BTEC national

Health & Social Care

Book 1

Series editors:
Beryl Stretch • Mary Whitehouse

Contributors:
Carolyn Aldworth • Marilyn Billingham
Lynda Mason • Neil Moonie • Beryl Stretch
Hilary Talman • Mary Whitehouse

www.harcourt.co.uk

✓ Free online support
✓ Useful weblinks
✓ 24 hour online ordering

01865 888058

Heinemann is an imprint of Harcourt Education Limited, a company incorporated in
England and Wales, having its registered office: Halley Court, Jordan Hill, Oxford OX2 8EJ.
Registered company no: 3099304

www.harcourt.co.uk

Heinemann is the registered trademark of Harcourt Education Limited

Text © Carolyn Aldworth (Unit 3), Marilyn Billingham (Unit 7), Lynda Mason (Unit 2), Neil Moonie
(Units 1 and 4), Beryl Stretch (Unit 5), Hilary Talman (Units 8 and 22) and Mary Whitehouse
(Units 6 and 44)

First published 2007

12 11 10 9 8 7
10 9 8 7 6 5 4 3 2 1

British Library Cataloguing in Publication Data is available
from the British Library on request.

ISBN 978 0435 49915 0

Typeset and illustrated by 7 Tek-Art, Croydon, Surrey, UK
Cover photo: Masterfile
Picture Research by Zooid Pictures
Printed by Printer Trento s.r.l., Italy

Websites
Please note that the examples of websites suggested in this book were up to date at the time
of writing. It is essential for tutors to preview each site before using it to ensure that the URL
is still acccurate and the content is appropriate. We suggest that tutors bookmark useful sites
and consider enabling students to access them through the school or college intranet.

Contents

Acknowledgements

Special thanks go to Nina Hockeridge and Karen James at Coleg Morgannwg, and Karen Cunliffe at Riverside College, Halton for their help in providing background material in Unit 6

The publishers would also like to thank the following for permission to quote:
Page 85: Nursing and Midwifery Code of Conduct cited with permission of Nursing and Midwifery Council www.nmc-uk.org; page 89: BCHS charter Complaints Policy cited with permission of Warwickshire County Council www.warwickshire.gov.uk; page 108: extract from 'Home Life: a code of practice for residential care' produced by Centre for Policy on Ageing, 1996 www.cpa.org.uk; pages 111, 126: extracts from 'Commission for Social Care and Inspection' 2006 www.csci.gov.uk The 'In context' on page 355 is adapted from 'How AIDS and starvation condemn Zimbabwe's women to an Early Grave' by Daniel Howden, the *Independent* 17 November 2006. On page 389: 'Children Learn What They Live' is taken from *Children Learn what they Live,* © 1972 by Dorothy Law Nolte and 1998 by Dorothy Law Nolte and Rachel Harris and used by permission of Workman Publishing Co., Inc., New York. On page 409: Breda Cullen's comments on the test she devised to measure the body's immune response to bacteria in a wound are quoted with her permission.

Photo credits
P2: © Harcourt Ltd / Jules Selmes; p9: © Science Photo Library / Mauro Fermariello; p10R: © Alamy / Image State; p10L: © Harcourt Ltd / Studio 8 / Clark Wiseman; p16: © Harcourt Ltd / Gareth Boden; p19: © Harcourt Ltd / Tudor Photography; p48: © Harcourt Ltd / Gareth Boden; p60: © Alamy / John Robertson; p67:
© Harcourt Ltd / Jules Selmes; p97: © Richard Smith; p106: © Harcourt Ltd / Gareth Boden; p109: © Alamy / Photofusion Picture Library; p113: © Royal College of Nursing; p114: © Science Photo Library / Dr Kari Lounatmaa; p133T: © Alamy / Medical-on-Line; p133B: © Photographers Direct / Blinding Services; p135: © Photographers Direct / GBC Productions United Kingdom; p138: © Harcourt Ltd / Tudor Photography; p143: © Photographers Direct / GBC Productions United Kingdom; p150: © Harcourt Ltd / Jules Selmes; pp152, 184, 196: : © Alamy / Rex Argent; p162: © Alamy / Picture Partners; p167: © Richard Smith; p169: © Alamy / Sally and Richard Greenhill; p174L: © Alamy / Elmtree Images; p174R: © Alamy / Andrew Parker; p186: © Photofusion Picture Library / Paul Doyle; p191: © Alamy / Adrian Sherratt; p200: © Science Photo Library / Susumu Nishinaga; p206: © Getty Images / PhotoDisc; p210: © iStockPhoto / Rafal Zdeb ; p270: © Harcourt Ltd / Jules Selmes; p334: © Harcourt Ltd / Martin Sookias; p345: © Getty Images / Hulton Archive / Rischgitz; p347: © Alamy / Photofusion Picture Library; p361: © Alamy / Image Source; p372: © Jupiterimages / Photos.com; p378: © Getty Images / PhotoDisc; p381R: © Rex Features / Focus / Everett; p385: © Harcourt Ltd / Jules Selmes; p392: © Harcourt Ltd / Jules Selmes; p395: © Harcourt Ltd / Gareth Boden; p397: © Corbis ; p406: © Harcourt Ltd / Mark Bassett; p407: © Harcourt Ltd / Jules Selmes; p466: © Harcourt Ltd / Jules Selmes; p492: © Medical-on-Line

The cover photograph is © Masterfile, and the photos in the icons are credited as follows: *Thinking points, Remember, Theory into Practice* and *Assessment* © Photos.com; *In context* and *Reflect* © Harcourt Ltd / Jules Selmes; and *Knowledge check*: Harcourt Ltd / Peter Morris

Introduction

Health and Social Care is a fascinating and growing area. You have chosen an excellent way to study it more closely and perhaps you will use this programme as a way into the professions, into higher education or straight into work. Or you may just be interested in the subject. Whatever helped you make your decision to do this course, welcome to the BTEC National Health and Social Care course book. It is specifically designed to support you if you are enrolled on the following programmes:

- BTEC National Award in Health and Social Care
- BTEC National Certificate in Health and Social Care
- BTEC National Diploma in Health and Social Care.

These qualifications are further divided into several different pathways: Health and Social Care, Social Care, Health Studies or Health Sciences. The contents of this book will provide you with the core units that you will need for any of these pathways, and four additional interesting and useful units which will fit into these programmes. The table opposite explains how the units we cover fit into your specific programme.

We are also providing a second book (Book 2) to give you yet more units for your study and you will find details about this either from your tutor or teacher or on our website: www.harcourt.co.uk.btechsc.

The aim of this book is to provide a comprehensive source of information for your course. It follows the BTEC specification closely, so that you can easily see what you have covered and quickly find the information you need. Examples and case studies from health and social care are used to bring your course to life and make it enjoyable to study. We hope you will be encouraged to find your own examples of current practice too.

You will often be asked to carry out research for activities in the text, and this will develop your research skills and enable you to find many sources of useful health and social care information, particularly on the Internet.

In some units of the book you will find information about different care settings and professionals which will be of great practical help to you in furthering career choices.

The book is also a suitable core text for students on HND, foundation degree and first-year degree programmes. To help you plan your study, an overview of each unit and its outcomes is given at the beginning of each unit. There is a wealth of information in these two books that you will find useful for a long time in your training.

■ A note about language

There are many terms in use for people who receive care and people who give care so, to prevent any confusion, we have standardised the use of such terms in this book.

For general, non-specific contexts, we have used the term 'service user' for an individual receiving care and, specifically, for those in a care setting. We use the term 'patient' for those receiving care through health care settings, e.g. when attending the family doctor or a hospital, and the term 'client' in a counselling context.

Similarly, we have approached the term 'carer' in an informal way and use 'professional' for an individual who is specifically trained or working in a formal setting using a value-based system.

The units and the pathways

Whether you have enrolled to study for the BTEC National Award, Certificate or Diploma, along the pathway of Health & Social Care (H&SC), Social Care (SC), Health Studies (HS) or Health Sciences (HSc), this book provides all the core units you need, plus four further units to develop your understanding of your chosen field.

▼ How each unit fits into each programme

Unit and title	Pathway	Core	Specialist
Unit 1 Developing effective communication	All pathways	All levels	
Unit 2 Equality, diversity and rights	All	All levels	
Unit 3 Health, safety and security	All	All levels	
Unit 4 Development through the life stages	All	All Certificate pathways All Diploma pathways	Award H&SC
Unit 5 Fundamentals of anatomy and physiology	All	All Certificate pathways All Diploma pathways	Award H&SC
Unit 6 Personal and professional development	All	All Certificate pathways All Diploma pathways	
Unit 7 Sociological perspectives	All	Certificate H&SC All Diploma pathways	Award H&SC Certificate: SC, HS, HSc
Unit 8 Psychological perspectives	All	Certificate H&SC All Diploma pathways	Award H&SC Certificate: SC, HS, HSc
Unit 22 Research methodology for Health and Social Care	All		All Certificate pathways All Diploma pathways
Unit 44 Vocational experience	All		All Certificate pathways All Diploma pathways

Guide to learning and assessment features

This book has a number of features to help you relate theory to practice, to reinforce your learning from both classwork and placements, and to help you to study independently. It also aims to help you gather evidence for assessment. You will find the following features identified in the sample spread below in each unit.

Your tutor should check that you have completed enough activities to meet all the assessment criteria for the unit, whether from this book or from other tasks.

Tutors and students should refer to the BTEC standards for the qualification for the full BTEC grading criteria for each unit (www.edexcel.org.uk).

Learning features

In context

Interesting examples of care situations are described in case studies to help you relate practice to theory. They will show you how the topics you are studying affect real people and their experience of health or social care.

Key terms

These define issues and vocabulary that have been used in the text and which are important for your understanding in relation to your studies and work in health and social care. They are gathered together in the glossary on page 500.

Reflect

These are opportunities for individual reflection on, or group discussions about, your experiences in a health and social care context. They will widen your knowledge and help you reflect on issues that impact on health and social care.

Remember!

These highlight important points to reinforce your learning or to give you practical tips.

Theory into practice

These practical activities allow you to apply theoretical knowledge to health and social care situations. Make sure you reinforce your learning by completing these activities as you work through each unit.

1.1

In context

Surraya is a 'linkworker' at a busy hospital trust. She is based in the Department of Public Health Awareness and responds to staff who require her services. Today she is working in the ear, nose and throat department, translating some deaf awareness posters from English into Bengali. These will then be used in the waiting room.

Tomorrow, she will be working with the community midwife in some parenting classes – she will be interpreting the information for Bengali first-time expectant mothers.

1   **What other kinds of health information are likely to need translation services?**

2   **What is the difference between interpretation and translation?**

3   **How do you think service users will feel about this service? What kind of worries may they have?**

Cultural enrichment

It should be fairly obvious by now that, if all the benefits we have already explored (diverse food types, new languages, the arts etc) are available and accessed by everyone, we will be culturally enriched.

Key terms

Equality This means that individuals are all treated equally.

Rights This describes the roles and responsibilities attached to being an individual living and working within a wider society.

■ Tolerance

Tolerance doesn't just mean putting up with something or someone. It has a much wider meaning and it is important to recognise this. In society and in the workplace we do not have to be friends with everyone but we do have to behave at all times in a professional and caring manner, towards both our service users

Theory into practice

When you are at your work placement, look around and try to identify all the measures that have been taken to keep staff and service users safe. For example, carpets provide a non-slip surface for residents and remove the risks associated with spillages, which can lead to people slipping. Try to think of all the dangers that your service users would face if no measures had been taken to provide a safe environment. This will help you to realise how much thought goes into planning a safe environment for service users and staff.

For people to feel that they belong, there is a need for everyone's circumstances and background to be valued and respected. Alongside this lies a need for positive relationships between people from different backgrounds in all the social and economic places in which they might meet, for example, schools, workplaces and neighbourhoods.

Health and social care teams need to demonstrate social cohesion in the way individual members work together and support each other. As we have already said, most care teams are multicultural: it is important for these teams to support each other and to uphold the rights of every single member.

Reflect

What actions could be taken by a hospital trust to contribute towards a cohesive society at a local level?

Remember!

Visiting tradesman are experts in their trade, not care practice. They need to be made aware of the nature of the client group so that they do not unintentionally place people at risk.

Legislation on the web

There is also an Appendix to this book which summarises key aspects of legislation that apply across several units. You should look at these whenever a piece of legislation is mentioned in the text of any of the units. This will help reinforce your learning about the key features of each Act and how the legislation relates to the theory and practice being discussed in the units. You will find this on our website: www.harcourt.co.uk/btechsc.

A number of health and social care professionals and teachers have contributed to this book to enable you to develop your knowledge. Each of them has expertise in a particular area and a wide teaching experience.

We do hope that you enjoy your course and find these books an excellent support for your studies. Good luck!

Beryl Stretch and Mary Whitehouse

Theory into practice

Write a short report describing either:

- how accessible your college is for people who are wheelchair users, or
- how easy it is for wheelchair users to do their shopping in your local high street.

■ Iatrogenesis or 'doctor-generated' illness

Iatrogenesis refers to illness generated by medical activity and practice. It was a term introduced by Ivan Illich (1976) and was part of his more general attack on, and criticism of, industrialised society and its large bureaucratic institutions. However, it is still very much part of current debate. Particular areas of concern include the side-effects of drugs, the risks attached to medical drugs trials and concerns about infections spread within hospitals. Illich identified three major types of iatrogenisis:

- clinical iatrogenesis – the unwanted side-effects of medical intervention
- social iatrogenesis – medicine has gained so much power and status that people too quickly and easily place themselves in the hands of the professional and become mass consumers of medical products
- cultural iatrogenesis – society becomes over-concerned with perfect health, so making it difficult to develop positive attitudes towards impairment and to cope appropriately with death.

■ The clinical iceberg

Official statistics on levels of illness are sometimes called 'the clinical iceberg' because it is thought that the 'true' levels of illness are largely concealed; this is because people who are ill do not necessarily visit their doctor. This may be for a wide range of reasons.

Assessment activity 1.1

Describe different concepts of ill health.

1 Drawing on examples from your placement and from other life experiences, describe the different concepts of ill health introduced in this unit:

- disability
- iatrogenesis
- the sick role
- the clinical iceberg. **P1**

Grading tip for P1

You can provide evidence of linking theory to practice by using well-chosen examples to illustrate concepts.

Take it further

Consider how concepts of ill health may help care workers in evaluating their own care practice.

Knowledge check

1 Explain what 'valuing diversity' means.
2 List the key aspects of the care value base.
3 Explain the consequences of making assumptions about people that are not based on fact.
4 List three ways of demonstrating respect for an individual.
5 Describe the purpose of a code of practice in the workplace.
6 List three ways of actively promoting anti-discriminatory practice.
7 Explain which circumstances would allow confidentiality to be broken.
8 List five benefits of diversity to society.

Unit 1 | Developing effective communication **[3]**

Assessment features

Activities and assessment practice

Activities are provided throughout each unit. These are linked to real situations and case studies and they can be used for practice before tackling the preparation for assessment.

Grading icons

Throughout the book you will see the **P**, **M** and **D** icons. These show you where the tasks fit in with the grading criteria. If you do these tasks you will be building up your evidence to achieve your desired qualification. If you are aiming for a Merit, make sure you complete all the Pass **P** and Merit **M** tasks. If you are aiming for a Distinction, you will also need to complete all the Distinction **D** tasks. **P1** means the first of the Pass criteria listed in the specification, **M1** the first of the Merit criteria, **D1** the first of the Distinction criteria, and so on.

Preparation for assessment

Each unit concludes with a full unit assessment, which taken as a whole fulfils all the unit requirements from Pass to Distinction. Each task is matched to the relevant criteria in the specification.

Knowledge checks

At the end of each unit is a set of quick questions to test your knowledge of the information you have been studying. Use these to check your progress, and also as a revision tool.

Developing effective communication

Introduction

In health and social care work, you will need to communicate with a range of people. You will work with people who have different lifestyles, personalities, cultures and personal needs. You will find yourself in a wide variety of formal and informal work situations. During all of these different encounters you will need to feel confident that you can support others in a caring and professional way. This unit is designed to help you to identify and analyse the effectiveness of your own communication skills.

How you will be assessed

You will be assessed through an assignment that will include reports of your own practical communication work in the role of a carer. A variety of assessment practice tasks are included throughout this unit to help you prepare your work.

After completing this unit you should be able to achieve the following outcomes:

- Understand effective communication and interpersonal interaction
- Understand factors that influence communication and interpersonal interactions in health and social care settings
- Know how patients/service users may be assisted by effective communication
- Be able to demonstrate your own communication skills in a caring role.

Thinking points

Anita is a care worker who has worked in a day centre and as a home care worker. Below you can read some statements that service users have made about Anita:

> 'She is like a ray of sunshine – she always smiles and cheers me up when I feel down.'

> 'She makes you feel important – she always has time for you, even when she is very busy.'

> 'She is so easy to talk to – she takes an interest in you. I would say she makes you feel special – not just one of the crowd.'

> 'She is a very special person, very kind and considerate. There aren't very many people like her – it's a sort of magical touch – you feel different when she is around.'

Anita has excellent interpersonal skills – a 'magical touch'. Anita's skills enrich her own life and the lives of other people. You may have met professional carers who have these skills; you may also have encountered people who are less skilled. Why do some people have good 'people skills' while others have difficulty getting on with others? This unit explores how interpersonal and communication skills can be understood and how you can develop your skills.

In context

Imagine that you go on a wonderful holiday to a faraway country. But one day while you are there, you wake up in a hospital! You do not know what has happened to you but you are unable to get out of bed without assistance. The staff and everybody around you cannot speak your language and you cannot make much sense of their facial expressions or gestures. You have no one to communicate with. You do not know how long you will have to stay there. You cannot ask for assistance in order to get food or drink or to go to the toilet. The staff do not attempt to communicate with you because they cannot understand your language.

1 **How might a lack of effective communication put you at risk and how might it affect you emotionally?**

2 **Just because people speak different languages, does this mean that communication cannot take place?**

3 **Is communication just about passing on information or is there an important emotional aspect to communicating in a care setting?**

Communication between people enables us to exchange ideas and information but it involves much more than simply passing on information to others. Communication enables people to feel safe, to make relationships and to develop self-esteem.

Poor communication might make a service user feel vulnerable, worthless or emotionally threatened.

There are many different types of communication. Communication between people might involve:

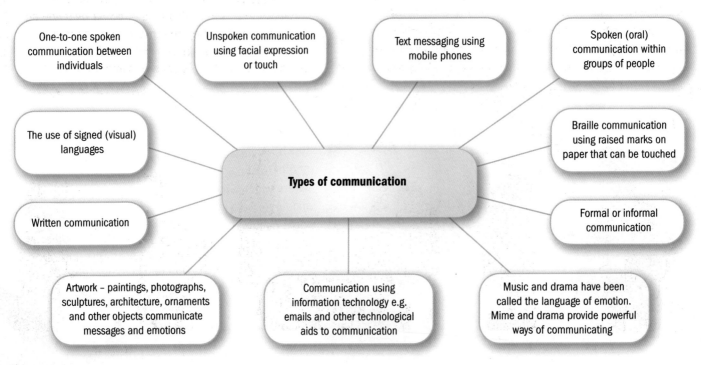

One-to-one spoken communication between individuals	Unspoken communication using facial expression or touch
Text messaging using mobile phones	Spoken (oral) communication within groups of people
The use of signed (visual) languages	Braille communication using raised marks on paper that can be touched
Written communication	Formal or informal communication
Artwork – paintings, photographs, sculptures, architecture, ornaments and other objects communicate messages and emotions	Communication using information technology e.g. emails and other technological aids to communication
	Music and drama have been called the language of emotion. Mime and drama provide powerful ways of communicating

Types of communication

▲ Figure 1.1 Types of communication

Reflect

New technology, such as the mobile phone, provides new opportunities to contact and communicate with people. Can you think of ways in which mobile communication may be important within health care?

Remember!

Several years ago a study of teenage mobile phone users was carried out in Japan. It found that the teenagers considered it rude to make voice contact with friends over the phone without first sending text messages to make sure that a voice call would be welcome. This group had automatically developed their own social rules about creating the right emotional atmosphere for conversation!

One-to-one conversations

When you start a conversation with someone you don't know very well you should always try to create the right kind of feeling. It is important to create the right emotional atmosphere before you can go on to discuss complicated issues or give people information. It is important that the other person feels relaxed and happy to talk to you. Very often people will start with a greeting such as 'Good morning'. You need to help other people to relax by showing that *you* are friendly and relaxed. Once you have created a good feeling, you can move on to the business – the things you want to talk about. When it is time to finish the conversation, you will want to leave the other person with the right kind of emotions: you might say something like 'See you soon' to show that you value them. Formal conversations can be understood as involving a three-stage model where it is important to have an emotional warm-up stage and a winding down stage as well as a 'business' or exchange of information stage in the middle.

Reflect

You must have experienced conversations where other people come straight to the point without warm-up or lead-out. An example might be someone in authority who makes demands on you: 'Right (your name). I want you to get this work finished and I want it on my desk first thing in the morning!' How does this abrupt and cold message make you feel? You might decide to do what the other person wants if they have power over you. Tutors, parents and employers might have this kind of power over you so they may feel that they don't need to be sensitive to your emotions. But how might you affect service users if you imitate this style of communication?

Warm-up, small talk

Business

Lead-out

 Figure 1.2 Interaction often involves a three-stage process

Group communication

Taking part in a group discussion involves some additional issues as compared to one-to-one communication.

- **Group 'atmosphere'**: group discussion only works well if people want to be involved. Sometimes people feel threatened if they have to speak within a formal group of people or they might stay quiet because they are worried about the reaction of others. It is important that the group has the right emotional atmosphere. Formal groups often use humour or other friendly behaviours to create the right group feeling to encourage people to talk. Creating the right group atmosphere involves 'maintaining' the group and so this aspect of group communication is often called group maintenance.

- **Group leaders**: some groups such as team meetings or classroom discussions have a leader or chairperson. Having a leader is very useful because they can help people to take turns in talking and encourage people to express their ideas. Group leaders often encourage people to focus on a particular task within a group.

- **Thinking through what you are going to say**: in formal groups it is important to think through your points before sharing them with the whole group. Because of this extra preparation, talking to a group can feel very different from talking in a one-to-one situation.

- **Taking turns**: when a group does not have a leader or chairperson it is important that group members have the skills to take turns in talking. When a speaker is finishing, they usually signal this by lowering their voice tone, slowing the pace of talking and looking around at other people in the group. The next person to talk knows that it is their turn by watching the eyes of other group members. People often fail to take turns in speaking and then everybody talks at once. If everybody is talking then nobody is listening!

- **Use of space**: if people sit in a circle then everyone can see everyone else's face. This is very important because group feeling and turn taking often depend on people being able to understand the messages in other people's faces. If people sit behind each other or in rows, then some of the group cannot see others' faces. Bad seating or standing positions can make group communication harder.

Reflect

Think about group meetings that you have attended. Can you identify the atmosphere – the beliefs and values that help to give the group its identity? Are people good at taking turns? How good is the group leader at encouraging people to be involved and at encouraging the right atmosphere in the group?

Stages in group formation

Communication in groups can also be influenced by the degree to which people feel they belong together. When people first meet in a group they often go through a process of group formation. Many groups may experience some sort of struggle before people unite and communicate effectively. One of the best-known theorists to explain group formation stages is Tuckman (1965). Tuckman suggests that most groups go through a process involving four stages. These are:

1 forming
2 storming
3 norming
4 performing.

The first stage (forming) involves people meeting for the first time and sharing information. The second stage (storming) involves tension, struggle and sometimes arguments about the way the group might function. The third stage (norming) sees the group coming together and consciously or unconsciously agreeing on their **group values**. Once a group of people have established common expectations and values, the group will reach the fourth stage of being an effectively performing group.

Key terms

Group values Group members need to share a common system of beliefs or values in order for the group to communicate and perform effectively. You may be able to identify these values when you watch a group at work.

In context

Five care workers who work with adults with learning difficulties are talking to each other in a group meeting.

Speaker 1: I'm worried about the cookery sessions – I don't think we give enough help and support. For example, Drew nearly burned himself last Tuesday and no one was watching what he was doing.

Speaker 2: But he didn't burn himself and he is learning to become independent. I think it's important to let people take risks. I would never have become independent if my parents hadn't let me take risks.

Speaker 3: So are you saying safety doesn't matter then?

Speaker 4: I can't believe you just said that! We were discussing the importance of independence and you turn that round by saying that we are negligent!

Speaker 3: Well, I don't think you take safety seriously enough. These are vulnerable people you know – they can easily hurt themselves if they're not properly supervised.

Speaker 5: Look, it's obvious that both safety and independence matter. So why is it that we're talking about the issues as if they were only about safety – or only about independence?

Speaker 3: Well, I agree that both are important but I think safety comes first.

Speaker 4: No, I don't think things can be that simple. A total concentration on safety will result in us failing to help people to become independent – there's got to be a balance.

1   **Using Tuckman's theory, which is the most likely stage of group formation that this group is at?**

2   **Can you identify different norms that are being argued about in the group?**

3   **This group later performed and worked together effectively. From the brief conversation above, what system of group values do you think they would focus on?**

Speech and language: informal and formal communication

Informal communication

We often use informal communication when we know people well, for example, with friends and family. Some friends or family members may use terms that other people would not understand. Local groups might have their own ways of speaking, for example, some people in southern England might say things like 'Hi yer mate. How's it goin'?' If you belong to this group, you will appreciate this as a warm, friendly greeting.

But different groups of people use different informal language: it can be difficult to understand the informal communication of people from different social groups.

Formal communication

Health and social care work often involves the need for formal communication. For example, if you went to a local authority social services reception desk you might expect to be greeted with 'Good morning. How can I help you?' This formal communication might be understood by a wide range of people. Formal communication also shows respect for others. The degree of formality or informality is called the language 'register'.

Figure 1.3 Informality may be perceived as disrespect

Types of interpersonal interaction

Different localities, ethnic groups, professions and work cultures all have their own special words, phrases and speech patterns. These localities and groups may be referred to as different speech communities. Some service users may feel threatened or excluded by the kind of language they encounter. However, just using formal language will not solve this problem. The technical terminology used by care workers (often called **jargon**) may also create barriers for people who are not a part of that 'speech community'.

Key terms

Jargon Words used by a particular profession or group that are hard for others to understand.

Imagine that you went to the reception desk and you were greeted with the phrase 'What you after then?' It is possible that some people might prefer such an informal greeting. An informal greeting could put you at ease; you might feel that the other person is like you. But in many situations, such informal language might make people feel that they are not being respected. Being 'after something' could be a 'put down'; you might assume that you are being seen as a scrounger. So it is often risky to use informal language unless you are sure that other people expect you to do so. If you are treated informally, you may interpret this as not being treated seriously, or in other words 'not being respected'.

So is there a correct way to speak to people when you first introduce yourself? After all, if you are too formal you may come across as being pretentious or 'posh'. Usually care workers will adjust the way they speak in order to communicate respect towards different 'speech communities'.

Reflect

Service user: I 'ave to look after me mum like an' she's playing up, an' I can't do it without more help like.

Professional: You would be entitled to an assessment under section 1 of the Carers Recognition and Services Act 1995. Normally a person is assessed under section 47 of the NHSCCA 1990. Has your mother had a section 47 assessment?

Service user: So can you help me or not?

The two statements above represent speech from different speech communities. Can you work out what each person is really trying to communicate? Can you see how technical and legal terminology can exclude other people? Will the service user feel respected and valued by such a technical answer?

When people from different geographical areas use different words and pronounce words differently they are often using a different **dialect**. Some social groups use **slang** – non-standard words that are understood by other members of a speech community but which can't usually be found in a dictionary.

Key terms

Dialect Words and their pronunciation which are specific to a geographical community. For example, people who live in the north of England might use a different dialect from Londoners.

Slang Informal words and phrases that are not usually found in standard dictionaries but which are used within specific social groups and communities when communicating.

Non-verbal communication

Within a few seconds of meeting a service user you will usually be able to tell what they are feeling. You will know whether the person is tired, happy, angry, sad, frightened – even before they say anything. You can usually guess what a person feels by studying their non-verbal communication.

Non-verbal means 'without words', so non-verbal communication is the messages that we send without using words. We send messages using our eyes, the tone of our voice, our facial expression, our hands and arms, gestures with our hands and arms, the angle of our head, the way we sit or stand (known as body posture) and the tension in our muscles.

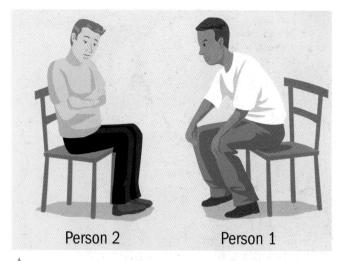

▲ Figure 1.4 You can see that person 2 is rejecting what person 1 is communicating

Posture: The way you sit or stand can send messages. Sitting with crossed arms can mean 'I'm not taking any notice'. Leaning back can send the message that you are relaxed or bored. Leaning forward can show interest or intense involvement.

The way you move: As well as posture, your body movements will communicate messages. For example, the way you walk, move your head, sit, cross your legs etc will send messages about whether you are tired, happy, sad or bored.

Areas of the body that send messages ▶

▲ Figure 1.5 Square-on orientation can communicate aggression

Facing other people: The way in which you face other people may also communicate emotional messages. Standing or sitting eye-to-eye can send a message of being formal or angry. A slight angle can create a more relaxed and friendly feeling.

Gestures: Gestures are hand and arm movements that can help us to understand what a person is saying. Some gestures carry a common meaning in most communities in the UK.

▲ Figure 1.6 Common gestures for 'good' and 'perfect'

Facial expression: Our face often indicates our emotional state. When a person is sad they may signal this emotion by looking down – there may be tension in their face and their mouth will be closed. The muscles in the

▲ A person's emotions can often be interpreted from facial expression

person's shoulders are likely to be relaxed but their face and neck may show tension. A happy person will have 'wide eyes' that make contact with you – their face will smile. When people are excited they will move their arms and hands to signal this.

We can guess the feelings and thoughts that another person has by looking at their eyes. We can sometimes understand the thoughts and feelings of another person by eye-to-eye contact. Our eyes get wider when we are excited, attracted to, or interested in someone else. A fixed stare may send the message that someone is angry. In European culture, looking away is often interpreted as being bored or not interested.

Most people can recognise emotions in the non-verbal behaviour of others. You will also need to understand how your own non-verbal behaviour may influence other people.

■ Non-verbal messages

When we meet and talk with people, we usually use two language systems: verbal language and non-verbal/body language. Effective communication requires care workers to be able to analyse their own and other people's non-verbal behaviour. Our body sends messages to other people – often without us deliberately meaning to send them. Some of the most important body areas that send messages are:

In context

In 2006 there was controversy over women who choose to wear a veil or 'niqab' as part of their religious identity. Some politicians argued that they felt uncomfortable conversing with people whose facial expression was hidden. Some newspapers argued that it was not possible to communicate effectively in interpersonal situations if the face could not be seen. But how important is non-verbal communication from the face? Most people are good at making sense of voice tone and pace of speech when they receive a telephone message. Face-to-face contact does give more information than you receive in a phone call but you still have eye contact with someone who wears a veil.

1 Is it always necessary to have a full range of non-verbal information in order to understand what someone is telling you?

2 If you cannot see someone clearly, what other non-verbal information can you sense in order to help you interpret their words?

3 How far is the debate about the veil concerned with clear communication and how far is it an issue about different social identities and norms?

Touch

Touch is another way of communicating without words. Touching another person can send messages of care, affection, power over them or sexual interest. The social setting and a person's body language will usually help you to understand what their touch might mean. But touch can easily be misinterpreted. You might try to comfort someone by holding their hand but they may interpret this touch as an attempt to dominate. Sometimes it can be a good idea to ask if you may touch, or gesture in a way that allows another person to refuse your touch before proceeding.

People may also look at, or feel, the degree of muscle tension that you show when you communicate with them. The tension in your feet, hands and fingers can tell others how relaxed or tense you are. If someone is very tense their shoulders might stiffen, their face muscles might tighten and they might sit or stand rigidly. A tense face might have a firmly closed mouth with lips and jaws clenched tight. A tense person might breathe quickly and look hot.

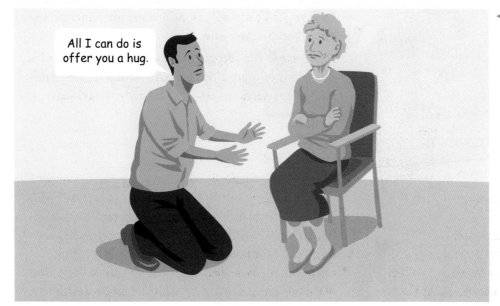

Figure 1.7 Gestures and words give the service user the option of refusing touch

Silence

One definition of friends is 'people who can sit together and feel comfortable in silence'. Sometimes a pause in conversation can make people feel embarrassed – it looks as if you weren't listening or interested. Sometimes a silent pause can mean 'let's think' or 'I need time to think'. Silent pauses can be OK as long as non-verbal messages which show respect and interest are given. Silence doesn't always stop the conversation.

When you do speak with other people, the tone of voice that you use will be important. If you talk quickly in a loud voice with a fixed tone, people may see you as angry. A calm, slow voice with varying tone may send a message of being friendly.

Proximity

The space between people can sometimes show how friendly or 'intimate' the conversation is. Different cultures have different behaviours with respect to the space between people who are talking.

In Britain there are expectations or 'norms' as to how close you should be when you talk to others. When talking to strangers we may keep 'an arm's length' apart. The ritual of shaking hands indicates that you have been introduced – you may come closer. When you are friendly with someone you may accept them being closer to you. Relatives and partners might not be restricted at all in how close they can come.

Proximity is a very important issue in health and care work. Many service users have a sense of personal space. A care worker who assumes it is fine to enter a service user's personal space without asking or explaining may be seen as being dominating or aggressive.

Reflective listening

We can often understand other people's emotions just by watching their non-verbal communication. However,

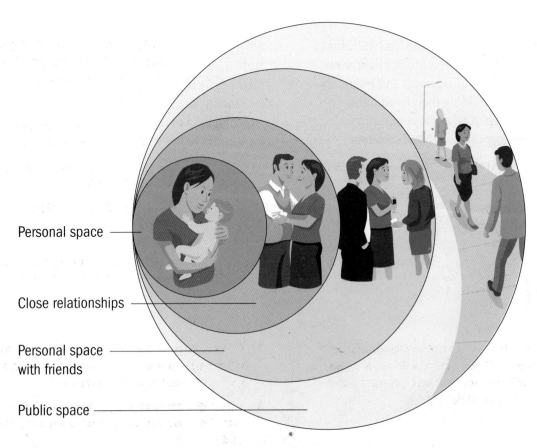

Personal space

Close relationships

Personal space with friends

Public space

▲ Figure 1.8 There are different expectations about personal space

we can't always understand someone's thoughts without good listening skills.

Listening skills involve hearing another person's words – then thinking about what they mean – then thinking how to reply to the other person. Sometimes this process is called 'active listening' and sometimes 'reflective listening.' The word 'reflective' is used because the person's conversation is reflected back (like the reflection in a mirror) in order to check understanding. As well as thinking carefully and remembering what a person says, good listeners will make sure that their non-verbal behaviour shows interest.

Skilled listening involves:

- looking interested and communicating that you are ready to listen

- hearing what is said to you
- remembering what was said to you together with non-verbal messages
- checking your understanding with the person that was speaking to you.

■ Checking understanding

We can learn about people who are different from us by checking our understanding of what we have heard. Checking understanding can involve listening to what the other person says and then asking questions. Reflection may also involve putting what a person has just said into our own words (paraphrasing) and saying it back to them to check we have understood what they were saying.

In context

Val is seriously in debt. She looks worried and says 'I don't know what to do. I haven't even got enough money to pay the rent.' She is not expecting to borrow money from you as she knows you cannot afford this kind of help. How can you respond in a supportive way? Consider some of the possibilities below:

Try to be reassuring e.g. 'I'm sure something will turn up.'	Unless you are an expert with detailed knowledge of the person's situation, reassurance is likely to sound 'false'. You may come across as trying to avoid the topic or trick the person.
Offer advice e.g. 'Why don't you see a financial adviser?'	Receiving unwanted advice can sometimes be very irritating. Many people may perceive advice as trying to avoid the issue i.e. 'please don't talk to me about your problems'.
Repeating what was said e.g. 'You haven't even got enough money to pay the rent.'	Parroting some phrases back to a person may sound mechanical. The person might say: 'That's what I just said – didn't you hear me?'
Reflecting the other person's message e.g. 'Worrying about the rent must be causing you a lot of stress.'	This shows that you have listened and it may be seen as an invitation to keep talking. Being able to talk to someone who is actively involved may make the other person feel supported.

1   What is the difference between saying things such as 'why don't you see an adviser or 'perhaps something will turn up' and just saying 'I don't want to talk to you about it'?

2   Can you explain the difference between just repeating or parroting the words you have heard and the idea of reflective listening?

3   Why might another person feel that you care about them because you can reflect back what they have said?

My message was understood.

Message sent

Message is 'reflected' back like an image in a mirror

▲ Figure 1.9 It is important to see our understanding reflected back to us

Theory into practice

Take a piece of paper. Divide it into four areas and write out four headings:

- Where I live
- An important thing that happened in the past
- Something I am looking forward to
- Where I work or study.

Any four headings will do – as long as you can talk in detail about the areas. Think through what you can tell another person about yourself. Then get together with another student who has planned their speech. Explain your four areas to each other. This should take at least 10 minutes. Then see what you can remember about the other person and how detailed and how accurate it is! How good are you at understanding and remembering?

When we listen to complicated details of other people's lives, we often begin to form mental pictures based on what they tell us. The skill of listening involves checking these mental pictures. Good listening involves thinking about what we hear while we are listening and checking our understanding as the conversation goes along – we reflect on the other person's ideas.

Good listening can feel like really hard work. Instead of just being around when people speak, we have to build an understanding of the people we communicate with.

Variation between cultures

Skilled carers use a range of conversational techniques when working with others. These include being sensitive to variations in culture.

Culture means the history, customs and ways that people learn as they grow up. People from different regions of Britain use different expressions. Non-verbal signs vary from culture to culture. White middle-class people often expect people to 'look them in the eye' while talking. If a person looks down or away a lot, it is a sign that they may be dishonest, or perhaps sad or depressed. In some other cultures – among some black communities – looking down or away when talking is a sign of respect.

No one can learn every possible system of **cultural variation** in non-verbal behaviour but it is possible to learn about the ones that are used by the people you are with! You can do this by first noticing and remembering what others do i.e. what non-verbal messages they are sending. The next step is to make a guess as to what messages the person is trying to give you. Finally, check your understanding (your guesses) with the person. This involves reflective listening and thinking carefully about the person's responses.

Key terms

Cultural variation Communication is always influenced by cultural systems of meaning. Different cultures interpret verbal and non-verbal communication behaviours as having different meanings.

In context

Andreas is a middle-aged man who is talking to a care worker about his son's care. He is standing face to face with an upright posture, closer than an arm's length to the care worker. He is also moving his arms in large sweeping gestures, talking in a loud forceful voice and at a fast pace. Another worker has said that she thinks Andreas may become aggressive and wonders whether the centre's manager should be alerted.

1 **Can you identify how the concept of cultural variation might be relevant to understanding this situation?**

2 **Can you think of possibilities other than anger and aggression that might explain each of the non-verbal behaviours described above?**

3 **Can you describe some ways in which you could check out what particular non-verbal behaviours might mean during a conversation?**

Care workers must be careful not to assume that statements and signs always have the same meaning. Cultural differences and different settings can alter what things mean. There are a vast range of meanings that can be given to any type of eye contact, facial expression, posture or gesture. Every culture, and even small groups of people, can develop their own system of meanings. Care workers have to respect differences but it is impossible to learn all the possible meanings which phrases, words and signs may have.

The communication cycle

Michael Argyle (1972) argued that interpersonal communication was a skill that could be learned and developed in much the same way as learning to drive a car. Argyle emphasised the importance of 'feedback' in skilled activities. When you drive a car you have to change your behaviour depending on what is happening on the road. Driving involves a constant cycle of watching what is happening, working out how to respond, making responses and then repeating this cycle until you reach your destination.

Argyle argued that skilled interpersonal interaction (social skills) involved a cycle where you have to translate or 'decode' what other people are communicating and constantly adapt your own behaviour in order to communicate effectively. Verbal and non-verbal communication is not always straightforward. Communication involves a kind of code that has to be translated. You have to work out what another person's behaviour really means.

One way of looking at this cycle might be:

1 **Ideas occur**: you have an idea that you want to communicate.

2 **Message coded:** you think through how you are going to say what you are thinking. You put your thoughts into language or into some other code such as sign language.

3 **Message sent:** you speak, or perhaps you sign or write, or in some way send your message.

4 **Message perceived**: the other person has to sense your message – they hear your words or see your symbols.

5 **Message decoded**: the other person has to interpret or 'decode' your message i.e. what you have said. This is not always easy as the other person will make assumptions about your words and body language.

6 **Message understood**: if all goes well then your ideas will be understood but this does not always happen first time!

The communication process might look something like this:

1. Ideas occur

2. Message coded

3. Message sent

4. Message perceived

5. Message decoded

6. Feedback – what was understood

Figure 1.10 Stages in the communication cycle

In context

Anita is talking with Margaret, whose partner has died.

Margaret: It was just so sudden. I can't believe it. I don't know how I'm going to cope.

Anita: It must have been a terrible shock.

Margaret: I'll say it was – I just feel so anxious. I know I won't be able to cope.

Anita: Can you tell me a little about your life together?

In this brief example, Anita has been careful not to jump to conclusions or offer advice about what she is being told. There is no helpful advice or information that Anita can offer. Anita was careful to reflect back what Margaret said. This resulted in a communication cycle where Margaret can now begin to share her worries.

1   **Can you identify why it is so important for care workers to say back what they think they have heard?**

2   **Can you explain what might have happened if Anita had responded with 'Don't worry, you'll feel better as time goes by'?**

3   **Can you explain how understanding the communication cycle can help care professionals to demonstrate skilled communication?**

Communication needs to be a two-way process where each person is trying to understand the viewpoint of the other person. Communication is a cycle because when two people communicate they need to check that their ideas have been understood. We can learn about different people by checking our understanding of what we have heard. Effective communication involves the process of checking understanding that is involved in reflective or active listening. And this process of monitoring the development of understanding is identified in the theory of reflective listening and in the idea that communication involves a cycle.

Remember!

Most communication with service users is likely to involve the building of understanding using an active process of reflecting on what the service user is communicating. Communication can be seen as involving a process or cycle of building an understanding.

Assessment activity 1.1

Describe different types of communication and interpersonal interaction, using examples relevant to health and social care settings.

1   You should make notes of conversations and interactions that you have while you are on work placement. Naturally it will be important that you do not record real names or details that could identify the people you have worked with. You can use these notes in order to identify and describe examples of different kinds of communication.

Grading tip for P1

You may be able to identify many of the different types of communication/interaction as set out in the diagram on page 4 during your work placement experience.

Because you will also be providing evidence of two interactions in the role of a carer in P5, you will describe different types of communication and interpersonal interaction as an introduction to the details of your interaction work.

Describe the stages of the communication cycle.

2   Using notes you have made during your work placement experience you may be able to identify examples of interactions between people that involve the communication cycle. You will then be able to use these examples in order to describe the stages of the communication cycle within the interaction.

Grading tip for P2

You could also design a poster explaining the importance of the communication cycle and describing how the communication cycle works within an interaction in a health or care setting.

Communication and language needs and preferences

Preferred spoken language

Steven Pinker (1994) estimated that there may be about 600 languages in the world that are spoken by more than 100,000 people. There are many more minority languages. Some people grow up in multilingual communities where they learn several languages from birth. But many people in the UK have grown up using only one language with which to think and communicate. Learning a second language later in life may mean that many people cannot communicate their thoughts as effectively as they might have done using their **first language**. The first language that people have learned to think in therefore becomes their preferred language.

First language The first language that a person learns to speak is often the language that they will think in. Working with later languages can be difficult as mental translation between languages may be required.

Reflect

How many languages can people in your local community communicate in? Do people you know who communicate in more than one language think in more than one language?

Use of signs and symbols

Gestures made with hands or arms, written symbols or diagrams such as traffic signs, all communicate messages to people. Braille (see page 37) provides a system of communication using raised marks.

Signed languages

Language does not have to be based on sounds that are heard. Signing systems such as British Sign Language (BSL) (see page 37) provide a full language system for people who do not use spoken language.

Written communication

There is a Chinese saying that 'the faintest ink is stronger than the strongest memory'! Written records are essential for communicating formal information that needs to be reviewed at a future date. When people remember conversations they have had, they will probably miss some details out and also change some details. Written statements are much more permanent and, if they are accurate when they are written, they may be useful at a later date.

Pictures and objects of reference

Paintings, photographs, sculptures, architecture, ornaments and other household objects can communicate messages and emotions to people. People often take photographs or buy souvenirs to remind them of happy experiences and emotions. Sometimes an object – such as a cuddly toy – can symbolise important personal issues and provide a source of meaning and comfort for an individual. Some people with communication difficulties do not identify with photographs or drawings but they may identify with an object such as a toy.

◀ Children can communicate through play using objects

Communication passports

Communication passports are usually small personalised books containing straightforward practical information about a person and their style of communication. The passport may help health and care workers to understand the personal and communication needs of a person with communication difficulties. Communication passports often include photographs or drawings that may help care workers to gain a better understanding of the person who owns the passport. They are put together by working with the person with communication difficulties and his or her carers; the person tells their own story of their likes, dislikes and communication styles.

Technological aids to communication

Information technology offers a wide range of facilities to help with communication. It is possible to provide enlarged visual displays or voice feedback for people with visual impairment. Electronic aids to communication can turn speech into writing – such as the minicom for people with a hearing disability or voice typing

for people with dyslexia. Electronic communication systems can be activated by air pressure, so that a person can communicate via an oral tube connected to computerised equipment. At a more simple level, aids such as flash cards or picture books can also improve communication with people who do not use a spoken or signed language. Text messaging using a mobile phone provides an effective way of staying in touch for many people; for people with a hearing disability, text messaging may provide a major form of communication.

Reflect

When you send text messages to friends, do you use symbols and shortened words that would not be acceptable in more formal academic work? If you send emails, do you use abbreviations, symbols and special terms or do you only use formal English? Do you think it should be acceptable to use 'texting' symbols and abbreviations for academic work? How formal should English be?

Many service users will have specific communication needs. It may be important to employ an interpreter if a service user uses a different language such as BSL. Some carers learn to use communication systems such as Makaton, in order to help them communicate with service users. Hayman (1998) notes the following points for communicating with people with hearing impairments:

- Make sure the person can see you clearly.
- Face both the light and the person at all times.
- Include the person in your conversation.
- Do not obscure your mouth.
- Speak clearly and slowly. Repeat if necessary, but you may need to rephrase your words.
- Do not shout into a person's ear or hearing aid.
- Minimise background noise.
- Use your eyes, facial expressions and hand gestures, where appropriate.

If people have limited vision, it may be important to use language to describe issues that a sighted person might take for granted, such as non-verbal communication or the context of certain comments. Touch may be an important aspect of communication; some registered blind people can work out what you look like if they can touch your face in order to build an understanding of your features.

It is always important to choose the right style of language in order to communicate with people from different language communities.

Environment

It is very hard to hear what someone is saying if there is a lot of background noise. It is very difficult to make sense of other people's facial expressions if you can't see their face properly due to poor lighting. Rooms with awkward seating positions might mean that a group of people cannot see each other comfortably. People sometimes feel uncomfortable if they are trying to communicate with a person who is too close or at a distance. A room that is too hot, stuffy or cold may inhibit communication if it makes people feel tired or stressed.

The environment also plays an important role in the effectiveness of aids for communication. For instance, hearing aids will amplify background noise as well as the voice of the speaker. A noisy environment may therefore be difficult and unpleasant for someone who is using a hearing aid. Good lighting will be critical for someone who supports their understanding of speech with lip reading.

Responding to behaviour

In context An interview with Anita

Interviewer: You must have to deal with some awkward people?

Anita: Some people seem difficult at first but I usually find a way to get on with them. It is partly about your attitude. I never have enough time to do the practical work but I always make time to listen and take an interest in the people I work with. I always like to leave people feeling more cheerful than when I went in.

Interviewer: But some people must wind you up?

Anita: They do but I never 'rise to the bait'. I stay calm and think carefully about how to respond. If they are angry and critical, I don't get angry and critical back. But I don't let them push me around either! The key thing is to remember that they wouldn't have care services if everything was perfect in their lives. You have to put yourself in their shoes and then you can usually find a way to help them feel OK.

1   Do you think that Anita has good assertion skills?

2   If Anita did behave aggressively towards service users, what would be the risks for Anita and her service users?

3   Why is it important that Anita listens to and takes an interest in people?

Being assertive

Fear and aggression are two of the basic emotions that we experience. It is easy to give in to our basic emotions and be either submissive or aggressive when we feel stressed. **Assertion** is an advanced skill that involves controlling the basic emotions involved in running away or fighting. It involves a mental attitude of trying to *negotiate*, trying to solve problems rather than giving in to emotional impulses.

Key terms

Assertion Assertion is different from both submission and aggression – it involves being able to negotiate a solution to a problem.

During an argument, an aggressive person might insist that they are right and other people are wrong. They will want to win while others lose. The opposite of aggression is submission. A submissive person accepts that they will lose, get told off or be put down emotionally. Assertive behaviour is different from both these responses. In an argument, an assertive person will try to reach an answer where no one has to lose or be 'put down'. Assertion is a skill where 'win-win' situations can happen – no one has to be the loser.

To be assertive a person usually has to:

- understand the situation that they are in (including facts, details and other people's perceptions)
- be able to control personal emotions and stay calm
- be able to act assertively using the right non-verbal behaviour
- be able to act assertively using the right words and statements.

Some of the emotions, attitudes and behaviours involved in assertion are summarised in Table 1.1 on the following page.

Staying calm and in control of your emotions, displaying respect for others, using reflective listening and building an understanding of another person's viewpoint are all part of being assertive. Assertion is the skill of being able to understand another person's viewpoint while being able to help them to understand your viewpoint. Assertion skills create a situation where negotiation is possible.

Assertion does involve a special kind of attitude – you are going to stick up for yourself – but you are not trying to dominate or get power over other people. You are

In context

Either Mitesh or Anil will have to go on the care rota to work on Saturday but neither wants to – they both want Saturday free. Mitesh says, 'I really want Saturday free and I did ask first.' Anil could respond with:

- **aggression**: *You always want your own way, don't you? Well, I'm fed up with it. I need Saturday more than you do and I'm not coming in. That's it – I don't care what you say!*
- **assertion**: *I want Saturday free the same as you do. Let's talk it through. I don't agree that the person who asks first should always get what they want. I'm sure we can come up with some sort of agreement.*
- **submission**: *Oh that's a shame. I'm sorry. I suppose I'll have to work then.*

1   With a submissive response, Anil will lose and Mitesh will get what he wants. But what are the likely consequences for their ability to work together as team members?

2   An aggressive response will not necessarily result in winning. Both people could become trapped in a cycle of aggressive responses. What is the difference between 'sticking up for yourself' in an aggressive or in an assertive way?

3   Assertion can be seen as the most skilful response to make. Can you identify the skills that Anil would need in order to make this approach work?

Aggressive behaviour	Assertive behaviour	Submissive behaviour
Main emotions		
Anger	Control of own behaviour	Fear – wanting to please
Attitudes		
Trying to win	Trying to create a situation where everyone wins	Accepting that you will lose
Wanting your own way	Negotiating with others	Letting others dominate
Making demands	Trying to solve problems	Agreeing with others
Behaviours		
Not listening to other people	Listening to other points of view	Not putting your own views across
Putting other people down	Showing respect for others	Withdrawing or showing fear
Shouting or talking very loudly	Keeping a clear calm voice	Speaking quietly or not speaking at all
Body language		
Fixed eye contact, tense muscles, waving of hands and arms, looking angry	Varied eye contact, relaxed face muscles, looking 'in control', keeping hands and arms at your side	Looking down, not looking at others, looking frightened, tense muscles

Table 1.1 The differences between aggressive, assertive and submissive behaviours

trying to get the best outcome for everyone. It is very easy to be aggressive – it is in our 'animal nature' to attack people who cause us problems.

Your communication with service users should involve understanding and responding to their emotional needs.

Self-esteem

Service users are vulnerable people. Many service users do not have the emotional security that comes from a clear sense of **identity** and a high level of **self-esteem** and a positive **self-image**. If you dominate and threaten the people you work with, you are likely to damage their self-esteem. If they don't feel valued, children are not likely to develop a secure identity and adults may have difficulty maintaining a working sense of who they are. Aggressive responses may damage a service user's self-esteem.

Key terms

Identity This is how a person understands him- or herself. A person's identity will include self-esteem and self-image together with other social and personal issues that a person identifies with.

Self-esteem This is how you value or feel about yourself.

Self-image This is how you see or imagine yourself.

In context An interview with Anita continued …

Interviewer: You said that you like to leave people feeling cheerful. It sounds like you are a bit of an entertainer.

Anita: No, my job is very practical – housework, shopping and that sort of thing. But I am also a professional carer and part of caring is to be sensitive to people's feelings. Some people feel very uncomfortable having to have a stranger look after them. If you don't pick up on how they feel and you just work in a cold, mechanical way then they are going to stay afraid and worried. A lot of the time people try to get at you because they are frightened. If you can make people feel safe, if you can give them something emotionally – perhaps remind them of something good – well, then it makes their day and it makes my day too!

Interviewer: So, care workers have to meet the self-esteem needs of service users as part of their job?

Anita: Yes, I suppose you could put it like that.

1   **What is self-esteem?**

2   **How might Anita pick up on a service user's feelings? What verbal and non-verbal messages might she notice?**

3   **Anita talks about 'reminding people of something good' but how could she get to know about good things that might exist for different service users?**

Whether you work with children, older people or people with health needs, or physical or learning disabilities, you can always think of ways in which you can increase another person's self-esteem.

Appropriate non-verbal behaviour	• smiling • relaxed body posture • looking interested • being calm
Appropriate communication	• correct level of formality • language appropriate to speech community • appropriate preferred language • use of technological aids
Listening skills	• taking an interest • willingness to build an understanding of a service user's views

Table 1.2 Aspects of communication that increase self-esteem

In context   An interview with Anita continued ...

Interviewer: Can you give some examples of ways in which you can influence a service user's self-esteem in a positive way?

Anita: Well, it's little things that make people feel good. First, people feel valued if you remember things about their life. If you show that you are taking an interest, it shows that you think they matter – that they have value. I think it always helps to give people a choice about how they want work done, what products they want and so on. I think people need to feel in control of their lives in order to maintain a sense of self-esteem. Then I think it's important to listen to people. If people listen to you then you matter, don't you? If people cut you short – well, then, perhaps you're not worth much. I think some people enjoy talking about past times. Some people have lived fascinating lives. Learning about a person's life story can help you to find ways to help them feel valued.

Interviewer: Maintaining their identity?

Anita: Yes, no matter how much trouble you've got, it is important to hang on to all the good things in your past.

1 **What is meant by identity?**

2 **Can you explain why talking about a person's life story should help to maintain identity and meet self-esteem needs?**

3 **Anita will not use set phrases when she responds to people. Why is it that making individual responses to service users will show more value than using phrases such as 'have a nice day'?**

Barriers to communication

Communication not received

There are different types of barriers that can block effective communication. The first obvious type of barrier is when information is not received. An example would be speaking to a deaf person who uses a signed language. The sounds are not received. Communication fails because an appropriate language system has not been used and no information is communicated.

Barriers in the environment can also prevent sounds from being heard, or non-verbal messages from being seen.

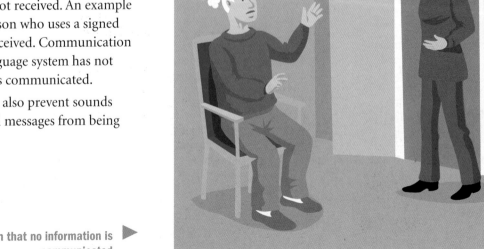

Figure 1.11 Barriers can mean that no information is communicated ▶

Remember!

The following ideas can help to reduce communication barriers in the environment.

- Improve the lighting.
- Reduce any noise.
- Move to a quieter or better-lit room.
- Work with smaller groups to see and hear more easily.
- Organise any seating so that people can see and hear each other.

Communication not understood

A second type of barrier exists when information is received (for example, seen or heard) but is not 'decoded' correctly. In other words, the information is not understood. An example of this kind of barrier might be where people from different speech communities attempt to communicate. A person using slang, jargon or complex technical terminology might be heard, and something of their message might be 'decoded', but a person who does not understand the technical terminology will not have understood the message.

For example, a service user might ask, 'Excuse me, where is the loo?' and a care worker, misunderstanding her

speech community, might say 'yer down the apples and pears an' y' can't miss it.' If the service user does not understand rhyming slang (apples and pears = stairs) they will have heard a reference to two types of fruit but still have no idea where the loo is! There is a barrier to making sense of the information that has been communicated.

Remember!

The following ideas can help to reduce communication barriers where there are language differences.

- Communicate using pictures, diagrams and non-verbal signs.
- Use translators or interpreters.
- Increase your knowledge of jargon, slang and dialects.
- Re-word your messages – find different ways of saying things.
- Speak in short, clear sentences.

Understanding is distorted

A third type of barrier is when information gets through, and you think that you have understood the message, but what you understand is distorted by perception (your understanding is wrong). Assumptions, values and beliefs and stereotypes can distort the way we 'decode' messages. A wide range of emotional and psychological factors can act as barriers that result in distorted communication.

> So you see the situation is quite serious. You have a difficult choice to make.

> I'm frightened!

> This threatens my self-esteem.

> How will I cope?

> But I don't actually need to do anything, do I?

Figure 1.12 Psychological factors can create barriers to communication by distorting perception of a message

Interviewer: How do you know if service users really understand what you are talking about?

Anita: It's not easy but sometimes you can tell from a person's face. If they look puzzled, or if they don't respond, then you know you've got to try and explain something in a different way. But some people will nod and smile although they haven't understood you. So the best way is to try and keep the conversation going and hope that they will say something back to you that shows that they have understood. For example, I had to explain I would come at a different time. Now, I couldn't ask a direct question like 'Can you remember what I just told you?' If I did that, people would be offended – they would feel I was treating them like a child. So instead I asked them about what they would be doing on the day that I had to change my time. They said that I would be coming at 10 o'clock – and that was wrong – and I was able to remind them of the change. One way of preventing misunderstanding is to just keep somebody talking.

1 **Can you explain why Anita does not like to ask questions like 'What did I just tell you?' or 'When am I coming next then?'**

2 **Can you identify some reasons why people might nod and smile as if they understand you even if they don't understand what you have tried to communicate?**

3 **Anita likes to keep the conversation going with service users in order to overcome barriers. By doing this, she can get feedback on what they have understood. Can you use the idea of the communication cycle to explain what she is doing?**

Where the first and second type of barriers exist, it will usually be obvious that communication has failed. Distorted understanding is not always easy to identify. Reflective listening may help you to check what has been understood or what barriers may exist to communication.

Types of communication: difficult, complex or sensitive

Some communication between people is simply about sharing or 'transmitting' information. For example, someone might want to know what number bus to catch, or they might ask for a drink of water etc. A great deal of communication in care work involves building an understanding of another person and providing emotional support. Burnard and Morrison (1997) argue that caring and communicating are inseparably linked. Care workers have to care about the people they work with in order to communicate effectively.

Reflect

Imagine you had to support a person in any of the situations below:

- a mother whose child was killed in a road accident several weeks ago
- someone who has just been diagnosed as HIV-positive
- someone who says they want to die because they can't bear to live following the death of their partner.

What can you say?

There is no advice or information that is likely to be helpful in the situations above but many people do want someone to be with them. Communication in this situation may focus on emotional needs rather than the 'transmission of information'.

Engebretson (2004) uses the idea of 'a caring presence' to explain what is needed in these situations. Creating a **caring presence** is about sharing an understanding of the feelings that service users may be experiencing. Sometimes just being with a person who is lonely, anxious or depressed can provide comfort. If you believe that your carer understands your needs and is concerned about you, then just knowing that they are near you can help you to feel supported. Non-verbal communication may sometimes communicate emotions and feelings more effectively than words.

Key terms

Caring presence A caring presence involves being open to the experience of another person through a 'two-way' encounter with that person.

If you can support people just by the way you are 'present with them' this may be because you have developed a sense of empathy. Empathy involves a caring attitude where someone can see beyond his or her own assumptions about the world and can imagine the thoughts and feelings of someone else. Gerard Egan (1986) defined empathy as 'the ability to enter into and understand the world of someone else and communicate this understanding to him or her'. A care professional who can empathise will be able to imagine the emotions associated with the pain and grief that another person is experiencing.

Barriers to emotional communication

Sometimes care workers can feel stressed by the emotional needs of service users. Listening to others might involve hearing about frightening and depressing situations. Carers sometimes stop listening in order to avoid unpleasant emotional feelings. A lack of time, tiredness or a desire to avoid emotional stress can create a barrier to providing caring communication.

It is important that health and care workers can work out if a situation simply requires the sharing of information or whether a more sensitive, caring approach to communication is needed.

Barriers associated with personality and psychological needs

Building an understanding of another person and establishing a 'caring presence' can be very difficult where the personality or self-esteem needs of another person create a barrier. Many people who are depressed or anxious experience negative thoughts that 'just come to them'. Attempts to understand these thoughts and feelings may feel like hitting a brick wall. It can feel as if there is an emotional barrier that prevents the person from experiencing any positive emotions. The case study on the next page demonstrates this.

In context

Alex: I can't go on. I just don't want to live any more. You won't understand but it's just no good – I've lost everything.

Worker: But would you like to tell me? I would like to try to understand.

Alex: But you can't know what it feels like. I mean you've got everything – everything has gone wrong for me. I've got no job, no money, no partner, no one cares. I've got nothing to live for. I'd be better off dead, wouldn't I?

Worker: I can understand that you feel very bad – but are things really as hopeless as they feel?

Alex: Yes, they are! You might think I could get a 'crap' job down the road but I can't live with that. I used to be important and I can't give that up. I don't want to live in some awful flat with social services telling me how to budget. No. I'd be better off dead. I just want to get it over with!

There is no simple way of removing this barrier but some skilled therapists might continue to listen and learn about the person – keep the person talking in the hope that they might use the understanding they have developed in order to positively influence the person's self-esteem.

The conversation continued with the worker using her understanding of Alex.

Worker: So when you were in charge of your own business, you enjoyed the challenges. You didn't let anything get you down?

Alex: Yes, but that was then. It's all different now. I've lost it all.

Worker: But you've been a very successful person, who could cope with so much. Why is it that you have to give up now?

Alex: I can't explain it – I just feel so bad.

Worker: Well, tell me about how it felt when you had that great success we were talking about. I would like to imagine what it felt like.

Read the information on probes and prompts below and answer the following questions.

1 **Can you identify how the professional worker has used questions, probes and prompts in order to keep the conversation going?**

2 **Can you explain how the worker may have used a cycle of communication in order to build up an understanding of Alex's thoughts?**

3 **Can you explain the importance of building an understanding of, or of developing empathy with, another person during a difficult, complex or sensitive interaction?**

The professional worker in the case study above is not 'just talking' – she is trying to steer the conversation round to positive memories. The worker is using her understanding of Alex's past to try and lead the conversation around the barrier of negative and depressed thoughts. If the worker is successful, the conversation might lead to Alex increasing his level of self-esteem.

Talking through difficult, complex or sensitive issues will involve the verbal skills of asking open questions and using probes and prompts within the conversation.

- **Open questions** – these cannot be answered with a yes or no answer – they require a person to think about their answer. Open questions are likely to involve a complex cycle of communication in order to discuss issues. They include questions such as 'How would you describe your quality of life?'

- **Probes** – these are very short questions such as 'Can you tell me more?' Probes are used to dig deeper into the person's answer – they probe or investigate what the other person has just said.

- **Prompts** – these are short questions which you offer to the other person in order to prompt them to answer. Prompts are questions such as 'Would you do it again?'

Assessment activity 1.2

Explain how the communication cycle may be used to communicate difficult, complex and sensitive issues.

Communication about difficult, complex and sensitive issues will depend on feedback – you will need to check whether you have understood the other person. There is always the risk that you will not understand what another person is trying to communicate.

You will need to explain how reflective listening techniques might help you to clarify your understanding. If you have used notes from your placement in order to describe the communication cycle, or if you have designed a poster, you will need to explain in detail the importance of feedback and checking what you understand. **M1**

Grading tip for M1

You should role-play or simulate a conversation that involves emotional issues – this may help you to explore the importance of reflective listening. An example of an emotional situation that could be acted and recorded in class would be where one person is acting what their feelings might be, following the death of a pet. You will need to use a range of skills including probes and prompts and reflective listening in order to keep the conversation working.

In order to explain how the communication cycle is used, you will need to go beyond a simple description of the stages of coding and decoding messages. You will need to describe the difficulties involved in arriving at a situation where you can truly understand what another person is communicating. You should discuss the importance of reflective listening techniques in achieving this understanding.

Barriers associated with cultural differences

Culture refers to the different customs and assumptions that communities of people adopt. Different ethnic and religious groups may have different cultures, but different age, occupational and geographical groups also make different cultural assumptions.

Words and non-verbal communication can be interpreted differently depending on the context and on the culture of the person using them. For example, the word 'hot' can have different meanings depending on the context in which it is used and the culture of the person using it. In a formal context, 'hot' refers to having a high temperature. But in other speech communities an object might be 'hot' if it has been 'stolen' or if it is perceived as 'very desirable'. A hot person might be very good at something, or be someone who is overcome with sexual desire! If communication is interpreted only from a fixed cultural standpoint, then serious misunderstandings can arise. If you are going to make sense of spoken and non-verbal language then you must understand the context and the intentions of the speaker.

Reflect

How many words can you think of that mean quite different things depending on the cultural context in which they are used? Some obvious words to start with are *cool*, *hard* and *wicked*.

An example of a non-verbal **cultural difference** might be the hand gesture of the palm up and facing forward; in Britain this means 'Stop, don't do that' whereas in Greece it can mean 'You are dirt' and is a very offensive

Key terms

Cultural difference Communication is always influenced by cultural systems of meaning. Different cultures interpret words, phrases and body language differently.

gesture. Why do the same physical movements have different meanings? One explanation could be that the British version of the palm-and-fingers gesture means, 'I arrest you, you must not do it' whereas the Greek interpretation goes back to medieval times when criminals had dirt rubbed in their faces to show how much people despised them.

Remember!

The following ideas can help to overcome the barriers associated with cultural differences.

- Try to increase your knowledge of different cultures.
- Try to identify different possible cultural interpretations of words and non-verbal behaviour.
- Avoid making assumptions about people who are different.
- Use reflective listening techniques to check that your understanding is correct.
- Be sensitive to different social settings and the form of communication that would be most appropriate in different contexts.
- Consider involving advocates who will represent the best interests of the people that you are working with.

In context

Jasmine is a member of a youth group; she often sits with her arms crossed and her head turned away. She avoids eye contact. When asked if she feels OK, she does make eye contact, changes her body posture and says she is happy to be in the group.

1 **What messages would crossed arms and avoidance of eye contact normally send?**

2 **How many reasons can you think of to explain why someone might sit with their arms crossed, deliberately avoiding eye contact while other people are speaking?**

3 **How can you find out what an individual's body language means?**

It is important not to make assumptions about non-verbal messages – they should always be checked. Non-verbal messages can mean different things depending on the circumstances of the people who are sending them.

Values and belief systems

In context An interview with Anita continued …

Interviewer: There is an awful lot of theory to understand about communication, isn't there? How do you manage to take all this in and use it when you work with people?

Anita: I just go in with the right attitude – it's a sort of feeling. If you've got the right attitude then you tend to say and do the right things anyway. I enjoy meeting people and getting to know them. I value everyone I work with; I think of them as important people. I am interested in their lives and I listen to what they tell me. I think values – what you believe in – are at the heart of how you work with people. All the theory like verbal and non-verbal helps you to understand what might be happening, but just knowing about these ideas isn't enough when you work face-to-face with people.

1 **Can you identify what values Anita uses when she talks to service users?**

2 **Can you explain what Anita means when she talks about 'If you've got the right attitude then you tend to say and do the right things anyway'?**

3 **Can you explain what Anita means when she says that theory helps you to understand but that just knowing theory isn't enough?**

If a person does not feel valued – if a person feels emotionally threatened during an interaction – then this will create a barrier that is likely to lead to misunderstandings.

Figure 1.13 It is important to learn about other people's beliefs in order to avoid barriers to communication

It is important to try to learn about the beliefs and values of other people in order to make sense of what they are trying to communicate

Assumptions and stereotypes

When someone has fixed ideas that they use to classify people as 'all being the same', it is called **stereotyping**. Stereotypes may create barriers to building an understanding of another person. Once you have classified people you think that you know what they are like. You might believe that you don't need to listen to a person because you already know what their needs are. Stereotypes can create a barrier because people stop listening and checking their understanding of other people's communication.

Key terms

Stereotyping This is a fixed way of thinking involving generalisations and expectations about an issue or a group of people.

Theory into practice

Get together with your colleagues and discuss what assumptions and stereotypes older people might have about 16- to 19-year-olds.

An example of a stereotype that creates a barrier to communication might be disability. Disabled people are often stereotyped as damaged versions of 'normal' people. When disabled people are classified in this way, they might be pitied and ignored. People with communication differences are sometimes assumed to be awkward or mentally limited. Older people are sometimes seen as demented or confused if they do not answer questions quickly, correctly and clearly.

Use and abuse of power

The General Social Care Council (GSCC) Code of Practice for Social Care Workers (2002) requires all workers to respect individuality and support service users to control their own lives. However, there is always the danger that, if a care worker is short of time, they will seek to control the service user. It is an abuse of **power** if care workers deliberately control and manipulate service users.

Key terms

Power In the context of interpersonal behaviour, 'power' means the ability to influence and control what other people do.

In context An interview with Anita continued …

Interviewer: You said that people are sometimes afraid to have care services. Why is that?

Anita: Well, I think that people are afraid that you will come in and take control – order them about, tell them how they should live their life and so on.

Interviewer: So it's about power then?

Anita: Yes, being caring is all about valuing other people and not trying to manipulate and control them, but it's very difficult sometimes. I don't have enough time to get everything done and there is always the temptation to just take over and do everything my way in order to get it done quickly. It's easy to think that you know best but if you take this attitude you will upset people. You always have to involve and 'work with' people rather than 'working on' people. You have to find out what people think, you have to respect their wishes and you have to let people choose how they want things done.

Interviewer: But don't some people like to leave you to it?

Anita: Yes. Some of the men say, 'You do what you like, you buy me whatever you think I need – I don't care anymore.' But this is a problem too. Sometimes people lose control of their life and give up – they become 'helpless'. People in this situation want you to make all the decisions – have the power. I still try to find out about their preferences and try to encourage them to make choices.

1 Can you identify reasons why 'taking over' and not bothering to communicate with service users is wrong?

2 Can you explain why Anita still tries to encourage people to make choices even when – to begin with – they want her to take control?

3 Can you explain what is meant by power in the context of interpersonal behaviour?

Building an effective working relationship involves helping a service user to take control, or stay in control, of their life. This is often called 'empowerment'. See the section on empowerment on page 38.

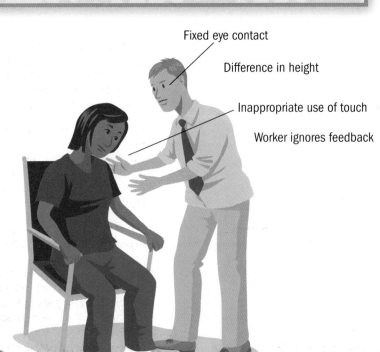

Fixed eye contact

Difference in height

Inappropriate use of touch

Worker ignores feedback

Figure 1.14 These non-verbal messages express power and domination ▶

Disability

In context

Zana arranged to interview a 40-year-old woman who has a hearing disability. Zana sat with her back to a bright window and decided to talk very loudly to give the woman more chance to hear her. After introducing herself, Zana asked, 'When did you go deaf? It must be terrible not to hear properly.'

The woman later said, 'I didn't like the interview at all. At first I thought Zana was very angry and aggressive – she kept shouting. I couldn't see her face so I couldn't really hear what she was saying. I couldn't understand what she was asking. She seemed to think I was deaf but I can hear when my aid is working. I felt she looked down on me as if I wasn't worth anything.'

1 **Can you identify any physical barriers to communication in this example?**

2 **Can you identify any barriers involving miscommunication of information?**

3 **Can you identify any barriers associated with perception including assumptions, values or stereotypes that might prevent effective communication between these two people?**

People with a disability often experience barriers associated with all of the issues identified in this section. Some practical ideas for addressing barriers involving disability are suggested in the table below.

Visual disability	• Use language to describe things. • Assist people to touch things (e.g. touch your face to recognise you). • Explain details that sighted people might take for granted. • Check what people can see (many registered blind people can see shapes, or tell light from dark). • Check glasses, other aids and equipment.
Hearing disability	• Don't shout. Use normal clear speech and make sure your face is visible for people who can lip-read. • Show pictures or write messages. • Learn to sign (for people who use signed languages). • Ask for help from, or employ, a communicator or interpreter for signed languages. • Check that hearing aids and equipment are working.
Physical and intellectual disabilities	• Increase your knowledge of disabilities. • Use pictures and signs as well as clear, simple speech. • Be calm and patient. • Set up group meetings where people can share interests. • Check that people do not become isolated. • Use advocates (see page 35) – independent people who can spend time building an understanding of the needs of specific individuals to assist with communication work.

Table 1.3 Ideas for reducing barriers to communication where people have a disability

In context

Joseph is 86 and lives in residential care. He came into care because he could no longer cope alone. He has arthritis, a hearing disability and poor memory. Joseph moved to the UK from Jamaica 50 years ago. The home is some distance from his friends and he receives few visits. Care workers do not know much about Joseph's history or cultural background. The home is short-staffed and care workers have little time to talk with him. Care workers have difficulty understanding Joseph's accent and some of the words that he uses. Because Joseph has poor hearing he does not always respond appropriately when he is asked

questions. Some of the care workers say that Joseph is 'confused'; one said, 'There is no point talking to him – he can't understand anything anyway!' Joseph feels isolated and distressed.

1   Can you identify some of the barriers to communication that exist for Joseph?

2   Can you provide some ideas for overcoming the barriers to communication that you have identified in this situation?

3   Can you explain why these barriers might reduce Joseph's self-esteem?

Assessment activity 1.3

Describe factors that may influence communication and interpersonal interactions with particular reference to health and social care settings.

1   You must describe factors that influence communication in health and social care settings. Your work placement notes will help you to identify specific interactions that will enable you to describe examples of these factors. **P3**

Grading tip for P3

Some of the factors that may influence communication are summarised in Figure 1.15 below.

The nature of communication: spoken language signs and symbols, written and electronic systems

Cultural differences and preferred spoken language systems

The environment – lighting, noise and the ability to see or hear others

Emotional needs associated with personality, self-esteem and issues such as depression and anxiety

Communication is influenced by . . .

Attitudes – the ability to be assertive and to respond to others in an appropriate way

Content of communication – communication in difficult, complex or sensitive situations

Disability and preferred methods of communication

Values and beliefs – the risk of assumptions and stereotypes

▲ Figure 1.15 Factors that influence communication

There are a range of services that may assist people to communicate or help to remove the barriers to effective communication.

Support services

Advocates

Sometimes, when people have a very serious learning disability or illness (such as dementia), it is not possible to communicate with them. In such situations, care services will often employ an advocate. An advocate is someone who speaks for someone else. A lawyer speaking for a 'client' in a courtroom is working as an advocate for that person and will argue the person's case. In care work, a volunteer might try to get to know someone who has dementia or a learning disability. The volunteer tries to understand and then communicate the service user's needs and wants. Advocates should be independent of the staff team and so can argue for the service user's rights without being influenced by what is the easiest or cheapest thing to do.

Advocacy often makes sure that people's needs are not overlooked but it is not straightforward; volunteers may not always understand the feelings and needs of the people for whom they are advocating. Some people argue it would be better if service users could be trained and supported to argue their own case. Helping people to argue their own case is called self-advocacy.

Interpreters and translators

Interpreters are people who communicate meaning from one language to another. This includes interpreting between spoken and signed languages such as English and British Sign Language. Translators are people who change recorded material from one language to another.

Translating and interpreting involve the communication of meaning between different languages. Translating and interpreting are not just technical acts of changing the words from one system to another. Many languages do not have simple equivalence between words. Interpreters and translators have to grasp the meaning of a message (decode the message) and find a way of expressing it in a different language system. This is rarely easy, even for professional translators.

Take it further

Look up a website where the content is written in a language other than English. Use an automatic translation system available on the Internet to automatically translate the language into English. Very often descriptions of hotel accommodation etc are extremely funny when they are automatically translated. An automatic system often uses strange and sometimes inappropriate words to interpret the original text. Translation is not just a matter of swapping words over!

Interpreters may be professional people who are employed by social services or health authorities in order to communicate with people who use different spoken or signed languages. They may also be friends or family members who have sufficient language ability to be able to explain messages in different circumstances.

Interpretation and translation are vital in any setting where communication is blocked because individuals rely on different languages or communication systems. Many people live in communities where English may not be the first language. When these people need to access health care or social services, or when members of these communities need legal support, they will need the services of translators and interpreters. People who use signed languages may also need assistance from interpreters and translators – see page 37 for further details of signed languages.

Some issues associated with using interpreters

Translation and interpretation involves conveying what a person means from one language to another. This is not as simple as just changing words or signs from one system to another. When an interpreter works with people, they will become part of the communication cycle.

Important issues in interpretation include:

- **Knowledge of the subject matter** – an interpreter is likely to be more effective when they understand the issues involved. A professional interpreter may be able to explain details of legislation or procedures for claiming benefit because they understand the issues. If a relative or friend is acting as an interpreter, they will have to make sense of the technical details before they can communicate clearly. Knowledge of a language is not always enough to ensure clear and effective communication.

- **Trust** – it is important that people have confidence in somebody who is acting as their interpreter. People from specific communities may find it hard to trust a member from a different community. Many women may not feel safe and confident discussing personal issues using a male interpreter. The issue may not be about the interpreter's language competence, but about the interpreter's ability to understand and correctly convey what a person wants to say.

- **Social and cultural values** – many people may feel that it is inappropriate to discuss personal details using an interpreter of the opposite sex. Some deaf people do not feel confident using interpreters who have not experienced deafness themselves. The choice of an interpreter must support the self-esteem needs of people who need to access interpretation services.

- **Confidentiality** – confidentiality is a right (Data Protection Act 1998) as well as an ethical issue. Professional interpreters are likely to offer guarantees of confidentiality. Using a relative or volunteer may not necessarily provide people with the same guarantee of confidentiality.

- **Non-judgemental support** – a professional interpreter is likely to offer advanced inter-personal skills which include the ability to remain non-judgemental when undertaking interpretation work. Volunteers, relatives and friends may have language competence, but they may not necessarily be able to interpret meaning without biasing their interpretation.

In context

Jai is 10 years old. His mother and father do not speak English as a first language although Jai has grown up to be multilingual. Jai's mother is in poor health and needs to explain her problems to a health worker. Jai is expected to provide the necessary interpretation of his mother's problems into English.

1   Can you identify some of the problems that may arise if Jai has to interpret for his mother?

2   Can you identify some of the emotional risks that Jai might experience in such a situation?

3   Can you explain why the services of a professional interpreter might be more appropriate in this situation?

Speech therapists

Speech therapists provide assessment and therapy for people with speech, language or other communication problems. Speech therapists may work with children, people with physical or learning difficulties or people with neurological problems such as Parkinson's disease. A range of communication approaches and therapy will be used in order to improve people's communication abilities.

Counsellors

Counsellors use advanced communication skills combined with knowledge of psychological theory in order to help people. All counsellors spend time listening to, and building an understanding of, their client's problems. They will then work within a particular psychological model in order to support a person to change or develop some aspect of their life. Many counsellors act as private practitioners – some of them specialising in specific areas of therapy such as grief counselling, self-harm, drug dependency, alcoholism or health needs. Many GPs refer patients to specific counselling services associated with the practice. Various voluntary agencies such as MIND (mental health) and RELATE (relationship guidance) employ counsellors or refer people to counselling services.

Mentors

Mentors are usually people who are highly experienced in a particular job or activity; they advise others who are new to the activity or less experienced. Mentors will need effective communication skills coupled with some ability to explain issues and provide guidance. If a person is referred to as a mentor, it might be assumed that they will provide guidance based on their experience and knowledge of an issue.

Befrienders

Befrienders seek to create a supportive relationship with others. A befriender will have good communication skills that enable them to listen to, and build an understanding of, a service user's views and feelings. A befriender will work 'as if' he or she was a friend. Befrienders will not be assumed to have any particular psychological knowledge.

Psychologists

The term 'psychology' originally meant the study of the mind. Clinical psychologists work in the field of mental health and sometimes provide assessment and therapy to people who have emotional or psychological problems such as depression and anxiety. Many psychologists work in other areas of human behaviour. Educational psychologists work in the field of learning and human development, while occupational psychologists focus on human behaviour within a work setting.

Preferred language

Spoken and written English are not the preferred system of communication for everyone (see page 18 for further details of preferred languages and technological aids to communication). The first (or main) language of many deaf people may be a signed language. People who are registered blind may use Braille as opposed to written text in order to read information.

British Sign Language

The British Deaf Association states that British Sign Language 'is the first or preferred language of nearly 70,000 Deaf people in the United Kingdom'. The British Deaf Association explains that British Sign Language (BSL) 'belongs to Deaf people. It is not a communication system devised by hearing people. It is a real language which has evolved in the UK's Deaf community over hundreds of years'. The British Deaf Association campaigns for the right of Deaf people to be educated in BSL and to access information and services through BSL, arguing that the Deaf community is a 'linguistic and cultural minority and is not measured in medical terms'. Many Deaf people argue that the Deaf community should be identified as 'culturally Deaf' by using a capital 'd' for Deaf. This emphasises that 'Deaf' people use another language system as opposed to 'deaf' people who are perceived to be impaired.

Further details of BSL can be found at www.britishdeafassociation.org.uk.

Details of signs and a finger spelling alphabet can be found at: www.british-sign.co.uk and at: www.royaldeaf.org.uk.

Makaton

Makaton is a system for developing language that uses speech, signs and symbols to help people with learning difficulties to communicate and to develop their language skills. People who communicate using Makaton may speak a word and perform a sign using hands and body language. There is a large range of symbols to help people with learning difficulties to recognise an idea or to communicate with others. Further information on Makaton can be found at www.makaton.org.

Braille

Braille (a system of raised marks that can be felt with the fingers) provides a system of written communication based on the sense of touch for people who have limited vision. The communication system known as Braille was first published by Louis Braille, a blind 20-year-old, in 1829. The system is now widely adopted as the form of writing and reading used by people who cannot see written script.

Modern computer software can translate written material into Braille, which can be printed out using special printers. Further details on Braille can be found at www.brailleplus.net.

Supporting service users

Supportive communication involves building an understanding of the service user's needs through effective reflective listening skills. It may also be important to use 'warm' friendly non-verbal behaviour that expresses interest in another person such as:

- effective eye contact (making varied and appropriate contact with another person's eyes)
- a relaxed and calm body posture
- smiling – looking friendly rather than 'cold' or frozen in expression
- hand movements and gestures that show interest
- slight head nods while talking that communicate messages of 'I see,' or 'I understand,' or 'I agree'
- an appropriate gentle tone of voice.

Being supportive involves being aware of your own behaviour and monitoring how it is affecting others. It may also be important to come across to other people as being genuine. Being genuine involves not acting or 'playing a role' when you interact with service users. Supportive skills are sometimes defined as the ability to:

Reflect

Imagine that you feel sad about something and that you explain your problems to a friend. How would you feel if your friend did not look at you and instead seemed interested in what was happening outside the window? How would you feel if your friend just 'parroted' the things you said back to you? How would you react if they just said things like 'I know', or 'Yes' without sounding sincere or interested?

Being a good friend involves supportive behaviour. How good are you at showing others that you understand their feelings?

- build an understanding of another person
- be perceived as warm and friendly
- be perceived as genuine and sincere.

Empowerment

Reflect

Imagine you went into a shop where the shop assistants were unfriendly and ignored you. How would this affect your self-esteem?

Most people would be angry if they were ignored but their self-esteem would not suffer greatly because they would think, 'I'm not using this shop again – I'll take my business elsewhere.'

Now imagine that you receive the same treatment every day. Imagine that you live with people who are unfriendly and ignore you. How will this affect you and your self-esteem?

If other important people treat you as if you don't matter, it is hard for you to value yourself. The key difference between being mistreated in a shop and mistreated in a care setting is one of power. If you hold the power, your self-esteem will not be vulnerable. If you think that other people have all the power, your self-esteem is likely to be at risk. **Empowerment** involves believing that you can make choices and control your own life.

Key terms

Empowerment This enables a service user to make choices and take control of their own life. The opposite of empowerment is dependency.

In order to empower others, care workers need to understand the unique story of each person. An empowering approach must never involve stereotyping

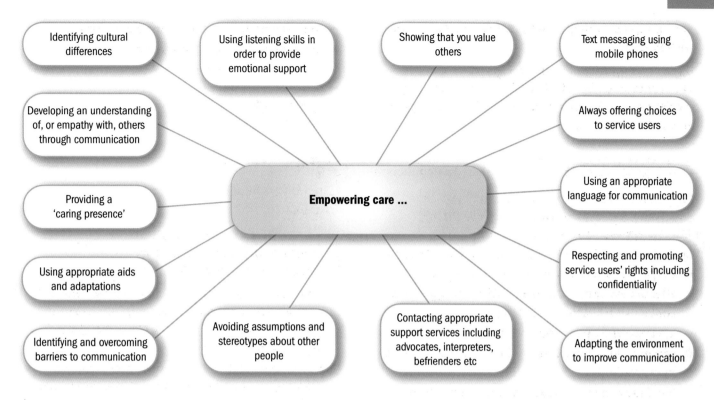

▲ Figure 1.16 Aspects of empowering communication

– seeing a group of people as 'all being the same'. Empowerment involves:

- a value system where the worker understands that their life experiences will be different from others
- supporting service users to take control of important decisions
- service users and carers enjoying an equal status.

The care worker is not a person of higher status than the service user.

Promotion of rights

As well as general human rights, service users have a range of rights that are established in national standards, codes of practice and legislation. Patients and service users may be seen as having the following rights.

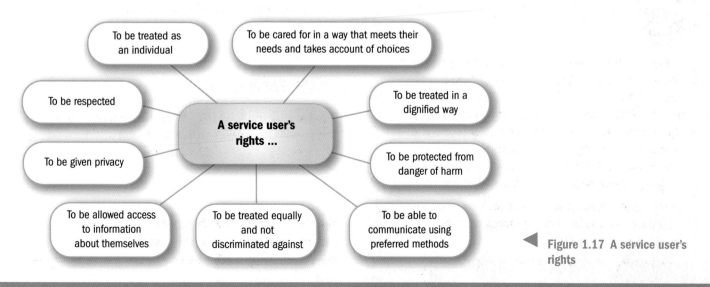

◀ Figure 1.17 A service user's rights

Maintaining confidentiality

Confidentiality is an important right for all service users because:

- they may not trust a carer if the carer does not keep information to themselves
- they may not feel valued or able to keep their self-esteem if their private details are shared with others
- a professional service which maintains respect for individuals must keep private information confidential
- there are legal requirements to keep personal records confidential
- a service user's safety may be put at risk if details of their property and habits are shared publicly.

Trust

If a service user knows that their care worker won't pass things on, they may feel confident about sharing what they really think and feel.

Self-esteem

If a care worker promises to keep things confidential, then it shows that they respect and value the service user.

Safety

Care workers must keep personal details confidential in order to protect service users' property and personal safety. If your home is empty and other people know where you keep your money, someone may be tempted to break in.

Staying professional

Medical practitioners and lawyers have always kept strict confidentiality as part of their professional role. If service users are to receive a professional service, care workers must copy this example.

Assessment activity 1.4

Identify how the communication needs of patients/ service users may be assisted, including non-verbal communication.

1. In order to demonstrate this outcome you will need to identify some communication needs such as language needs – needs that can be met through technology and emotional needs. You must identify how you would use verbal and non-verbal communication to assist effective communication.

Grading tip for P4

You could use notes of interactions you have experienced while on placement to help you to identify needs. You might also undertake some role-playing activities where you simulate different situations involving communication difficulties. If you simulate communication needs associated with different languages or disabilities, your experiences will enable you to identify and perhaps make a presentation about communication needs and ways in which you can assist people. You could also identify communication needs and methods for assessing these needs through the design of posters.

Grading tip for M2

You must go into more detail and identify a range of specific communication needs. The summary table below could give you a starting point for explaining the needs that service users may have and how those needs can be met.

In order to explain needs, you must provide a greater depth of information about communication needs than if you were simply identifying needs.

Explain the specific communication needs patients/ service users may have that require support, including the use of technology.

2   You must explain how specific communication needs can be supported. You should write a report that draws on work you have undertaken in simulations, or in making presentations or designing posters.

Specific communication needs of service users

Need	Type of support
Visual disability	Assistive equipment including glasses, magnifiers and IT software to enhance display. Improved environmental conditions including lighting. Use of oral communication, Braille.
Hearing disability	Assistive equipment including hearing aids, minicom, IT support, text messaging. Improved environment such as reduced background noise. Visual communication, BSL signers, interpreters.
Physical disability	Assistive equipment – to produce language. Use of signs and symbols, speech therapy.
Learning difficulty	Use of signs and symbols, Makaton, communication passports and advocates.
Spoken language differences	Interpreters, translators, use of signs and symbols and visual communication.
Cultural differences	Listening skills, identifying the risk of assumptions and stereotypes.
Emotional support	Using listening to develop understanding and empathy, the importance of a caring presence.
Psychological problems including depression, anxiety, self-esteem and personality needs	Listening skills, befriending, counselling, psychotherapy and psychological support.

Whatever the specific communication need all service users will have a right to supportive communication that conveys respect and value.

Table 1.4 The needs that some service users may have and how those needs can be met

Analyse how communication in health and social care settings assists patients/service users and other key people.

3   You will need to write a report which provides a range of examples of interactions, explaining the strengths and weaknesses of various support services, support technologies, language systems and supportive, empowering approaches to communication.

Grading tip for D1

At this level you must go into greater depth and analyse how communication can assist the physical and emotional well-being of service users and other key people.

In order to analyse how communication assists people in health and social care settings you will need to explain a range of issues involved in communication and discuss the advantages, disadvantages and strengths and weaknesses of different approaches.

You should practise describing interactions and reviewing their effectiveness before you present evidence of your own practical work. To begin with, you might watch videos or film clips of interpersonal interactions. You should practise identifying and describing different behaviours that you have seen and/or heard in recorded material. As you become more confident you can **role-play** or simulate communicating in care settings. You should practise identifying and describing communication within these role-plays and **simulations**.

See 'Preparation for assessment' at the end of this unit (page 45) for detailed discussion of how you can demonstrate your communication skills.

Key terms

Role-play This involves acting out a role. You have to behave in such a way that other people can – at least temporarily – believe in the character you are portraying.

Simulation This does not require you to act or portray a character. If you simulate a conversation, you simply say (or sign) the appropriate responses. You do not expect people observing your behaviour to perceive you as anyone but yourself. Both simulation and role-play involve thinking through appropriate responses but role-play involves a greater level of acting skill.

Assessment activity 1.5

Describe two interactions that you have participated in, in the role of a carer, using communication skills to assist patients/service users.

1   You must provide an account of two interactions where you have taken the role of a carer and used your communication skills to assist others.   **P5**

Grading tip for P5

Unit guidance recommends that one of these interactions should be on a one-to-one basis and the other interaction should be a group interaction. At least one of the interactions should be observed by a course tutor, or workplace supervisor, using a checklist or witness statement as supporting evidence.

Review the effectiveness of your communication skills in the two interactions undertaken.

2   Having described your two interactions you must consider how effective they were.   **P6**

Grading tip for P6

You should consider whether you were able to communicate clearly and if you were effective in providing emotional support to others. You can describe their non-verbal behaviour to help you discuss this issue. If people smiled, if they made frequent eye contact, if they were relaxed, if their non-verbal behaviour copied your behaviour – then this may provide evidence of an appropriate emotional atmosphere. What did people say to you? Perhaps the other person said, 'I enjoyed talking with you' or 'Will you be here tomorrow? It would be nice to talk again.' Then you have evidence that your communication was seen as supportive. Did other people respond to you in a group setting? Did they chat with you at the end of the group meeting?

Your interactions need not have worked out perfectly but you must at least review how your work communicated with and supported other people.

M3 Explain how your communication skills could have been used to make the interactions more effective.

3   You must explain how your communication skills could have been used to make the interactions more effective. You must go beyond a description of the feedback you got from other people and you must use your knowledge of communication theory to help you think of ways in which you could have made the interactions more effective.   **M3**

Grading tip for M3

For a merit you need to go into greater detail. Even if your performance was very well received, even if everyone else enjoyed your company – there might still be ways in which you could have improved your performance. In a one-to-one situation you might have developed an understanding of the other person – but if you had more time and involvement could you develop this understanding into empathy? You may have clearly communicated your points in a group but could you have influenced people to a greater degree by linking your points to the values and beliefs that people share within the group? Could you have timed your points more effectively? You might not be looking for things have gone wrong in order to write about ideas for improving your communication. Naturally, if you did encounter barriers or problems in communicating, then it might be easy to suggest ways of improving such an interaction.

D2 Analyse the factors which influenced the interactions undertaken.

4   For a distinction you must analyse the factors that influenced the interactions. This means that you must go into greater depth than simply explaining possible improvements.

Grading tip for D2

When you analyse, you will be breaking down your description of events in order to identify how aspects of communication can be explained. You will also use key terms and theory in order to explain what you think was happening during your interactions.

At distinction level you will need to discuss the theory behind improving communication as well as the theory that explains what was happening in both your individual and group interactions.

Knowledge check

1   Why is tone of voice categorised as a non-verbal rather than a verbal issue?

2   Is it true that effective caring communication can be defined as 'clear, concise transmission of information between people'?

3   What does coding and decoding messages within ordinary everyday communication mean?

4   What is reflective listening and why is it important?

5   Rachel says, 'I never let anyone else win an argument with me – I always get my own way!' Is it correct to describe Rachel's attitude as being assertive?

6   If you met a person who said, 'I can't hear you, I need to put my glasses on' what sense could you make of this communication?

7   How can stereotyped thinking create a barrier to communication?

8   Is it possible for a person who has no knowledge of the English language to be able to sign using British Sign Language?

9   What is an advocate?

10 What problems might arise if a relative (with the necessary language skills) acts in place of a professional translator?

Grading criteria		
To achieve a pass grade the evidence must show that the learner is able to:	To achieve a merit grade the evidence must show that, in addition to the pass criteria, the learner is able to:	To achieve a distinction grade the evidence must show that, in addition to the pass and merit criteria, the learner is able to:
P1 describe different types of communication and interpersonal interaction, using examples relevant to health and social care settings **Assessment activity 1.1 page 17**		
P2 describe the stages of the communication cycle **Assessment activity 1.1 page 17**	**M1** explain how the communication cycle may be used to communicate difficult, complex and sensitive issues **Assessment activity 1.2 page 29**	
P3 describe factors that may influence communication and interpersonal interactions with particular reference to health and social care settings **Assessment activity 1.3 page 34**		
P4 identify how the communication needs of patients/service users may be assisted, including non-verbal communication **Assessment activity 1.4 page 40**	**M2** explain the specific communication needs patients/service users may have that require support, including the use of technology **Assessment activity 1.4 page 41**	**D1** analyse how communication in health and social care settings assists patients/service users and other key people **Assessment activity 1.4 page 41**
P5 describe two interactions that they have participated in, in the role of a carer, using communication skills to assist patients/service users **Assessment activity 1.5 page 42**		
P6 review the effectiveness of own communication skills in the two interactions undertaken. **Assessment activity 1.5 page 42**	**M3** explain how own communication skills could have been used to make the interactions more effective. **Assessment activity 1.5 page 43**	**D2** analyse the factors that influenced the interactions undertaken. **Assessment activity 1.5 page 43**

Preparation for assessment

■ Describing what you see

In order to provide evidence of your communication skills **P6** you must identify your own verbal and non-verbal behaviour. You must explain how you used eye contact, whether you smiled or not, facial orientation, body posture, how calm and relaxed you were etc **P1**. You should also provide examples of things that you said and the responses that you received. This will enable you to describe the degree of formality you used, how you used feedback (the communication cycle) and perhaps whether you used reflective listening **P2 M1**. If you can identify your actual verbal and non-verbal behaviour, then you can work out how effective it might have been and how you can improve it **M3 D2**.

You need to say more than 'I behaved in a friendly manner and tried to cheer the other person up'. Anyone reading this sentence can understand what you were trying to do but there is no evidence of your actual behaviour. What does 'being friendly' involve in terms of verbal and non-verbal behaviour? What does 'cheering another person up' involve?

■ Pitfalls to avoid

Naomi is practising describing an interaction; her work involves the following generalised statements. These statements all fail to communicate what her behaviours really were.

Naomi's statements	Why these statements do not explain what happened
Mrs B looked sad and lonely so she was pleased to talk.	'Sad and lonely' do not describe behaviours – we need to know what Mrs B's non-verbal behaviour involved. Did she look down or away from Naomi? Did she fail to respond? What evidence was there that she was pleased to talk – did she say so? Did her facial expression communicate that she was happy?
I used the communication cycle as we talked.	What does 'using the communication cycle' involve? Naomi needs to provide examples of the process in order to evidence her claim.
I looked at her in a supportive way.	Naomi needs to describe the process of smiling, making varied eye contact, the angle of her head and perhaps body posture and orientation. This evidences what 'supportive way' means.
I used the right level of formality in the way that I spoke.	Naomi needs to give examples and then explain why these examples were the 'right level' for the situation she was in.
I remembered to look interested as I listened to what she said.	What non-verbal behaviours are involved in looking interested? Naomi needs to describe eye contact, body posture, angle of head etc.
The conversation was warm and friendly.	This is too generalised – what were the behaviours? Naomi probably used reflective listening skills. If she gives an example and describes her reflective skills, this would give her evidence.
I think the conversation went very well.	Naomi needs to say why – the way Mrs B responded will give her evidence of how effective the conversation was. She needs to describe what Mrs B said and what her non-verbal behaviour involved.

Describing an interaction involves practice in using many of the key terms involved in this unit. It will be important to get feedback from colleagues, tutors and work experience supervisors in order to develop your own skills of reporting your work.

■ Giving feedback

You will help other students to develop their skills and they will help you by giving you feedback on the way you have described interactions.

Describing or analysing an interaction usually involves an act of 'interpretation'. There is usually some room for different ideas and perceptions. So it is important to avoid making judgements about other people. If you can say things like, 'I've got an idea – I think you could have spoken less and encouraged the service user to say more', you may help someone to review the effectiveness of their conversation. If you say things like, 'That was rubbish – you annoyed her', you fail to draw attention to the detailed issues and you are likely to create an emotional barrier to understanding. You might practise your own communication skills when you give feedback on other people's communication.

■ Reporting interactions in health and social care

You must provide evidence of your communication skills in interactions **P5**; guidelines recommend that one of these interactions should be in a one-to-one situation and the other should be a group interaction. The interactions should take place in a work experience environment.

It is very important that any notes or reports that you write are confidential. This means that it should not be possible to identify service users or care professionals involved in your interactions. It is also ethically important that people involved have given their consent for you to report interactions with them. People must not be stressed or threatened by the work that you are doing. For these reasons it is very unlikely that you will be able to get permission to make a visual or audio recording of your interactions.

Instead you should take notes immediately after a conversation, and immediately after your involvement with a group of staff or service users. These notes will help you to describe your interactions. You will not be able to remember everything that you said or did, or to remember everything that other people did. You should aim to recall some of the key things you said and to remember the responses others made to you. You should try to describe some of the non-verbal behaviours you saw in others and that you used **P3** **P4**. The checklist opposite may help you to remember examples of issues in your own communication work.

If you can describe two interactions you have been involved in, then you can use the feedback you received to help you review the effectiveness of your own communication skills. You may also be able to use evidence from your two interactions to contribute towards an explanation of specific communication needs **M2** and an analysis of how communication and health and social care can assist people **D1**.

One-to-one interaction
- How did you start and finish your interaction? Did you try to meet emotional needs? ☐
- Could you identify a communication cycle involving feedback on your understanding of the other person's ideas? ☐
- Did you use effective reflective listening? ☐

Group interaction
- Were you able to take effective turns in speaking? ☐
- Could you identify group values and/or purposes within the group? ☐
- Was there a group leader? How was the interaction managed? ☐

All interactions
Non-verbal communication
Can you identify examples of the following:
- eye contact ☐
- facial expression ☐
- voice tone ☐
- position of hands and arms ☐
- gestures ☐
- body posture ☐
- touch and proximity? ☐

Verbal communication
- How far did you encourage others to talk? ☐
- Did you reflect back what others said? ☐
- How appropriate was your use of language and level of formality? ☐
- Did you use any open or closed questions? ☐
- Were any technological aids to communication involved? ☐

Barriers to communication
- Could everybody see and hear each other clearly or were there any barriers to receiving information? ☐
- Were there any barriers to interpreting communication, such as language differences? ☐
- Were there any barriers to understanding, such as cultural differences, assumptions or stereotypes? ☐

Feedback
- What responses or feedback did you get from others? ☐
- Were any difficult, complex or sensitive issues involved? ☐
- How far were you able to understand the points that others made? ☐

Resources and further reading

Argyle, M. (1972) *The Psychology of Interpersonal Behaviour*, second ed. Harmondsworth: Pelican

Burnard, P. (1996) *Acquiring Interpersonal Skills*, second ed. London: Chapman & Hall

Burnard, P., Morrison, P. (1997) *Caring and Communicating* Basingstoke and London: Macmillan Press Ltd

Egan, G. (1986) *The Skilled Helper* Monterey, California: Brooks/Cole Publishing Company

Engebretson, J. (2004) 'Caring presence: a case study' in *Communication, Relationships and Care* Robb, M., Barrett, S., Komaromy, C., Rogers, A. (eds) London & New York: OU & Routledge

Hayman, M. (1998) 'A Protocol for People with Hearing Impairment', *Nursing Times*, Vol. 94, No. 43

Pinker, S. (1994) *The Language Instinct* Harmondsworth: Penguin

Tuckman, B. (1965) 'Development Sequence in Small Groups', *Psychological Bulletin*, Vol. 63, No. 6

Useful websites

Braille
www.brailleplus.net

British Sign Language
www.britishdeafassociation.org.uk

Makaton
www.makaton.org

Signs and finger spelling alphabet
www.british-sign.co.uk and at
www.royaldeaf.org.uk

Equality, diversity and rights

Introduction

Health and social care is a sector which treats every individual, whether service user or staff member, as an individual who is unique in their own way.

At the heart of this philosophy lies the care value base which seeks to treat people equally and fairly while actively demonstrating and promoting rights, respect for diversity and the culture of the individual.

Treating people differently (negatively or positively) due to their race, religion or any other aspect of their life is not acceptable practice and would be considered discriminatory. Clearly, any form of discrimination has the potential to affect a service user's treatment, self-esteem, self-identity and ultimately their physical and mental well-being.

It is essential, therefore, that all health and social care workers are fully aware of the impact of equality, diversity and rights on themselves, their teams and the service users they work with. A sound knowledge of policy, legislation and practice has to underpin all your future studies, and indeed working practices, in health and social care if you are to provide a high quality service for others.

With this in mind, this unit offers you the opportunity to gain a good grounding in equality, diversity and rights as a sound preparation for future career development or studies at a higher level. In this unit we will look at the issues and barriers around disability and disadvantage from a societal and economic point of view (a social model) including:

- prejudice, stereotypes and labelling
- organisational procedures and practices
- inaccessible information, buildings and transport
- policies, charters, actions and non-actions.

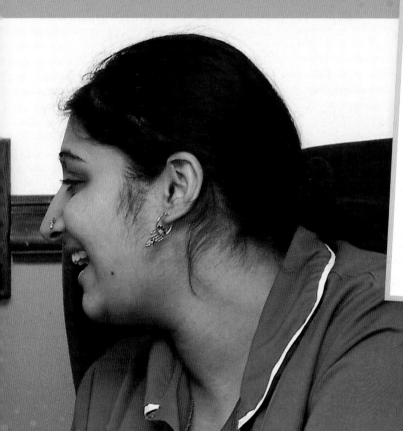

Thinking points

It is well known that a lack of knowledge about something can lead to a whole range of misunderstandings and negative behaviours. This is certainly the case when it comes to equality, diversity and rights. Unless we know and understand the issues surrounding cultural difference, we cannot work effectively in the health and social care services.

As you prepare to embark on this unit, spend a few minutes reflecting and thinking about why a unit like this, dedicated to equal opportunities, forms a core part of studying the issues related to working in health and social care. Make some notes about your thoughts. Later in the unit you will be asked the same question to see if your response has changed as a result of your studies.

It may also prove helpful to think about the actual words 'equality, diversity and rights'. What do you understand about each word? How have you (or others) used them in the past? Again, think about why they form a central part of your studies.

How you will be assessed

You will be assessed against the learning outcomes for this unit. After completing this unit you should be able to achieve the following outcomes:

- Understand concepts of equality, diversity and rights in relation to health and social care
- Understand discriminatory practice in health and social care
- Understand how national initiatives promote anti-discriminatory practice in health and social care
- Understand how anti-discriminatory practice is promoted in health and social care settings.

The concepts of **equality**, **diversity** and **rights** are enshrined within the British legal system. They are, therefore, underpinned by legislation and guidance. This aims to make sure that every individual is treated fairly, has their unique identity valued and respected, and ultimately has their rights upheld at all times.

Key terms

Equality This means that individuals are all treated equally – there are employment laws in place which ensure that organisations treat everyone equally.

Diversity This means recognising that everyone is different in some way. Importantly this also means 'valuing' the difference.

Rights This describes the roles and responsibilities attached to being an individual living and working within a wider society.

Within health and social care, these rights form the core values of every health and social care worker. It is clearly essential for a care worker to recognise the need to treat every individual equally and the need to challenge and, if necessary, 'fight for' the rights of those individuals in their care.

Alongside equality and rights comes diversity – again, in health and social care, it is important to recognise and value the differences amongst those people we are caring for. Often the 'differences' can and do affect the health care or treatment we provide. Therefore, we must ensure that all the aspects of a person are considered when planning health care routines with, and for, an individual (holistic care).

Reflect

Think about the words equality, diversity and rights. What is your current understanding of each word? How have you (or others) used them in the past?

The benefits of diversity

Britain is a multicultural society. This means that people from different countries and backgrounds are living and working together in our villages, towns and cities. Health and social care teams and service users are, therefore, made up of people from different backgrounds and cultures. The range of behaviours and beliefs experienced by all are therefore 'diverse'. We are all individuals in our own right and expect to be valued and respected for the diversity, skills and knowledge that we bring to the people we live, work and mix with and wider society in general.

The benefits of diversity should be clear to everyone but this is often not the case. It is well recognised that many people actually fear something or someone that is different from them and this can be particularly true of people who feel vulnerable when they are in need of treatment or health and social care. Yet having access to a wide range of cultures, skills and expertise should mean that we as a population have exciting opportunities to access new forms of treatment, care, learning and new experiences to meet our needs at every turn.

The social and cultural benefits of diversity

The benefits of diversity go beyond the health and social care sectors to encompass other aspects of our lives as Figure 2.1 below demonstrates.

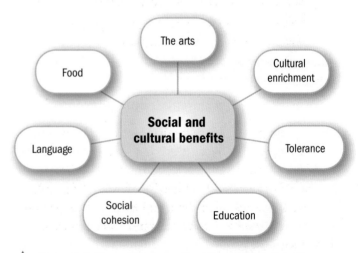

▲ Figure 2.1 The social and cultural benefits of diversity

◼ The arts

One benefit of living in a socially diverse society is the easy access we all have to a range of different traditions and art forms from around the world. Museums and galleries now feature displays and exhibitions that reflect the heritage and beliefs of many different societies. Theatre often offers the opportunity to gain insight into other cultures and, in some cases, languages. For example, many cinemas now offer films originating in other countries.

In context

Victoria came across a film called 'The Camel that Cried' in her local video rental shop. On reading the cover, she discovered that it was about a family living a nomadic life in Mongolia. She thought she would give it a try.

The film was actually sub-titled but Victoria was so engrossed in the film that she didn't notice after a few minutes. She felt overwhelmed by the end of the film and couldn't wait to recommend it to her friends and family. She had learnt so much about life in another place. She promised herself that one day she would visit Mongolia.

1 **How did the film affect Victoria's plans?**

2 **How do you think her attitudes towards other people and cultures might be affected?**

3 **What other benefits might Victoria gain from watching films such as this one?**

The arts can prove helpful to the work of a health and social care professional as they can provide some insight into the cultures and beliefs of other societies. They can help you to understand the needs and wants of people from backgrounds other than your own. Learning about 'the arts' is a good way to understand and appreciate difference.

Reflect

How have the arts enriched your life? What aspect of the arts do you and your friends enjoy? Have you considered trying out something new?

◼ Food

Another benefit of living in a diverse, multicultural society is the wide variety of foods that are available. This should be taken into consideration by health and social care workers as they plan diets for individuals. It is important to recognise that many people enjoy foods that are flavoured with spices, herbs and fruits. Expecting people to eat traditional British foods is probably outdated, although it should be remembered that many (particularly older) people may prefer simple foods that are prepared without the use of spices and 'exotic' vegetables.

Our food choices are developed from an early age and for some people experimentation is a way of life. Asking people about their food likes and dislikes and providing a choice in menu planning demonstrates active respect for diversity.

Reflect

Curry has been voted Britain's favourite food. Which foods do you and your family enjoy eating? Do you know which countries the ingredients originate from?

◼ Education

Equality and diversity are high on the agenda for all educational institutions, whether they are the funders or providers of education. Our education systems focus on every individual, ensuring that everyone has an opportunity to succeed, no matter what their background. Our education system has benefited from cultural diversity in many different ways. For example, the subjects studied in schools and colleges now include the cultures and religions of a wide range of different groups of the population, as well as a wide range of modern foreign languages.

The celebration of tradition and culture is now seen on all syllabuses in one form or another. The education system has also benefited from diversity through the contributions made by teachers and managers from diverse cultural backgrounds. They often bring new perspectives and break down traditional, possibly outdated, ways of working; this is to the benefit of the educational system and those who study and work within it.

The inclusion of equality, rights and diversity in the training and development of health and social care workers has seen huge improvements in the way individuals are treated and cared for by those workers. Most organisations include training on equal opportunities as part of their induction process. In-service training ensures that ongoing education about rights and responsibilities is included in all workforce development.

▲ Figure 2.2 'How can I make life different for my children?'

Take it further

It is interesting to note that up to 40 per cent of people on incapacity benefits have no qualifications at all, which can seriously disadvantage them. Carry out some private research to find out how the health of the individual and the family is affected by whether or not they have educational qualifications.

■ Language

The English language is already formed from a complete mix of other languages ranging from French through to Latin, Germanic, Celtic and Nordic. New groups of settlers into the country are also bringing elements of their language with them. These new words are slowly being assimilated into everyday speech. For example, Diwali and Eid are two celebrations that most people will have heard of and understand at some level. Other words regularly used in the English language include 'bungalow' and 'pyjamas' – do you know where they originate from?

Other language users bring additional benefits. For example, having the opportunity to live and work with people from other countries and cultural backgrounds offers everyone the chance to learn something new and different. Colleges of further education and schools offer the opportunity to study modern foreign languages at every level, so that people can travel and work abroad as part of the European Union agreement. The teachers of these languages are often from that cultural background and can add value by sharing cultural norms and behaviours with their students.

Within the health and social care system, the arrival of new languages has led to the development of new ways of working. For example, it is now possible and practical to follow a career in interpretation and translation in the health service: this could be providing a service for deaf

In context

Surraya is a 'linkworker' at a busy hospital trust. She is based in the Department of Public Health Awareness and responds to staff who require her services. Today she is working in the ear, nose and throat department, translating some deaf awareness posters from English into Bengali. These will then be used in the waiting room.

Tomorrow, she will be working with the community midwife in some parenting classes – she will be interpreting the information for Bengali first-time expectant mothers.

1   What other kinds of health information are likely to need translation services?

2   What is the difference between interpretation and translation?

3   How do you think service users will feel about this service? What kind of worries may they have?

service users or for clients who do not have English as a first language in a variety of different settings.

■ Cultural enrichment

It should be fairly obvious by now that, if all the benefits we have already explored (diverse food types, new languages, the arts etc) are available and accessed by everyone, we will be culturally enriched.

■ Tolerance

Tolerance doesn't just mean putting up with something or someone. It has a much wider meaning and it is important to recognise this. In society and in the workplace we do not have to be friends with everyone but we do have to behave at all times in a professional and caring manner, towards both our service users and our colleagues. While we may not share or hold similar beliefs and traditions, we should at the very least understand the concepts attached to another person's beliefs and respect their right to hold that belief or follow that tradition as long as it does not harm anyone else.

■ Social cohesion

'Cohesion' means sticking together. Social cohesion is a difficult concept but can perhaps be explained by the use of the word 'community' instead of 'social'. A cohesive community is one where there is a common sense of 'belonging' for all the individuals and communities living in one place (that place could be a geographical area such as a 'ward' or a town or even a country). For people to feel that they belong, there is a need for everyone's circumstances and background to be valued and respected. Alongside this lies a need for positive relationships between people from different backgrounds in all the social and economic places in which they might meet, for example, schools, workplaces and neighbourhoods.

Health and social care teams need to demonstrate social cohesion in the way individual members work together and support each other. As we have already said, most care teams are multicultural: it is important for these teams to support each other and to uphold the rights of every single member.

Reflect

What actions could be taken by a hospital trust to contribute towards a cohesive society at a local level?

Take it further

Abuse towards staff in accident and emergency departments is well known. While much of this is as a result of alcohol, some cases of abuse have been directly related to staff race. Discuss with others how you might support a team member or other colleague who is experiencing racist abuse.

Employment

When an individual is entrepreneurial and perhaps uses their skills and knowledge to start a new business, opportunities for employment (new jobs) are created. There are many examples of 'alternative therapies' which have come from other cultures. For example, acupuncture, massage and reike therapists are now employed in the hospice movement to bring relief to, and manage the stress of, many of the service users being treated there. Clearly over time, new therapies are offering employment and educational opportunities within the health and social care sector for the local population.

Theory into practice

Use the Internet to find an overseas medical appliances company that supplies medication or other health care products to the National Health Service (NHS).

Remember!

Almost 30 per cent of Britain's doctors and 43 per cent of Britain's nurses were born in another country.

■ Expertise

The example of doctors and nurses originating from other countries highlights how diversity enriches our health services with new levels of expertise and knowledge. There is a wide range of medical advancements that have originated abroad (facial transplants is one example, alongside heart transplants which originated in South Africa) and are now being used to improve medication and treatment services in this country. A lot of our research into medical

▲ Figure 2.3 The NHS has a zero tolerance approach towards personal attacks on their staff

The economic benefits of diversity

The economic benefits of diversity can be clearly seen through the contributions that are made to society at all different levels by those people living and working in the community. For example, links are made to other countries in terms of imports and exports and the knowledge economy can be transferred from one country to another simply by employing or working with an individual from 'overseas'. In terms of health and social care, the economic benefits of diversity can be seen through the knowledge and practice that new practitioners bring into the country. In some cases, new treatments can save 'bed time' in hospitals. Other examples include new IT systems (that originated overseas) that mean service users receive more information and a faster service.

conditions and social care facilities comes from other countries. Finland produced much of our knowledge relating to coronary artery disease and heart attacks: its findings have informed the medical profession and the public health service about the kind of preventative action we should be taking in this country. Many of the coronary artery disease prevention policies adopted by our government are based on studies carried out abroad.

Assessment activity 2.1

Explain the benefits of diversity to society.

1   Produce a leaflet for a family from eastern Europe who intend to live in Britain to explain the benefits of living in a culturally diverse society. Make sure you explain how society as a whole benefits from cultural diversity.   **P1**

Grading tip for P1

To help you produce work of a high standard, you may find it helpful to carry out some personal research into the benefits of living in a culturally diverse society. You could visit a range of community centres or use the Internet to find out more about different cultures. You could include this information as case studies in your leaflet. You should include at least three examples of social/cultural benefits and two examples of economic benefits.

Terminology

Recognising the value and importance of diversity is essential for a health and social care professional but it is also important to understand and use the appropriate terminology (words or jargon) to describe issues within equal opportunities. So, for example, in this unit you are expected to understand the meaning of words such as equality, diversity, empowerment etc and to be able to use them in the right context. Clearly, unless

you understand the meaning applied to such words in the context of good practice in health and social care, you cannot participate appropriately in the provision of good practice in the workplace and in the wider community.

Therefore, we are going to explore the key words and terms that you need to understand and to be able to use comfortably in all your units of study.

Equality

The meaning behind this word can perhaps be best 'summed up' as 'all people have the same value'. However, this does not mean treating all people in the same way – we need to recognise and value diversity. The word 'equality' is often linked to 'opportunity' creating a new term 'equal opportunity'. All workplaces should have an 'Equal Opportunities policy' not least because the law states that they must have one. These policies aim to create a 'level playing field' in the workplace to try and make sure that all people are treated equally in relation to:

- access to work
- pay and conditions of work.

Equal Opportunities policy also covers access to services, and organisations must make sure that service users are not subject to discrimination through the actions, or indeed lack of action, of the staff employed to care for them. Under Equal Opportunities it is expected that all individuals will experience the same level of high quality service, no matter what their background or beliefs and values may be. As our health care system is based on 'need' rather than an ability to pay, individuals should have access to the treatment and care that they require, when they require it.

Reflect

Do individuals access the health service when they 'need' it or is there some limiting factor in place? What might prevent an individual accessing a consultant doctor when they have a health problem?

In context

Tahir Ahmed has been living and working in London since 2001. He is from Bangladesh and is still struggling a little with his English. He is able to get by from day to day – he can access banking services and is able to carry out his work as a park ranger without too much difficulty.

He has just been to see his GP because of a cough and has had his blood pressure taken for the first time. He has been told that it is too high and to see the nurse. When he sees the nurse, she gives him information on blood pressure, cholesterol, weight and urine. Tahir cannot understand the technical points the nurse raises with him but feels too embarrassed to ask for clarification. He is given two leaflets on blood pressure and cholesterol but cannot understand them. He has decided 'not to worry' – it won't matter in the long run!

1   **Has Tahir been able to gain access to this service?**

2   **What could the organisation do to improve the service to Tahir?**

3   **How could an Equal Opportunities policy be better adhered to in this case?**

Equity

Equity means 'fairness'. In health and social care, equity can be about ensuring that all people have fair and equal access to services, such as doctors, treatment and medication. It also highlights the need to all service users that they can, and should, expect fair and equal treatment from the funders of medical care and the providers of health services no matter where they live in the country.

Theory into practice

Use the Internet to research back issues of national newspapers to look for articles about women who have received or not received specialist drugs for the treatment of breast cancer.

Discuss your findings with others to answer the question 'Is the health service equitable for all individuals?'

Diversity

This is the term we use to describe the range of differences between all individuals. It is important to recognise, acknowledge, accept and value those differences. It is expected that all health and social care workers recognise that there are key differences between people that could affect their health and health care in a variety of ways. For example, gender has the potential to affect how long people live (in general women live longer than men), religious observance can affect the food choices made by individuals and ethnic origin can affect a person's experience of ill health. However, it is important to recognise that none of these should be allowed to act as a barrier between the individual and the health professional or caring service that is working with them. Indeed, respect for, and understanding of, diversity has the potential to enhance health care and an individual's experience of being cared for.

Remember!

Valuing diversity is all about respect for people.

Theory into practice

Make your own glossary of terms as you go through this section. Write any key words you don't understand in a notebook and then use a dictionary to find a definition for each one.

Rights

Rights are often linked with responsibilities. This means that everyone has access to basic human rights and in turn has a responsibility towards other people's basic human rights. In UK law, 16 human rights have been incorporated into our legal systems. These are:

- right to life
- prohibition of torture
- prohibition of slavery and forced labour
- right to liberty and security
- right to a fair trial
- no punishment without law
- right to respect for private and family life
- freedom of thought, conscience and religion
- freedom of expression
- freedom of assembly and association
- right to marry

- prohibition of discrimination
- protection of property
- right to education
- right to free elections
- abolition of the death penalty.

These rights are taken from the Human Rights Act, 2000 and, as you might expect from reading them, have the potential to affect every aspect of life. Observing and applying these rights are central to the way we provide treatment and care for our service users in the health and social care system.

Remember!

Every individual has the right to live their life in the way they choose, as long as it does not affect anyone else in a harmful way.

Take it further

Discuss with another individual how the 'right to life' could be infringed by doctors and family members making decisions about people receiving life support in a hospital. Use the Internet or past newspaper articles to help you gather information for the discussion.

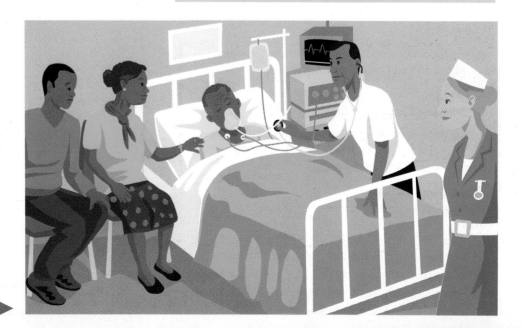

Figure 2.4 Who should make the decision to 'switch off'?

Opportunity

Every individual should have the same treatment or care opportunities open to them as every other person. These opportunities range from access to jobs through to becoming transplant patients or having access to life-saving medicines. It is expected that health and social care workers make sure that all their service users are aware of the opportunities available to them. In some cases this means bringing information to the client's attention and in other cases it might mean involving other health professionals in the care or treatment of the individual.

In context

Monica has rheumatoid arthritis which has begun to severely restrict her movements. She is struggling to make meals for herself and cannot remember the last time she managed to pour hot water from the kettle. Her home care assistant has suggested that she ask for an assessment visit by the occupational therapist: they will be able to make special adaptations to her environment which might make life easier for Monica.

1   **What more could the home care assistant do to make this 'opportunity' become a reality for Monica?**

2   **How could an occupational therapist make a difference to Monica's environment?**

3   **Use the Internet to find out more about aids to help individuals with mobility difficulties.**

Difference

This word takes us back to the discussion on diversity. We know that every individual is different from any other. Even twins are different, as they are individuals in their own right with their own talents, aspirations, needs and wants. There are some obvious differences which

will affect health and social care provision such as age, gender, physical ability and disability. However, we need to recognise that, no matter what the difference, each individual and their differences deserve to be respected and valued.

Overt discrimination

Discrimination is illegal in the UK and there is wide-ranging legislation in place to support any individual who feels unfairly discriminated against. Discrimination can take place for a variety of reasons. For example, three common causes of awards that are made to individuals in discrimination cases are because of:

- sex discrimination
- race discrimination
- disability discrimination.

Discrimination can be hidden or it can be clear and 'up front' (overt). An example of overt discrimination would be paying a male nurse more money than a female nurse for the same job because of his gender. In the health care sector, overt discrimination is more likely to be seen in the way a patient is treated by staff.

In context

Rea is in a nursing home. She has been ringing her bed buzzer for the last hour – she is desperate to use the toilet but she has been told she must not get out of bed. She calls out for help to Peter, the senior male nurse, as he passes the door of her room. He totally ignores her and thinks, 'She can wait until my private patients have been seen – she isn't even paying for her own nursing care.' Rea knows that others are being better looked after than she is but, as she said to her sister on visiting day, 'What can I do about it? I am only an old woman needing help.'

1   **How is this overt discrimination?**

2   **What might be the long-term effect on Rea?**

3   **How might other service users feel knowing the situation Rea is in?**

Covert discrimination

Covert discrimination is the opposite of overt. Therefore, covert discrimination can best be described as hidden or masked in some way. For example, three people applying for a job as a nurse would be shortlisted (called for an interview) using the same criteria. However, if the shortlisting panel decided not to call someone for interview based on their name or the area they lived in, this would be covert discrimination (hidden).

Stereotyping

Stereotyping describes the belief that all people are the same in certain circumstances. It is highly likely that you will have experience of many stereotypes, as stereotypical attitudes are developed as part of the socialisation (growing up) process. Examples of stereotypes in health and social care could be:

- all runners have bad knees and should put up with the pain
- overweight people are lazy and do nothing to help their situation
- female nurses are 'good time girls'
- male nurses are likely to be gay.

Reflect

What stereotypical examples have you come across in daily living? How accurate are they likely to be?

Stereotyping individuals is a dangerous practice. The end result can be discrimination against individuals based on totally wrong assumptions. Making assumptions about people is poor practice and often leads to gossip and hurt. The problem with making assumptions about individuals is that it can turn into discriminating activity. At this point it is a harmful and illegal practice.

Labelling

Labelling is another form of discrimination. Unfortunately, we often do this without even recognising that we are doing it! A label is a word or term applied to an individual that is considered to 'sum them up'. Examples of frequently used labels are all around us:

- fat
- uneducated
- mean
- weak.

Reflect

Think about the times you have come across labels such as these. How were they used? What message did the labels give you? Make a note of any labels that have been applied to you in the past. Were they fair? Did they reflect the real you? How would you label yourself?

Clearly, having a label applied to an individual can and does take away their identity. The danger in health and social care (or any other situation) is that people lose their dignity and can be treated less well as a result.

In context

Michael has been labelled 'sneaky' by the mental health unit that has organised his admittance into residential care. All the care workers have been 'warned' about him by the senior officer at the care home.

1 **How might Michael's treatment and care in the home be affected by the label that has been applied to him?**

2 **How can he get rid of a label that he probably does not even know exists?**

3 **How have Michael's rights been affected by this event?**

▲ The lack of safe play space leads children to play in dangerous streets

Prejudice

The easiest way to describe this term is by understanding that prejudice is usually demonstrated by individuals who show a negative attitude towards some groups or individuals within the population. The term is often used to describe the way people sometimes judge others without knowing them. The judgements are made on the basis of labels and stereotypes and not the individual in question. Once we realise that the term 'prejudice' is based on the term 'pre-judgement' we can easily see the true meaning.

Again, the danger of prejudice is that in health and social care, people will be treated disadvantageously because of someone else's lack of knowledge about them. In other words, discrimination results from prejudice.

Disadvantage

In health and social care, we often take 'disadvantage' to mean an experience of life chances that is lower than that of the average person. In other words, individuals and families from poor economic areas can (and usually do) experience a poorer health status than those people living in more affluent areas. Unfortunately, it is also true that you are more likely to find poorer health care services in these economically deprived areas. This has the potential to add to the burden of ill health already experienced by the population.

It has also been shown that access to a good education may be more limited in these disadvantaged areas. This in turn can prevent people knowing how best to use the health and social care services that could be available to them. In addition, housing is often of a poorer quality and parks and play areas are unavailable in the immediate vicinity. This leads to more road accidents involving children. As you can imagine, this list is not exhaustive. Clearly, there are many other aspects of life including employment and income that have the potential to 'disadvantage' whole families and their communities in the health stakes.

Beliefs

Our beliefs reflect the way we see the world and the opinions we have about what is happening around us. For example, religion, and how we feel about it, reflects part of our belief system. Beliefs are formed over many years and are very powerful in terms of the way they influence our behaviour towards other people and indeed our behaviour towards ourselves. For example, if we believe fat in food is not a problem or will not 'affect us' and consequently eat a high-fat diet, we will more than likely develop heart or circulatory disease at some point in the future. If we believe that violence in certain situations is acceptable, we are more likely to end up in the accident and emergency department of our local hospital trust!

Values

Our values are those things we believe are important and are formed and developed as we grow and go through the 'socialisation' process. Values are mainly developed through the influences of other people (often our families and friends) and our personal experiences. Clearly then, our values are based upon a great range of different things. For example, some people do not eat animal flesh because of their moral or ethical values; others may avoid using cars because of their stance upon the environment. The value an individual places on themselves (feelings of self-worth and self-esteem) can affect their attitude and behaviour towards seeking medical help when they become unwell. Feelings of low value towards yourself also affect access to many of the screening services that are available through the health service.

In context

Lillian has just reached her fiftieth birthday. Almost immediately she is invited to a breast screening appointment to check that she is not developing cancerous cells in her breasts. She puts the appointment to one side and thinks to herself, 'I don't need to bother with that – it's not important in my life at the moment. I need to concentrate on looking after my grandchildren so that Claire can go to work.'

1 What do you think Lillian's core values are? Discuss your thoughts with another person.

2 How have Lillian's values affected her choice not to take up the breast screening opportunity?

3 What might be the results of this decision on Lillian and her wider family?

Vulnerability

This term is used to describe the condition of people who are potentially 'at risk' from something or someone else. For example, older people who are frail and sick may be 'vulnerable' to colds in winter (and so flu vaccinations are offered to some groups of the population). Individuals with Alzheimer's disease may be more vulnerable to abuse because of challenging behaviour patterns and an inability to protect themselves. The role of the health and social care professional is key to the health and safety of vulnerable people as they have a responsibility to keep individuals safe from harm.

Abuse

Abuse is the term applied to a wide range of negative behaviours which have the potential to harm or damage individuals in a variety of ways. Abuse can be:

- physical, for example, hitting someone or neglecting their health needs

- mental, which could be related to humiliation, fear and exploitation
- sexual, relating to inappropriate physical contact
- verbal, which can be used to intimidate, and cause fear in, the individual involved.

Empowerment

To empower someone means 'to enable an individual (or group of people) to take control of their lives (or in some cases to carry out specific tasks and actions)' rather than relying on other people. Helping to empower service users is a core part of the care value base for health and social care staff. There are a variety of different ways in which empowerment can happen. For example, on a macro (whole population) level some people would argue that the NHS, and therefore the government, is too paternalistic. In other words, it tells us what to do and when and how, when in fact we should be 'empowering' individuals to take control of, and responsibility for, their own health, and health workers should leave us to make our own decisions. At an individual level (micro) we could see patients having access to their health records as 'empowering' as they could take more control over their health and even question health professionals about the content and issues involved.

Theory into practice

The Surestart Children's Centre initiative is all about empowering parents to make a difference to their own lives and futures and those of their children. Nursery care and adult education work together 'hand in hand' to bring about positive and lasting change to a family's circumstances.

Use the Internet to find out more about the ways the parents of young children can be empowered to have more control over their own lives and those of their children.

▲ Figure 2.5 Independence brings a sense of well-being

Independence

This word is often linked to 'empowerment'. In its simplest sense, independence is about enabling individuals to live life to the full without having to rely on others to carry out tasks for them or tell them how and when to do something. All health professionals aim to have client independence at the centre of a health care regime. A good health professional will always strive to carry out caring and health tasks *with* their service user, never *for* them. Independence is closely linked to feelings of positive well-being and control, each of which has been shown to improve overall health.

Interdependence

This term is used to describe the way in which a group of services (or individuals) rely on one another in some way. In health and social care it is used in a variety of ways but a good way to see it in action in this unit is through the work of a multi-disciplinary health care team. Each member of the team has a key role to play in improving or caring for the health of an individual and no one role is more important than another. The case study below demonstrates this.

In context

Mrs Ormerod is 94 years old. She lives alone in a three-bedroom semi but stays downstairs now as she cannot get around any more. Her home care assistant arrives at 7.30 a.m. to help her wash and dress and makes her breakfast for her. At lunchtime, the 'meals on wheels' service visits and bring her a hot meal with a plate of sandwiches for her evening meal. Her home care assistant returns at 8.00 p.m. and helps her back to bed. Once a week the speaking library collects her tapes and leaves her two new ones. She attends day care once a week at the residential care home three miles away. She is collected by the volunteer transport service and returned home by the social care ambulance service.

1 **How are these services interdependent upon each other?**

2 **How would Mrs Ormerod be affected if the 'meals on wheels' service should fail to carry out their responsibilities?**

3 **What difference do you think services working together like this makes to the life of Mrs Ormerod?**

Racism

This term is used to refer to a whole range of negative behaviours or 'unfair' treatments and behaviour patterns towards other people based on ethnicity or race.

Sexism

'Sexism' has the same meaning as the term 'racism' except that the unfair treatment and behaviours are based on gender.

Homophobia

This word literally means 'fear of homosexuals'. People who are homophobic sometimes discriminate against an individual, or individuals, on the basis of their sexual orientation. While attitudes towards sexuality have changed significantly over the years there are still a minority of people who do this.

Reflect

Do any of the words above and their explanations trigger a strong response in you? If so, perhaps you should stop for a minute and consider why. What has happened to you that has influenced these feelings and beliefs? Understanding ourselves is key to bringing about change in our behaviour.

Remember!

Over 80 per cent of homosexuals have been subjected to verbal abuse at some time as a result of their sexuality.

Health and social care settings

In this unit you are asked to explore equality, diversity and rights in relation to four key health and care settings that service users regularly access. These are:

- residential care
- day care
- nursing care
- domiciliary care (home care).

Residential care settings

Residential care involves a service user leaving their own home and moving into a setting that will allow them to live their lives in a safe and secure environment that can cater for their social care needs. The service user shares the accommodation with other people who usually need the same type of care and attention as they need themselves.

Theory into practice

Arrange a visit to a residential care home and interview two people to find out what they think are the benefits and disadvantages of living in residential care.

Find out how they are helped to maintain their independence.

Day care settings

Day care is provided by a range of different settings, for example, hospitals and residential care homes. It is used by individuals on a daily basis. It serves a variety of different purposes, for example, the provision of physiotherapy and occupational therapy services, and it can be provided in a variety of different ways by different day care providers. In the main, day care is used to support care that takes place in the home. An example is shown in the case study below.

Another form of day care can be found attached to hospitals. In this example, service users may be collected by ambulance from home and taken to the centre. Once there, they may have the opportunity to be treated by health care professionals. For example, physiotherapy may be provided for those who need it and an occupational therapist may take the opportunity to carry out assessments on some individuals. It is possible for some people to attend a day care centre more than once a week. It is important to recognise that every situation and every individual should be assessed for day care on an individual basis.

Nursing care settings

This kind of care, as the title implies, relates to the care provided by trained nursing staff. This in turn means that the service users are often ill in some way. Their care needs involve treatment and medication in a variety of different settings. However, when we discuss nursing care we need to remember that there are several different types of nursing. For example:

- practice nurse
- health visitor
- Macmillan nurse
- ward nurse
- school nurse
- occupational health nurse
- midwife

In context

Olive, who is 83, lives at home with her elderly husband, Bill. He manages to get her up in the morning and prepares and cooks all her meals. In fact, he runs the home and looks after Olive's 'every need'. However, he finds that he cannot bath Olive safely any more and needs help with this task. He also needs some respite from caring for her every minute of the day. His local community centre has just had a day care centre built onto the side of it to take seven people each day. Olive now attends every Tuesday from 9 a.m. to 4 p.m. She

is given a bath by carers and has the opportunity to socialise with other service users while Bill has a well-earned rest at home.

1   **How does day care affect the lives of Olive and Bill?**

2   **What other services do you think could be provided at this day care centre?**

3   **How are interdependence and empowerment demonstrated in this scenario?**

- mental health nurse
- paediatric nurse.

Each of the nursing jobs specialises in a particular kind of care and works in a range of different settings with specific client groups i.e.

- school nurses are often based in schools and health centres
- mental health nurses could be based in hospitals, GP practices or the community.

For the purposes of your study you should concentrate on those nursing staff who care for people with health needs. A hospice is a good example of a nursing care setting that could be ward-based (where the patients are actually living there) or could be accessed on a day care basis.

Theory into practice

Select two of the nursing jobs and research the qualifications, job role and key settings involved. Identify ways in which both types of nurses can work towards the empowerment of their client groups. Prepare a presentation to share your findings with others.

Remember!

Nursing care doesn't necessarily involve someone being ill. Having a baby doesn't mean that a mother is ill and a school nurse doesn't only work with sick children.

Domiciliary care settings

The word domiciliary means 'at home' so we can see that this setting involves all the health and social care work being carried out in an individual's own home. The kind of service provided in the home can vary from something relatively simple, such as preparing and cooking meals, through to the medical care that could be required for someone who is terminally ill. Clearly, a wide range of health professionals could be involved in a domiciliary setting depending on the needs of the individual.

Take it further

Research the role and responsibilities of a Macmillan nurse in a domiciliary setting.

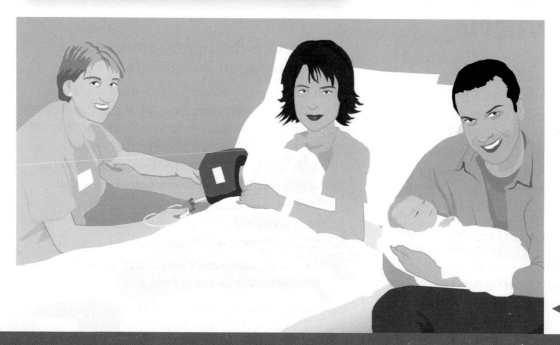

Figure 2.6 Sick or well?

Active promotion of equality and individual rights

Having a good understanding of the key concepts and settings used in health and social care is central to all job roles within the sector. Alongside this is a need to recognise and understand the health and social care professionals' role in actively promoting the rights of others. The word 'active' is dynamic and implies that 'action' will be taken wherever and whenever appropriate. In other words, promoting the rights and equality of others is something that should be central to care and health roles.

The principles of the care value base

Putting the patient/service user at the heart of service provision is central to the role of a care and health worker. This is underpinned by an extremely important code of practice known as the care value base.

There are seven key aspects to the care value base. These are of equal importance and should form the basis of all relationships with service users and work colleagues. They include:

- the promotion of anti-discriminatory practice
- the promotion and support of dignity, independence and safety
- respect for, and acknowledgement of, personal beliefs and an individual's identity
- the maintenance of confidentiality
- protection from abuse and harm
- the promotion of effective communication and relationships
- the provision of personalised (individual) care.

We can break down these statements further into key words and actions. For example, to be 'service user centred' we must ensure:

- inclusivity
- participation
- access
- honesty and openness
- trust
- respect
- confidentiality
- safety
- choice.

■ Promote the rights, choices and well-being of individuals

Furthermore, if we follow the care value base in our everyday work with individuals, we will automatically be promoting an individual's rights and choices. This will have a positive effect on their feelings of well-being and their sense of control over their lives, no matter what their situation. Therefore, we must make sure that we:

- promote and demonstrate equality at every opportunity
- respect diversity and demonstrate this publicly
- promote independence and take appropriate action to increase this for every individual that we work with

▲ Inclusivity means everyone is involved

- challenge stereotypes and those people using them
- improve an individual's life chances by ensuring access to services to meet their needs
- improve the overall quality of the service that we and others are providing for our service users.

Take it further

Find out what 'inclusivity' is and then write short notes on its importance in the health and social care sectors.

Discuss with others the importance of contributing to the overall improvement of the service being provided to individuals.

Clearly, these are challenging roles and responsibilities for every health and social care worker regardless of the sector or setting that they work in.

■ Anti-discriminatory practice – empowering individuals

If we remain 'true' to the care value base at all times, we will be able to demonstrate anti-discriminatory practice. However, in order to actively promote our approach, we should be prepared to challenge others who may inadvertently (or even deliberately) discriminate. This could mean challenging colleagues and service users about their use of language or the application of labels or stereotypes. We should never accept that 'this happens'. Instead, we should seek to bring about change that will improve the lives of the individuals we work with (even when they don't know that we are doing it!).

Challenging discriminatory attitudes and language is a way of indirectly empowering our service users. A more direct way is to work with individuals to encourage them to maintain, regain or gain independence as far as they are able. For example, we should:

- encourage choices and decision making
- work *with* our service users
- encourage independent activities
- offer opportunities and strategies for improvements in physical, intellectual, emotional, social and spiritual well-being (PIES)
- promote individuality at all times.

■ Dealing with tensions and contradictions

There are always difficult areas and decisions to be taken in the provision of health care for others. We will see many examples of this as we work through this unit: for example, confidentiality and the need to 'pass on' information in certain circumstances or the need to allocate tight resources to the care of one individual or another. How do health professionals decide 'who gets what'? It is important to recognise that no one individual has the 'burden' to carry alone.

Team work is an essential part of health care and when this is used alongside guidance, high quality standards and evidenced-based practice, decisions become easier and fairer.

Once again, the underpinning values of the care value base will help you to find effective methods for dealing with some of the difficulties we have identified. If we keep the service user at the centre of decision making, we should be able to keep some of the tensions involved in funding and service provision to a minimum. Funding is always difficult and there are occasions when we cannot provide all the services we would want to. However, remember we can take our concerns to line managers and supervisors for other action at a higher level.

For more information on dealing with conflict, look at pages 93–94 of this unit.

Staff development and training

Health and social care workers need regular training and development in order to keep up-to-date and use best practice at all times. In terms of the care value base, it is essential that the training enables workers to fully understand their roles and responsibilities as well as increasing their knowledge about individual rights and equality of opportunity.

Training and development does not just consist of attending college or gaining qualifications. While these are obviously important for career development, the knowledge required to provide sound, high quality care can be derived from a variety of sources. (see Figure 2.7 below, for example).

The practical implications of confidentiality, and the recording, storing and sharing of information

The care value base (and the law) demands that health and social care workers maintain service user confidentiality at all times. By 'confidentiality', we are referring to all the information relating to our service users and the records associated with them, whether these are written or computerised.

Whenever you are handling information, it is important that you respect your service users' wishes, follow the guidance and procedures of your organisation and comply with the requirements of the law. Bringing these three key aspects together will help to ensure that you actively promote your service users' rights.

From the outset it is important to remember that you should only collect information that is needed and then it is extremely important that the data should only be used for the purpose for which it was intended.

▲ Figure 2.7 Sources of training and development

All records must be kept safe and secure and each workplace must have a policy or guidelines for staff to follow as regards maintaining confidentiality.

Theory into practice

The law says service users must be allowed access to any personal information relating to them upon their request.

1   What might be the implications of this legislation for health care practice?

2   How might a nurse be affected by this law?

3   How might a service user be affected by this individual right?

Take it further

Obtain a copy of a confidentiality policy and make notes of the contents and their purpose in promoting access and individual rights.

The practical aspects of confidentiality can place huge demands on organisations as well as the individuals concerned. For example:

- Where can paper-based records be stored?
- Who should have access to them?
- How can they be kept secure?
- How long should they be kept?
- What kind of information should be recorded?
- How often do they need to be updated or reviewed?

The list is similar to that for electronic records but for these we should also consider:

- Who has access to passwords?
- What happens when the system fails?
- Who will carry out the necessary training?
- Who carries out repairs and can they see the information?

Take it further

Complete a questionnaire based on the questions listed to enable you to obtain answers to the questions posed. Once your questionnaire is completed, approach a care organisation to obtain their responses.

Individual rights

In order to explore this section, you may find it helpful to revisit the earlier section on 'rights' which explained the way rights in health and social care are built upon the foundations of the Human Rights Act. When we discuss rights in health and social care, we are referring to those 'rights' which form part of the care value base. For example an individual's rights to be:

- respected
- treated equally and not discriminated against
- treated as an individual
- treated in a dignified way
- allowed privacy
- protected from danger and harm
- allowed access to personal information
- able to communicate using their preferred method
- cared for in a way that meets their needs and takes account of their choices, and protects.

By now, these rights should be very familiar to you. Some of them have been touched upon in the section covering terminology (see page 55). Here, however, we will explore these rights further through the use of activities and case studies that will enable you to reflect upon a variety of situations.

The right to be respected

All individuals have the right to expect and receive respect, no matter what their age or circumstance. It is a basic human right. Health care professionals need to demonstrate their respect for the individual through the way they approach, communicate with and treat each person they are involved with.

Respect for others has to be at the core of a health worker's responsibility. Respect is not only about preserving 'dignity', it is about respecting an individual's core beliefs and wishes and respecting the need for choice and privacy. Respect is about acknowledging an individual's rights to choose the kind of health care they want, even when this choice clashes with your own opinions.

Demonstrating respect requires:

- good communication skills
- patience
- acceptance of choices made
- skilled interactions between the health worker and the individual.

In context

Albert has had a stroke and cannot move his right side at all. He has been in hospital for four days and is on a ward with 12 other men. He needs to have a bed bath and Nurse Baker has been asked to carry out this procedure. Nurse Baker is feeling very harassed by a huge workload but he goes off to prepare. He approaches Albert and gently touches his hand, saying 'Good morning', and asking him if he would like a bath to help him feel more comfortable. The curtains are closed while Nurse Baker removes the bedclothes and then takes off Albert's pyjama jacket explaining everything to him as he goes along. Once his arms and chest are washed, the nurse puts Albert's jacket back on and then removes his pyjama bottoms. He uses a towel to cover Albert as he washes each section of his lower body so he does not feel exposed. Once he is finished he makes sure Albert is comfortable and dry before re-covering him with the bedclothes and opening the curtains.

1 **What practical strategies is the nurse using to demonstrate respect for Albert?**

2 **What skills and knowledge are being demonstrated by the nurse as he deals with Albert in a sensitive situation?**

3 **What more could the nurse have done to demonstrate respect for Albert?**

The right to be treated equally and not discriminated against

As we have already said, all individuals have the right to be treated equally and not discriminated against. Health care professionals must take particular care to see that they do not discriminate in any part of their practice. We need to remember that it is possible to discriminate without even realising that we are doing it. In many care settings, health professionals work with groups of people. It can prove difficult not to develop 'favourites' and spend more time with them than with other service users who may not be quite so popular!

The right to be treated as an individual

Treating people as individuals is central to the care value base. By recognising and valuing difference we can treat all people as individuals. Abraham Maslow (see page 74 and Unit 8 for details of Maslow's hierarchy of needs) identified some key similarities in the needs of all human beings. For example, we all need warmth, shelter and food, followed by love and other aspects of basic need. While it is important to recognise that we all share these basic needs, we must also recognise that we have individual needs based on difference. Treating everyone the same 'regardless' is failing to respect diversity.

Jack Straw is a Member of Parliament for Blackburn in Lancashire. His constituency is mainly made up of 70 per cent of individuals from the indigenous population and 30 per cent from Asian heritage backgrounds. Following one of his recent 'surgeries' (2006) (when members of the public can speak to their MP, often to ask for help) Mr Straw commented that it would be helpful if the Asian heritage women would remove their face veils from their faces during conversations with him.

This comment was reported in the local press and very soon became national news. It caused outrage amongst sections of both communities, with letters, TV interviews and debates taking place over a period of several months. Many of the comments and views expressed said that:

- The request was disrespectful.
- The women were being discriminated against.

- They were not being treated with dignity.
- Their right to privacy was being infringed.
- Their right to choice was being eroded.

The other side of the argument noted that:

- Communication methods were being infringed (lip reading for the hard of hearing, hidden body language).
- The veil caused a barrier towards social integration and could, in fact, act as a tool for increasing segregation.
- The veil also had the potential to cause fear related to the hidden face of a robber or the fact that terrorists could hide behind the veil.

Theory into practice

Use the Internet to find out more about this situation and the debate it opened up. In small groups, discuss the following issues:

- Do you agree with any of the views expressed?
- What arguments can you put forward to support these opinions?
- How might the veil affect/not affect access to health and social services?

Reflect

How can an individual's rights be upheld on both sides of this argument? How might this kind of conflict be dealt with in a health or social care setting?

We all have the right to be *respected and treated equally and as an individual* in our everyday lives. However, as we have just seen, this is not always easy to achieve. The health and social care worker often has to 'juggle' a range of situations and opinions in order to demonstrate and uphold these rights for the service user they are working with.

The right to be treated in a dignified way

All individuals deserve to be treated in a manner that preserves their dignity and self-worth. Look back to the earlier case study about Albert on page 70 and remind yourself of how simple the maintenance of dignity can be. All health workers should be sensitive and aware of the needs of people in their care, especially during times when the body and its functions could be exposed.

The right to be allowed privacy

Privacy is a basic human right, as long as the individual is not going to harm themselves or anyone else. All human beings have the right to expect that:

- their treatment and care will be kept private
- no information about them will be passed to people who have no right of access (confidentiality)
- their dignity will be maintained throughout any procedures necessary.

Have you finished, Mark?

▲ Figure 2.8 Privacy *is* possible

Reflect

How would you want your privacy to be maintained if you had to undergo an operation for a bowel disorder? Think about procedures during an initial consultation and then the treatment that might be required in a large ward setting.

Take it further

Write a short case study based in a health or social care setting (use one of the four highlighted in this chapter) to demonstrate an individual's rights being upheld. Give the case study to a member of your group and ask them to identify the rights being upheld.

Treating people with dignity and allowing them privacy is not always easy to achieve but, with thought and care, the needs of individuals can be met.

In context

Agnes, who is 85, has fallen and broken her hip. She has been lying in her bathroom for over three hours waiting for it to get light so that she can use her alarm to alert her neighbours (she didn't like to disturb them in the middle of the night).

By the time the ambulance arrives, Agnes has soiled herself and is in tears because she is in pain. On arrival, the paramedics ask the neighbours (who are watching with great interest) to move into the sitting room. The paramedics immediately set about reassuring Agnes. They cover her with a blanket while making her comfortable on the stretcher, before taking her out to the waiting ambulance which has been reversed right up to the door.

1   **How did the paramedics demonstrate respect for Agnes?**

2   **How did they help to maintain her dignity and privacy in a difficult situation?**

3   **What would have been the effects upon Agnes if the neighbours had been allowed to remain?**

The right to be protected from danger and harm

All patients and service users have the right to expect their carers to keep them safe from danger and harm. To ensure this happens, all hospitals and nursing homes must have a health and safety policy which spells out necessary action, rules and regulations that must be followed to keep staff and service users safe and healthy. In many hospitals you will find a 'locked door' policy, especially on children's wards and wards caring for vulnerable adults. In these cases, entry to the ward is managed by an intercom system.

Reflect

In most hospitals you will find hand wash gel available outside each ward and sometimes in each room. Visitors are expected to clean their hands before and after entering the ward.

• Why do you think the hand wash has been made available?

• Who is being protected?

• Use the Internet to find out which danger or harm is being protected against.

The right to be protected and kept safe from harm may seem a fairly straightforward process. In most situations, keeping the service user safe during their treatment or care will happen without the care worker even thinking about it. However, is it always this simple? Let's consider what happens when things go wrong. Consider the following (extreme) cases.

In context

In 1991, Nurse Beverley Allitt was arrested and tried for the murder of four young children and the attempted murder of at least another nine patients in her care.

At all times, Allitt demonstrated deep empathy and feelings for the parents of the children involved. Later, during the investigation, Allitt was diagnosed with Munchausen's Syndrome by Proxy. This is a form of attention-seeking through other people. (Use the Internet to find out more about this condition.)

During the police investigation it was noted that patients' notes were missing from the hospital. Sections of the patients' missing care notes were later found in Beverley's home.

1 **How did the health care system fail to protect these children from harm?**

2 **Whose rights were abused?**

3 **What action/s (if any) do you consider could have been taken by line managers or others to prevent this tragedy?**

Take it further

Use the Internet to find out about the case of Harold Shipman and make notes of the ways in which services failed to maintain the rights of the individuals and families involved.

The right of an individual to be allowed access to information about themselves

In addition to service users having and expecting privacy, they also have the right to access and see their health records and the information stored about them. The Freedom of Information Act became law on 1 January 2005. This means that all health care workers (and those from other sectors and industries) must

respond to all written requests for information within 20 working days. Health professionals must:

- keep their records in order
- be able to find information quickly and easily
- enable colleagues to find information quickly and easily in case they are absent.

Reflect

What skills will be required from health workers to ensure that they can respond to the Freedom of Information Act effectively?

The right to communicate using an individual's preferred methods of communication and language

All individuals have a preferred method of communication and a preferred language. For example, think about yourself and your family:

- Which language do you prefer to speak in the home?
- Would you use a different language in a public environment?
- Would you want to use communication aids?

What you have identified for yourself is likely to be different for another person. However, it is important to recognise that, without good communication between a patient and their health worker, the treatment and recovery process is likely to be slower than is ideal.

Using a preferred communication method is key to overall 'good communication' in health and social care. This can be particularly challenging for the health care workers involved. However, it is important to overcome any difficulties because, without good communication between an individual and their care worker, the care service or treatment and recovery process are likely to be ineffective and fail to meet an individual's needs.

Offering individuals the opportunity to communicate in their preferred language can have huge implications for the organisation providing the care service. For example, there will be a need to:

- employ staff who communicate in the same language as service users
- buy in the skills of interpreters and translators
- have information available in a variety of formats, for example, leaflets, pictures, tapes etc
- ask an individual's family members to be involved in the communication process.

In context

Woodlands is a care home for young people with physical and learning disabilities. At the moment there are 20 young people in residence but two of these will be leaving soon and another three will take their place. Of these 20 young people, four of the individuals come from Asian heritage backgrounds and speak Punjabi and Urdu, one young woman is profoundly deaf and has limited vision and one comes from eastern Europe and has not yet managed to learn English.

1 **How can the care home best meet the needs of this mix of service users in order to ensure their communication preferences are honoured?**

2 **What actions and activities might you use to communicate with a deaf service user?**

3 **What 'tensions and conflicts' might the manager of this care home have to deal with?**

Take it further

Debate the following issue in two groups and then make recommendations for the use of 'family members' as interpreters.

- Asking family members to interpret on behalf of an individual is a good way to allow communication in a preferred language.
- Family members should never be asked to interpret health-related information for family members as confidentiality may be breached.

Reflect

At the beginning of this unit you were asked about your thoughts relating to equality, diversity and rights. Has your thinking changed at all and, if it has, what is different? Consider how studying equality, diversity and rights might improve the work of a health and social care practitioner and improve the well-being of individual service users.

The right to be cared for in a way that meets needs, takes account of choices and protects

Essentially, this aspect of the unit, which explores individuals' rights, is a summary of everything we have discussed. In order to meet individual needs and account for choices we have to make sure that all other rights are protected and promoted. For example, you cannot provide care that meets an individual's needs without taking into account:

- privacy
- dignity
- individuality (for example, the freedom for an individual to follow their own beliefs and values and make their own choices)
- equality and respect
- protection and safety.

■ Meeting needs

Maslow's hierarchy of needs demonstrates that it is essential to meet an individual's basic health needs prior to other needs. The model argues that warmth, food and shelter are the building blocks upon which other needs can be balanced. So once an individual's basic care needs have been met we can concentrate on meeting higher-level needs such as social and intellectual ones.

■ Taking account of choices

Valuing choice is a central part of the care value base. Making choices does not have to be as significant as choosing a hospital or place of residence – we can make a difference to health and social care outcomes by offering quite simple choices.

Figure 2.9 Choice should be part of everyday life

It is the act of choosing that gives an individual a sense of control over their lives. When illness or infirmity strikes, many individuals feel disempowered; at such times, making even simple choices becomes vital to restoring feelings of control, self-esteem and self-belief. Often it is the simple choices that make a huge difference to the everyday lives of the individuals involved.

As you might expect, simple choices would include:
- choosing from a menu
- deciding which clothes to wear
- when to have a bath or shower.

Reflect

Many hospitals and hospices now put pain control into the hands of the individual following an operation. This has been shown to reduce distress and the experience of pain. Why do you think self-medication has been shown to aid recovery?

2.2 Discriminatory practice in health and social care

Discrimination within health and social care can arise for a wide range of different reasons. The root causes of discrimination are often referred to as the 'bases of discrimination' and we will now explore them in more detail.

In February 2005, the government announced that they would be carrying out a 'root and branch review' of the causes of discrimination in British society. When Jacqui Smith from the cabinet office announced the review, she said:

'We need to look to the future and question why deep seated patterns of disadvantage remain so that we can improve opportunities and help the new Commission for Equality and Human Rights make a strong impact from the start.'

Clearly, from a health and social care perspective, this review supports our efforts to provide the best service possible by seeking to develop a 'better understanding of the underlying and long term barriers faced by many individuals and groups in society'.

Bases of discrimination

We already know that the main bases of discrimination are:

- culture
- disability
- age
- social class
- gender
- sexuality
- health status
- family status
- cognitive ability.

Each of these reasons for discrimination is used by individuals and groups within society to exclude others from life's chances. It is part of our role and responsibility, as health and social care workers, to understand these bases of discrimination and the effects they can have on the health and well-being of our service users. This knowledge should then be used to 'champion' our service users' rights and challenge discriminatory attitudes and behaviours.

Culture

An individual's culture is formed through the social interactions that they have been exposed to when they were 'brought up'. Their behaviours and beliefs are formed by the family and the community in which they live and can be classed as a pattern that demonstrates the culture to which they belong.

Therefore, it is easy to see that if the culture of the health care worker and that of the individual clash there is the potential for conflict and discrimination.

In December 2004 the Islamic Human Rights Commission published a report called 'Social Discrimination: Across the Muslim Divide'. The report identified that about 80 per cent of Muslims had experienced some form of discrimination. The reason for the discrimination appeared to be based on perceived differences in morals, values, norms, standards, beliefs and attitudes. In other words 'cultural incompatibility' appeared to be a key factor in the amount of discrimination experienced.

Muslims who practised their religious observances reported more discrimination than those who did not practise the faith. The report went on to say that for some individuals there is a 'double penalty'. This happens when there is more than one base of discrimination applied to a single individual. For example, being a dark-skinned, practising Muslim increased the amount of discrimination experienced by individuals.

Take it further

Working with others, research those factors which combine to create an individual's 'cultural background' and discuss why different cultures may fail to integrate successfully together.

Disability

This is another potential source of discrimination. Most people realise that children often behave differently towards other children who have physical or mental disabilities. Unfortunately it isn't only children who behave differently – some adults do too. Health care workers could discriminate either positively or negatively depending on the ability of an individual.

We have already seen evidence earlier in this unit of government action to reduce disability discrimination: every organisation is required to have a policy on this subject.

Age

By 2050 one in five people will be over the age of 60 in developed countries. This will clearly put a huge strain on the resources available to care for and treat those needing medical assistance. However, age is already another cause of discrimination within developed countries and is an issue that has already caused a great deal of debate within the health and social care systems. There are some service providers who would argue that it is possible to be too old for certain kinds of treatment and that resources should be used on those young enough to benefit from the treatment provided.

Reflect

During 1999, Age Concern published a report which argued that the NHS was 'ageist'. Many older people had been denied treatment for cancer, high blood pressure and organ failure requiring transplant. The medical establishment pointed out that there was a shortage of organs and that they had a duty to make sure the recipient was fit and well enough to receive a transplant. It may well be that older people are too frail or sick to make the best use of treatments on offer.

Discuss with others your views on treatments (such as those listed above) for older people.

Social class

'The Registrar General's Scale of Social Class' is one way of grouping people according to their occupations. See the description on page 340. (Unit 7).

Social class can be the basis of discrimination for a variety of reasons. The higher social classes are said to 'look down' on the lower social classes. This could be because of different speech patterns, levels of power or the amount of money earned (although this is less relevant these days).

Theory into practice

Use the Internet to find out more about the Registrar General's Social Classification System and then arrange to talk to people from each division. Discuss with others whether you really can tell any difference and whether a social classification is helpful to the work of a health and social care worker.

It has been well documented by a variety of sources for many years (see the Acheson Report, 1998) that doctors and other health workers are more likely to offer a better service to those people who are articulate and can 'stand up for themselves'. As you might expect, these are the people who are well educated, have good jobs and are therefore earning good rates of pay. Obviously then, in some cases, doctors are potentially discriminating against those people who are less articulate than themselves!

Gender

Discrimination can occur simply because an individual is male or female. In the past, employers failed to offer the same promotion prospects and pay to men and women as it was generally held that women were unable to match the skills and knowledge attained by men. While this is no longer the case, some women's groups still feel that there is a 'glass ceiling' (a point in a woman's career when it proves almost impossible to proceed any further). For example, in health and social care there are still more male medical consultants than female.

Reflect

Have you ever been excluded from an activity because of your gender?

Sexuality

This term is generally used to refer to an individual's sexual orientation. Again, this can be the basis of discrimination if the health care worker is homophobic (prejudiced against gay and lesbian people).

Health status

Another cause of discrimination can arise from the level of good health or illness being experienced by an individual at a given moment in time. It is possible for health care workers to discriminate in favour of an individual who is more ill (or less ill) than another. This kind of discrimination could occur because of the amount of work and the actual work patterns associated with caring for the individuals involved.

Family status

The type of family an individual comes from also has the potential to be the source of discrimination for some people. It is less common to find discrimination occurring as a result of single-parent status but same-sex parents and other family groupings might form bases of discrimination for some individuals.

Reflect

What are your views on children being born to lesbian parents? Would you be in danger of discriminating against either the parents or the children? Why do you think you should not let your personal views lead to discriminatory attitudes and behaviours when working in health and social care?

Cognitive ability

This term is often used to mean 'level of intelligence'. The way an individual processes information in their brain can be the cause of discrimination, particularly for those people with learning difficulties. Health care staff may find these people challenging to work with and inadvertently apply labels to them, not realising that they are in effect discriminating against their client groups.

Discriminatory practice

Discriminatory practice can be demonstrated through a wide variety of actions and behaviours. Sometimes this happens through simple thoughtlessness and sometimes, sadly, intentionally.

Infringement of rights

When we are exploring discriminatory practice, it is important to recognise that what we are referring to is the 'infringement of an individual's rights'. As we have previously said, all individuals have an entitlement to have their rights respected, acknowledged and followed. Health and social care professionals have a duty to promote the rights of their patients and service users and to challenge those people who may infringe the rights of others. In the past, services have been accused of not letting service users know about some of the facilities that could be available to them: this is because practitioners knew there was no funding available to support the provision of the service. This can be seen as an infringement of the individual's rights.

Covert or overt abuse of power

As we have seen, covert means 'hidden' and overt means 'out in the open'. Using and abusing power and authority to discriminate against individuals is not acceptable behaviour. Health and social care professionals have to use their power when working with individuals in a variety of ways. For example, social workers and carers have to make decisions about the level of care an individual will receive each day, and doctors make decisions, as part of their everyday function, about who will receive treatment, and when. However, if this power is used negatively, individuals can be disadvantaged in their access to health care.

Prejudice

Prejudice is pre-conceived judgements (pre-judgements) about people and their characteristics or behaviours. We know that decisions are often made in the health and social care sector prior to meeting an individual – this is because 'information' is usually provided beforehand.

For example, if you visit your GP and ask for a referral to the local hospital, the doctor will send the request to the Patients Referral Unit who must then decide if you really need the appointment. It is possible to find prejudice occurring at this and other levels.

Reflect

How might prejudice be demonstrated at the Patients Referral Unit and what could be the outcomes of this?

In context

Elaine has just come on night duty to care for a 14-bedded ward of medically ill patients. During the handover, her colleague Irene provides a report on the patients and their care during the day. Irene says, 'The diabetes patient has had her blood tests but the type 2 is still waiting, the asthma case is still on oxygen and the thyroid's surgical wound is healing well. Other than that, there's not much to report.'

1 **How have labels been used in this case?**

2 **What might the effects of this information be on Elaine?**

3 **How are individuality and rights being infringed?**

Stereotyping

Stereotyping occurs when assumptions are made about groups based on information relating to just a small number of people. As a result, many individuals or groups of the population might have labels applied to them which could affect the health care they receive.

Labelling

The action of giving people labels (identified by Howard Becker in 1963) is usually carried out by people who hold power in society. The labels are mostly negative and can

place individuals outside social acceptance. Within health and social care, giving an individual a label can certainly affect the care they will receive. Many care givers are accused of seeing the label and not the individual.

Bullying

This term is used when someone uses their power or position to intimidate another individual. Bullying can also be classed as abuse. Bullying can be demonstrated through physical actions as well as through verbal or

In context

Martha has lived in a nursing home for three years. She knows she is a challenging individual for the nursing team because of her physical disabilities but she does try to help them move her around as much as possible.

She is worried in case 'that Arthur' will be on duty this evening because, no matter how she tries, she cannot please him. She hates the way he just bursts into her room and manhandles her into the hoist and

wheelchair to take her for dinner. Her upper arms are really sore from last night and she knows she must not complain or tell anyone else or she will be left in her room again without a meal.

1 **How does this scenario demonstrate bullying?**

2 **Why does Martha feel that she cannot complain?**

3 **What action could be taken to help Martha achieve her rights?**

written actions that lead to mental health and distress issues. In health and social care we could find bullying occurring at a range of different levels or through a range of different circumstances. For example, it is possible for one member of staff to bully another or for a manager to bully their team members. It is important to remember that all forms of bullying are discrimination and should not be allowed to go unchecked.

When bullying situations occur in the workplace, it is possible for staff to respond and, with support, to challenge this offensive behaviour. However, when bullying occurs between service users or between a member of staff and an individual in their care, it can become much more difficult to handle.

We need to remember that harassment is also a form of bullying and should be challenged wherever it occurs. Examples of bullying and harassment could include:

- threatening words
- nicknames
- offensive jokes
- personal, physical or verbal attacks
- exclusion from treatment/medication etc.

Reflect

Did you know that more women than men suffer from harassment and bullying? Why do you think this might be?

Abuse

It is important to remember that all forms of discrimination are a form of abuse, whether this is bullying, denying someone choice or applying labels to individuals. You might have heard of cases of physical and other types of abuse occurring in some workplaces and have probably heard stories of individuals being prosecuted for their part in the action. However, this is rare and would usually only occur because of a lack of staff training and support. In some cases, stress (due to a work overload) can contribute to abusive situations occurring.

The effects of discriminatory practice in health and social care

Discrimination has the potential to affect individuals in wide-ranging ways. In health and social care, the effects of discrimination can be catastrophic and even end in the death of a service user. Anyone planning a career in health and social care should be aware of the potential negative effects caused by discrimination. We will explore them here.

Marginalisation

As you might expect, marginalisation means being pushed to the margins of society. In other words, you are unable to participate fully in the health and social care services that are available. Marginalisation can occur at both micro and macro levels. Governments have been accused of marginalising groups of the population in terms of their health and social care needs.

In context

The drug rehabilitation centre for Prestpool is closing due to a lack of funding, even though there is a strong culture of drug use in the area. Local pressure groups are lobbying the health and social care services to ask for other provision to be considered but no one seems to be listening. When a local councillor was asked for her views she said, 'Where would we put another centre? No one wants these people in their backyard!'

1 **Why do you think drug users could be marginalised?**

2 **Should drug services be funded as a matter of priority? If not, why not?**

3 **What would your views be of a drug service located in your neighbourhood?**

Disempowerment

People who are discriminated against (especially by powerful groups in society such as health care professionals) are often totally disempowered. This means they are not able to take action for themselves, have no way of fighting the discrimination and, sadly, lose the will to do something about it.

Take it further

Use the Internet to research infertility treatment and those people who can and cannot access this service. Find out how some people react to being refused treatment and what has happened to some individuals as a result.

Individuals can be disempowered through another form of discrimination – 'the health worker knows best' syndrome.

In context

Harry is a World War II veteran who has cared for his wife, Pat, at home for the last 10 years. She has a form of dementia and her condition is slowly getting worse. Pat's home carer feels that she is getting too much for Harry to care for and they have arranged for her to be admitted into a residential care home without Harry's approval.

Harry is devastated and wants his wife back home but the authority involved will not let this happen. Harry has now applied to the legal system to fight the case but feels he cannot manage on his own. He has made contact with the ex-servicemen's support network and they are going to help him fight the case.

1   **How is disempowerment demonstrated in this case?**

2   **What could Harry have done if he had not been an ex-serviceman?**

3   **What other support networks might have been available to Harry?**

Low self-esteem and self-identity

If we have high self-esteem and self-worth, it means that we appreciate our own worth and value ourselves highly. Conversely then, having low self-esteem means that we feel helpless and powerless to cope and can even feel depressed.

People who are discriminated against are in real danger of developing low self-esteem which can lead to them being unable to cope with life's challenges and changes. This is particularly important for those individuals who have to cope with illness or changes in their social condition. If they are to cope well, they need to believe in themselves and their ability to manage, whatever situation they are in. Health care workers need to pay attention to an individual's self-esteem and constantly work at improving this – this is a good method for helping individuals to cope positively with their situation.

Restricted opportunities

Discrimination, as we have already seen, has the potential to prevent access to health and social care services. This could be through the attitudes and beliefs of the health care workers who fail to value all individuals or it could be through the effects of low self-esteem.

Negative behaviours including aggression and criminality

Another effect of discrimination can be seen in the behaviour of individuals. This is particularly noticeable in children, who often display negative behaviours in order to gain attention, even when that attention is negative! Negative behavioural traits can also be displayed by adults and young people as a result of discrimination and low self-esteem. However, in these cases the behaviour can take on a much more 'sinister' appearance. It may manifest itself as aggression towards those holding power (including health care professionals or those working in the employment and judicial services) and through criminal activity such as drug taking, burglary and physical violence.

Loss of rights

There have been cases in the national media of care homes, secure or forensic units (places of security for people with dangerous psychiatric behaviours) and individual carers being accused of systematically discriminating against the people in their care and overriding their individual rights by the use of power or force. Older, vulnerable people in residential or nursing care homes are at particular risk of abusive situations because of the high power base of those caring for them.

There are occasions when statutory powers are used legitimately to override individual rights. In these cases, doctors and judges can take decisions together to place people in places of safety for their 'own good'. Another example of the use of statutory powers in operation is when social workers need to work with others such as the police or medical service to take children from unsafe homes and place them in centres of safety.

2.3 How national initiatives promote anti-discriminatory practice

The law provides service users, individuals and health care professionals (as well as others) with the basic principles and guidelines which must be followed when dealing with individuals in any given situation. The obligations attached to each specific piece of legislation must be followed or sanctions will be applied to those breaking the law.

Conventions, legislation and regulations

No one expects a health or social care worker to know all the details of every law that promotes anti-discriminatory practice in health and social care.

However, it is important that you understand the major legislative framework and the basic principles involved. These should then be applied to all aspects of caring for individuals.

Law or regulation	Areas covered
European Convention on Human Rights. 2000	This convention forms the basis of the human rights that have been agreed by the UK. The declaration aims to gain universal recognition and observance of Human Rights and Fundamental Freedoms. The countries that have 'signed up' to the agreement aim to follow all the 66 articles identified within the convention (see page 57 for examples).
Sex Discrimination Act, 1975	The Sex Discrimination Act is there to protect both men and women. It is designed to give everyone equal rights in relation to employment and services. It deals with both direct and indirect discrimination on the grounds of gender.
Mental Health Act, 1983	This act protects the rights of those people with mental health difficulties or learning disabilities. The intention is to protect individuals from exploitation by others. The act also serves to protect wider society from individuals who display dangerous behaviours.
Mental Health, Northern Ireland Order, 1986	This act covers the treatment of people with mental health problems in Northern Ireland and the issues involved in caring for people with learning disabilities. It also covers aspects of compulsory treatment and the detention of people in hospital without their consent as well as the protection of individuals from exploitation by others.
Convention on the Rights of the Child, 1989	This convention was held by the United Nations General Assembly and reaffirmed that children's rights require special protection. They called for a continuous improvement of the situation of children all over the world. Aspects of the convention have been followed through The Children Act (see below) and the Every Child Matters policy.
The Children Act, 1989	This act protects children and their rights. Through the act children are: • protected from significant harm • supported fully if they are in care • safe and cared for suitably by the setting of standards for nurseries and residential schools.
Race Relations (Amendment) Act, 2000	All public sector organisations must have a due regard and hold the duty to promote racial equality. This means that they should promote equality of opportunity and promote good relations between people of different ethnic backgrounds. Encouraging racial hatred is unlawful and any form of discrimination on the grounds of colour, nationality or race is illegal.
Disability Discrimination Act, 1995	This act protects the rights of people with disabilities. It places a duty on organisations to explore how they can overcome barriers and increase access to their services for people with a disability. Reasonable adjustments should be made and equipment provided to enable equal access.
Human Rights Act, 1998	This act enables all individuals to take action against authorities including the police and government if they feel their rights have been affected negatively. All care and health establishments are included in this act and must therefore respect the main rights covered.
Data Protection Act, 1998	This act is designed to protect information held about individuals. All organisations must register as a data user and follow the rules provided. Examples of these are: • Data must have been collected through lawful means. • The information held should only be used for the purpose agreed and must be relevant to the situation. • The information must be stored securely. • Individuals must be allowed access to all their personal information on request.
Nursing and Residential Care Homes Regulations, 1984	This act places a duty on care and nursing providers to register their service and manager with the appropriate authority (for an annual fee). Local councils and health authorities then have a duty to regulate the standard of care being provided. This means that the authorities have the right to enter and inspect premises and services, to make recommendations for change and if necessary close establishments that are under-performing.

Law or regulation	Areas covered
Care Standards Act, 2000	This act replaced the regulation of duties carried out by local authorities and health authorities under the Registered Homes Act, 1984. The Care Standards Act expanded a new system for regulating health and social care provision to include domiciliary, fostering and family care as well as residential home care. A series of national minimum standards have to be applied to all services with the intention of putting the individual at the centre of the caring process.
The Children Act, 2004	This act underpins the Every Child Matters policy which aims to transform children's services by bringing them all together under Children's Trusts. The key duty in this act is one of co-operation between services to be sure that children: • are healthy and safe • enjoy life and achieve • make a positive contribution • achieve economic well-being.
Disability Discrimination Act, 2005	This act has amended the Disability Discrimination Act of 1995 to include making it unlawful for operators of transport to discriminate against people with disabilities. It is also now unlawful for owners of private clubs and landlords of rental properties to discriminate on the basis of disability. The act also includes protection for people with HIV, cancer and multiple sclerosis, as well as ensuring that equality of opportunity is promoted across the public sector.
Mental Capacity Act, 2005	This act provides a framework that empowers and protects vulnerable people. It allows others to take decisions on behalf of people who lack mental capacity. However, decisions must always be in the best interests of the individual concerned. For the first time there is a clear test to assess 'capacity', which will lead to action being taken in the best interests of the individual.
Age Discrimination Act, 2006	This is the final strand of equality legislation and aims to prevent discrimination as a result of an individual's age. The act covers all aspects of employment and vocational training. For example, an individual's chances of promotion or selection for a job should never be jeopardised by their age.

Table 2.1 Key legislation concerning the caring of other people

Clearly, along with legislation such as this come rights and responsibilities for each and every one of us. While an act can give 'freedom of speech' to the individual, alongside this comes a responsibility for that individual not to promote discrimination against other people when using their 'right to freedom of speech'.

▲ Figure 2.10 'Protesting' does not give individuals or groups the right to discriminate or incite others to do so

Codes of practice and charters

Codes of conduct

Codes of conduct or codes of practice are designed to guide and advise health and social care workers on their roles, rights and responsibilities. They also help individuals and service users to identify the kind of support and behaviour they can expect from the person caring for them.

Most health and social care professions have a charter or code of practice which members follow.

All codes of conduct and charters use the care value base as a starting point for the content and the messages they are giving. For example, the box below includes a selection from the Nursing and Midwifery Council Code of Conduct. Here you can see clearly the expectations placed on a nurse or midwife in terms of duty and behaviours.

Take it further

Use the Internet to research the Code of Practice for Social Care Workers. Make notes of the key differences between the social care code and that followed by nursing and midwifery staff.

Nursing and Midwifery Council Code of Conduct

1   Introduction

The purpose of the NMC code of professional conduct standards for conduct, performance and ethics is to:
- inform the professions of the standard of professional conduct required of them in the exercise of their professional accountability and practice
- inform the public, other professions and employers of the standard of professional conduct that they can expect of a registered practitioner.

As a registered nurse, midwife or specialist community public health nurse, you must:
- protect and support the health of individual patients and clients
- protect and support the health of the wider community
- act in such a way that justifies the trust and confidence the public have in you
- uphold and enhance the good reputation of the professions.

You are personally accountable for your practice. This means that you are answerable for your actions and omissions, regardless of advice or directions from another professional.

You have a duty of care to your patients and clients who are entitled to receive safe and competent care.

You must adhere to the laws of the country in which you are practising.

2   As a registered nurse, midwife or specialist community public health nurse, you must respect the patient or client as an individual.

You must recognise and respect the role of patients and clients as partners in their care and the contribution they can make to it.

You are personally accountable for ensuring that you promote and protect the interests and dignity of patients and clients, irrespective of gender, age, race, ability, sexuality, economic status, lifestyle, culture and religious or political beliefs.

You must promote the interests of patients and clients. This includes helping individuals and groups gain access to health and social care, information and support relevant to their needs.

3   As a registered nurse, midwife or specialist community public health nurse, you must obtain consent before you give any treatment or care.

All patients and clients have a right to receive information about their condition. You must be sensitive to their needs and respect the wishes of those who refuse or are unable to receive information about their condition. Information should be accurate, truthful and presented in such a way as to make it easily understood. You may need to seek legal or professional advice or guidance from your employer, in relation to the giving or withholding of consent.

You must respect patients' and clients' autonomy – their right to decide whether or not to undergo any health care intervention – even where a refusal may result in harm or death to themselves or a foetus.

What are the Codes?

The Codes are the first statutory codes of practice for social care workers and their employers. They provide a clear guide for all those who work in social care, setting out the standards of conduct that workers and their employers should meet. They also mean that service users, carers and the wider public will know what standard of conduct and practice they can expect. There are two Codes:

- The Code of Practice for Social Care Workers – this sets out the standards of professional conduct and practice required of social care workers.
- The Code of Practice for Employers of Social Care Workers – this sets out the responsibilities of employers in the regulation of social care workers.

Why are the Codes important?

The Codes play a key part in regulating the social care workforce and in helping to improve levels of public protection. Adherence to the Codes will be a condition of joining the Social Care Register. Social care workers who breach the Codes could be removed from the register, while employers who break them could face sanctions.

The Codes apply to anyone working at any level in any social care setting. Over time, one million-plus social care workers in the UK will be invited to register with their relevant social care regulatory council. This will be one of the following:

- the General Social Care Council in England
- the Care Council for Wales
- the Northern Ireland Social Care Council
- the Scottish Social Services Council.

The Codes also apply to all employers in private, voluntary and statutory sectors.

What should I do with the Codes?

Whether you are a social care worker or a social care employer you need to comply with the Codes.

Individual social care workers should take personal responsibility for ensuring they adhere to the Code of Practice for Social Care Workers. Everything in them can be put into practice straightaway.

Charters

Most organisations have 'charters' which tell the service user what they can expect from that service. A charter sets out rights and responsibilities in an easy-to-read and accessible format. A charter is used by a range of different individuals and organisations. For example, the Inspectorate (the organisation with the responsibility for ensuring standards are upheld) may start their review of an organisation by reading the charter and then asking service users about their perception of the organisation and its aims i.e. does the service live up to expectations?

Take it further

The text below is taken from Warwickshire County Council Better Care Higher Standards Charter.

We aim to provide a high standard of service by:

- *treating people with politeness, honesty and respecting their dignity*
- *having the best people to deliver our services*
- *promoting independence and supporting people to take part in the community*
- *working in partnership with people who need the services*
- *involving service users and carers in decisions about the care they receive and giving them enough information to make informed choices*
- *helping service users and carers to have a voice through advocacy and other representative organisations*
- *respecting and listening to what people say whatever their background*
- *making sure that people feel able to complain about the standard of service provided and that they are assured they will not be treated badly because they complain*
- *making sure people feel able to let agencies know where service provision is not working well.*

How does this charter meet the care value base and promote equality, diversity and rights in health and social care?

Organisational policies and procedures

Within the health care sector there is a wide range of policies, guidelines and procedures in place in different organisations to support equality, diversity and rights. We have already seen an outline of the legislation that is designed to support individuals and groups within the population at a national level (see pages 83–84). Now we will explore many of the actions that can be taken at a more local or organisational level, for example those services and actions that managers and health and social care workers can use and take to further support those people in their employment or care.

Positive promotion of individual rights

Positive promotion of equality and rights is often seen on notice boards displaying key policies and guidelines. Health care settings are required by law to display health and safety regulations but you are just as likely to see the confidentiality policy displayed alongside. This is intended to give service users reassurance as they enter care, perhaps for the first time, and to remind staff of their duty regarding confidentiality.

In many health care settings, staff are able to contribute to the development of policies and procedures that help to promote individual rights. For example, a charter in the workplace might outline the behaviours expected from staff towards their service users but equally it should include a section on the responsibilities o[...] towards each other and the staff who are [...]

Other examples of positive promotion [...] rights could include handbooks that ou[...] and responsibilities of staff and their service users. And of course, there is always the example of the charter which, if made readily available (perhaps located on walls, in leaflets and other service user information), would serve as an example of positive promotion.

■ Dignity in Care campaign

Dignity in Care is a national initiative launched in November 2006 that aims to ensure that all older people are treated with dignity and respect, as is their right. It is intended to make a real difference to the lives of older people receiving services from health and social care. You can find out about the campaign from the website www.dh.gov.uk/dignityincare.

Advocacy

There are many occasions when an individual is too ill or frail to speak for themselves. In cases such as these they have the right to expect an advocate's help. An advocate is a person who will speak on behalf of the service user. An advocate can be:

- a fully trained and employed individual
- a member of the individual's family
- a family friend or neighbour
- a member of staff.

In context

Manham hospital has finally put together a 'zero tolerance' policy against physical and verbal abuse in the accident and emergency department (A&E) following the third attack on one of their doctors. The staff in the department have worked together with the health and safety officer, the police and the human resource department to develop the policy which they hope will protect the staff and patients in A&E and elsewhere.

The main message of the policy is that any patient displaying abusive or violent attitudes towards the staff or other patients will be asked to leave.

1   Why is this an example of positive action?

2   Whose rights are being protected in this action?

3   Which rights are being protected?

▲ Figure 2.11 There are advocates working at every level for the individual

Whoever speaks on behalf of the service user must remember that they are putting the views of the individual forward and not their own perception of those views. They will need to be clear about the difference between the individual's views and those of the organisation caring for them. In many health care settings you will find guidelines for staff on accepted behaviour for those acting in the role of advocate.

Take it further

Look back at Unit 1 for more information on advocacy. You could also use the Internet to research more about the role and responsibilities of an advocate.

Work practices

Work practices must demonstrate equality and rights across the organisation at all times. All organisations will have policies and procedures that cover confidentiality, disability discrimination, health and safety, bullying and harassment to mention but a few. There is no point having these policies if staff and service users are not aware of them or do not follow the guidelines within them. A central part of health care training is the promotion of these policies. Staff are expected to know the contents and comply with them at all times, alongside making sure that service users are also aware of the policies and procedures. Failure in this respect would result in disciplinary action and, if necessary, dismissal.

Staff development and training

Once a health care professional has qualified they are expected to continue with personal and professional training to update their skills and knowledge. Remember, technology is moving fast and a health or social care worker can soon become outdated in their practice if they don't move with the times. A service user has the right to expect to have their treatment and care carried out to the best possible standards.

In exactly the same way, it is important to recognise that training and development on equality and rights should also be updated and kept fresh in the minds of the staff employed in the organisation.

Quality issues

An organisation must always strive to do better and ensure it provides services of the highest quality. Maintaining the standards around equality and rights is difficult for any organisation but not impossible. An organisation has to consider:

- how they can monitor the policies and their effectiveness
- how they can update the content to keep in line with legislation
- what staff training is required
- what impact the policies are having on their service.

Finding out the answers to these questions and others like them is central to the role of quality control.

Reflect

How might a hospital trust find out if their confidentiality policy is working or not?

Complaints procedures

All organisations must have a complaints procedure which will be inspected when audits are carried out. However, each organisation's complaints procedure will be different. They will, of course, contain roughly the same information but the wording will vary from one organisation to another.

In general we could expect a complaints procedure to follow the pattern shown opposite.

**Figure 2.12 ▶
An example of
a complaints
policy**

WARMSHIRE COUNTY CARE SERVICES
Complaints Policy

This leaflet outlines the ways you can make a complaint if you are dissatisfied with our services. If you feel that you have a complaint to make about our service or the way you have been treated then follow the simple guidelines shown below.

It is often simpler to refer your complaint to the member of staff with whom you have been dealing. They may be able to sort the issue out immediately for you.

If you prefer not to speak to the member of staff then please ask to see their supervisor or line manager.

Failing either of these two options you can:

- use the attached form to make a complaint
- write a letter and send it to us
- ask someone else to write the letter on your behalf and send it to us.

Our staff are here to help you and you will not be discriminated against because you have made a complaint.
....

Please return this form to:
Warmshire County Care Services, Heaton Place, Warmshire.

Please state your complaint below and continue on a separate sheet if necessary.

Your complaint will be acknowledged within one week and will be dealt with within 28 days.

Your details:
Name: ....

Address: ....
....
....

Telephone number: ....

In context

Maple Leaf day centre is based in East Wertham where there is a high population of Asian heritage people. The service users coming for day care are mainly from the Indian sub-continent and one or two people have Irish backgrounds. The centre manager has decided that the workforce needs to reflect the population better so she has set a target to try and employ more nurses from Asian heritage backgrounds. She is using the newspapers and local schools that are accessed by the local population to advertise job vacancies. However, she knows that when it comes to appointing people into the posts, she must fill the jobs on merit only or she will be breaking the law!

1 **What difference will it make to the health and well-being of service users to have staff who reflect their own backgrounds?**

2 **Why might it be difficult to attract workers from different cultural backgrounds?**

3 **What else could the manager do to attract workers from all cultural backgrounds?**

Affirmative action

This is sometimes called positive action or positive discrimination, which means favouring one individual over another because they come from a minority group. This is illegal in Britain under the Race Relations and Sex Discrimination Acts unless special amendments are agreed. However, in an organisation where the workforce does not reflect service users or the community they are based in, it is acceptable to set targets for the recruitment of staff from particular backgrounds and take positive action to meet these targets.

Anti-harassment

All organisations must have a policy that deals with the issue of harassment. This should be made available to staff and be updated and monitored regularly. UK laws aim to prevent harassment or bullying on the grounds of race, ethnicity, sex, gender, religion, sexual orientation and disability.

Harassment is defined by the way actions make individuals feel, not by the intentions of the person accused of carrying out the harassment. In other words, the perpetrator may not realise that their actions amount to harassment.

Confidentiality

The Data Protection Act of 1998 provides clear guidelines about the use of personal information. The guidelines restrict the use of service user information to ensure that only relevant information is collected and that it is stored in a secure place. Alongside this is a professional responsibility for all health and social care workers to maintain service user confidentiality at all times.

Every service user has a right to expect that the information they disclose to a health and social care worker will be kept safe and secure. This means that a health care worker should:

- never gossip about individuals and service users
- never discuss service user information in the hearing of other people
- never leave notes lying around for others to read
- never disclose information to a third party without permission.

All organisations should have a policy that outlines their confidentiality procedures. This is usually written in such a way that it gives service users confidence in the organisation and their staff. However, it is important to recognise that some information cannot be kept confidential. This should be highlighted on the confidentiality policy so that all service users know what to expect.

Information that cannot be kept confidential from the people who should act on it (for example, supervisors) is any that:

- puts the life of another individual in danger
- puts the life of the service user in danger
- discloses abusive or potentially abusive situations.

I'm sorry but I can't discuss this with you.

▲ Figure 2.13 It is important to maintain confidentiality at all times

In context

Marika is on evening duty in the local nursing home for people with heart and circulatory disorders. She is extremely busy and trying to complete three jobs at once. The telephone rings and a man asks how Norman's operation has gone. Marika replies, 'He is doing fine – the heart bypass seems to have gone well.' The caller thanks her and ends the call.

On putting the receiver down Marika suddenly thinks, 'I should not have done that!'

1 **What should Marika not have done?**

2 **What can she do about the situation?**

3 **What might she need to consider in the future?**

Human rights

It is expected that all health and social care organisations will adhere to best practice and follow the guidelines linked to human rights. While these may not be made explicit through a 'Human Rights Policy' pinned to the wall for everyone to read, the guidelines and other organisational policies that are adopted and followed will demonstrate quality practice that is based on the human rights principles.

2.4 Promoting anti-discriminatory practice

The active promotion of anti-discriminatory practice

If these ethical values are applied to all individuals then equality and rights should be met. The care value base is built upon ethical principles and places the service user at the heart of provision.

Ethical principles

These are principles or ways of working that are based on moral beliefs and judgements. Key ethical principles are:

- justice
- autonomy (maintaining or increasing the independence of service users)
- beneficence (taking actions that benefit service users)
- non-maleficence (not doing harm to service users).

Putting the patient/service user at the heart of service provision

Actively promoting equality and rights puts the service user at the heart of provision which keeps them in mind at all the key points of service. For example, the planning and implementation of all services should (as far as possible) be carried out with the service user and built around their specific needs. In health and social care one model does not fit all! In some of the health and social care settings, meeting individual needs can be challenging to achieve but with forward planning and flexibility it is always possible.

When several people share the same living space there are certain expectations of everyone. For example, meals are often planned to take place at a specific time i.e. breakfast at 8 a.m. and dinner at 6 p.m. – you may find that there is a reading room and a television room and so it can be assumed that reading and television watching takes place in the allocated rooms. So what happens when an individual wants something different?

This is where a flexible, client-centred approach is the key to success. The key principles that each setting must adhere to are:

- providing service users with active support
- promoting individuals' rights
- offering choices and ensuring well-being
- promoting anti-discriminatory practices
- empowering service users.

Providing service users with active support

Active support, as we have already discussed, involves taking the appropriate action to support a service user when they need assistance or guidance. It does not mean 'taking over'. Many service users are reluctant to ask for support and will try to deal with issues themselves (or at the very least 'keep it in the family'). Therefore, providing active support requires a sensitive approach.

Support can take many forms and it is important to recognise both the forms and the amounts of support that may be required. All of our service users are individuals and will therefore need varying amounts of support, in some cases on a daily basis. The main forms of support could be summarised as:

- service-related advice and guidance (access, rights etc)
- the provision of service-related information (medication, appointments, care planning etc)
- physical support (dressing, eating, washing, moving etc)
- social support (entertainment, friendships, listening ears)
- mental health support (coping strategies, encouragement, confidence building).

Promoting individuals' rights

The promotion of individual rights takes many forms and includes the need to help service users express their needs and preferences. Many individuals can and do express their needs and wants quite forcefully and are very able to 'speak up for themselves' but there are other individuals who will need help and support.

Reflect

What kind of service user is likely to need help and support to express their needs?

Service users who might need help to express their needs include those who:

- are ill
- are frail
- have learning difficulties
- use a second language.

However, you may have identified others. Whatever the reason for needing assistance, the support comes in the form of good communication!

To support individuals to express their needs you will need to:

- keep service users informed
- ask questions
- use a preferred method of communicating
- listen
- not make assumptions
- ask for help from others if necessary.

Offering choices and ensuring well-being

Active promotion of equality and individual rights can also be demonstrated in the way we work individually with our service users. For example, offering people a choice related to their care and treatment can make a huge difference to the way people feel and respond to the service. Choices around food, clothing and personal care are key to the services offered by health and social care assistants. As you can imagine, choosing your own clothes for the day and the food you want to eat at mealtimes are central to feelings of well-being and a sense of control over your daily life.

Reflect

How would you feel if someone else made these decisions on your behalf?

However, in health and social care, choice is being taken into much wider avenues through the way we access and use the public services available to us.

■ Promoting anti-discriminatory practices

All health care workers have a responsibility to promote anti-discriminatory practices. This can include informing service users of their rights, challenging discriminatory practices and keeping themselves up-to-

date with current legislations and policy guidelines to help ensure the best possible service is provided.

■ Empowering service users

Empowering individuals is another key role for the health professional. As you are already aware, this is about enabling individuals to feel that they have control over their lives and that they can take action as appropriate.

Balancing an individual's rights with the rights of others

Balancing the rights of one individual with the rights of another can be difficult to achieve but certainly not impossible. In the main, the health and care worker needs to develop good negotiating skills and an open communication style. Balancing rights is often about dealing with conflict and tensions.

Dealing with conflicts

Dealing with conflicts and tensions is all part of the daily work of a health and social care professional. In some

In context

Helen is only 53 but already she needs to have a hip replaced. She has been in constant pain for the last three years and feels that she cannot 'take any more'. She has been on a waiting list for over 18 months and has gone along to visit her GP to see if anything can be done to speed up the operation.

Her GP looks on the Internet at the waiting times in a range of hospitals for hip replacements. She finds one 200 miles away that could see Helen in two weeks' time if she is willing to travel. Helen asks her GP to make the necessary arrangements as her husband will take her to the appointment. She knows she will not get any visitors while she is in hospital as it is too far

for her family to travel. But she feels that this would be preferable to having to wait another eight months for her treatment at the local hospital trust.

Discuss with others how this choice could affect Helen and her family. What would influence your choices if you were in the same situation as Helen?

1   **How is Helen's right to choice promoted here?**

2   **How might her well-being be affected by the choices she makes?**

3   **Who else might need to be involved in the choices Helen makes?**

cases the tensions might be between a service user and a carer or between two service users. In addition, there is also the possibility of tensions occurring between services. No matter what the situation is, a resolution must always be found if the individual at the centre of the care process is to receive high quality provision.

In the main, there is only one way that staff at any level can learn how to deal with issues arising in their daily work in a positive and successful manner. This is through staff development (training, education and workplace experience).

Dealing with conflict requires a range of skills including:

- seeing all sides of an argument
- being willing to listen and take action
- taking action quickly and not leaving things to fester
- not taking sides (but the service user must come first)
- looking for quick, but appropriate, solutions.

Theory into practice

Arrange a visit to a residential care home and interview two people to find out what they think are the benefits and disadvantages of living in residential care.

- Find out how they are helped to maintain their independence.
- Explore how choice for the individual is balanced against the needs of running an organisation that serves several people.
- Make notes of your findings to present back to your peers.

Identifying and challenging discrimination

Within health and social care, the promotion of anti-discriminatory practice takes place at a whole range of different levels. Actively identifying and challenging discrimination is achieved through:

- government policies and guidelines implemented at local level
- training and development
- awareness-raising events
- challenging work colleagues when discrimination is evident
- challenging the use of inappropriate language wherever it is found
- whistle blowing when rules are broken (reporting inappropriate behaviours to line managers and other authorities).

In context

Eric always sits in the television room to read. It is a lovely room with good views over the garden and, most importantly, it contains the comfortable chair he has claimed for sitting in and reading the daily newspapers.

Since Monica arrived he has found it intolerable to read in there as she needs the television on very loudly in order to hear the sound. He has complained to the manager of the rest home but doesn't suppose there is much she can do.

The manager has asked Eric if he would like to have 'his' chair moved to the conservatory which

has a different view of the garden but is warm and comfortable. 'What a good idea,' he thought. 'I most certainly would like that,' was his response.

1   How is this case study an example of conflict resolution?

2   What communication skills is the manager displaying?

3   Why might this scenario be described as a 'win-win' situation?

In context

Paul works as a mental health nurse in a small residential mental health trust that specialises in helping young adults with eating disorders. He is trying to encourage local volunteers to come into the centre to work with the young people. He has designed a series of workshops and posters to dispel some of the myths around young people with eating disorders.

At a meeting of the volunteers' group, he spends a great deal of time explaining how the media can influence the eating habits of young people. He emphasises that, for many individuals, low self-esteem is a recognised trigger factor in the development of

eating disorders. It is not just about wanting to get rich and famous as highly paid models.

As part of the session Paul has arranged for some of the volunteers to meet the residents of the centre so that they can get to know each other better.

1   What methods is Paul using to promote anti-discriminatory practices?

2   What aspects of the care value base is he following directly or indirectly?

3   How does the media influence the way people think about others?

Assessment activity 2.4

Describe how legislation, codes of practice, rules of conduct, charters and organisational policies are used to promote anti-discriminatory practice.

1   Produce a handbook or other form of guide for use by staff in a care setting that describes how legislation, codes of practice, rules of conduct, charters and organisational policies are used to promote anti-discriminatory practice.

Explain the influences of a recent or emerging national policy development on organisational policy with regard to anti-discriminatory practice.

2   Your handbook should include a section that explains the influences of a recent or emerging national policy development on organisational policy with regard to anti-discriminatory practice.

Grading tip for P4

It would be helpful to obtain a copy of a staff handbook from your work placement. You could then use this as a guide. However, do make sure that you don't copy it.

Grading tip for M1

Use the Internet to help you choose an emerging or recent policy development and then arrange to interview a member of staff from a health and social care setting. Ask them to tell you about the policy and the changes they are having to make as a result of the new legislation or guidelines.

Evaluate how a recent or emerging policy development influences organisational and personal practice in relation to anti-discriminatory practice.

3   The handbook should also include an evaluation of how a recent or emerging policy development influences organisational and personal practice in relation to anti-discriminatory practice.

Explain how those working in health and social care settings can actively promote anti-discriminatory practice.

4   Continue the handbook you produced for P4, introducing a series of case studies that explain to new members of staff the ways in which they can actively promote anti-discriminatory practice.

Explain the difficulties that may be encountered when implementing anti-discriminatory practice.

5   You should also include an explanation of the difficulties that may be encountered when implementing anti-discriminatory practice.

Grading tip for D1

When you are interviewing the individual from a health and social care setting, remember to ask them about how the policy or development has affected their working practice in relation to anti-discriminatory practice. You could then turn the information into case studies and use them as examples in your staff handbook.

Grading tip for P5

Use your own knowledge and studies to show active promotion of anti-discriminatory practice. A good point to remember is the word 'active' i.e. taking action before anything happens.

Grading tip for M2

Remember, most difficulties involve working with people and helping individuals to understand their roles and responsibilities.

Personal beliefs and value systems

Our personal beliefs and value systems drive us as individuals to react and behave in certain ways.

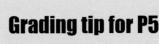

Some influences on our beliefs and values include:

- culture
- past events
- socialisation
- environmental influences
- health and well-being.

■ Culture and beliefs

As we have already noted, an individual's culture has the potential to clash with that of someone else. As a health or social care worker you must take especial care to make certain that your personal culture and your beliefs do not interfere with the caring services you provide to others.

In context

Claire was involved in a road traffic accident when she was 17. Her boyfriend at the time was driving too fast and skidded around a bend. He was killed instantly and she was left with a fractured pelvis, a broken leg and spinal injuries. It took more than six months for her injuries to heal and she has never got over the death of her boyfriend. Now, at the age of 28, she still won't learn to drive and prefers to use public transport at every opportunity. This has seriously affected the kind of employment open to her as many jobs require car ownership and driver status.

1   **How has Claire's well-being been affected by the past event?**

2   **How will her future be affected in the long term?**

3   **How might she influence the development of her family and friends?**

■ Past events

The things that have happened to you, your friends and your family will all have had a strong influence on the person you have developed into. These events have more than likely influenced some of your health behaviours. For example, if you were afraid of the dentist as a young child, you may be unwilling to make regular appointments for your six-monthly check-ups! This in turn could influence your future decisions about your own children's dental care and so the next generation is affected by something that happened in the past.

■ Socialisation

Socialisation is the process all human beings go through as they grow and develop. It is about learning to live in society. The way we are brought up, the people we mix with and the education we receive, all combine to influence our culture, beliefs and values.

Reflect

Consider the kinds of events that have shaped your current behaviours. Hopefully they will not be as terrible as the example shown here but they will still strongly influence your behaviours and beliefs. Now is probably a good point to identify your own values and beliefs and some of the events that have influenced the person you have become.

▼ **Children quickly absorb the norms of the culture they grow up in**

Reflect

How have your friends affected the way you think about other people? Have they influenced your beliefs about groups of the population? Did you label and stereotype others as a result of being together? It is very likely that you did!

Reflect

Think about your own health.
- Are you very healthy?
- Are you physically unfit/fit?
- Are you overweight/underweight?
- Do you take medication?
- Do you have physical/mental disabilities?

How do these 'conditions' affect your values and beliefs? How would you describe yourself? Are you sick or well?

■ Environmental influences

The environment in which you are brought up has an influence, in addition to that of your family and friends, on your personal development. The influence of environment is so strong that stereotypical attitudes have grown and developed around certain situations. For example:

- council estates 'breed' work-shy individuals
- troublemakers and drug users always live in high rise flats
- people who live on suburban estates are 'nice people'.

These statements are clearly unacceptable – people must be judged on an individual basis and not have stereotypical labels applied to them. Some situations *do* have an influence but each individual will respond differently to them.

■ Health and well-being

People's health status and sense of well-being can have a strong influence on the way they feel about themselves, on their beliefs and values, and on their consequent behaviour.

For most people, health and well-being are things that have the potential to change on a daily basis, depending on what is happening at the time. Many people who take medication would never describe themselves as 'ill'. People with physical disabilities often do not describe themselves as 'disabled' so why should we apply labels just because we work in the health and social care field?

However, it is important to recognise that if you do want to work in health and social care, your own level of health needs to be good. That is:

- you should be capable of carrying out the required work to a high standard
- you should not need to take significant amounts of time off work (think about your responsibilities to service users and team members)
- you should have a positive attitude towards health and well-being.

Developing greater self-awareness and tolerance of differences

It is very helpful to know yourself, and how you react to certain situations, if you are working in health and social care. Having insight into your own beliefs and behaviours and where they come from is a useful starting point for changing negative attitudes.

Committing to the care value base

A good starting point for bringing about changes in your own attitudes and behaviours towards other people is to revisit the care value base. Think hard about what it is asking you to do. If you cannot commit to the values outlined, you should not be considering a career in the caring services!

Take it further

Use the chart below to reflect upon your own socialisation process. What events and which people have had the strongest influence on you? How have these influences affected your values and beliefs?

Having considered the people and the events that have affected your development, reflect upon your own values and beliefs regarding equality, diversity and rights for other people. What actions could you take to help you change where necessary?

	Who or what	Consider why	Influences on your beliefs and behaviours
People who influenced me	Mother	She was a single mother who worked hard and held strong values about respect for others.	• I have a strong work ethic. • I don't approve of people who are lazy. • I always say 'please' and 'thank you'. • I have high expectations of my children.
Events that influenced me			
The environment that influenced me			

Careful use of language

Careful use of language is part of good communication which, in turn, is an underpinning value of the care value base. It is possible to discriminate against individuals or cause upset and confusion through your use of language. As we have already discussed, jargon should never be used with service users as they might not understand what we are saying (possibly excluding them from important information). Service users should always be enabled to use their preferred method of communication and it is part of your role and responsibility to help them do this.

Another aspect of language use is related to your choice of words. Clearly, swear words need to be avoided but so do discriminatory words and terms. It is important to be aware of 'political correctness' but it is also important not to take this too far and lose sight of the individual.

Try to avoid using gender-based terms but don't take it to extremes. For example, 'chair' is a good option instead of 'chairman'. It is also important to think before you speak because, in caring situations, your choice of words will greatly affect your relationship with others.

In context

Selina is new to her job as a care assistant and has been asked to assist Imran in getting out of bed and preparing for the day. Imran is a wheelchair-user and is unable to walk. On entering his bedroom, Selina says, 'Good morning, Imran. Are you capable of getting out of bed by yourself?'

Imran is furious although he doesn't show it to Selina. However, all he can think to himself is, 'What does she mean ... capable?'

1 Why do you think Imran was furious at the use of the word 'capable'?

2 What could Selina have said instead?

3 What would you do differently in a similar situation?

If you wish to develop a career in health and social care you must work within the legal, ethical and policy guidelines that are in place. Think about current legislation and your views on this and the way it has the potential to affect both you and your service users.

As you reflect on this unit, it should be clear to you which way you want your career to develop. Working in health and social care is very rewarding but also extremely challenging. Maintaining and promoting equality, diversity and rights is central to the caring process and without this, no matter how skilled and knowledgeable you are, you will never be successful with service users and employers.

Assessment activity 2.5

Describe ways of reflecting on and challenging discriminatory issues in health and social care.

1   Describe ways of reflecting on and challenging discriminatory issues in health and social care.

Grading tip for P6

Once you have completed your group work on exploring ways of reflecting on and challenging discrimination, write a short report of your findings.

Analyse how personal beliefs and value systems may influence your own anti-discriminatory practice.

2   Spend some time thinking about how your own personal beliefs and value systems may have influenced your practice. Record your thoughts in a short report or you might prefer to use a grid (such as the one shown above on page 99).

Grading tip for M3

When you are analysing your beliefs and values, remember there can be both positive and negative influences. You should demonstrate that you are aware of this and have some ideas of practical things you could do to overcome any negative influences.

Evaluate practical strategies to reconcile your own beliefs and values with anti-discriminatory practice in health and social care.

3   Evaluate practical strategies to reconcile your own beliefs and values with anti-discriminatory practice in health and social care.

Grading tip for D2

Remember this assessment uses the words 'practical strategies' i.e. it is asking you to concentrate on those realistic and achievable actions that you could take to reconcile your beliefs and values with anti-discriminatory practice. A grid such as the one opposite might help you present your findings.

Behaviour or belief to be changed	Practical ways of achieving changes	Strengths and weaknesses of the strategy
Everybody should eat meat – the protein is needed for a physically healthy body.	Find out about other food sources of protein and their effects on the body.	<ul><li>Time for research</li><li>The need to access reputable sources of information</li><li>Helps to improve my nutritional knowledge which I could pass on to service users</li></ul>

Knowledge check

1 Explain what 'valuing diversity' means.

2 List the key aspects of the care value base.

3 Explain the consequences of making assumptions about people that are not based on fact.

4 List three ways of demonstrating respect for an individual.

5 Describe the purpose of a code of practice in the workplace.

6 List three ways of actively promoting anti-discriminatory practice.

7 Explain which circumstances would allow confidentiality to be broken.

8 List five benefits of diversity to society.

9 Describe the difference between covert and overt discrimination.

10 Name three bases of discrimination.

Preparation for assessment

The evidence for this unit could be presented in a variety of ways but should include a written report as a central part of the evidence collection. The report could be divided into two halves. For example, Part 1 concentrates on anti-discrimination policy and practice and the effects it can have on an organisation and on the staff and service users involved. Part 2 is all about you and your beliefs about anti-discriminatory practice.

■ Part 1

Use your work placement to gather the evidence you require to achieve a pass for this unit of study. You will need to plan and prepare your approach prior to starting in your chosen workplace. You should discuss the outcomes required for this unit with both your tutor and the manager or supervisor based in your work placement.

1 Using your work placement as an example and, extending this to society as a whole, explain a minimum of seven benefits (including economic ones) of diversity. **P1**

2 While in your workplace setting, carry out a small-scale survey of three members of staff to find out why they think promoting equality, recognising diversity and respecting rights is important in health and social care. Find out from your respondents how they actively promote anti-discriminatory practice as part of their everyday work routines. Once the survey is complete, produce a report to summarise your findings, using at least eight examples of the recognised terminology used in the specifications, to explain the importance of promoting equality, recognising diversity and respecting rights. **P2**

3 Include a section in your report that explains how those working in the setting are (or could be) actively promoting anti-discriminatory practice. **P5**

4 When producing your report, carry out additional personal research so that you can include a section that explains the potential effects of discriminatory practice on the service users in your workplace setting. **P3**

5 While on your work placement, collect together examples of codes of practice, rules of conduct, charters and other examples of organisational policy and procedures. Make yourself familiar with their content. Using the examples you have collected, and additional personal research if necessary, describe how legislation, rules of conduct, charters and organisational policies are used to promote anti-discriminatory practice in your workplace setting. **P4**

6 Discuss with a senior member of staff recent external (national) policy changes that have had an impact on the organisation. Find out what *changes* they have had to make internally to their policies and practices as a result of the new policy. Don't forget to ask for details about any staff training that will be required to make sure that all staff are kept up-to-date. **P4**

7 If you are aiming for a merit or distinction it would be helpful to include a discussion about the strengths and weaknesses of the new policy. Ask about *how* it will make a difference to the service users and the staff involved in the provision of care. Find out if the policy 'goes far enough' or whether it has any shortcomings **D1**. It would be helpful to include some questions that require the member of staff to explain the difficulties that can be encountered when implementing anti-discriminatory practice **M2**. For example, how do they make sure everyone is up-to-date? What about the financial costs of making changes? And, of course, how do they make sure their service users know their rights? Making

sure everyone is informed and up-to-date etc is likely to pose difficulties for the management of an organisation. So find out how they handle difficulties such as these and include the information in your report.

8   If you are aiming for a merit or distinction you will need to include information in your report about the strengths and weaknesses of the policy that you should have discussed while in your workplace setting. Use your discussions to find out about the *influences* of a recent or emerging national policy development on organisational policy, with regard to anti-discriminatory practice.   **M1**

■ Part 2

The second half of your report needs to concentrate on your personal development and should show that you are able to reflect upon your views and feelings. In other words, that you have the potential to become a reflective practitioner.

1   You should use the work you completed earlier in this unit to help you provide evidence. For example, re-read some of the case studies that explore challenging discrimination in the workplace and then think about the kinds of activities that you could do to help you reflect.

2   You must ensure that your report includes a description of the ways of reflecting on, and challenging, discriminatory issues in health and social care. Your report should also describe the necessary changes to the organisation and to the staff team's work routines.   **P6**

3   In order to gain a merit, you will need to provide an analysis of how your personal beliefs and value systems might influence your own anti-discriminatory practice. Again, you might find it helpful to re-read the section that covers beliefs and value systems and reflect again on how your own beliefs have affected your attitudes towards anti-discriminatory practice.   **M3**

4   If you are to gain a distinction, you will also need to include a discussion of the strengths and weaknesses of three strategies that could help you to overcome any negative beliefs and values you may hold, to make sure that you provide a high quality service to all individuals. If you are aiming for a distinction, make sure your report includes an evaluation of practical strategies to reconcile your own beliefs and values with anti-discriminatory practice in health and social care.   **D2**

Once you have completed a first draft of your report, check the content against the criteria required for the level of award you are aiming to achieve (pass, merit or distinction). You should do this before you complete your report, as evidence of your knowledge and understanding of this key issue in health and social care.

Resources and further reading

Acheson, D. (1998) *Independent Inquiry into Inequalities in Health* London: HMSO

Hogg C., Holland K. (2001) *Cultural Awareness in Nursing and Healthcare* London: Hodder Arnold

Kallan, E. (2004) *Social Inequalities and Social Injustice: A Human Rights Perspective* London: Palgrave

Moonie, N. (2004) *Diversity and Rights in Care* Oxford: Heinemann

Thompson, N. (2003) *Promoting Equality,* second ed. London: Palgrave

Useful websites

Commission for Racial Equality
www.cre.gov.uk

Dignity in Care
www.dh.gov.uk/dignityincare

Disability Rights Commission
www.drc.gov.uk

Employers Forum on Age
www.efa.org.uk

Equal Opportunities Commission
www.eoc.org.uk

Mental Health Foundation
www.mentalhealth.org.uk

National Council for One Parent Families
www.oneparentfamilies.org.uk

Royal National Institute for the Blind
www.rnib.org.uk

Stonewall
www.stonewall.org.uk

The Gender Trust
www.gendertrust.org.uk

The UK coalition of people living with HIV and Aids
www.ukcoalition.org.uk

Grading criteria

To achieve a pass grade the evidence must show that the learner is able to:	To achieve a merit grade the evidence must show that, in addition to the pass criteria, the learner is able to:	To achieve a distinction grade the evidence must show that, in addition to the pass and merit criteria, the learner is able to:
P1 explain the benefits of diversity to society **Assessment activity 2.1 page 55**		
P2 use recognised terminology to explain the importance of promoting equality, recognising diversity and respecting rights in health and social care settings **Assessment activity 2.2 page 66**		
P3 explain the potential effects of discriminatory practice on those who use health or social care services **Assessment activity 2.3 page 82**		
P4 describe how legislation, codes of practice, rules of conduct, charters and organisational policies are used to promote anti-discriminatory practice **Assessment activity 2.4 page 95**	**M1** explain the influences of a recent or emerging national policy development on organisational policy with regard to anti-discriminatory practice **Assessment activity 2.4 page 95**	**D1** evaluate how a recent or emerging policy development influences organisational and personal practice in relation to anti-discriminatory practice **Assessment activity 2.4 page 96**
P5 explain how those working in health and social care settings can actively promote anti-discriminatory practice **Assessment activity 2.4 page 96**	**M2** explain difficulties that may be encountered when implementing anti-discriminatory practice **Assessment activity 2.4 page 96**	
P6 describe ways of reflecting on and challenging discriminatory issues in health and social care. **Assessment activity 2.5 page 100**	**M3** analyse how personal beliefs and value systems may influence own anti-discriminatory practice. **Assessment activity 2.5 page 100**	**D2** evaluate practical strategies to reconcile own beliefs and values with anti-discriminatory practice in health and social care. **Assessment activity 2.5 page 100**

Health, safety and security

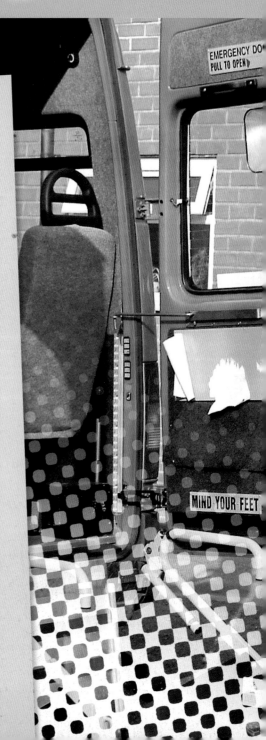

Introduction

This unit introduces you to health, safety and security issues in health and social care settings. Health and safety is so ingrained in practice, we tend to forget how vulnerable service users are. We take it for granted that our workplace will be safe. However, as a practitioner you will have to consider what risks exist, and to be able to plan an environment that will keep your service users safe.

You will gain a thorough understanding of potential hazards and how legislation, policies and procedures work to reduce risk. You will learn what responsibilities employees and employers have for health, safety and security.

Finally you will learn how to deal with hazards when out and about in your local environment.

How you will be assessed

This unit will be internally assessed by your tutor. A variety of exercises and activities is included to help you understand all aspects of health and safety in health and social care environments, and prepare for the assessment. You will also have the opportunity to work on some case studies to further your understanding.

After completing this unit you should be able to achieve the following outcomes:

- Understand potential hazards in health and social care
- Understand how legislation, guidelines, policies and procedures promote health, safety and security
- Understand roles and responsibilities for health, safety and security in health and social care settings
- Know how to deal with hazards in a local environment.

Thinking points

This unit provides you with vital information that should be understood by all health and care workers. Even as a student on placement you have a responsibility for the safety of yourself, your colleagues and your service users. You may one day hold a position of great responsibility, such as the manager of a day care centre, a modern matron or you may own your own care home. Jobs like these bring a lot of responsibility, and health and safety is a major area for concern. You may know someone, or have heard of someone, who has received compensation for an accident that has happened to them at work. Virtually all accidents are preventable, and as a manager it would be your responsibility to anticipate danger and put into place measures that would reduce the risk of potentially hazardous situations.

Even if you decide that you do not want to work at a senior level in care, you still need to understand how to prevent accidents, incidents and illness. If you are unaware of potential hazards and their consequences, you will not be able to act to prevent them. You will need to be observant, quick to act and able to devise safe ways of managing tasks.

It would be awful to think that a tragedy could have been avoided if only you had thought ahead and acted differently. Hindsight would be a wonderful thing if only we had the benefit of it! We do have foresight, though, so we have to use that instead.

Hazards

Hazards potentially exist for staff, visitors and service users, if care is not taken to minimise **risk**. Hazards can relate to **health**, **safety** and **security**. However, it would be unreasonable to remove the opportunity for service users to be able to take risks, if they so wish. A balance must be achieved between exposing people to unreasonable risk, and over-protecting them to the extent that they cannot identify dangerous situations.

Key terms

Hazard Hazard means anything that can cause harm.

Risk Risk is the chance, high or low, that someone will be harmed by a hazard.

Health hazards These include incidents leading to illness.

Safety hazards These include incidents leading to injury or to damage to equipment or buildings.

Security hazards These include intruders, theft of property or information, and service users either being abducted or leaving without consent.

'Responsible risk-taking should be regarded as normal, and residents should not be discouraged from undertaking certain activities solely on the grounds that there is an element of risk. Excessive paternalism and concern with safety may lead to infringements of personal rights. Those who are competent to judge the risk to themselves should be free to make their own decisions so long as they do not threaten the safety of others.'

Source: *Home life: a code of practice for residential care*
Centre for Policy on Ageing, 1996

Reflect

Think about a time when you had an accident. What caused the accident? It could, for example, have been lack of concentration, lack of skill or untidiness. Almost all accidents are preventable. Could yours have been prevented?

Working environment

For health and social care workers the working environment can include a variety of settings, including residential and nursing homes, day centres, hospitals, health centres and clients' own homes. Some jobs involve taking clients out, perhaps on holiday, to the shops, or to an appointment. A paramedic's working environment could be anywhere.

■ Residential and day care settings

In a residential or day care setting, much is done to ensure that service users, and therefore staff as well, are protected from harm.

Environmental hazards could include:

- objects left on the floor
- slippery floors
- equipment left in corridors, on stairs or blocking fire exits
- worn carpets
- trailing flexes
- hot surfaces.

Hopefully you will never witness such hazards, but it would be easy to forget that hazards exist. This is the danger of protecting people too much, including yourself. It is an important skill to be able to anticipate and avoid danger.

Theory into practice

When you are at your work placement, look around and try to identify all the measures that have been taken to keep staff and service users safe. For example, carpets provide a non-slip surface for residents and remove the risks associated with spillages, which can lead to people slipping. Try to think of all the dangers that your service users would face if no measures had been taken to provide a safe environment. This will help you to realise how much thought goes into planning a safe environment for service users and staff.

■ Service users and visitors

People can also pose a hazard in health and social care settings. Service users can pose a danger to each other or to you and other staff. Service users might be violent and unpredictable, or may be carriers of infectious diseases, such as hepatitis and HIV.

Sometimes the environment is particularly hazardous, such as working in close proximity to patients undergoing cancer treatment involving radioactive implants.

Hazards associated with staff will be discussed under the headings 'Poor staff training' and 'Poor working practices' on pages 112 and 113.

Visitors to the setting could also create hazards, perhaps by leaving external doors open, allowing confused service users to leave the building unaccompanied.

Remember!

Visiting tradesman are experts in their trade, not care practice. They need to be made aware of the nature of the client group so that they do not unintentionally place people at risk.

■ Out and about

Sometimes you and another care worker might have to take service users to other premises, perhaps to the local hospital, the library, and shops or on an outing.

Before embarking on such a trip, the potential risks should be considered. Service users are at greater risk of hazards in an unfamiliar environment because they may become confused and the risk of falls is increased. Being involved in an incident, such as a fire, in strange surroundings can be bewildering so it is important that the accompanying member of staff familiarises him- or herself with evacuation procedures. Taking service users on an outing poses even more potential risks.

◀ Health and safety are much harder to control in the wider environment

■ Private homes

Some health care workers carry out their job in service users' homes. Such people include community nurses, social workers, home care assistants, midwives and health visitors.

A private home is not designed as a working environment. People are entitled to arrange their home as they please. Community care staff can advise service users about ways to improve safety in the home, such as removing loose mats, installing extra handrails and replacing low chairs with higher ones but there is no obligation on the service user to follow this advice. However, home care workers should not risk injury from moving and handling people at home. A hoist can be supplied for community care staff and relatives to use. Training, of course, should be given to relatives before allowing them to use the hoist, otherwise they could cause themselves or the service user injuries.

Another risk to lone workers, such as home care assistants, social workers, community nurses, GPs and health visitors, is their vulnerability to attack by aggressive clients or by members of the public when out visiting in the community. Staff are often required to work unsocial hours, including evenings and nights. Social workers may have to take children into foster care. This is often a highly distressing experience for parents, children and social workers. Community care staff sometimes visit on foot and may have regular patterns of visits making them vulnerable targets for attack.

It is vital that you are aware of the hazards you and other care workers face and the policies and procedures developed to keep everyone as safe as possible.

In context Assaults on NHS staff increasing

There were 118,000 reported incidents of violence against NHS staff in 2003. Assaults are becoming more common and more violent.

Staff have been threatened at gunpoint, and with knives, while others have been physically assaulted, resulting in injuries such as broken noses and fractured cheekbones. Nurses have been sexually assaulted on duty and threatened with things like broken bottles.

There is growing concern about attacks on community care staff, such as district nurses and midwives, who work on their own visiting people's homes, not always knowing who is in the house and what kind of situation they are walking into. There may be people in the house who are under the influence of alcohol or drugs, who may be violent, and staff are very vulnerable. Aggressors can even be relatives or patients themselves.

Nurse Jane Smee said she was attacked by a male patient who had been acting in a restless manner since arriving in Accident and Emergency earlier in the morning. The man kicked her in the stomach and then tried to attack other patients. The attack was so severe Jane had to go to be examined herself to rule out internal injuries. She was off work for a week, and felt very nervous on return.

Source: http://news.bbc.co.uk/1/hi/scotland/4533420.stm#

1 **What could be done to increase the safety of frontline accident and emergency staff?**

2 **Is it acceptable for community care staff to be expected to risk their personal safety?**

3 **What should happen to perpetrators of assaults on care personnel?**

Poor working conditions

Working conditions include aspects of your job such as the hours you work, the staffing levels, ventilation, lighting and staff relations.

Despite considerable improvements in the quality systems governing health and social care, there is still an issue over staff turnover and staff shortages. This can lead to staff rushing their work and not always following procedures properly, which can increase the risk of injuries and accidents.

■ Rates of pay

The pay rates for care assistants remain low, with workers often only paid the minimum wage, or just above. While many staff work to high standards despite low wages, others may feel undervalued and disinclined to follow policies and procedures designed to keep them and their service users safe. It is also important that there is a suitable mix of staff – it is no help to have a high number of inexperienced staff and few experienced ones.

■ The demands of care work

Staff shortages can result in staff being expected to work overtime. You will soon realise that care work is physically and mentally demanding, and too much overtime is likely to result in staff that are not able to perform to their best ability. Staff that are tired are more likely to make mistakes, such as miscalculating drug dosages. They are also likely to be less alert, and may miss a sign that a service user is becoming unwell.

'Too often people receive care that is patchy and fragmented, as care homes and home care services struggle to recruit and retain high quality staff. Because of the difficulties with recruiting staff, vital recruitment checks are often overlooked, placing people at risk. Social workers remain the poorest-paid professionals and care workers are getting an increasingly poor deal.'

'Vacancy rates in social care are higher than for all other employment sectors in England. Around one in four residential homes for children, adults and older people do not have, or cannot recruit, sufficient staff. Shortages of staff have a direct impact on the quality of care.'

Source: *www.csci.gov.uk 2005*

▲ Figure 3.1 Stress can have a detrimental effect on the quality of care given

■ Stress levels

Stress is another cause of staff shortages. Stress can manifest itself in a variety of ways including anxiety, insomnia, digestive disorders, high blood pressure and mood swings.

■ The physical environment

The physical environment can have a profound impact on the well-being of service users. Poor ventilation will increase the spread of airborne infections, such as colds and flu. However, service users should never be in a draught and should always be warm enough. It is easy to think the temperature is adequate when you are rushing around but remember that people who are elderly or disabled find it more difficult to maintain their body temperature.

Fumes or smoke should not contaminate fresh, clean air. Ventilation should also remove stale air and provide air movement.

Rooms should be centrally heated and it should be possible to control the temperature in each individual bedroom.

Lighting in communal rooms should be normal domestic lighting, bright enough and positioned to enable people to be able to read and enjoy other activities. Emergency lighting, which comes on if there is a power failure, must be provided throughout the home.

These form part of the National Minimum Standards. You can find more information in the Department of Health document 'Care Homes for Older People' which can be viewed on www.dh.gov.uk.

Poor lighting can be particularly hazardous to elderly residents and anyone with poor vision. You should take special care when looking after people with limited vision to position them in a well-lit area. It is also helpful to ensure that there is a good contrast between objects and surroundings. For example, a light coloured plate on a dark tablecloth, or a dark door in a white surround.

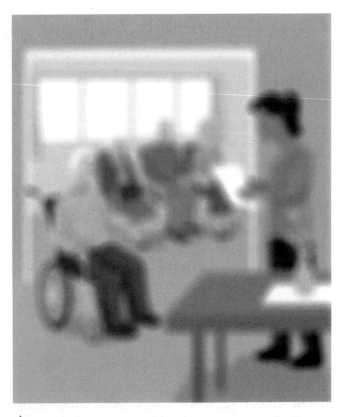

▲ Figure 3.2 Imagine trying to find your way around a busy care home with poor vision like this

Take it further

If you are interested in understanding better the effect of visual impairment take a look at this website: http://www.disability.auckland.ac.nz.

There are a series of simulated photographs showing the effects of a variety of different visual impairments.

Poor staff training

It is vital that you receive training when you start a new job and that you continue to receive training regularly to ensure that you are working effectively and safely.

Reflect

Think about your first day on placement, work experience or when starting a new part-time job. You may well have felt lost, incompetent and uneasy. You may even have done something wrong and got into trouble. The main reason you felt this way was because you didn't know what to do, because you needed training.

Making a mistake in some working environments is not disastrous. However, in others it can be very serious indeed.

Health and social care training has been designated as a government priority area. There is an increased awareness that care staff can easily put themselves and their service users at risk if they do not know the correct techniques and procedures. For example, a person who has had a stroke can easily sustain a dislocated shoulder if lifted from the armpit. This is an example of unintentional abuse. Care staff may also sustain injuries themselves. Lack of training can also increase the risk of spread of infections, such as **MRSA**, hepatitis and gastro-enteritis.

Key terms

MRSA MRSA is short for methicillin-resistant Staphylococcus aureus. It is sometimes known as a 'superbug' because it has developed resistance to many antibiotics. Even the antibiotics that are effective against MRSA have to be given in much higher doses over much longer periods to be successful.

Staff must also be made aware of fire evacuation procedures; without proper training there is a risk that people can be trapped in a burning building. Fire training should be carried out on the first day of a new job, to ensure that staff and service users can be quickly and safely moved to a designated area in the case of fire.

A comprehensive induction programme for new staff is a statutory requirement. Many care settings provide all new staff with training in food hygiene, moving and handling and first aid. Some also provide specific training relevant to the client group; regular updates keep all staff informed of current practice.

Remember!

National care standards require care homes to have at least 50 per cent of staff trained to NVQ Level 2 Health and Social Care, or an equivalent qualification. This cannot include the registered manager or qualified nurses.

Poor working practices

If you do not follow procedures correctly you can put yourself and others at unnecessary risk. Food hygiene must be scrupulous in care settings. Elderly people and young babies are particularly at risk of serious, and sometimes fatal, complications if they contract food-borne infections, such as salmonella, Clostridium difficile and E. coli.

Good practice in infection prevention and control

Guidance for nursing staff

Royal College of Nursing | **wipe it out** RCN Campaign on MRSA | Kimberly-Clark

▲ Nurses are acutely aware of the need to reduce the incidence of MRSA in hospitals

■ MRSA

The recent media coverage of the incidence of MRSA in hospitals has highlighted the devastating effects that over-prescription of antibiotics and poor personal hygiene practices can have.

The number of cases of MRSA in the UK has been rising sharply. There were 2422 reported cases in 1997, rising to 7684 from 1 April 2003 to 31 March 2004. However a fall was noted from 1 April 2004 to 31 March 2005 to 7212 cases. About 15 per cent of cases result in death.

MRSA is often associated with patients in hospitals but can also be found in the nose or throat, or on the skin of patients in the community. It is not usually necessary to treat MRSA organisms. The organism Staphylococcus aureus is found on many people's skin and does not generally cause major problems. People who carry

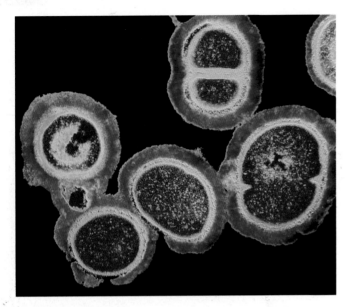

▲ The MRSA bacillus

MRSA bacteria can also cause scalded skin syndrome and, very occasionally, toxic shock syndrome.

For more information about MRSA you could look at the NHS Direct website: www.nhsdirect.nhs.uk.

■ Hazardous waste disposal

Care workers need to take particular care when disposing of hazardous waste including soiled dressings, nappies and incontinence pads. These should all be disposed of by depositing in a yellow clinical waste bag. These bags are incinerated, thus destroying any microorganisms.

Remember!

Protective disposable gloves should always be worn when dealing with potentially infectious waste.

MRSA are usually very healthy and are considered to simply be carriers of the organism.

People can become carriers of MRSA by direct contact with the organism. If the bacteria are on the skin then they can be spread by touch. If the organism is in the nose or the lungs it may be passed on by droplet spread, by breathing or coughing over someone.

In patients who are otherwise well the bacteria often disappear once they leave hospital. Sometimes, however, they do not, and this may mean that precautions need to be used again if the patient has to be readmitted to hospital. As long as other members of the household are healthy, special precautions are not required at home.

If MRSA gets inside the body, perhaps into the bloodstream through a wound, or into the lungs, it can cause serious infections such as:

- osteomyelitis (bone marrow infection)
- septicaemia (blood poisoning)
- septic shock (a complication of septicaemia that causes a fall in blood pressure and organ failure)
- septic arthritis (infection of the joint)
- meningitis (inflammation of the tissues that surround the brain and spinal cord)
- abscesses anywhere within the body
- endocarditis (infection of the heart lining)
- pneumonia (lung infection).

▲ Figure 3.3 All sharps, such as needles and scalpel blades, should be safely disposed of in a sharps bin

Syringes and needles can cause needle stick injuries (accidental puncture of the skin with a used needle) if not disposed of in a sharps box. There is a small but significant risk that HIV and hepatitis B virus can be contracted by needle stick injuries.

Administering medication

Carelessness when administering medication can also put service users at risk. Medication could be given to the wrong person, or the wrong dose might be given if care is not taken. This can have devastating consequences. For example, in 2005, two nurses miscalculated the dose of a drug to slow down the heart rate of a baby boy. The baby was given ten times the dose he should have received and died.

Theory into practice

Try to get into the habit of reading newspapers. Cases involving poor practice are often reported. As future carers you can benefit from others' mistakes. Try to work out how the errors occurred. Not all mistakes are made by staff being lazy.

Remember!

As a student on placement you should never be asked to give out medication.

Safety policies

Hazards can also be caused by not following safety policies, such as fire policies, requiring staff to keep escape routes clear. Blocked fire exits impede the escape of staff and service users in an emergency, increasing the risk of people becoming trapped in a building.

Obstruction of passages with equipment and boxes can also cause hazards to service users and staff.

Materials stored near to a heat source such as a radiator, boiler or electric heater can catch fire, so care should be taken with blankets, cardboard, newspapers and other flammable materials.

In context

Kendra Clarke started a new job as manager of Firbanks Residential Home in March 2004. The previous manager had resigned after an inquiry into the death of a resident following a fall. The inquiry identified a concern over the number of falls that had occurred at the home.

One of Kendra's first actions was to examine the accident book. There had been 57 falls in the home in the previous 12 months. She felt this figure was very high and she set about analysing the reports.

Many of the falls appeared to have occurred when residents had been walking unaccompanied around the home. Some had tripped over obstacles while others had simply overbalanced. Kendra decided to carry out a risk assessment for every resident with respect to their mobility.

Suggest six measures Kendra could implement to try to reduce the number of falls.

Equipment

Equipment must be functioning correctly and fully maintained at all times. There should be a schedule for checking equipment to ensure it will not cause injuries to staff or service users. This might include fire-fighting equipment, hoists and diagnostic equipment, such as ECG and X-ray machines. If any of this equipment is faulty it will not work properly which, in the case of diagnostic equipment, could lead to a false diagnosis.

Computers are now part of the care industry as much as in any other field of work. The same attention to health and safety must be paid to their use as in an office. Incorrect positioning can cause repetitive strain injury, prolonged exposure to the screen can put strain on vision, and incorrect sitting position can lead to orthopaedic problems, such as back strain or neck pain.

Cord pulls for call systems should be within easy reach of service users. Over-stretching in itself could cause a fall, and an out-of-reach cord pull is useless to someone who has fallen over. Precious time is lost in coming to the assistance of service users, during which time their condition could deteriorate and make the situation much more serious.

Substances

A number of substances are used in care settings that are hazardous if misused. Cleaning fluids could cause chemical burns to the throat and oesophagus if swallowed in error.

Even when medication is given correctly, there can be risks. Arthritis tablets can cause stomach ulcers, sedatives for anxiety can lead to drowsiness and increase the risk of falls, diuretics (water tablets) can cause incontinence and dehydration.

Some service users may be allergic to certain foods. Nuts, shellfish and eggs are common allergens. In sensitive individuals, contact with even a tiny amount of such foods can cause a severe life-threatening reaction, known as anaphylactic shock. In less sensitive people an unpleasant rash, vomiting or diarrhoea can occur.

Key terms

Anaphylactic shock Anaphylactic shock is a sudden, severe allergic reaction causing a sharp drop in blood pressure, a rash, and breathing difficulties. It is caused by exposure to an allergen, such as nuts, shellfish or bee venom. The reaction can be fatal if emergency treatment such as injection by an EpiPen is not given immediately.

Incidents

Hazardous incidents might include severe weather conditions such as floods or heavy snowfall. This might make it impossible for community workers to visit clients at home. Problems with power supplies, such as electricity cuts or an interruption to the water supply, can be much more hazardous for service users who may need electricity to power vital equipment, such as automated peritoneal dialysis for kidney failure.

The entry of an intruder to a care setting is another example of an incident. The intruder may be intent on harming a service user, or stealing property or information. For people who live in their own homes this can be extremely distressing.

In some settings service users can come and go as they please. However, in a setting where there are people who are confused, or young children, this would be inappropriate. The risk of road traffic accidents is very real in this situation. Anyone who is confused may become disorientated and get lost. In colder weather they may develop hypothermia if they are inadequately dressed or suffer a fall.

If service users do go out, you must know that they have left the building, and they must be able to get back in on their return.

Fires cause particularly difficult problems in health and social care settings. Large organisations, such as hospitals and large care homes, often divide the building into zones which can be separated in the case of a fire by substantial fire doors that automatically close when the alarm sounds. This removes the necessity for evacuating anyone who is not in the immediate vicinity of the fire. It is extremely difficult to evacuate very ill patients, some of whom are reliant on equipment to survive. Those who do have to be evacuated can usually be moved into an adjacent zone. This avoids them being exposed to inclement weather and ensures there is still access to electricity and oxygen supplies.

In smaller establishments this may not be the case.

Accidents

There are many accidents that can result from hazards in the workplace. A fall can be very serious in a frail, elderly service user. Whereas you would almost certainly recover from a fall, older people are more likely to sustain a fractured neck or femur, which can then lead to pneumonia. Head injuries are another consequence of falls. In 2005, 2007 people aged 75 years and above died as a result of falls, compared to 35 people aged 15 to 24 years.

Poor manual handling can result in dislocation of joints of service users and back injuries for care workers. Service users have also been dropped in the past by carers.

Lack of care with wheelchair footrests can lead to cuts and bruising of the lower legs. Rough handling of the frail and elderly can result in tearing of fragile skin. Carelessness while dealing with casualties who have spinal injuries can lead to permanent disability.

Assessment activity 3.1

Use work placement experiences to explain a minimum of six potential hazards in a health and social care setting.

Imagine that you are on placement at Ash Lodge, a converted farm building in a rural location a short distance away from other buildings and next to a busy main road. You need to produce a list of health and safety hazards that the staff and service users face, and explain what injuries or illnesses could result from them.

P1

You need to consider:

- the internal and external environment
- the experience and competence of the staff employed
- potential visitors
- the mental and physical condition of the service users
- care procedures that will be carried out.

1 What are the main hazards that exist in this care setting?

2 What are the particular risks to people with Alzheimer's disease to themselves and to their fellow service users?

3 What hazards could be caused by visitors?

Grading tip for P1

You must ensure that you *explain* the hazards. Just listing them is not sufficient.

3.2 How legislation, guidelines, policies and procedures promote health, safety and security

Legislation and guidelines

The UK has one of the lowest accident rates in the world. The Health and Safety at Work Act 1974 is one of the main reasons for this. **Legislation** over the last 30 years has helped bring about significant improvements in health and safety in the workplace (such as a reduction in fatalities of nearly two-thirds since the act was introduced). Even now over 200 people are killed each year at work in the UK and over 150,000 are injured. Two million people suffer from illnesses that have been caused, or made worse, by their work.

Health and safety law applies to employees, the self-employed, people on work experience, apprentices, volunteers, mobile workers and homeworkers.

There are a number of pieces of legislation and **guidelines** that you have to work within as a health and social care worker.

Health and Safety at Work Act 1974

The Health and Safety at Work Act 1974, also referred to as HASAWA or HSW, is the main piece of legislation covering occupational health and safety in the United Kingdom. The Health and Safety Executive is responsible for enforcing the Act and a number of other **regulations** relevant to the working environment.

■ Key requirements

Employers are responsible for the health and safety of employees, workers from other organisations and visitors while they are on the premises. They must:

- carry out a thorough risk assessment before opening for business, and it should be updated regularly
- ensure that there is a health and safety policy written for the setting and appoint someone to be responsible for health and safety
- keep a record of all accidents and incidents
- provide safety equipment, written health and safety information and training
- ensure the workplace is fully insured. Employers compulsory liability insurance and public liability

insurance must be taken out, in case an incident occurs and the business is found to be at fault.

Employees (including yourself when on work experience, even though you are not paid) also have responsibilities under the Health and Safety at Work Act 1974. You must:

- take reasonable care of your own, and other people's, health and safety
- not deliberately do anything that could jeopardise someone else's health or safety.

In context

Anita Patel has just started her first placement. She has never been on placement before. She is on work experience at Riverside Day Centre. She has been told that the day centre caters for older people with dementia.

As she arrives on her first day she finds the front door open. She enters leaving the door as she found it.

Anita reports at the day centre manager's office to say that she has arrived, and is asked to go through to help give out the drinks.

Half an hour later she hears a commotion and realises that one of the service users is missing. She doesn't see how it could have anything to do with her as it is only her first day.

Is she right?

Look through the list of employer and employee responsibilities. Discuss with your peers who you think was at fault and why. What should have been done to prevent this incident occurring?

Regulations under the Health and Safety at Work Act 1974

Over the years since the HASAWA was first passed additional regulations have been added to reflect changes in practice, technology and understanding. These regulations include:

- Manual Handling Operations Regulations 1992
- Reporting of Injuries, Diseases and Dangerous Occurrences Regulations (RIDDOR) 1995
- Control of Substances Hazardous to Health Regulations (COSHH) 2002
- Food Safety Act 1990
- Food Safety (General Food Hygiene) Regulations 1995
- Management of Health and Safety at Work Regulations 1999
- Data Protection Act 1998
- Fire Precautions (Workplace) Regulations 1997.

■ Manual Handling Operations Regulations 1992

The main requirements under these regulations are:

- Avoid manual handling operations that involve a risk of injury, as far as reasonably practicable.
- Assess all manual handling operations which cannot be avoided.
- Take steps to reduce the risk of injury during those operations that cannot be avoided.

In order to reduce the risk of injury from manual handling you should:

- encourage the service users to move independently whenever possible
- plan your lift
- use lifting aids when service users cannot move independently or when moving heavy objects
- avoid twisting your body
- avoid lifting from the floor
- keep the load close to your body
- avoid repetitive lifts.

Take it further

There is a network of Disability Living Centres around the UK. Find out where the nearest one is and try to arrange a visit. They display a range of equipment to assist people who have physical and sensory impairments with daily-living activities. Look at the range of lifting, moving and handling aids that are available.

If you are ever in a position to need to buy such equipment for a care setting, you can try equipment out before buying it, to ensure that it will suit the purpose for which you intend to use it.

▲ Figure 3.4 Always plan a lift beforehand to reduce the risk of injuries

■ Reporting of Injuries, Diseases and Dangerous Occurrences Regulations (RIDDOR) 1995

These regulations require you to report the following to the local council or the Health and Safety Executive (HSE):

- death or **major injury**
- an incident leading to someone being absent from work for three or more days
- **reportable diseases**
- potentially **dangerous occurrences** that did not lead to injury or disease.

Key terms

Major injury Major injuries include fractures, dislocations, loss of sight, unconsciousness, poisoning and any injury resulting in someone requiring resuscitation.

Reportable diseases Reportable diseases relevant to health and social care workers include hepatitis, tuberculosis and meningitis.

Dangerous occurrences These include fire, electrical short circuit, needle stick injury and collapse of lifting equipment.

The information enables the local council or the HSE to ascertain why, where and how risks occur and to investigate serious accidents and near-accidents. They can then help and advise organisations on how to prevent or reduce injury, ill health and damage to property. If at some time in the future you are working in a senior post and an incident occurs, it would be your responsibility to submit the report.

■ Control of Substances Hazardous to Health (COSHH) 2002

COSHH requires employers to:

- assess the risks posed by hazardous substances such as body fluids and sharps
- devise and implement precautions to prevent or control exposure to hazardous substances

- ensure procedures are followed
- carry out health surveillance to identify early signs of disease
- prepare plans to deal with accidents, incidents and emergencies
- ensure staff are adequately trained and supervised.

The job of a senior manager in a health or social care setting would be to consider what substances pose a threat to care staff. The main risk to care workers would be exposure to cleaning chemicals and to body fluids including blood, urine, faeces, vomit and sputum.

The blood of individuals infected with human immunodeficiency virus (HIV), hepatitis B or hepatitis C poses a risk to health care workers and so a risk assessment would be carried out to ascertain the best way to keep staff safe.

The person carrying out the risk assessment has to consider the seriousness of the conditions identified as possible threats to health.

HIV, for example, takes on average nine years to develop into full-blown acquired immunodeficiency syndrome (AIDS) without treatment. Once AIDS has developed the person might only expect to live for one to two years. However, since better HIV treatments have become available, those who take the medicines as prescribed tend to do very well.

For more information about what it is like living with HIV look at www.hivinsite.ucsf.edu.

Remember!

To protect yourself from HIV infection when working in health and social care:

- wear protective gloves when dealing with blood (and a face mask if likely to be sprayed with blood)
- wash your hands after any incident involving blood
- cover cuts and wounds with waterproof dressings
- never put the cover back on a needle after use
- ensure all equipment is properly sterilised.

Managers should watch staff periodically to ensure that they are following these procedures properly.

Any member of staff who is accidentally exposed to potential infection must be started on an anti-HIV drug, such as AZT, which has been found to be 80 per cent effective in preventing HIV infection. In this case you would not wait for signs of infection to appear before starting prophylactic (preventative) treatment.

Staff must be trained to ensure they know how to keep themselves safe from harm.

Take it further

Investigate the health risks of being infected with hepatitis B and C. What measures do health and care settings have to take to reduce the chances of staff being infected?

■ Food Safety Act 1990

Under the Food Safety Act 1990 it is illegal to sell food unfit for human consumption. The act gives powers to environmental health inspectors to inspect food and seize food unfit for human consumption and condemn it. Any establishment breaching food hygiene standards can be served a notice of improvement, and can, in extreme circumstances, be closed temporarily or permanently if the practices are considered to be a health hazard. Businesses can be prosecuted for breaching standards.

■ Food Safety (General Food Hygiene) Regulations 1995

Food Safety (General Food Hygiene) Regulations 1995 aim to prevent cases of food poisoning by stipulating that:

- food areas are kept clean and good standards of personal hygiene are maintained
- foods are cooked thoroughly
- foods are kept at the right temperature
- cross-contamination is prevented.

Health and social care settings need to have a kitchen that meets all the requirements of the regulations. If you look at the kitchen at your work experience placement you should notice it is run on a commercial basis. There

will, for example, be separate chopping boards for raw and ready-to-eat foods. The kitchen should be easy to keep clean, with surfaces that are smooth and without cracks and crevices where food can accumulate, such as stainless steel. There should be a separate hand washing basin; staff cannot use the same sink as that used for food preparation. Hand washing should take place frequently, and especially after touching raw meat, and after visiting the toilet. Sometimes the sink will have elbow taps, to prevent germs being transferred back onto the hands when turning the taps off.

If you are asked to help prepare food at your placement, you must practise good hygiene, and preferably complete a food hygiene certificate. This should ensure that you understand the risks of poor practice. It is easy for food to become contaminated if raw foods, especially meat, come into contact with foods which are not going to be cooked, or have already been cooked.

No one should have any dealings with food preparation who has been suffering from an infection such as vomiting and diarrhoea.

▲ Figure 3.5 Food must be stored correctly and use-by dates must be adhered to

■ Management of Health and Safety at Work Regulations 1999

The Management of Health and Safety at Work Regulations 1999 (the Management Regulations) generally make more explicit what employers are required to do to manage the Health and Safety at Work Act. Like the act they apply to every work activity. The main requirement of employers is to carry out a **risk assessment**.

Employers with five or more employees need to record the significant findings of the risk assessment.

Risk assessment should be straightforward in a simple workplace such as a typical care home.

It basically states that employers must:

- make arrangements for implementing the health and safety measures identified as necessary by the risk assessment

- appoint competent people (often themselves or company colleagues) to help them to implement the arrangements
- set up emergency procedures
- provide clear information and training for employees
- work together with other employers sharing the same workplace.

This might involve the employer holding meetings to discuss health and safety issues, such as managing challenging behaviour; one care worker might be appointed as the challenging behaviour representative, meaning that they might attend specialist training in the field. They could then cascade this information down to other colleagues by running training sessions for them. They might also be involved in developing strategies to use during episodes of challenging behaviour.

■ Data Protection Act 1998

The Data Protection Act 1998 relates to personal information held in paper and electronic format.

Information held should be relevant and not excessive. It should have been obtained for lawful reasons and should be accurate and current. The information should not be held for longer than is necessary. Information should be protected against unauthorised access and accidental destruction.

Health and social care services necessarily hold a lot of sensitive information about their service users. It is vital that this information is only used for legitimate purposes. You may have access to home addresses, sometimes meaning properties are empty. Diagnoses of service users are highly confidential. Not everyone wishes their relatives to know what is wrong with them. Some information may be embarrassing for people, for example if they are incontinent.

Accidental destruction of medical information could have very serious consequences, such as loss of information about allergies.

When you are at work placement you too will have access to some information. You must never disclose this information to an unauthorised person, such as a member of your family. Be very wary of giving any information over the telephone; it is usually best to hand calls over to permanent staff. Do not let callers pressurise you into disclosing sensitive information.

Even after a service user has died, their records cannot be destroyed. The Department of Health requires records to be retained for at least eight years after someone has died. Records of treatments given to children and maternity records must be kept until they are 25 years of age, unless the child has died, in which case they will be destroyed eight years after the child's death. This should give plenty of time for notes to be accessed if there are any complications later on that could be attributed to treatments given.

In context

NHS Connecting for Health is delivering the National Programme for IT to modernise computer systems in the NHS. The aim is to improve patient care and services. The National Programme for IT will connect over 30,000 GPs in England to almost 300 hospitals and give patients access to their personal health and care information, transforming the way the NHS works. Some of this system came into operation on 1 April 2005. A fact sheet all about Connecting for Health, including statements about confidentiality, can be downloaded from:
http://www.connectingforhealth.nhs.uk/about

Privacy Statement

'Under the Data Protection Act, we have a legal duty to protect any information we collect from you. We will only use your information for the purpose we have described and we do not pass on your details to any third party or government department unless you give us permission to do so. We use leading technologies to safeguard your data, and keep strict security standards to prevent any unauthorised access to it.'
Source: *http://www.connectingforhealth.nhs.uk*

1 **What are the potential consequences if someone managed to breach security and hack into the NHS computer system?**

2 **Many private companies sell contact details to third parties, who use the information to target potential customers. Do you think the NHS should do this to raise extra money for improved services? Give reasons for your answers.**

■ Fire Precautions (Workplace) Regulations 1997

The Fire Precautions (Workplace) Regulations require business premises to:

- carry out, monitor and review a fire risk assessment
- plan for an emergency
- provide staff with information about risks and training in fire prevention and emergency procedures
- nominate fire officers
- fit fire detectors and alarms, and emergency lighting
- ensure that there are means of escape, which are clearly signed
- provide firefighting equipment.

Health and social care organisations need to think very carefully about how they would keep staff and service users safe in a fire. Sometimes it might be inappropriate to evacuate people, for example those who are very sick or frail. In these circumstances the building could be adapted to create safe zones. Fire safety doors will hold a fire back for about two hours – plenty of time for the fire

▲ **Figure 3.6 Fire exits must always be kept clear of obstructions for easy evacuation**

service to arrive and take charge of the situation. Service users can be moved, in bed if necessary, into an adjacent zone, to be kept safe from a fire.

Policies and procedures

Every workplace has to produce their own health and safety **policies** and **procedures** to state how they will operate under the legislation. The Health and Safety at Work Act 1974 states that organisations must have a health and safety policy. Most organisations also have a range of policies and procedures linked to the regulations discussed earlier. These would include:

- manual handling policy
- disposal of body fluids
- fire procedure
- first aid policy.

Other policies and procedures are only relevant in certain settings, such as:

- challenging behaviour policy
- medication policy.

Policies and procedures reflect the unique nature of individual organisations. Every building is slightly different, service users differ from one setting to another, and policies may also reflect the requirements of local authorities. Unfortunately most policies are long and complex and include a lot of formal legal jargon. It would be impossible to include a full example within this chapter. Below is an example of the wording of a policy statement and a short procedure to give you an idea of the difference between the two.

Theory into practice

Fire Policy Statement
The Trust will meet all statutory requirements for fire safety for all buildings for which responsibility is held.

Fire Procedure Statement
On discovering a fire raise the alarm by breaking the glass in the nearest fire point.

Leave the building by the nearest fire escape.

Assemble at Fire Assembly Point B.

As a group, collect a selection of health and safety policies and procedures from your work placements. Compare the policies and procedures, looking for similarities and differences.

Take it further

Try to write basic policies for two care homes to allow residents to go out shopping. You need to consider two things. Firstly, is there any legislation related to the topic that would have to be incorporated into your policies and procedures? Secondly, what factors, relevant to each setting and its service users, will have an impact on your policies?

The first home is a residential care home for the elderly. It is situated in a suburban area, 100 metres from a row of local shops.

The second care home is for young adults with learning disabilities and is situated in the middle of a busy town centre.

How health and safety requirements affect service delivery

Legislation, policies and procedures all have an effect on health and social care service delivery. As a care student, you will learn the importance of care values when dealing with service users, for example, maintaining dignity, offering choice and promoting independence. Sometimes there has to be a compromise on these values for the health and safety of both staff and service users.

Working practices

■ Activities

Activities are an important part of the care you deliver to the service users. People of all ages and abilities can enjoy games, art and craft. They provide mental stimulation, an opportunity for social interaction and give people something other than their illness or situation to focus on. However, activities have to be chosen with due regard to health and safety. For example, if you are working with clients who are prone to aggressive outbursts, it would not be appropriate to set up an activity using sharp knives. Wherever possible, activities should be adapted to allow people to participate, perhaps by engaging extra helpers.

Reflect

Medical professionals recognise that horse riding provides significant benefits for people with a range of disabilities. The movement of the horse gradually makes the rider more relaxed and supple, reducing spasms and improving balance, posture and co-ordination.

Riding offers an element of risk, often denied to many people, especially those who have been affected by an accident or serious illness and offers them the chance to regain mobility and a sense of achievement. People with congenital disabilities discover a new freedom in movement.

Riding for the Disabled is an organisation that relies heavily on volunteers, as most riders need a leader or side helper. Without these volunteers this activity would not be safe for many of the participants, some of whom have visual impairment, balance or co-ordination difficulties.

■ Procedures

Many procedures in health and social care settings are covered by legislation, policies and procedures. The administration of medication is a good example.

The Care Standards Act 2000 and the Regulation of Care (Scotland) 2001 require nursing homes, care homes, day care settings and children's residential homes to be registered with the appropriate body. Each of these bodies has laid down national minimum standards for care, and as part of this they monitor administration of medication during the inspection process. Anyone responsible for administration of medication should receive extra training.

Wherever possible, service users should be encouraged to administer their own medication. This preserves their independence and enables them to access medicines, such as painkillers, as required, just as you would. However, this does not mean that the staff do not have any responsibility. For example, the service user should have a personal lockable drawer or cupboard to prevent other service users being able to access their drugs. Some service users may find it easier if their medicines are arranged into a 'monitored dosage system' with a different compartment for breakfast, lunch time, tea time and bed time (see Figure 3.7).

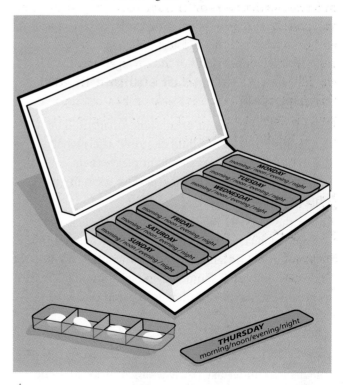

▲ Figure 3.7 A monitored dosage system

been discussed under the Health and Safety at Work Act 1974 and the Management of Health and Safety at Work Regulations 1999. The outcome of a risk assessment will determine whether or not you consider that the activity poses too much of a risk to allow it to go ahead. This can result in service users being prevented from participating in something they would enjoy.

■ Storage and use of equipment and materials

Any piece of equipment or substance that could be dangerous if misused should be stored safely when not in use. Service users should not leave their belongings where staff or other service users might trip over them.

Under the COSHH regulations chemicals, such as cleaning materials, must be locked away when not in use, and should not be left unattended when they are in use. For example, bleach should never be left in toilets in care homes in the way that it often is in a domestic setting.

Risk assessment

The need to undertake risk assessment prior to doing activities with service users, or taking them out, has

Roles and responsibilities of employers and employees

The promotion of health and safety can be influenced by the **roles** and **responsibilities** of employers and employees.

Activity The journey as well as activities during the visit.	Hazard and Risk Something with the potential to cause harm and potential risk	Likelihood 1 = low 5 = high	Severity 1 = low 5 = high	Risk Likelihood and severity 1 = low 5 = high	Recommendations To remove risk or reduce likelihood or severity
Travelling on minibus	Children distracting the driver, potentially causing a road traffic accident	1	5	5	

▲ Figure 3.8 A risk assessment template

■ Employers

Employers are the company or the statutory body you work for. The managers of the organisation act on behalf of the employers and take responsibility for the operation of the organisation.

Employers promote health and safety by ensuring that all necessary policies and procedures are in place to meet the legal requirements for health and safety. Some employers go over and above statutory obligations, providing extra benefits to enhance the health and safety of employees. This might include on-site health provision, private health insurance or good terms and conditions of employment. This raises the self-esteem of the workforce and encourages staff to stay. By ensuring that staff are experienced, well-trained and committed to the reputation of the organisation, there will be a positive effect on the health and safety of the service users.

Managers can have an enormous influence on the quality of care delivered if they show they are committed to high standards. An enthusiastic manager can inspire staff to take pride in their work.

■ Employees

There are a wide variety of job roles in the health and social care sector, including professional staff, such as nurses, occupational therapists and social workers, and skilled staff, such as care assistants, youth workers and early years workers.

It is the responsibility of staff providing direct care to consider the health and safety of the service users at all times. It would be easy for care workers to cut corners. You often work behind closed doors with vulnerable clients who are not usually in a position to complain if health and safety procedures are not followed. It is therefore imperative that you maintain high standards without supervision.

Health and safety are a key part of the General Social Care Council Induction Standards, and it is the employers' responsibility to ensure new staff receive this training.

Assessment activity 3.2

Describe how key legislation in relation to health, safety and security influences health and social care delivery.

Riverside Residential Children's Centre caters for 10 children aged 11 to 16 years with severe emotional and behavioural difficulties.

The centre provides education, behavioural psychotherapy and adventurous activities in a highly structured environment to give children a structured and purposeful lifestyle.

1 What health and safety legislation would this establishment have to adhere to?

2 How would legislation affect the delivery of care at this centre?

Using examples from work experience describe how policies and procedures promote health, safety and security in the health and social care workplace.

3 What policies and procedures, on top of the standard health and safety policy, would have to be written for such a specialist provision?

4 How would the policies you suggested help to keep the staff and children safe?

Grading tip for P3

Describe the accidents, incidents and illnesses that should be prevented if the policies and procedures are followed properly.

Grading tip for P2

Describe the way care is delivered and link this to legal requirements.

Explain how legislation, policies and procedures are used to promote the health, safety and security of individuals in the health and social care workplace.

5   Explain how imposing restrictions or requirements by law increases the chance that staff and service users will remain safe and well.

M1

Grading tip for M1

Think about the consequences to a care business of flouting health and safety legislation?

Using examples from work experience, evaluate the effectiveness of policies and procedures for promoting health, safety and security.

6   What evidence would tell you whether or not policies and procedures work to keep people safe and well?

D1

Grading tip for D1

Think about statistics or observations.

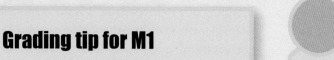

3.3 Roles and responsibilities for health, safety and security in health and social care settings

Employers' and employees' roles

As has already been stated, it is the employer's role to oversee the health, safety and security of their staff, visitors to the premises and the service users. Employers can delegate responsibility for health and safety to employees, managers, health and safety representatives and the service users themselves. However, it is still their role to take ultimate responsibility for health and safety.

It is the role of the employees to keep themselves, their colleagues, visitors and service users safe from harm.

Employers' responsibilities

Employers are responsible for the health and safety of employees, visiting workers from other organisations and visitors while on the premises.

This means that if there is an incident where someone is hurt, or contracts an infection, or if security is breached,

it is the employer who will be investigated to ensure that all regulations were being followed at the time of the incident, and that everything practicable had been done to keep the person safe.

Legal and organisational requirements

■ Health and safety representative

Every organisation will have a different approach to the management of health and safety. Broadly speaking, someone will be appointed to oversee health and safety on behalf of the employer, so the employer must be certain that they are capable of carrying out this role. When appointing someone to the post, a person specification should be written to help to select suitable candidates from everyone who applies.

Staff holding qualifications such as a BTEC National Diploma in Health and Social Care, and NVQ Level 2 or 3 in Health and Social Care will have studied for a health and safety unit. Employers may feel it is essential that staff being considered for the post should hold, or be willing to undertake, a Health and Safety at Work qualification. This should give them an in-depth knowledge of legislation and how to manage health and safety in the workplace. Sector-specific qualifications such as First Aid at Work, Manual Handling Trainer, COSHH Training, a Certificate in Infection Control, would also be useful.

Take it further

Ask the manager at your work placement what qualifications they would require when appointing a health and safety representative. Ask them if they would expect the person to hold these qualifications when they are appointed, or whether the person would be sent on training courses.

■ Policies and procedures

Health and safety policies and procedures must be written specifically for the setting. They should also be monitored regularly to ensure that they are keeping staff, visitors and service users safe.

Following any incident, the employer, or the health and safety representative, should review policies and procedures and consider whether the reason the incident occurred was due to any weakness in the systems in place.

■ Training

Training sessions must be put on for staff. All new staff should be given health and safety training within the first week of employment, to ensure they know what to do in the case of a fire, and any immediate threats to their health and safety. They would not be allowed to manually handle any service users without the appropriate training.

■ Supply of equipment

Employers must ensure that safety equipment is provided for staff. This would include disposable protective gloves and aprons, moving and handling equipment, and sharps boxes.

■ Risk assessment

It is the responsibility of the employer to anticipate danger and to put into place measures to reduce risk. This is done through the process of risk assessment (see pages 126–127). As an employer you would delegate the responsibility of carrying out risk assessments to appropriate staff. For example, a senior care worker could carry out a risk assessment on the manual handling of a new resident. It is the responsibility of the management to ensure the senior care worker has the correct training to be able to carry out the task. Here again, the responsibility for training may well have been delegated to an experienced member of staff.

■ Records

A record must be kept of all accidents and incidents. This is normally achieved by providing an accident book, which has to be completed whenever an accident or untoward injury occurs.

Take it further

Figure 3.9 on page 131 shows an example of an accident form. If you have had an accident, or witnessed one, complete the form. Alternatively, you could make up your own scenario.

■ Insurance

The workplace must be fully insured. Employers Compulsory Liability Insurance and Public Liability Insurance must be taken out, in case an incident occurs and the business is found to be at fault. Should an employee be seriously injured, compensation would have to be paid for any loss of income or costs incurred as a result of the injury. Occasionally workers are so badly injured that they are unable to work again; this type of insurance ensures that a person is still able to have a similar standard of living to that which they had before the accident. Some people may need long-term treatment, such as physiotherapy, or special equipment, such as back support to relieve back pain. All of these items are expensive, so it is reasonable to expect compensation.

EXEMPLAR ACCIDENT FORM

About the person completing the form:

Full name:

Job title:

Signature

About any witnesses:

Full name:

Job title/Status

Signature

About the injured person:

Name:

Home address:

Post code:

Home tel no:

Date of birth:

Gender:

Age:

About the accident:

Date of accident: ___/___/___

Time of accident: ___:___ hrs

Location of accident:

Injury (e.g. fracture)

Part of the body injured:

About the type of accident:

What happened? (tick if applies)

☐ Equipment failure
☐ Slip on wet surface
☐ Tripped over object
☐ Injured while moving something
☐ Fell
☐ Trapped by something collapsing
☐ Inhaled gas/fumes
☐ Electric shock
☐ Asphyxiation
☐ Assault
☐ Exposure to fire
☐ Struck by moving object
☐ Other

Describe the accident using factual information:

About prevention of a recurrence:

Can you identify any way the accident could have been prevented?

Date form completed: **Review date:**

REVIEW

Outcome at review:

Was the injury (tick if applies)

☐ A fatality?
☐ A major injury?
☐ Serious enough to require 3 or more days off work?
☐ Serious enough to require hospital treatment?

Did the injured person (tick if applies)

☐ Become unconscious?
☐ Need resuscitation?
☐ Remain in hospital for 24 hours or more

If any of the above ticked, accident must be reported to HSE.

Prevention:

What has been done to prevent future similar accidents?

Review date: ___/___/___

Name of person reviewing accident:

Name in full: ___/___

Job role:

▲ **Figure 3.9** An example of an accident form

Disposal of hazardous waste

The employer is responsible for ensuring that hazardous waste is disposed of correctly, by arranging for the collection of potential sources of infection. Clinical and medical waste would include soiled dressings and incontinence pads which contain body fluids. Employers should ensure that such waste is disposed of in yellow bags in clearly marked bins. There should also be a lockable large bin outside where staff can deposit these yellow bags once they are full. Either the local council or a specialist private company will collect these.

Recruitment of suitable staff

It is the employer's responsibility to ensure that all staff, including students like you, are suitable for the job role for which they have been appointed. Under the Department of Health's Protection of Vulnerable Adults scheme (PoVA) all staff working in care homes, domiciliary care (providing care in the service user's own home) and adult placement schemes (for adults with learning disabilities) must be checked by the Criminal Records Bureau (CRB) against the PoVA list, to ensure that they have not previously harmed a vulnerable adult or placed a vulnerable adult at risk of harm. Similarly those working with children should be checked for previous offences.

Employees' responsibilities

Following procedures

It is irrelevant how much is invested in health and safety by employers if employees do not follow organisational policies and procedures. Employees cannot claim compensation in the case of an accident or incident if they were not following procedures. You must use equipment provided, attend training, and adhere to all guidance that has been put in place for your own safety.

Risk assessment

As a student you are unlikely to be more than an observer in a formal risk assessment. However, if you are on placement and a risk assessment is being carried out, do take the opportunity to observe. You may be allowed to do the assessment under the supervision of a qualified member of staff, who will take responsibility for the assessment.

Risk assessments for direct care can include manual handling, where the ability of the service user to transfer themselves, perhaps from bed to chair, will be observed, and the most suitable equipment identified to minimise the risk of the service user falling or developing sore skin from friction.

In context

Suzanne started a BTEC First Diploma in Health and Social Care a year ago. When she enrolled she brought all her evidence for her CRB check to college. Two weeks into the course she went into town for a Saturday night out with her friends. They all drank a lot of alcohol and, as they were walking through the streets, a fight broke out. Police were soon on the scene and one of Suzanne's friends was arrested. Suzanne attacked the police officer, kicking and hitting her. Consequently she was also arrested.

Suzanne went to court and was found guilty of assaulting a police officer. She was given a Community Rehabilitation Order. Suzanne did not tell her tutor at college and went out on placement all year working with vulnerable adults and children. The offence did not come to light until this year, when a new CRB check was carried out at the beginning of the BTEC National Diploma in Health and Social Care course.

Discuss with your group the issues in this case.

Could anything be done to prevent this type of incident occurring?

Another example of risk assessment in direct care involves assessing the risk of a service user developing **pressure ulcers**.

Key terms

Pressure ulcers Once known as pressure or bed sores, these are areas of damage to the skin and deeper tissue which can affect all patients. They can give discomfort and become infected. In extreme cases, they can damage muscle and bone, leading to a longer stay in hospital.

There are several tools used to assess the risk of pressure ulcers developing. The most frequently used tool is the Waterlow score. Factors such as the weight, mobility, skin type and continence status of the service user all combine to give a score. The higher the score, the more likely the service user is to develop pressure ulcers. Once the risk has been established, it will be decided how often the service user should have their position changed. There are various types of equipment designed to relieve pressure, usually by spreading the pressure over a larger surface area. Examples include decubitus mattresses and water beds. These can be used in conjunction with frequent changes of position to further reduce the risk of these debilitating ulcers occurring.

■ Checking rights of entry and taking appropriate actions

Working in the care sector means that you are working with very vulnerable people and you have to be careful that everyone entering the building has a legitimate reason for visiting. Most settings now keep the front door locked, so visitors have to ring a bell to gain entry. As a student you may well answer the door to visitors. You should always ask who they are and whom they wish to visit. Check with a member of the permanent staff that there are no restrictions on visitors for that resident.

If you are working in an early years setting, there may be children whose parents have restricted access (imposed by a court order). It is essential that you are aware of

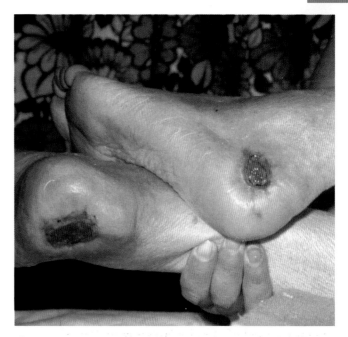

▲ Pressure ulcers are caused by people staying in the same position for a long time. Tissue is effectively starved of oxygen as it is compressed between the bed or chair and the bones of the service user

▲ Pressure-relieving mattresses distribute the weight over a larger surface area to reduce pressure

this. You also need to know what the procedure is at your placement if a visitor arrives who is not allowed to see the service user; you need to avoid getting into a situation where you could be in danger.

Identifying and minimising health, safety and security risks

When working in a care environment, it is your responsibility to identify hazardous situations. If you notice something dangerous, you must not ignore it.

A spillage could cause someone to slip, or if it is a hazardous substance, it could cause the spread of infection. The least you should do is to report the spillage and put up a warning sign. Not all care settings have domestic staff on the premises at all times, so the responsibility to clean up a spillage may fall to care staff. If this is so, you must follow the procedure in the case of a hazardous substance.

Objects causing trip hazards or blocking fire exits should always be moved.

Any faulty equipment must be reported, so accidents can be avoided and repairs can be arranged.

If you notice an external door has been left unlocked or open, shut it and lock it, but then check whether it was open for a reason.

Monitoring of working practices

It is the responsibility of senior staff to monitor working practices, such as hand washing, correct moving and handling techniques and **aseptic techniques**.

Key terms

Aseptic technique This is the method used to keep the patient or service user as free from contamination as possible. It is used to prevent microorganisms entering wounds and other susceptible sites, which could cause infection. You need to use sterile equipment and fluids during medical and nursing procedures that pierce the skin.

It is vital that staff are confident about their abilities and don't feel threatened by senior staff who are monitoring their skills. They also should feel able to ask for a demonstration and supervision if they are not confident.

Respecting the needs, wishes, preferences and choices of individuals

When deciding how to carry out procedures in a care setting it is important to respect the needs, wishes, preferences and choices of individuals. However, the health, safety and security of staff and service users will always have to come first.

Theory into practice

Discuss the following scenarios with your peers. What health, safety and security issues are involved in each of the following?

- A confused service user wants to go outside in very cold weather without a coat on.
- An 83-year-old man with emphysema wishes to continue smoking, even though it will worsen his condition.
- A 20-year-old man with learning disabilities wants to go into town on his own for the first time.

Safe storage and use of materials and equipment

As an employee it is imperative that you store and use materials and equipment as dictated by manufacturer's instructions, legislation, policy and guidance.

You must ensure that you put any hazardous substances away in an appropriate place when not in use. For example, flammable materials must be stored away from a heat source.

Staff responsible for medication must ensure that the drug cupboard is locked and that the drug trolley is locked to the wall unless in use. When service users are self-medicating, medication must be inaccessible to other residents. In some organisations this is achieved by giving service users a key to a small medication cabinet in their room. An alternative solution is to ask them to carry their medication with them in a bag around their waist. This is to prevent others accessing the medication.

Medical supplies, such as syringes and needles, should be locked away. A balance has to be reached between keeping service users safe and making supplies accessible in an emergency.

Some items may have to be stored in the refrigerator, particularly vaccines and liquid medicines.

Tidiness is essential when working in a care environment, both to prevent trips, and to ensure items can be found quickly in an emergency situation.

Dressings and other dry goods must be kept in an area free from moisture.

■ Dealing with spillages and waste

Spillages must be dealt with according to procedures.

Gloves and aprons should be worn to carry out this task.

The disposal of clinical waste has already been discussed on page 132. Dry waste must not be stored near a heat source, due to the risk of combustion.

■ Following manual handling procedures

You must follow procedures for manual handling, using equipment correctly. Qualified and experienced staff will carry out risk assessments for moving and handling for each service user.

■ Reporting health and safety issues

As a care worker, it is your responsibility to report any hazards you identify. Do not leave it to someone else. An accident can be prevented through vigilance.

■ Completing health and safety records

Health and safety records can include completing accident reports, risk assessments and routine maintenance checks on the condition of equipment and substances (for example, checking the use-by-date of medications).

■ Work within the limits of your role

It is vital that you limit your work activities to those you are trained for, and confident about. If you are under 18 years of age, you are also restricted under the Care Standards Act.

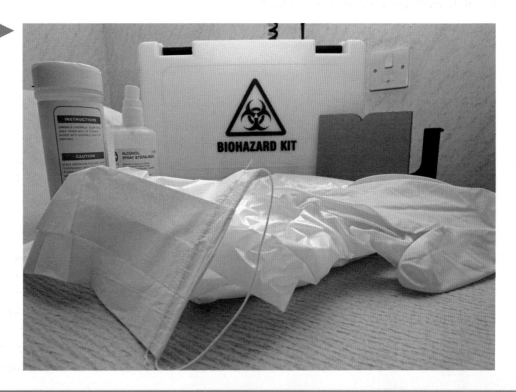

Blood, urine and vomit should be dealt with by sprinkling with granules that absorb the liquid, enabling it to be scooped up. The area should then be disinfected

Assessment activity 3.3

Examine the roles and responsibilities of key people in the promotion of health, safety and security in a health or social care setting.　**P4**

Ekwueme Oniolo is the officer-in-charge of a day centre for adults with learning disabilities.

Aspects of health, safety and security can include the following:

- staff training
- providing, using and maintaining equipment
- disposing of waste
- storage of equipment and supplies
- risk assessment
- policies, procedures and the law
- staff welfare.

1　What would Ekwueme do in his role as manager to ensure the health and safety of the staff and service users?

2　What would the employees' responsibilities be towards the health and safety of themselves, their colleagues and their service users?

Complete the table below to differentiate between employers' and employees' responsibilities.

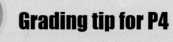

Grading tip for P4

The manager is responsible for ensuring everything is in place to keep staff, visitors and service users safe, and that legal requirements are fulfilled, whereas employees must follow the rules and work in a safe way.

Aspect of health and safety	Employers' role	Employees' role
Staff training	Assess training needs of staff. Select a competent training provider or deliver training.	Attend training, listen, participate, complete any coursework, and put into practice what has been learnt.
Providing, using and maintaining equipment		
Disposal of waste		
Storage of equipment and supplies		
Risk assessment		
Policies, procedures and the law		
Staff welfare		

As a care worker you could potentially work with a variety of different clients in many different settings. Before you take a service user out you need to plan ahead to be sure that you are not likely to endanger them. This may involve visiting the environment beforehand to familiarise yourself with any actual or potential hazards.

Patient/service user group

You would particularly need to consider the client group, as a safe environment for one client group could be dangerous for another.

For any outing a risk assessment should be carried out. Some organisations have a stock of risk assessments for a range of activities and outings. If a stock risk assessment is used, always read it through and consider the individuals who will be participating. It may be that some risks exist with a particular individual in that group, even though they are not relevant to other participants.

If practical, visit the venue prior to the trip. This will give you a much better idea of hazards. If it is not possible to visit, have a telephone conversation with staff at the venue, and discuss any concerns you have.

■ Older people

If you are taking older people out, you need to be aware of their physical and cognitive abilities. Outside paths may be uneven or slippery. The path may be too narrow for an accompanying carer to be able to walk alongside.

Older people are more likely to be affected by extremes of temperature, so make sure they are wrapped up well in cold weather, with a hat to reduce heat loss. In warm weather hats should be worn to protect from sunburn. You should take drinks with you.

Do consider the availability of toilet facilities when choosing venues, including disabled toilets.

■ Cognitive impairment

Some older people develop Alzheimer's disease or other forms of dementia. This affects their ability to remember recent events. It can also affect their communication skills, reasoning and understanding of the world around them.

They can become disorientated, even in familiar surroundings. There must be adequate numbers of staff on hand when taking out service users with dementia – they will need close supervision.

■ Sensory impairment

People with sensory impairment, such as hearing loss or poor vision, present other potential problems. A person who is blind will usually have a care worker with them all the time, whereas this isn't necessarily the case with people who are deaf. The main danger for anyone who is deaf is that they will not hear verbal instructions, announcements or warnings. Special arrangements need to be made to ensure they will be alerted in an emergency situation, such as in the case of a fire.

■ Physical impairment

Wheelchair users may need to follow different instructions in the case of a fire. Large public buildings often have safe areas where wheelchair users can assemble during a fire emergency. These areas will be protected by fire doors that can withhold fire for about two hours. The fire service can be alerted on arrival. Other buildings, such as theatres or pubs, may be less well designed to cope with wheelchair users in an evacuation. You may need to consider whether these are suitable venues, or if you would want to position wheelchair users just next to the fire exit, to enable them to be quickly evacuated alongside other users.

■ Children

Children pose a different set of challenges. Young children have poor awareness of danger and need close supervision on outings. You may need to enlist the help of other adults, such as parents, to increase the child/adult ratio. You may need to consider having adult

Play parks are designed with safety in mind, but still have to provide some challenge to children

volunteers checked with the Criminal Records Bureau. In this case you would need to plan well ahead. Checks can take several weeks. You would also need to consider whether any of the children need special care during a trip, for example, if they have a physical or learning disability, chronic illness or behavioural disorder.

Environments

The types of environments to which you might take service users are many and varied. Each will have different potential hazards.

■ Local parks and play areas

While generally a safe environment, free from traffic, you may need to consider whether there are any potential dangers posed by other park users. If young people use the park as a safe place to skateboard, it could create a hazard to elderly people who might be unsteady on their feet.

Unfortunately some parks are frequented by drug abusers, who may leave used needles on the ground. This would be extremely hazardous to inquisitive young children. Another threat to children in a park could be dog faeces. Dog owners have become much more

responsible in recent years about picking it up but you do need to be vigilant. Toxicara is a roundworm that can be present in the faeces of dogs that haven't been wormed. The chances of a child being infected are fairly low, with about two cases per million population annually. Total blindness in either one or both eyes is exceptionally rare. However, children should be encouraged to use good hygiene practices and thoroughly wash their hands after playing in any area where dogs have been.

Parks are an ideal place to take children to allow them to get some exercise. However, accidents do happen and a well-equipped first aid kit should be taken to deal with insect bites, stings, cuts and sprains. It is also wise to take a mobile phone and contact and medical details for everyone on the trip.

It is important that children are able to assess risk for themselves. You can discuss with children what dangers exist and encourage them to work out what measures they must take to keep themselves safe.

It is also essential that children are kept in sight at all times to stop them being approached by strangers, or adults who are prohibited from seeing individual children. This is also essential to prevent children from wandering off unaccompanied.

In context

Hayley Singleton worked at the Little Red Hen day nursery. She decided to take the children over to the children's playground opposite the nursery, as the equipment was more challenging for the children. There were swings, a slide, a spider's web climbing frame and a roundabout. The staff got the children ready, wrapping them up warmly in their hats, coats and scarves and putting on their wellies.

There were three nursery staff and eight children. They crossed over the busy road. Two children had to hold the hand of another child, as there were not enough adult hands to go round. They went into the playground. The children were very excited and rushed off to start playing. Cody started to climb up the steps of the slide but lost confidence halfway up. Phoebe started making her way back through the gate, towards the busy road. Tom was walking towards the swings where Kuan-Lin, who was a bit older, was already swinging. Saleem

and Maddy started to climb up the spider's web and Tyrone was crying because he had trodden in some dog faeces. At least Megan was playing happily on the roundabout.

Hayley soon decided that there was too much risk to the children's safety, and decided to take them back to the nursery. Four children started crying because they didn't want to go back and refused to hold the hand of either an adult or another child.

1 **What were the main hazards of this trip?**

2 **Why was the trip so risky?**

3 **If Hayley had carried out a thorough risk assessment beforehand, what might she have done differently? Think about other risks as well as the incidents that did happen.**

■ Local tourist attractions

Theme parks, zoos and farms are popular venues for trips with children, whereas elderly service users are more likely to visit garden centres or stately homes. All such venues will have public liability insurance and have to work within health and safety legislation. This will give some protection to visitors. You certainly should expect equipment and buildings to be safe and cafes should meet food hygiene requirements. Risk assessments should focus on the specific nature of the service users. For example, you should avoid exposing anyone with epilepsy to strobe lighting at a theatre performance or on a theme park ride. Some service users might be prone to nervousness, motion sickness or vertigo. As a care worker you need to be prepared to stay with someone who doesn't wish to participate.

Allergies are another condition to be aware of when taking service users on trips. Pollen from plants and animal dander (minute particles of fur and skin) are common allergens. Asthma can be triggered or a skin reaction (urticaria). You may have service users who are allergic to insect bites, or wasp or bee stings.

Remember!

When on a visit you are primarily there to support service users and help them to enjoy their day out. You should not feel resentful if you have to miss out because someone does not want to participate. You must not make them feel embarrassed or inadequate for opting out.

When choosing a venue to use, try to select somewhere that all participants will enjoy and that will not aggravate medical or psychological conditions.

These can cause an extremely severe reaction leading to anaphylactic shock (see page 116). Susceptible individuals should carry an adrenaline injection and accompanying staff must be trained to use it in an emergency (although normally the service user will be able to self-administer).

In context

Marta Krygowski is the manager of Broad Oaks, a residential home for three young people who are physically disabled and aged between 16 and 25 years. The residents have decided that they want to go to Alton Towers for the day. Marta is very enthusiastic about her job and always encourages the service users to behave in a manner appropriate to their age. She is keen to facilitate this trip and sets about carrying out a risk assessment for the trip. The home has an adapted minibus which is regularly used, so the staff are used to loading and unloading residents safely. It is a longer journey than normal but, other than that, Marta's main concern is about helping the young people to safely access the theme park rides – the main reason for going.

Marta looked at the Alton Towers website and was delighted to find that the park would be able to accommodate the service users, as long as they were accompanied by two carers each.

1   **What are the main hazards associated with this trip?**

2   **What would Marta need to take with her on the day to cope with caring for these individuals?**

3   **Have a look at the Alton Towers website to see the arrangements for visitors with disabilities: www.alton-towers.co.uk.**

■ Shopping malls

Adult service users often find it very difficult to get out to shops due to transport difficulties and perhaps the need to be accompanied. Physical safety is not usually an issue as floors are level and malls are often indoors and protected from the elements. However, there could be a risk of service users becoming disorientated and the fire procedure should be established ahead of the trip. Care needs to be taken to keep the service users' valuables safe. For example, do not hang handbags on the back of wheelchairs. Shopping can be a very enjoyable outing, allowing service users to choose presents and cards for friends and families, or to buy new clothes for themselves.

In context

Mario Rossi works for a voluntary organisation which provides summer breaks for teenagers with visual impairment. This year they have decided to take the young people shopping and are looking for a suitable venue. Some of the young people have guide dogs and others use canes. From previous experience, Mario knows that some of the guests will not want to walk around with a sighted guide all the time, so he is trying to find a venue that will be suitable. The essentials include a guide in Braille and large print, a level floor with few trip hazards, access to toilets and eating places within the complex, Braille labels on lift buttons and shops that are well laid out with wide aisles. He decides to take them to the Bluewater shopping mall in Kent.

1   **What hazards might still exist on a trip like this, despite the care that has been put into choosing the venue? What risks would the young people face?**

2   **Do you think the benefits outweigh the risks?**

3   **Make a list of measures that shopping malls can take to make them suitable for a wide variety of disabilities.**

Risk assessments for visits to the local environment

When carrying out a risk assessment for a visit you will need to identify all the hazards that potentially exist for the whole trip, including the journey, and specific hazards related to any activities planned. For each hazard you identify you will need to assess the risks, and plan how to minimise the chances of the service users coming to any harm. You may be able to make recommendations about how to improve the venue to increase health and safety.

Assessment activity 3.4

Carry out a health and safety survey of a local environment used by a specific patient/service user group.

Imagine you are taking a group of people with visual impairment to a shopping centre. If you were planning such a trip, you would need to find out as much about the surrounding area as you could. If possible you should survey the venue in advance. If you can identify all the potential hazards beforehand, it is much more likely that you will have a safe and successful trip.

1 Identify all the hazards the service users might face.

2 Describe the risks from each hazard you have identified.

P5

Grading tip for P5

Consider the specific difficulties that would be faced by the service users and which make the environment particularly hazardous.

Assess the risk associated with the use of the chosen local environment and make recommendations for change.

3 Suggest ways that the risks could be minimised.

4 Make recommendations about how the environment could be changed to make it safer.

You could use the sample risk assessments form on page 127.

M2

Grading tip for M2

Think of ways the environment could be made safer for service users with visual impairment.

Justify recommendations made for minimising the risks, as appropriate, for the setting and service user groups.

5 Explain your recommendations for the improvements suggested.

D2

Grading tip for D2

Give detailed explanations of how the recommendations you have suggested would make the shopping centre safer for people with visual impairment.

It is recommended that all care workers complete a recognised first aid qualification. The information included in this section is no substitute for attending a course and practising first aid techniques under the supervision of a first aid instructor. If you do have to administer any first aid, always reassure the casualty during treatment.

■ Action at an emergency

It is imperative that you do not put yourself in any danger in an emergency situation. On approaching the scene of an accident or incident:

- stop and think
- check for danger from fire, fumes, moving vehicles, falling masonry, chemicals or body fluids
- protect yourself with vinyl gloves if you are likely to come into contact with blood or other body fluids
- do not move the casualty unless they are in extreme danger by staying in the same position.

■ Emergency first aid

Once you are happy that you will come to no harm, approach the casualty to assess their condition.

If the casualty is unconscious, follow the steps below.

- Gently tap the casualty, introduce yourself and ask if they are all right.
- If they respond, leave them in the position you found them in and try to find out what is wrong.
- If there is no response, shout for help from a bystander. If there is no bystander, carry on to the next stage.
- Check that the casualty is breathing. If not, ask the bystander to call the emergency services. If there is no bystander, go and call the emergency services yourself, as you need to have help on the way.
- Even if you suspect back injuries, roll the casualty onto their back. Your first priority is breathing.
- Open the airway by tilting the head back. This will draw

▲ **Figure 3.10 The open airway position**

the tongue away from the back of the throat and breathing may restart with no further action. There are techniques to reduce the risk of worsening neck injuries but they are beyond the scope of this chapter. Try to attend a first aid course if possible.

- Place your ear and cheek over the mouth of the casualty. Listen and feel for breaths, while looking for the rise and fall of the chest.
- If the casualty is breathing normally, put them in the recovery position and examine for other signs of injury.
- Keep a close eye on their breathing.
- If the casualty is not breathing, assume they have suffered a cardiac arrest. Kneel to one side of the chest and, with straight arms, place the heel of one hand on the breastbone and put the other hand on top, linking your fingers. Perform 30 chest compressions.

▲ **Figure 3.11 The recovery position**

- You will now have to breathe for the casualty, preferably using a resuscitation aid.
- Make a good seal around the casualty's mouth and, at the same time, pinch their nose and blow twice into their lungs to inflate them.
- Repeat this pattern of 30 compressions to 2 breaths until they start breathing on their own or until you can hand over to the ambulance service.

■ Bleeding, burns and shock

If you have established that the casualty is breathing normally the next most life-threatening situation is severe bleeding. If available, protective gloves should be worn.

External bleeding

- External bleeding from a limb should be controlled by applying firm pressure to the wound and raising the limb above the level of the heart.
- Ask a bystander to call an ambulance.
- If available, dress the wound with a large pad and bandage, keeping the pressure on as much as possible and maintaining the elevation.
- If blood starts to seep through apply another dressing on top – do not remove the first one.

▲ A resuscitation aid

Internal bleeding

Internal bleeding, caused by the rupture of an internal organ, such as the spleen or kidney, can result from a blow to the abdomen. You may not see any blood loss at all, although there may be signs of bruising. You might suspect internal bleeding from the history of the incident and the casualty may go into shock (see below).

Burns

Severe burns can be life-threatening, as a lot of fluid can be lost.

- Cool down the burnt area as quickly as possible by holding the area under running water or immersing in water for at least 10 minutes.
- Remove anything that might restrict the blood supply if swelling occurs, such as rings.
- Cover the area with clingfilm or a clean non-fluffy dressing.
- An ambulance must be called if the burn covers a large area of skin.
- Treat for shock (see below).

Shock

Signs of shock include pale, cold clammy skin, a fast pulse and fast breathing rate. The casualty may start to feel light-headed and nauseous.

- Lay the casualty down and raise their legs. Cover with a blanket or coat to retain heat.
- Be prepared to start resuscitation.

■ Medical emergencies

Some medical conditions can cause people to become ill suddenly and need urgent attention.

Asthma attacks

A severe asthma attack can be fatal. People who are asthmatic should always carry a reliever inhaler with them.

- Give the reliever inhaler straightaway.
- Sit the casualty down, and leaning forward over a table.
- If their breathing is severely restricted their lips will be blue. In this event, call an ambulance straightaway.

- If their colour is good, wait for 5–10 minutes, by which time their symptoms should have improved.
- If there is no improvement, keep administering the reliever inhaler every few minutes and call a doctor or an ambulance as you think appropriate.
- Keep administering the reliever while waiting for the ambulance to arrive.
- Be prepared to resuscitate.

Diabetes mellitus

People with diabetes sometimes become ill because their level of blood glucose is too low (hypoglycaemia). This is usually caused by the person not eating enough to balance out their insulin injection. Signs of hypoglycaemia include confusion or aggression, staggering, shaking, sweating and rapid pulse.

- Get the casualty to sit down.
- Give a sweet drink, spoonful of sugar or a piece of chocolate – anything containing sugar that they won't choke on if they lose consciousness. (Diet drinks will not work, as they do not contain sugar.)

Improvement should be rapid – within minutes.

- Once the casualty has recovered, give them more to eat or drink and then allow them to rest.
- If there is no improvement, the person may have too much blood sugar (hyperglycaemia). In this case, call an ambulance for urgent transfer to hospital.

Epilepsy

Although most people with epilepsy have their condition well controlled by medication, occasionally people do have seizures. There are many different types of seizure. The most severe seizure is a generalised seizure, involving the whole brain, where the person loses consciousness, goes stiff, falls to the ground and their body jerks, usually for a minute or two.

- During the seizure, try to protect the person as much as possible, by moving anything away from them that might cause injury.
- After the seizure put the person in the recovery position until they regain consciousness (see page 142).
- If they are known to be epileptic, it will only be necessary to call the emergency services if they are injured or if the fitting carries on.

Allergies

Most allergies are more of a nuisance than anything, causing, for example, a rash, itching or sneezing. However, occasionally individuals are highly allergic to certain substances (wasp and bee stings and nuts being prime examples).

Anaphylactic shock is the term used for this extremely severe reaction. Signs of anaphylaxis include swelling of the tongue and throat, blotchy skin and wheezing.

- Call an ambulance.
- Find out if the person carries emergency medication and, if so, help them to use it.
- Be prepared to resuscitate.

■ Fractures

The next most serious situation is a fracture.

Signs of a fracture include pain, loss of function, deformity, swelling, bruising, or a snap felt or heard by the casualty.

- Do not move the casualty unless they are in danger from environmental hazards.
- Ask a bystander to call an ambulance.
- Support the limb in the position found.
- If you do have to move the casualty, splint the limb using padding in any natural hollows. A fractured leg can be splinted to the good leg, a fractured arm should be supported in a sling.
- If the fracture is the femur (thighbone) the casualty may go into shock.

■ Sprains

The symptoms of a sprain can be very similar to a fracture so, if in doubt, treat as a fracture.

Symptoms include pain, swelling and loss of function.

- Elevate the limb.
- Apply a crepe or elastic bandage.
- Apply a cold compress.
- Keep checking circulation by pressing on the end of the finger or toe to see that pink returns to the tip quickly. This indicates a good blood supply.

■ Bites and stings

Allergic reactions to bites and stings have been covered under allergies.

- If the sting is visible, brush or scrape it off, being careful not to squeeze any more venom into the casualty.

- Ice can be useful to take away some of the pain initially and can reduce swelling. This is especially useful for stings in the mouth.
- Apply antihistamine cream or analgesic spray to external bites and stings.

Assessment activity 3.5

Demonstrate basic first aid skills.

As a group, role-play the following scenario and prioritise the injuries and casualties to decide the order in which you should act.

You are out on a trip taking Albert, aged 80, Daisy, aged 92, and Joan, aged 67, to the local shops. A car approaches and the driver loses control of the vehicle. You and the other two care workers, Samina and Josh, manage to run out of the way of the car, but it ploughs into the three elderly people, who were all in wheelchairs.

Daisy has been thrown from her wheelchair. She is bleeding from a head wound, her lower leg is obviously broken because it is bent halfway between the knee and ankle. She is moaning.

Albert has fallen from his wheelchair. He is slumped against a garden wall. He is unconscious but breathing. There are no obvious injuries.

Joan is screaming and blood is pouring from a large gash on her shin.

The car driver has got out of his car. He seems very shaken but does not seem to be hurt.

1 Show how you would protect yourself from harm.
2 Decide on the order in which you should deal with the casualties.
3 Decide how you would best use the three care workers.
4 Demonstrate the first aid treatment for each casualty.

Grading tip for P6

You must ensure that your actions are performed correctly, and in the correct order, or you could cause harm to yourself, a fellow first aider or the casualty.

Demonstrate first aid skills on a critically injured individual.

Continue with your role play. While you are waiting for the ambulance to arrive Albert's condition starts to deteriorate. His lips turn blue and you realise he has stopped breathing. Demonstrate how to perform cardio-pulmonary resuscitation using a mannequin.

Grading tip for M3

You must satisfy the assessor that you can perform CPR properly.

Knowledge check

1   Define the terms hazard and risk.

2   What makes children, those with learning and physical disabilities, the elderly and the mentally ill and those with sensory impairment more at risk of injury and illness?

3   How can employers make sure that staff use safe working practices?

4   What are the main pieces of legislation that cover health and safety in care settings?

5   What is the difference between a policy and a procedure?

6   What is the difference between employer and employee responsibilities for health and safety?

7   What is the reason for carrying out risk assessments?

8   What is the order of priority when dealing with a first aid incident?

Grading criteria

To achieve a pass grade the evidence must show that the learner is able to:	To achieve a merit grade the evidence must show that, in addition to the pass criteria, the learner is able to:	To achieve a distinction grade the evidence must show that, in addition to the pass and merit criteria, the learner is able to:
P1 use work placement experiences to explain a minimum of six potential hazards in a health or social care setting **Assessment activity 3.1 page 117**		
P2 describe how key legislation in relation to health, safety and security influences health and social care delivery **Assessment activity 3.2 page 128**		
P3 using examples from work experience describe how policies and procedures promote health, safety and security in the health and social care workplace **Assessment activity 3.2 page 128**	**M1** explain how legislation, policies and procedures are used to promote the health, safety and security of individuals in the health and social care workplace **Assessment activity 3.2 page 129**	**D1** using examples from work experience evaluate the effectiveness of policies and procedures for promoting health, safety and security **Assessment activity 3.2 page 129**
P4 examine the roles and responsibilities of key people in the promotion of health, safety and security in a health or social care setting **Assessment activity 3.3 page 136**		
P5 carry out a health and safety survey of a local environment used by a specific patient/service user group **Assessment activity 3.4 page 141**	**M2** assess the risk associated with the use of the chosen local environment and make recommendations for change **Assessment activity 3.4 page 141**	**D2** justify recommendations made for minimising the risks, as appropriate, for the setting and service user groups. **Assessment activity 3.4 page 141**
P6 demonstrate basic first aid skills. **Assessment activity 3.5 page 145**	**M3** demonstrate first aid skills on a critically injured individual. **Assessment activity 3.5 page 145**	

Preparation for assessment

1 When you are on your work placement, you need to discuss with your supervisor the hazards that exist for the service users in that setting. Consider the different parts of the placement, such as the kitchen, the day room, bedrooms, the dining room, corridors, stairs, the entrance and the grounds.

Also consider activities such as walking, eating and drinking, attending to hygiene, dealing with wounds and sores, using the toilet and cooking.

Explain the reasons why any hazards you identify exist for your service users. You must include at least six hazards.

Ask your placement if they would like you to change any details that could identify the placement. You could make a new name for the setting and not mention the location to ensure it cannot be identified. **P1**

2 When you are at your work experience placement, ask the manager or your supervisor if you could look at a copy of all the policies and procedures relevant to health and safety. Some organisations have more than others. Look at the policies and procedures and match them to the legislation. Some settings are reluctant to give out photocopies of their documents so while you are in placement, you could make some notes to summarise key responsibilities and procedures. Your tutor may have some examples that you could use instead. Make a table to show how legislation influences care delivery. You do not have to cover Fire Precautions (Workplace) Regulations 1997 for the syllabus, so look at the example below for that legislation, to help you to get started.

Legislation	How legislation influences health and social care delivery
Fire Precautions (Workplace) Regulations 1997 Provide staff with information about risks and training in fire prevention and emergency procedures.	At my work placement all new staff and students have a fire lecture on the first day. The staff handbook covers the fire policy and procedure. Your mentor checks that you have read it and understood it. All staff have a fire update annually. The training covers storage of equipment, fire exits, smoking policy, kitchen fire prevention and evacuation.

P2

3 By following policies and procedures, you are trying to prevent a variety of diseases, injuries and incidents from occurring. Select 4 policies from your work placement to use as examples.

Describe what illnesses and injuries should be prevented by following specific policies and procedures, such as the medication policy preventing poisoning or the restraint procedure preventing injury. **P3**

4 Consider why it is necessary to have health and safety legislation, policies and procedures, rather than just training workers and assuming that everyone will work to high standards. Think what the consequences might be if legislation, policies and procedures are not followed. Think more widely than about just the accidents and illnesses that might occur. **M1**

5 Consider what evidence might show that policies and procedures are effective. Where might this evidence come from? How could you obtain this information without causing offence? **D1**

6 Interview three different workers at your placement, including a manager, a care worker and an ancillary worker. Find out how they see their role in terms of responsibility for health and safety. Compare and contrast the three roles. **P4**

7 Choose a service user group from the list below:

- older people
- people with sensory impairment
- people with cognitive impairment
- children.

Choose a venue in your local area to visit and assess it for hazards from the perspective of a carer working with the group you have chosen. You could choose a local park, a local tourist attraction, a shopping mall or a children's play area.

During your visit look carefully at the layout, walking surfaces, equipment, proximity to a main road etc.

Identify the issues for health and safety associated with the venue for the service user group you have chosen. **P5**

8 Carry out a risk assessment, such as would be done by care workers prior to a visit. You could use the example risk assessment form on page 127 as a basis for this answer. **M2**

9 Consider how the venue could be improved to make it safer for the service user group you have chosen. Write a short report making recommendations for minimising the risks for service users at this venue. You must justify the recommendations you have made, so you will need to explain how the improvements would make the venue safer. **D2**

10 Ideally you should attend a first aid course to learn first aid. Your assessor will need to assess your ability to deal with fractures, sprains, bleeding, burns, asthma, epilepsy, diabetes, bites, stings and allergies. This will probably be done through simulation. **P6**

11 You need to know and be able to demonstrate how to deal with a critically injured person, such as a person who is not breathing, unconscious, or bleeding

seriously. Also you need to know your priorities if the casualty has more than one injury. Again this is likely to be assessed through simulation. **M3**

Resources and further reading

BBC News (20 May 2005) 'Baby died after decimal error' see www.news.bbc.co.uk/1/hi/england/leicestershire/4566427.stm

Centre for Policy on Ageing (1996) *Home Life: A Code of Practice for Residential Care* London: Centre for Policy on Ageing

Commission for Social Care Inspection (2005) *The State of Social Care in England* London: CSCI

Commission for Social Care Inspection (2006) *Handled with Care* London: CSCI

Department of Health (2002) *Care Homes for Older People, National Minimum Standards, Care Homes Regulations,* second ed. London: TSO

Epilepsy Action *First Aid for Seizures* see www.epilepsy.org.uk

Food Standards Agency (2002) *Guide to Food Hygiene* London: Food Standards Agency

Health and Safety Executive (2006) *Health and Safety Statistics 2005/6* Sudbury: National Statistics

Health Protection Agency Centre, Communicable Disease Surveillance Centre for the Department of Health, MRSA surveillance system, 2005

National Statistics (2006) *Mortality Statistics – Cause – Review of the Registrar General on Deaths by Cause, Sex and Age in England and Wales* Series DH2 No. 31 London: Office of National Statistics

Newtown Abbey District Council 'Dog Care: Aggression' see www.newtownabbey.gov.uk/dogs/toxocara.htm

Peiperl, L. HIVInSite (2006) 'What is the Average Life Expectancy of Someone with HIV?' see http://hivinsite.ucsf.edu/insite?page=ask–06–02–07

Resuscitation Council (UK) (2005) *Resuscitation Guidelines 2005,* first ed. London: Resuscitation Council (UK)

Richards, Y. et al (2003) *Pressure Ulcer Risk Assessment and Prevention*, first ed. London: Royal College of Nursing

University of Auckland Disability Services 'Simulations of Visual Impairment' see http://www.disability.auckland.ac.nz/awareness/index.cfm?pageName=impairment_160

Useful websites

BBC
www.bbc.co.uk

Commission for Social Care Inspection
www.csci.org.uk

The Department of Health
www.dh.gov.uk

Epilepsy Action
www.epilepsy.org.uk

Health Protection Agency
www.hpa.org.uk

The Health and Safety Executive
www.hse.gov.uk

NHS Direct
www.nhsdirect.nhs.uk

Royal College of Nursing
www.rcn.org.uk

Family statistics
www.statistics.gov.uk

Development through the life stages

Introduction

The study of lifespan development is about understanding the way we change over time. In this unit you will be able to identify some patterns in the course of human development and a range of factors that will influence how your life turns out. You will also need to make up your own mind about some very deep questions. Will you have a fixed life course where you can predict much of what will happen to you? How far is your life fixed for you by your genetics or by the social and economic environment you grow up in? How far can you choose to control your own life and can you try to ensure a happy old age?

How you will be assessed

In this unit you will be assessed through written assignment work. A variety of assessment practice tasks are included throughout this unit to help you prepare your work.

After completing this unit you should be able to achieve the following outcomes:

- Understand human growth and development through the life stages
- Understand how life factors and events may influence the development of the individual
- Understand physical changes and psychological perspectives in relation to ageing.

Thinking points

Can you become anything you would like to be or do you need to be born with certain abilities or born to the right parents? How do you understand the story of your life so far? Think about your physical features, your personality, your degree of health and fitness – how far have you chosen to be this way? How far are these things fixed for you by genetic or environmental influences? This unit will help you to explore and make sense of your own life story.

In context Janet's story

> Date is the 5th January 1959
> My life in the future
> When I am 15 I will be old enough to go from school.
> I will get a job in the factory for a bit.
> Then I will meet a boy and we will get married
> when I am 22. We will live in a nice
> house with a big garden.
> two I will have to children a boy and a girl
> and a dog.
> I will play in the big garden with my dog
> I will do house work until the children
> are grown up. When I am old I
> will be like my Nan and sit in a
> chair and not do much.
>
> Janet age 10

Figure 4.1 Janet's schoolwork from 1959

Talking to Janet now:

Janet: I kept all my old childhood things. I can't remember writing this but I'm glad I kept it – it makes me laugh! You really have no idea when you're a child what life is about. Now my life didn't turn out anything like I imagined. I stayed on at school until 16 then worked in an office. I did get married but then I got divorced. I never did get the dog.

Interviewer: Why did your life turn out so differently then?

Janet: Well, some things are fixed but a lot of things are not. To begin with, things just happened to me. I mean – I didn't really plan to marry, it just sort of happened – everybody got married, I did what everybody else did. Then I think it was a turning point in my life. I just thought: what am I doing? I don't like being with this person. Why do I have to live my life like this? Well, I learned to take control of my life. I started making my own choices – then everything changed.

Interviewer: So there is no destiny then. You would say that we can choose to be who we want to be?

Janet: No – that's not really true. Things happen to you that you don't choose. For example, I have arthritis – it stops me from walking very far. I can't exercise and I'm putting on weight. I get so angry when people tell me that I could improve my health if I just tried. Some things you can control, some things you can't. I think wisdom is to know what you can control and learning to cope with what you can't.

Janet thought she could predict her life course when she was 10, but her experiences turned out to be very different. Janet's life has been strongly influenced by genetic and social factors but she believes she is at least partly in control of what happens to her.

1 **Why didn't Janet's life follow a simple fixed pattern?**

2 **Why is it difficult to predict what will happen in your life?**

3 **How far can you choose how your life works out?**

Life stage	Age	Key features
Conception	9 months before birth	Egg and sperm fuse after sexual intercourse and create a new living being
Pregnancy (gestation)	9 months to birth	Physical development of embryo and foetus
Birth and infancy	0–3 years	Attachment to carers
Childhood	4–9 years	First experience of education
Adolescence	10–18 years	Identification with peer group – puberty takes place during this period
Adulthood	18–65 years	The right to vote, and manage one's own financial affairs, happens at 18
Older adulthood	65 years onwards	65 is the current age when men (and women born after 6 April 1955) receive a state pension
Final stages of life	variable	Physical 'decline'

Table 4.1 Life stages

Life stages

The human lifespan has been described in terms of life stages for centuries. The life stages are listed below. The age ranges of some life stages are defined by clear social criteria. However, the age ranges for certain stages can vary depending on the expert who is describing it.

Life expectancy

National statistics (2006) state that boys born in 2004 can expect to live to 77 while girls born in 2004 can expect to live to 81 years of age. So **life expectancy** at birth is 77 for males and 81 for females. A man who has already reached the age of 65 is expected, on average, to live until 82 while a woman who has lived to be 65 is expected to live until 85. So life expectancy at 65 for a man is a further 17 years and a further 20 years for a woman.

Key terms

Life expectancy Life expectancy is an estimate of the number of years that a person can expect to live (on average).

Can you map your 'life course'?

A **life course** describes the path of the human life cycle. Stages such as infancy, childhood and so on can be described alongside the social roles and expectations associated with different stages of the life course.

Key terms

Life course A life course is a map of what is expected to happen at the various stages of the human life cycle.

In the past many experts assumed that the human life course would be controlled by biology. Growth and development progress until adults are able to reproduce. As people get older a process of physical decline sets in and continues until the person dies. This view of the life course can be described as the 'springboard theory'.

In the past people often assumed that everyone would have similar experiences of the life course. Janet's story at the beginning of this unit provides an example of people's expectations.

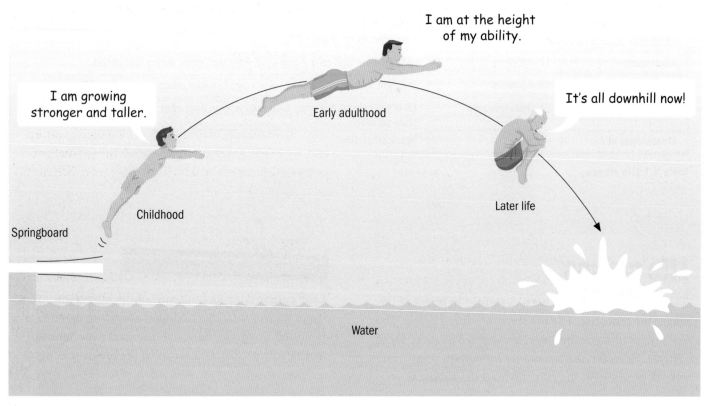

I am growing stronger and taller.

I am at the height of my ability.

It's all downhill now!

Early adulthood

Childhood

Later life

Springboard

Water

▲ **Figure 4.2 The 'springboard' model of the life course**

Bromley (1966) designed a three-page outline of the human life cycle, detailing physical and social development across the life course. Havighurst (1972) produced a theory of 'life tasks' that people had to cope with at the different stages of their life course. Levinson et al (1978) described a series of transitions that most people could expect to go through during their life course.

Nowadays it is much more difficult to describe the general life course. Biology no longer controls the adult life course! With the advent of reliable contraception, one in five young adults may deliberately choose not to have children. Many adults choose to delay starting a family until they have established their career. Some women even choose to freeze their eggs in order to postpone pregnancy until their forties. In recent times children have been born to mothers in their fifties and even sixties using artificial techniques.

Many people have multiple careers. People may retire from one career and start another. The state pension age is changing – it is realistic to expect that you may not retire until you are 68.

Health in later life is immensely variable – some people experience heart disease in their forties while others remain healthy and active into their nineties. Many people may continue to work part-time after retirement age. Huge variety is now possible in the human life course. Your adult life course may turn out to be quite different – even from that of your friends!

Reflect

Does your life have to be like the 'springboard' model? Do you have to 'take a dive' when it comes to intellectual, social and emotional development?

It is difficult to describe a general life course, or changes along the continuum of life, that will be true for most people. However, it is possible to describe some patterns of growth and development relevant to everyone.

Growth

Growth is a term used to describe an increase in quantity. For example, children grow taller as they get older. As height and weight increase we can refer to the increase as a process of growth.

Key terms

Growth Growth means an increase in some measured quantity – such as height or weight.

Development

The word **development** is used to describe changes that might be complex and involve a change in the quality of some ability, as well as a change in measured quantity such as height or weight. Most social, intellectual and emotional change across the lifespan is described in terms of development.

Key terms

Development Development is used to describe complex changes involving quality as well as straightforward increases in some measured quantity.

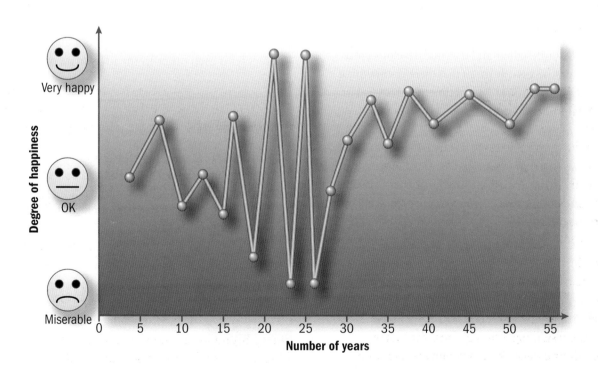

▲ **Figure 4.3 Happiness need not follow a 'springboard' pattern for most people. Your life will involve more than your biology**

People grow and they develop. **Maturation** is different again from either growth or development. The term 'maturation' is used when development is assumed to be due to a genetically programmed sequence of change. For example, your experience of puberty can be explained as caused by an in-built genetic process that unfolds as you grow older. Puberty can be seen as an example of maturation.

Key terms

Maturation This term is used when development is assumed to be due to a genetically programmed sequence of change.

Developmental norms

A norm is something that is expected. Certain sequences and developments are expected with respect to physical and intellectual development. Although there are norms it is important to remember that every child will develop in their own way. Norms describe an average set of expectations; if a child develops faster than the norm it does not mean that the child is necessarily 'gifted' and if a child develops more slowly, it does not necessarily mean that there is something wrong. The term 'milestones' is sometimes used instead of the term '**developmental norms**'.

Key terms

Developmental norms Norms describe an average set of expectations with respect to an infant or child's development.

Delayed development – potential causes and effects

Delayed development happens when a baby or young child has not shown developments within the expected time range. The term is usually restricted to development within the first five years of life. Delayed development may be caused by issues such as:

- brain damage (this can happen before and during birth or during infancy)
- poor social interaction with carers
- disease
- visual disability
- hearing disability
- poor nutrition.

Developmental progress will be checked by health professionals such as health visitors, although parents and GPs may be the first to notice problems. Children who appear to have delayed development will be referred to appropriate specialists for advice or therapy.

Human development – holistic development

Very few people experience their life in compartments labelled 'physical', 'intellectual', 'emotional' or 'social'. Most people experience a life course where all these issues come together as one whole. **Holistic** comes from the idea of 'wholism' – that things need to be understood as a whole. It is possible to analyse human development under separate aspects such as physical, intellectual, social and emotional development but all these aspects interact with each other in the life stories of real people.

Key terms

Holistic development People usually experience physical, intellectual, emotional and social development as a whole. Analysing development under these categories can help us identify issues but, in life, these aspects interact.

Physical development

Conception

Human life begins with conception. A fertile woman usually produces one egg cell each month, roughly two weeks after the last menstrual period. The egg cell travels from the ovary, along the fallopian tube towards the uterus. If sexual intercourse takes place while the egg is in the fallopian tube, then there is a possibility that a new life will be started. Millions of sperm are ejaculated by a man during orgasm. Just one sperm may fertilise the egg. Fertilisation means that the genetic material in the sperm joins with the genetic material in the egg to start a new life. Only about half of all fertilised eggs develop to become babies. Many eggs are lost without a woman knowing that fertilisation ever happened.

Pregnancy

Pregnancy begins when a sperm penetrates an egg. One to one-and-a-half days after this the single fertilised egg cell begins to divide. After two or three days there are enough new cells to make the fertilised egg the size of a pin head. This collection of cells travels to the lining of the uterus where it becomes anchored. The developing collection of cells is now called an embryo – it is attached to the wall of the uterus by a placenta. Once the embryo is attached to the uterus wall, a chemical signal stops the woman from having another menstrual period. After eight weeks, the embryo may have grown to between 3 and 4 cm, has a recognisable heartbeat and the beginnings of eyes, ears, mouth, legs and arms. At this stage the growing organism is called a foetus.

During the remaining seven months before birth, all the organs continue to develop. By 20 weeks, the foetus will have reached about half the length of the baby at birth. By 32 weeks, the foetus will be about half its birth weight.

Birth and infancy

At about nine months after conception the baby will be born. The newborn baby (or neonate) has to take easily digestible food such as mother's milk in order to grow. A newborn baby does not have a fully developed brain but can usually hear sounds, tell differences in the way things taste and identify the smell of their own mother or carer. Infants are born with various reflexes.

- A newborn baby will turn their head towards any touch on the cheek. This reflex is called the rooting reflex and helps the baby to get the nipple into their mouth to feed.

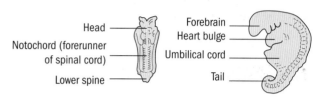

Weeks 1 and 2

Passage to the uterus
The egg is fertilised in one of the Fallopian tubes and is carried into the uterus

Fertilisation of egg in Fallopian tube

Ovary

Fertilised egg implants in wall of uterus

Head

Notochord (forerunner of spinal cord)

Lower spine

Forebrain

Heart bulge

Umbilical cord

Tail

Three weeks
The embryo becomes pear-shaped, with a rounded head, pointed lower spine, and notochord running along its back.

Four weeks
The embryo becomes C-shaped and a tail is visible. The umbilical cord forms and the forebrain enlarges.

Internal organs at five weeks
All the internal organs have begun to form by the fifth week. During this critical stage of development, the embryo is vulnerable to harmful substances consumed by the mother (such as alcohol and drugs), which may cause defects.

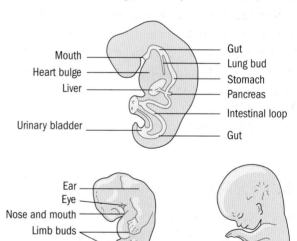

Mouth

Heart bulge

Liver

Urinary bladder

Gut

Lung bud

Stomach

Pancreas

Intestinal loop

Gut

Ear

Eye

Nose and mouth

Limb buds

Umbilical cord

Six weeks
Eyes are visible and the mouth, nose and ears are forming. The limbs grow rapidly from tiny buds.

Eight weeks
The face is more 'human', the head is more upright, and the tail has gone. Limbs become jointed. Fingers and toes appear.

 Figure 4.4 Embryo development

- If you place your finger in the palm of a baby's hand, they will grasp your finger tightly. This reflex is called the grasp reflex.
- If a baby is startled – perhaps by a loud noise – they will throw their hands and arms outwards, arching the back and straightening the legs. This is called the startle reflex.
- If a newborn baby is held upright with their feet touching the ground, they will make movements as if trying to walk. This is called the walking reflex.

Infants have the physical ability to recognise and interact with people. Babies prefer the sound of human voices to other sounds and soon learn to recognise their mother's voice.

Babies are helpless when it comes to muscle co-ordination and control. Babies cannot hold up their head, roll over, sit up or use their hands to move objects deliberately. The table below shows the average age for some types of body control.

Ability to lift head slightly	0–1 month
Ability to pass an object from one hand to another	6 months
Ability to roll over	6 months
Ability to crawl	9–10 months
Ability to stand alone	12 months

Table 4.2 Average ages for some types of body control

Children grow steadily at this time but less rapidly than during infancy. By the age of 6, a child's head will be 90 per cent of adult size, even though the body still has a lot of growing to do. Reproductive organs remain small until the onset of puberty.

Children's practical abilities continue to develop; at the age of 2, children may be able to run and to climb stairs one step at a time. By age 4, children may be able to kick and throw a large ball. By age 6 or 7, a child may be able to skip and ride a bicycle.

Puberty often starts for girls between the ages of 11 and 13, although some girls may begin earlier. Girls generally start puberty before 13 but boys generally start puberty later, often between 13 and 15 years of age. Puberty is a

Remember!

Physical development is not purely controlled by genetics. Berryman et al (1991) argue that records show that girls did not start puberty until 16 years of age in the 1860s. It seems that children start puberty earlier than in the past. This may be because of improved diet but, whatever the cause, you can see that the environment interacts with genetics in order to influence physical development.

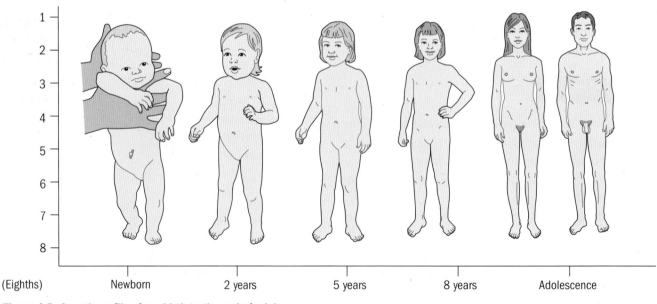

(Eighths)   Newborn   2 years   5 years   8 years   Adolescence

▲ Figure 4.5 Growth profiles from birth to the end of adolescence

development stage which prepares the body for sexual reproduction. It is triggered by the action of hormones that control sexual development. Both boys and girls may experience a 'growth spurt', where they grow taller at a faster rate than before.

Girls' sexual development during puberty includes the enlargement of breasts, the development of pubic hair, increased fat layers under the skin and the start of menstrual periods. Boys will experience the enlargement of their testes and penis, the development of pubic and facial hair and increased muscle strength. Boys' voices also 'break' and become deeper in tone. These major changes mean that adolescents look and behave very differently from children.

Young adults are often at the peak of their physical performance between the ages of 18 and 28. Most champions of highly active sport are aged between 16 and 30. Older adults generally tend to lose some strength and speed with age, although these changes are often unnoticed outside competitive sport.

Exercise can help develop physical fitness and athletic skills. An older adult could easily achieve a personal peak of fitness at 40 or 50 if they take up exercise late in life.

There are a number of age-related changes that slowly become apparent as we grow older. During their forties, many people find that they need to wear reading glasses. Some people cannot hear high-pitched sounds so well during late adulthood. Many adults show a thinning of hair, with hair loss being common in men.

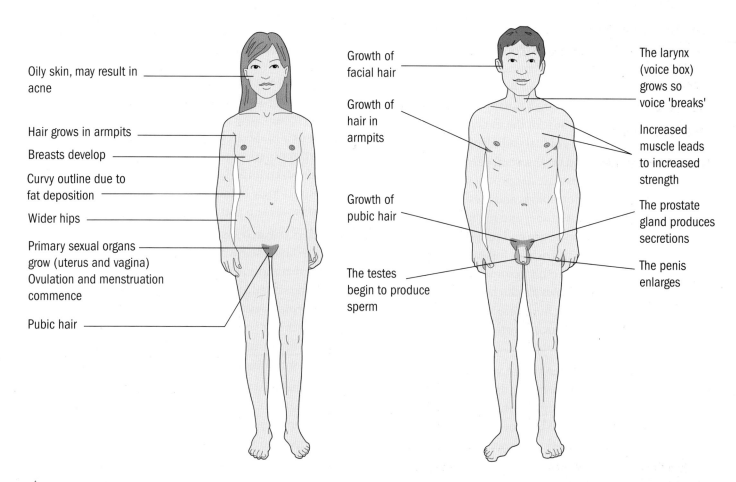

Oily skin, may result in acne

Hair grows in armpits

Breasts develop

Curvy outline due to fat deposition

Wider hips

Primary sexual organs grow (uterus and vagina) Ovulation and menstruation commence

Pubic hair

Growth of facial hair

Growth of hair in armpits

Growth of pubic hair

The testes begin to produce sperm

The larynx (voice box) grows so voice 'breaks'

Increased muscle leads to increased strength

The prostate gland produces secretions

The penis enlarges

▲ **Figure 4.6 Body changes at puberty in males and females**

In context

Since retiring, Jo works as a volunteer in a day centre. At first he found it very difficult to hear what people were saying. When talking to a colleague he said, 'It's strange that people here don't talk clearly – even the staff group mumble all the time. It can't be a problem with my hearing because I can understand my family all right.' Jo has since had a hearing check and now uses a hearing aid. He says, 'It's funny how you don't notice change – I really didn't believe I had a hearing problem but everything is much clearer now that I use a hearing aid.'

1 Would you generally expect problems with vision and hearing associated with ageing to develop slowly over time or would they be sudden crises?

2 Jo had a problem with hearing high-pitched sounds – he thought other people 'mumbled'. Would it have helped if other people had raised their voices and shouted at him or would it have caused more problems?

3 Why was Jo able to understand his family but not new people at the day centre? Why did he originally refuse to believe that he had a hearing loss?

The menopause

Women are most fertile (able to conceive children) in their late teens and early twenties. The risk of miscarriages and pregnancy complications rises with age. Between 45 and 55, women usually stop being able to have children because of the menopause. The menopause involves the gradual ending of menstruation (or having 'periods') and takes several years to complete. The menopause involves a greater production of hormones called gonadotrophins and these hormones can cause irritability, hot flushes and night sweats. Fewer sex hormones (oestrogen and progesterone) are produced by a woman's ovaries following the menopause and this may result in some shrinkage of sexual organs and sometimes a reduction in sexual interest. A reduction in sex hormones may also be associated with problems such as osteoporosis – see page 192.

Older adults in Britain often put on weight. 'Middle-aged spread' may happen because adults still eat the same amount of food as they did when they were younger although they have become much less active. Older adults are more at risk of disease and disability – see pages 189–193 for more details of the ageing process.

Intellectual development

We do not simply learn more as we grow older – we also develop more useful ways of thinking. Piaget (1894–1980) is a famous theorist who studied how our ability to think and reason develops. Piaget believed that there were four stages of intellectual development which mature or 'unfold'. In his theory, infants and children learn from experience but the ability to think logically depends on an underlying process. A 4-year-old cannot use abstract logic because they are not mature enough to think this way (no matter how well they are taught).

Nowadays research suggests that infants are more able to understand their world than Piaget thought. It also appears that most people take a lot longer than 11 years to become skilled at abstract logical thinking. Your ability to use formal logical thought may depend on how much encouragement you have received to think logically. The ability to use formal logic may not be part of a process of maturation – it might depend on your education.

Piaget's theory stops in adolescence but many theorists believe that adults continue to improve their thinking ability. Some psychologists suggest that there is a 'post-formal operations' stage of thinking where adults become more skilled in their ability to make flexible judgements. It may be that many adults develop an ability that could be called 'wisdom' as they grow older.

The sensorimotor stage: birth to 1½ or 2 years
Learning to use senses and muscles – thinking without language

- Babies are born with the ability to sense objects.
- Babies are also born with a range of reflexes such as the sucking reflex to enable them to feed. These reflexes lead to 'motor actions' controlling body muscles.
- The sensorimotor stage is a stage when thinking is limited to sensing objects and performing motor actions.
- Piaget believed that a baby would not have a working system for remembering and thinking about the world until they were about 18 months old.

The pre-operational stage: 2–7 years
Pre-logical thinking – thinking in language but without understanding logic

- Pre-operational means pre-logical; during this stage Piaget believed that children could not think in a logical way. Children can use words to communicate but they do not understand the logical implications involved in language.
- Piaget explained that pre-operational children cannot properly understand how ideas like number, mass and volume really work. A child might be able to count to 10 but might not understand what the number 10 really means. For example, in the case of 10 buttons stretched out in a line and the same number of buttons in a pile, a young child might agree that there are 10 buttons in the line and 10 buttons in the pile, but then they might say that there are more buttons in the line because it is longer!

The concrete operational stage: 7–11 years
A stage where logical thinking is limited to practical situations

- Children in the concrete operations stage can think logically provided the issues are 'down to earth' or concrete. In the concrete operational stage children may be able to understand simple logical puzzles.
- For example, if you ask a question such as 'Samira is taller than Corrine, but Samira is smaller than Leslie so who is the tallest?' you might find that the 7- or 8-year-old has difficulty in mentally imagining the information in a way that will enable them to answer the question. But if the child can see a picture of Samira, Corrine and Leslie they might quickly point out who is the tallest.

The formal operational stage: from 11 years +
Thinking using logic and abstract thought processes – adult thinking

- With formal logical reasoning, an adult can solve complex problems in their head.
- Formal logical operations enable adolescents and adults to use abstract concepts and theories in order to go beyond the limitations of everyday experience.
- Adults with formal operations can think scientifically. For example, an adult can use formal logic to reason why a car won't start. They can work out that perhaps the car won't start because the fuel is not getting to the engine or because there is insufficient air or an electrical fault; each theory can be tested in turn until the problem is solved.
- Abstract thinking enables us to think through complicated ideas in our head without having to see the concrete pictures.

Table 4.3 Piaget's stages of development

Language development

Reflect

Think back to your childhood; you can probably remember speaking to others without any conscious learning. Yet if you have tried to learn a second language after the age of 7 you have probably found it hard work.

Both Noam Chomsky (1959) and Steven Pinker (1994) believe that the ability to develop a signed or spoken language is genetically programmed into us. Chomsky states that we are born with a 'language acquisition device' that enables us to recognise and develop languages that we experience. Children do develop language extremely rapidly and it is likely that the ability to use language is genetically programmed in the same way as our ability to stand and walk. The ability to use language develops because of maturation – it is an unfolding of our biological potential. We need to experience other people using language but we do not need to be trained in order to speak.

▲ Infants may develop language as part of an unfolding process of maturation

Language development is outlined in the table below.

Age	The development of language
Around 3 months	Infants begin to make babbling noises as they learn to control the muscles associated with speech.
Around 12 months	Infants begin to imitate sounds made by carers such as 'da-da'; this develops into the use of single words.
Around 2 years	Infants begin to make two-word statements such as 'cat goed' (meaning the cat has gone away). The infant begins to build their vocabulary (knowledge of words).
Around 3 years	Children begin to make simple sentences such as 'I want drink'. This develops into the ability to ask questions, 'When we go?' Knowledge of words (vocabulary) grows very rapidly.
Around 4 years	Children begin to use clear sentences that can be understood by strangers. Children can be expected to make some mistakes with grammar 'We met lots of peoples at the shops today'.
5 years onwards	Children can speak using full adult grammar. Although vocabulary will continue to grow, and formal grammar will continue to improve, most children can be expected to use language effectively by age 5.

Table 4.4 The development of language

Theory into practice

Try to observe some young children and listen to the way they speak. You will probably find a great deal of variation, particularly in children under the age of 2½. Some children develop speech much more rapidly than others. Just because language development involves a maturation process it does not mean that every child will develop at the same rate.

Social development

There are great differences and cultural variations in the way individuals will experience social relationships during the course of their life. Some generalisations are listed below.

Life stage	Social development
Infancy	**Interacting with carers** Infants appear to have an in-built tendency to interact with carers. By 2 months they may start to smile at human faces. At 3 months they will respond when adults talk. At 5 months infants can distinguish between familiar and unfamiliar people. Infants make their first relationships as they form an emotional attachment to carers. In the later stages of infancy, infants will play alongside other children (parallel play).
Childhood	**First social learning** Young children are emotionally attached and dependent on the adults that care for them. Children begin to learn social roles and behaviour within their family context. This is called first or primary socialisation. A family environment might provide a 'safe base' from which to explore social relationships with other children through play. Children will learn to co-operate with other children (co-operative play). As children grow older they will become increasingly independent and begin to form friendships based on a sense of mutual trust. Friendships become increasingly important as children grow towards adolescence. Children may begin to form social networks or 'circles' of friends who like and agree with each other.
Adolescence	**Secondary social learning** During adolescence a person's sense of self-worth may be more influenced by other adolescents than by the family. Adolescents will copy the styles of dress, beliefs, cultural values and behaviours of their own network of friends. Historically, adolescence was seen as a time of 'storm and stress'. Adolescents have to cope with the development of their own sexuality (the impact of sex hormones at puberty) and the social transition to full independence from the family. Recent research suggests that many adolescents experience a smooth transition to adult roles without serious conflict with parents.
Adulthood	During early adulthood, friendship networks continue to be very important. For most people, early adulthood is dominated by the formation of adult sexual partnerships and by the need to find employment/establish a career. For many people marriage and parenthood represent major social developments in their life. Many adults in their forties and fifties experience time pressures that may limit their social activity. Mature adults may have to split their time between work, care of parents, other family commitments and wider social activities. Some mature adults report a reduction in the amount of social activity due to these pressures.
Older adulthood	Following retirement, older adults have more free time. However, many older adults may choose to increase their involvement with close friends and family rather than extend their network of social contacts. See page 185 for further details.

Table 4.5 Key aspects of social development

Reflect

When you were 15, did you feel great stress and conflict between yourself and your family? Is adolescence a time of 'storm and stress'?

Emotional development

The way we understand and feel about ourselves and other people develops as we grow older. Some key features of emotional development associated with life stages are set out below.

Life stage	Emotional development
Infancy	**Attachment** Bowlby (1953) argued that infants have an in-built need to form an attachment with a carer. The quality of this attachment may affect emotional development for the rest of the child's life. Ainsworth et al (1978) and Marris (1996) argue that the quality of our early attachment influences the assumptions we make about our self and others. Infants who are securely attached will grow up with the emotional resources needed to cope with uncertainty in life. Infants who are insecurely attached may have a reduced ability to cope with stress and major life events.
Childhood	**Understanding self and others** Children use their imagination to begin to understand the social roles that other people play. Children begin to imagine a 'me' – an idea of self. Relationships with other family members may influence how a child feels valued – a sense of self-worth. The way a child gets on with teachers and friends may influence their self-confidence. The child might develop a permanent sense of confidence or a sense of failure and inferiority.
Adolescence	**Identity** During adolescence this sense of self continues to develop. An adolescent needs to develop a secure sense of identity. Identity theory was first proposed by Erikson (1963). A person needs a clear understanding of identity in order to feel secure when working with other people or in order to make a loving sexual attachment. This may be a stressful time as self-esteem may depend on the development of identity.
Adulthood	**Intimacy** Erikson argued that the key task of early adulthood was learning to cope with emotional attachment to a sexual partner. This may involve not being too self-centred or defensive and not becoming emotionally isolated. **Staying involved** Later on adults may face a risk of emotional 'stagnation' when they lose interest in social issues. According to Erikson, the developmental task is to stay emotionally involved with social life.
Older adulthood	**Making sense of your life** Erikson argued that older people need to develop a secure sense of self that enables them to cope with the physical changes associated with ageing and death. People who fail to make emotional sense of life might experience emotional despair.

Table 4.6 Key features of emotional development

Assessment activity 4.1

Describe physical, intellectual, emotional and social development through the life stages.

Arrange a visit to a playgroup or nursery in order to identify some of the issues concerned with intellectual and language development that a person would not remember if they were to tell you their life story. **P1**

Grading tip for P1

Produce an outline map of life stages that might help you to identify issues when you listen to an older person's life story. If you can listen to a real-life story, you may be able to identify some of the physical, intellectual, social and emotional development issues at different stages of the person's life.

Life factors

In context It's just the way I am!

Jake is currently being held in a police cell following a 'road rage' incident. Jake rammed the car in front of him, got out and assaulted the driver of the car – all because the car in front had overtaken him. When questioned about his behaviour Jake said that the other driver had made him angry, 'I can't help it – it's just the way I am'.

Myrna is not tall but she weighs 115 kgs; her doctor has advised her to lose weight for the past two years but her weight continues to increase. She says, 'I've got friends who eat more than I do – yet they are as skinny as anything. No matter what I do, I just keep putting on weight. I can't help it – it's just the way I am'.

1 Jake and Myrna say they cannot be different – are some people fixed from birth to be overweight or aggressive?

2 What social and environmental factors might influence body weight and behaviour?

3 Perhaps Jake's anger and Myrna's weight are caused by nature (they were 'born that way') or perhaps social and environmental issues (the way they have been nurtured) have caused their problems. How far have Jake and Myrna chosen to be the way they are?

The nature–nurture debate

Historically, some philosophers and theorists have argued that we are born to be the way we are. Other theorists have argued that it is the way we are brought up and influenced by our surroundings that makes us the way we are. This historical argument is known as the nature-nurture debate.

Key terms

Nature Genetic and biological influences.

Nurture Social, economic and environmental influences.

■ Determinism

Leijla is 65 and unable to walk very far. One of the nurses who works with her says, 'These people bring it on themselves you know. I bet she never did any exercise.' Another nurse says, 'Oh, I don't think that's true at all. Her genetics will have caused her to be like this.'

Both the nurses' statements are 'determinist'. Determinism is the belief that your future is fixed or determined either by what you have genetically inherited or by your social environment and experience. In the story above, one nurse believes that the environment controls what happens while the other nurse believes that genetics control what happens.

■ Choice and interaction

The alternative to determinism is the belief that people can take control of their own lives through the choices that they make. In the past this has sometimes been labelled as the 'free will' viewpoint. Some people think that everything is fixed by nature or by nurture or that everything is a matter of choice. However, most people understand that the human life course involves an interaction of nature, nurture and the decisions and choices that people make.

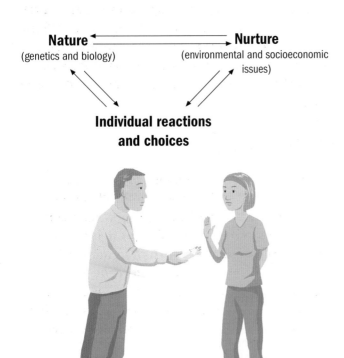

Your environment includes cigarettes.
Your genetics make you vulnerable to cigarette smoke.
What happens to you depends on your reactions and choices.

▲ Figure 4.7 Human development involves the interaction of nature, nurture and individual behaviour

Genetic factors

Each living cell in the human body has a nucleus with 23 pairs of chromosomes inside it. In each pair of chromosomes, one chromosome comes from the father and one from the mother. Each chromosome carries units of inheritance, known as genes, and these genes interact to create a new set of instructions for making a new person. Genes are made of a substance called deoxyribonucleic acid (DNA). The DNA contains the instructions for producing proteins – it is these proteins that regulate the development of a human being. Although half of your chromosomes come from your mother and half from your father, your genetic pattern can be quite different from the patterns of either of your parents.

Phenylketonuria (PKU)

This is a rare genetic condition which prevents a person from being able to process a substance called phenylalanine, which is found in most foods. This condition causes the build-up of harmful substances in the body that in turn damage the development of the brain and eventually kill the person.

Reflect

What if PKU 'ran in your family' and you might have a child with PKU? We cannot alter the defective gene so doesn't this sound terrible?

But despite this genetic condition being incurable, people who are born with PKU in the UK can go on to lead healthy lives. Nowadays newborn babies are tested for PKU (the 'heel prick' test) soon after birth. If a baby has PKU then they are given a specially controlled diet that restricts the amount of phenylalanine in their food. This means that the genetic condition will not result in damage.

Genetics and the environment interact. Sometimes it is possible to alter a person's environment so that genetic problems have no ill effects. Genetic issues do not always determine what will happen to you!

Cystic fibrosis

Cystic fibrosis is caused by a defective gene. This gene is thought to be carried by as many as 4 per cent of the UK population. The gene is recessive which means that children born to people who carry the gene will not develop cystic fibrosis unless

both parents are carriers. When both parents have the defective gene, there is a one-in-four chance that their child will be born with cystic fibrosis.

Cystic fibrosis results in the production of a defective protein that can cause the lungs, pancreas and intestines to become clogged with thick sticky mucus. People with cystic fibrosis may have problems with absorbing nourishment from food and they may also suffer from respiratory and chest infections. In the past, children with cystic fibrosis often had a very short life expectancy but modern medical treatments have succeeded in extending it.

Physiotherapy can help people to clear mucus from their lungs and various drugs can help breathing and control infection in the throat and lungs. People may be offered a special diet and drugs to help with food absorption. In the future it may become possible to use a form of genetic therapy to replace the faulty gene and so cure the condition.

Down's syndrome

Down's syndrome is a condition where a person inherits extra genetic information – usually a whole chromosome. This extra genetic information causes extra proteins to be made and these extra proteins disturb normal development. Down's syndrome is complex and people are affected differently. Some common physical features include being short, having a 'rounded' face, eyes that appear to slant upward, a short broad neck, a small mouth and a large tongue. Many

 Some people may need support in order to take control of their life

people with Down's syndrome have learning difficulties and health problems, such as heart problems and an increased susceptibility to illness.

People with Down's syndrome may develop differently but there is no biological reason why people with this genetic condition should not lead fulfilling and worthwhile lives. Those with the syndrome may need individually focused education and support in order to ensure a high quality of life. The consequences of Down's syndrome for an individual person will depend partly on the quality of care that other people provide.

Sickle-cell anaemia

Sickle-cell anaemia is an inherited disease that causes red blood cells to become sickle-shaped rather than round. These sickle-shaped cells have a shorter life than normal cells resulting in the blood becoming anaemic. These 'sickled' cells can also become stuck together resulting in sticky blood that can block blood vessels. People with sickle-cell anaemia may function normally but experience crises during which symptoms can include fever, pain, difficulty in breathing, kidney damage or loss of consciousness. People with sickle-cell anaemia may also run a higher risk of developing serious infections such as pneumonia.

When a person inherits only one gene for the condition (from either their mother or father) they are said to have 'sickle-cell trait'. This trait may result in problems if the person becomes short of oxygen, for example when mountain-climbing. When a person inherits a gene for the condition from both their mother and their father they are more likely to experience crises associated with the disease. People belonging to African and Mediterranean ethnic groups are more likely than other ethnic groups to carry genes for sickle-cell anaemia.

Asthma

Approximately one in 13 adults are treated for asthma – a disease that causes airways to the lungs to become swollen. The causes of asthma are not fully understood but genetic inheritance, diet and pollution may all contribute to causing the disease.

Biological influences before birth

The environment inside a mother's womb can have a dramatic influence on the development of a child. If a woman smokes or drinks during pregnancy then the nicotine or alcohol can affect the development of the foetus. Nicotine can limit the amount of blood and nutrition that reaches the foetus. Children born to mothers who smoke tend to weigh less at birth. If you smoke during pregnancy then it is possible that your child may have difficulties regarding attention and learning in school. Drugs can also damage a child in the womb.

Foetal alcohol syndrome

Alcohol can have a negative influence on a child's development before birth. Mothers who drink large amounts of alcohol when pregnant may give birth to children with foetal alcohol syndrome. Children with this condition tend to be smaller and to have smaller heads than normal. These children may also have heart defects and learning difficulties.

Infections during pregnancy

Infections such as rubella (a type of measles) and cytomegalovirus (a herpes-type virus) can attack the foetus if a mother becomes infected. Rubella is particularly dangerous during the first month of pregnancy. If a mother becomes infected in this period her baby may be born with impaired hearing or eyesight, or a damaged heart. Most women are vaccinated against rubella to prevent this risk. Cytomegalovirus can cause deafness and learning difficulties.

The extent to which these biological influences before birth affect the quality of a person's life will depend on the way in which deaf or disabled people are treated by others.

Environmental influences

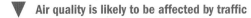
Pollution

Air and water pollution can influence development and be a major source of ill health. Historically, a lack of sanitation and sewerage in cities resulted in life-threatening diseases such as cholera. Until lead was removed from petrol, there were major concerns that lead pollution in the air might affect the brain development of young children. There are still concerns about air and water pollution.

Motor vehicles produce a range of pollutants, including carbon monoxide, nitrogen oxides, volatile organic compounds and particulate matter. People who live near busy roads may be particularly exposed to this pollution. Improved vehicle technology (such as the catalytic converter) is reducing air pollution. For example, carbon monoxide emissions fell by 55 per cent between 1991 and 2002, nitrogen oxides fell by 40 per cent and particulate emissions by 48 per cent. Power stations now burn less coal and there was a fall in sulphur dioxide

pollution of 72 per cent between 1991 and 2002.

Water pollution also appears to be decreasing. *Social Trends* (2005) reports that the water quality in rivers and canals in England and Wales has improved during the last 15 years. Rivers now contain fewer nitrates and have a higher concentration of oxygen.

■ Do we live in a chemical soup?

While official statistics report improvements in the levels of air and water pollution, there are concerns among some scientists that chemical pollution may be damaging the developing brains of children. For example, an article published in *The Independent* on 8 November 2006 quoted from American research; it suggested that as many as 202 chemicals used in household products may be leaking into the environment and could be causing developmental disability in young children. The article argued that 'the world is bathed in a soup of industrial chemicals which are damaging the intellectual potential of the next-generation'. These chemicals may be transmitted to children through air pollution, in food or in water.

▼ **Air quality is likely to be affected by traffic**

Socio-economic influences

Family

A family is a social group of people who are related genetically (historically called 'blood ties') or by marriage. There are four common types of family.

1 Extended – parents, children, grandparents and sometimes other relatives live together or near each other.

2 Nuclear – mother, father and children live together.

3 Reconstituted – as in a nuclear family, adults and children live together but the children are not all biologically related to both adults.

4 Lone parent – a lone parent lives with a child or with children.

Families can influence your development in the following ways.

- Families are where our first emotional relationships and attachments take place.
- They provide our first experiences of social interaction.
- Families influence our view of what is socially expected of us.
- Our experience of family life will influence what we assume to be normal or socially acceptable.
- The family home provides a setting that meets our physical needs for protection, food, shelter and warmth.
- Families can support each other emotionally and protect people from stress.
- Family members may help each other financially or practically. For example, families may support older relatives.

Every family is different. Some families may experience emotional stress for a variety of reasons including low income, poor housing or health problems. Stressful family environments may disadvantage children. It may be difficult to do schoolwork in an overcrowded house and it may be harder to develop self-confidence if there are constant emotional tensions at home.

Theory into practice

Every family is different but there may be some general advantages and disadvantages associated with different types of family. For example, there are more adults for children to interact with in an extended family. In groups, discuss some of the advantages and disadvantages you might expect to find with each type of family.

Community

Most family groups exist within a wider social context – the local community. Some families will be members of particular religious communities and the children will be part of a community associated with a mosque, church, synagogue or temple. Some families will belong to a street or village where there is a definite sense of neighbourhood community – where neighbours will meet together to discuss local and social issues. A sense of community may focus on a particular school where parents meet together.

The community in which you have grown up may have influenced both your parents' and your own attitudes and beliefs.

Reflect

What community or community groups do you associate with?

Media

Communities and families are influenced by information and opinions which are communicated by the media. Media include newspapers, radio, TV, the Internet (including Internet chat rooms), adverts, magazines and posters. Lifestyle choices such as choosing a healthy diet may be influenced by opinions and information available in the media.

Peer groups

As a child you will have learned a lot about social relationships when you played with other children. During adolescence we are very influenced by people of our own age group – our peer group. Attitudes and beliefs might be copied from the people we mix with – or at least from people who are seen as being similar to ourselves. Peer groups provide a second source of social learning after our first experiences of social learning in a family. The family is said to provide first or primary socialisation (social learning), while the people we mix with during adolescence provide a secondary source of social learning or socialisation.

Culture and beliefs

A **culture** can be identified by distinct aspects of language, self-presentation, religion, music, art, architecture and literature. Children learn the customs associated with their family's culture during childhood (see Unit 2 for further details). In the past, most children would have learned the culture associated with their local community. Everyone

Reflect

The media influences communities, peer groups and families. But how far do peer groups and communities influence the media? How far do you avoid a lot of what is presented on TV and just choose things that you and your friends see as important? How far are your values and attitudes controlled by the media and how far do you control what you absorb?

on a particular estate, street or village might have shared similar beliefs about religion, work and social roles. Today we live in a multicultural society where people in the same geographical location may belong to various different cultures. Many people identify with others over the Internet. To some extent people can choose to identify with a particular culture.

Key terms

Culture This is the collection of values, beliefs, customs and behaviours that might make one group of people distinct from others.

Figure 4.8 Our development is influenced by our family experiences and, later, by our peer group. Families and peer groups are influenced by the community and the media

Reflect

Think about the music you listen to, the websites you visit, the clothes you wear and the things you discuss with friends. How far have you simply copied the customs of others in your local community or neighbourhood? How far does 'nurture' control what you do and how far do you actively choose to be the way you are?

Social class and employment

Your occupation – what you do for a living – or your parents' occupations when you are young, determine your social class. *National Statistics* has a complex system for defining social class but the basic categories are set out in the table below.

1	Higher managerial and professional occupations: **1.1** Large employers and higher managerial occupations **1.2** Higher professional occupations
2	Lower managerial and professional occupations
3	Intermediate occupations
4	Small employers and own-account workers
5	Lower supervisory and technical occupations
6	Semi-routine occupations
7	Routine occupations
8	Never worked and long-term unemployed

Table 4.7 The National Statistics socio-economic classification – analytic classes

In the past many studies have shown that people in the higher social classes have enjoyed better health and lived longer lives on average than people in the lower classes. Recent studies still report a link between occupation and health. A study of the health of children and young people found that the average birth weight of children born to fathers in the lower social classes was less than the weight of children born to fathers in the higher classes. The study also reported more longstanding illness amongst children of parents in the lower occupations (*National Statistics*, 2004).

People in the higher occupations may earn more money, so are more likely to have better living conditions, more expensive homes and more lifestyle choices. Living on a low income may mean living in more stressful and less healthy conditions.

Income and expenditure

The economic resources that you or your family have can make a major difference to the quality of your life. A person's weekly income enables them to pay for their accommodation and to buy food and clothes. Income mainly comes from:

- wages from employment
- profits from your business if you are self-employed
- benefits paid by the government
- money from invested wealth, such as interest on bank accounts or bonds
- money raised through the sale of property you own.

Income is not distributed equally in the UK. The top 20 per cent of households get around 15 times more money each year than the poorest 20 per cent of households. But income is taxed and poorer households can claim benefits. So after tax and benefits, the richest 20 per cent are four times better off than the poorest 20 per cent of households (*National Statistics*, 2004).

Nowadays households with an income that is less than 60 per cent of 'median' income in the UK are considered to be living in poverty. People with a very low level of income are poor relative to the expectations of most people. Just over a sixth of Britain's population (17 per cent), were estimated to be living on a low income in the period 2001/2002 (*Social Trends*, 2004).

Key groups of people who have to live on very little money include:

- lone-parent families
- the unemployed
- the elderly
- the sick or disabled
- single earners
- unskilled couples (where only one person works in an unskilled job).

Income and employment

Being out of work is likely to mean that you live on a low income. You will also be affected if your parents live on a low income. *Social Trends* (2004) estimates that around 30 per cent of children (3.8 million children) live in low income households. It states that 'children living in workless families or households have a much higher risk of low income than those in families with one or more adults in full-time work'. Around three-quarters of children living in 'workless' or lone-parent families live in low income households.

The impact of low income

Paxton and Dixon (2004) quote research conclusions which show that: 'Children who grew up in poverty during the 1970s did worse at school, were six times less likely to enter higher education, and one-and-a-half times more likely to be unemployed – and earned 10 per cent less during their lifetimes than those who did not experience poverty as children.' They quote the following disadvantages of poverty:

- Poverty is associated with being a victim of crime; 4.8 per cent of people who earned under £5000 a year were burgled in 2003/4 compared to only 2.7 per cent of people who earned over £30,000.
- Poorer communities are more likely to live in polluted areas. 'In 2003 there were five times as many industrial sites in the wards containing the most deprived 10 per cent of the population and seven times as many emission sources than in wards with the least deprived 10 per cent.'
- Low social class is associated with an increased risk of dying young. 'In 2003 children of fathers in the lower social class were twice as likely to die within one year of birth, five times more likely to die in a traffic accident and fifteen times more likely to die in a house fire than those in the highest social class.'

Take it further

Use the Internet in order to look up recent statistics on the impact of low income on children and adults. The Office of National Statistics website (www. statistics.gov.uk) collects and reports statistics every few years on issues such as poverty. You may also see newspaper reports if major studies are reported in the press. In groups, discuss whether issues connected with poverty are improving or possibly getting worse.

Housing

People with high incomes often feel confident about their future and their ability to take out a mortgage to buy their own home. These people can also choose

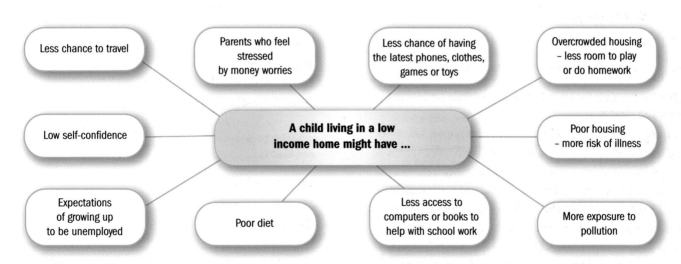

Less chance to travel

Parents who feel stressed by money worries

Less chance of having the latest phones, clothes, games or toys

Overcrowded housing – less room to play or do homework

Low self-confidence

A child living in a low income home might have ...

Poor housing – more risk of illness

Expectations of growing up to be unemployed

Poor diet

Less access to computers or books to help with school work

More exposure to pollution

▲ **Figure 4.9 Some problems a child may face if they belong to a low income family**

▲ Occupation and income will influence where you live – factors interact!

where they would like to live. People on low incomes tend to have less choice. They may have to rent property in more densely populated housing areas. Poor quality housing is associated with poor health. Dampness might increase the risk of allergic and inflammatory diseases including asthma. Poor housing is more likely to suffer from problems such as poor lighting, non-safety glass in windows, loose rugs and poor maintenance of stairs etc that may result in accidents.

Some older people on low incomes will worry about the cost of heating in their

homes. Older properties are often less well insulated than modern flats and houses so that people on low incomes might receive higher heating bills than people who are better off. Poor quality housing may result in the stresses summarised below.

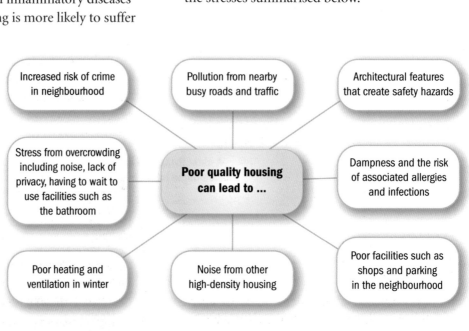

Increased risk of crime in neighbourhood

Pollution from nearby busy roads and traffic

Architectural features that create safety hazards

Stress from overcrowding including noise, lack of privacy, having to wait to use facilities such as the bathroom

Poor quality housing can lead to ...

Dampness and the risk of associated allergies and infections

Poor heating and ventilation in winter

Noise from other high-density housing

Poor facilities such as shops and parking in the neighbourhood

Figure 4.10 Stresses that may arise from living in poor quality housing ▶

Education

Some people may have better educational opportunities than others. The Acheson report (1998) noted that schools in deprived neighbourhoods were likely to suffer more problems than schools in more affluent areas. 'Schools in disadvantaged areas are likely to be restricted in space and have the environment degraded by litter, graffiti, and acts of vandalism. This contributes to more stressful working conditions for staff and pupils. Children coming to school hungry or stressed as a result of their social and economic environment will be unable to take full advantage of learning opportunities. Stress, depression and social exclusion may reduce parents' capacity to participate in their children's education.' The report also stated that low levels of educational achievement are associated with poor health in adult life.

Paxton and Dixon (2004) report that children from the highest social classes achieve more than twice the A to C GCSE grades compared with children from the lowest social classes. The majority of children from the higher social classes continue in education after the age of 16 while the majority of children in the lowest social classes leave education. People who leave education without qualifications are more likely to be employed in low income jobs than people who have good qualifications. Low income may be associated with poorer chances of achieving qualifications. A lack of qualifications may be associated with low income – creating a trap that is difficult to escape.

Reflect

Look at the analytic classes of the National Statistics socio-economic classification in Table 4.7 on page 172. What type of work roles would you expect to be open to people with no qualifications? How does educational achievement influence social status?

Gender

Eighty years ago women were considered to have a lower social status than men. Men and women did different types of work and had different social roles. (A social role means the way people expect you to act.) Adult women were usually expected to be responsible for childcare, housework, cooking and generally supporting a male 'breadwinner' whose social role was to work in order to provide money for the household.

Nowadays **gender roles** are less rigid than in the past with both men and women being expected to go out to work. However, there is still a gender pay gap with women who work full-time being paid on average only 82 per cent of men's earnings in 2004. A study by the Equal Opportunities Commission in 2004 argued that women are still massively under-represented in positions of influence in Britain. The majority of top jobs in politics, business, education, professional bodies and even trade unions are still held by men.

Key terms

Gender roles These are social and cultural expectations about the different ways in which men and women are expected to behave.

Surveys of the way men and women live at home still report major differences in gender roles. For example, a study reported in *Social Trends* (2004) found that household repairs and maintenance were still generally seen as a male responsibility, while doing the laundry, household cleaning and shopping for groceries was still very much seen as a female gender role or 'women's work'. It would appear that social expectations still have a powerful influence on the way men and women live their lives today.

Reflect

How far will other people's gender-role expectations influence your career and lifestyle and how free are you to choose your future?

Discrimination

People are often **discriminated** against because of their race, beliefs, gender, religion, sexuality, physical or mental ability, or age.

Key terms

Discrimination Treating some people less well than others because of differences.

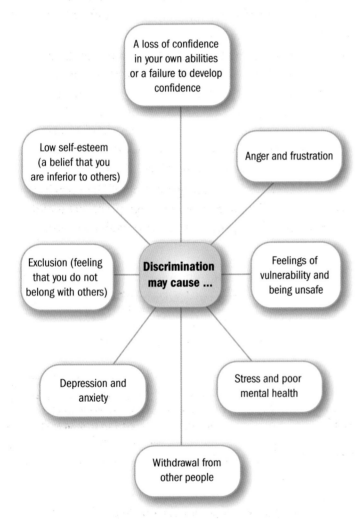

▲ **Figure 4.11 The effects of discrimination**

Discrimination could influence your development because it has a very negative impact.

See Unit 2 for more details of the issues surrounding discrimination.

Bullying

Discrimination may result in **bullying**. Like discrimination, bullying may undermine your self-confidence and can create stress, depression and anxiety.

Key terms

Bullying This is when an individual or group of people intimidate or harass others.

▲ **Figure 4.12 What bullying can involve**

Many children experience bullying at school but adults also engage in bullying. Because bullying can threaten a person's self-confidence, victims sometimes keep quiet about their experience. The Department for

Education and Skills stresses the importance of telling others – talking about the problem and getting support – in order to cope with and prevent bullying within an educational context.

Access to leisure and recreational facilities

Low income may restrict access to travel and other recreational activities. *National Statistics* (2006) reports that in 2002, 59 per cent of households with a low income did not have access to a car. Eighty-six per cent of households with high incomes had access to a home computer in 2002 but only 15 per cent of households with a low income had access to one. People with a low income may have more difficulty obtaining information about leisure activities and much more difficulty travelling to them if they live in neighbourhoods without regular public transport.

The issues in Figure 4.13 may create barriers to accessing leisure and recreational facilities.

Access to health and social care services

Areas with a high proportion of low income households may have poorer facilities than more wealthy areas. A range of studies has shown that life expectancy is shorter in deprived areas in comparison to that in more affluent areas of housing.

Although the National Health Service provides free health care for everyone, there are concerns that some groups of people may not receive the same quality of access to GP services and to preventative health services as others. Deprived areas may have greater difficulty in recruiting GPs and nurses.

A low income may make it difficult to get to health or care facilities. For example, *National Statistics* (2006) reports that 11 per cent of households without access to a car said they had difficulty in seeing their local GP compared with only 4 per cent of people with cars. People without home access to the Internet will have limited access to services such as NHS Direct.

There is concern that the reorganisation of NHS services may result in differences between geographical areas and the ease with which people can access hospital services.

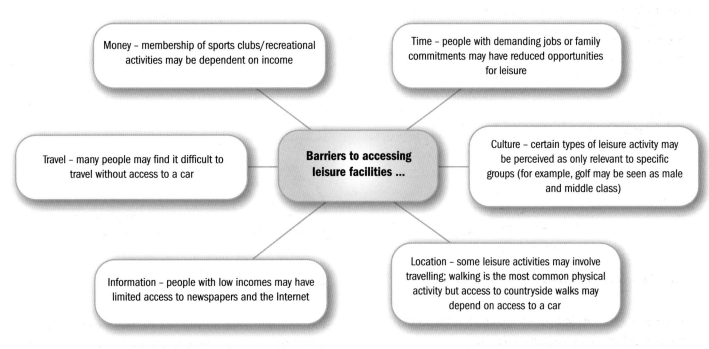

▲ **Figure 4.13 Barriers to accessing leisure facilities**

Theory into practice

Research recent press coverage of stories about NHS services, such as the development of 'super hospitals' and the availability of different types of treatment. Discuss any news stories that suggest differences in people's ability to access services or receive treatment.

Lifestyle

What leisure activities do you engage in? Do you exercise? Are you careful about your diet? How do you dress and present yourself when you are among your friends? These are some of the questions that will explain your **lifestyle**. Your lifestyle represents the way you choose to spend your time and money.

Key terms

Lifestyle This is how a person spends their time and money in order to create a 'style' of living.

To some extent your lifestyle is something that you choose. Your choices will be limited by the money that you have and influenced by your culture and the people in your life. People on low incomes have limited choices. Most people discover that they have developed habits connected to diet, exercise and use of alcohol. Many people never actively choose a lifestyle – it just happens – but people can choose to change their lifestyle. Some lifestyle issues are presented below.

Nutrition and dietary choices

People on a low income may eat a less healthy diet – higher in sugar and fat – than people who are better off. This is unlikely to be because they do not realise the dangers of their diet or because they are lazy.

Evidence comes from the Acheson report (1998) which argued that 'People on low incomes eat less healthily partly because of cost, rather than lack of concern or information'. The Acheson report also notes that people in low socio-economic groups:

- eat more processed foods containing high levels of salt thus increasing the risk of cardiovascular disease
- are more prone to obesity thus increasing the risk of ill-health
- are more likely to have babies with reduced birth weights (low birth weight is linked with the risk of cardiovascular disease in later life)
- are less likely to breastfeed their babies – breast-feeding helps to protect infants from infection.

People with a low income will find it harder to travel to supermarkets and stock up on cheaper food. Healthy food may cost more than processed food which contains higher amounts of sugar and salt. A low income may push people to choose an unhealthy diet, because it can be harder and more expensive to choose a healthy one.

Remember!

Government guidelines recommend that a healthy diet should include at least five portions of fruit and vegetables a day. *National Statistics* (2006) reported that only 14 per cent of men and 27 per cent of women in England were following this advice in 2004.

Theory into practice

Go to a large supermarket and look at the amounts of sugar and salt in budget or low-priced ready meals and compare these amounts with the sugar and salt content in more expensive pre-prepared food products. Can you find any evidence to suggest that a low income might influence people to choose products containing more sugar and salt?

Exercise

NHS Direct states that 'only 20 per cent of people in the UK get enough exercise to maintain a healthy lifestyle and satisfactory fitness level'. Regular exercise will help to prevent heart disease, prolong life and may help to prevent depression and various other illnesses. Many people spend their time on social activities or on career/work activities to the extent that they have little time left to exercise. In addition, some people have grown up within a culture that doesn't consider exercise to be important.

Reflect

How much time do you spend each week on exercise? Do you have the right lifestyle to maximise your health and enjoyment of life?

Stress

Hardly anyone chooses to be stressed but many people lose control of aspects of their life which leads to them feeling 'under pressure'. People with low incomes experience pressure when budgeting for food and clothes. Many people become stressed because of levels of debt. Other people become stressed because of work pressures or the pressure to gain good qualifications. Relationships can involve a great deal of stress, as can poor health. NHS Direct states that 12 million adults see their GP about mental problems each year: 'Most of these suffer from anxiety and depression, much of it stress-related'.

Key terms

Stress When we feel threatened we have a 'fight or flight' biological response. In other words, to either stay and fight or turn and run. If we cannot fight or run, then we experience 'stress'. Our body is ready for action but we cannot take action or reduce the threat. Eventually stressed people become exhausted and often anxious and depressed as a result.

A key issue is to feel in control. If you believe that you can manage the issues that are putting you under pressure, you may be able to cope with your stress. If you feel out of control, stress may lead to anxiety and depression. It is easier to feel in control if you have support from others and social, economic and time resources. Socio-economic factors will influence how well you can cope with stress.

Substance abuse

■ Alcohol

The Department of Health recommends that, in a day, men should not drink more than four units of alcohol and women should not drink more than three units. *National Statistics* (2006) states that 39 per cent of men and 22 per cent of women exceed this recommendation. Statistics also show that 22 per cent of men and 9 per cent of women have a lifestyle that involves heavy drinking.

■ Drugs

National Statistics (2006) reports that 14 per cent of men and 8 per cent of women said that they had taken illicit (illegal) drugs in the past year. Just under one in three young men and one in five young women reported that they had used cannabis.

■ Smoking

Amongst other serious risks to health, smoking is associated with heart and lung disease. Smoking is associated with socio-economic class. More people in manual occupations smoke than in the higher social classes.

Reflect

You may know of people who put their health at risk by excessive drinking, smoking or taking drugs. To what extent do you think these habits are deliberately chosen? How far are lifestyles copied from friends i.e. people just going along with what other people are doing? To what extent do people use alcohol, tobacco or other drugs in order to reduce stress in their lives?

Reciprocal influence

Leonie Sugarman (1986) discusses the theory of 'reciprocal influence'. Reciprocal means 'goes both ways' or 'give and take'. Biology and environment influence us – but then we go on to influence our biology and the environment around us. We make responses to the environment that we find ourselves in. For example, some people may respond to the stress of poverty and overcrowded housing by smoking, drinking and taking drugs. Smoking, drinking and taking drugs may damage physical health. Poor health may in turn increase problems of low income and negative life events. The whole thing is an interactive process or a 'vicious circle'. Just saying that pollution, or low income, can influence development does not explain very much. If you are going to make sense of someone's life you need to be able to understand how factors interact with each other and that the choices that a person makes also interact with life factors. You can influence your environment – and even your own biology.

In context Chris and Ian

Chris and Ian were born next door to each other 45 years ago. They went to the same school and both lived in similar types of family. Their parents both had similar income levels from similar jobs. Both Chris and Ian enjoyed good health during their early life.

Chris became very interested in sport while he was at school and eventually went on to work in the travel industry so that he would have opportunities to develop his interest in sail boarding. Chris has always been careful to exercise and control his lifestyle so as to maximise his physical fitness. At the age of 45 he says that he enjoys his life and has a high level of fitness and good health.

Ian worked hard at school and achieved good qualifications. His main recreation involved heavy drinking and smoking and he has continued to drink and smoke until recently. Ian has spent most of the last 25 years working in an office job – taking very little exercise. He has put on a lot of weight and now has high blood pressure. Ian is finding the stress of his job very difficult and says that he is unlucky with his health. He is afraid that he may soon have to give up work and have to live on a low income.

1   If both these people lived in similar circumstances and environments then how do you explain their different health levels now? Can an interest in sail boarding or working in an office be directly caused by DNA alone?

2   Can you explain how reciprocal influence may work to explain the differences between these two people? In other words, how might choices at one life stage have influenced events which in turn impact on a person's physical health later on?

3   Finally, can you explain how far Chris and Ian have chosen their lives and how far nurture and nature have determined their lives?

Assessment activity 4.2

Describe the potential influences of five life factors on the development of individuals.

1   You should arrange to interview someone about their life.

Grading tip for P2

You can use this life story to identify an example of how each of the five different life factors has influenced the person.

Discuss the nature-nurture debate in relation to individual development.

2   You should make a guess as to how some factors might have interacted in a person's life to influence their development. **M1**

Grading tip for M1

'Discuss' means to talk and write about the arguments for the role of nature, nurture and individual choice. You can practise your discussion skills using real or fictitious life stories. You should guess how some factors have interacted in a person's life to influence their development.

Evaluate the nature-nurture debate in relation to development of the individual.

You will need to be able to answer the following questions if you are to evaluate the debate.

3   How far is it useful to talk about human development in terms of certain aspects being mainly nature (genetics and biology) or mainly nurture (environment, socio-economics and lifestyle)?

4   How far can people influence or even control their own development through the choices that they make?

5   Genetics and environment interact but can you give examples of how this interaction might work in relationship to individual development?

6   Can you explain how human development might involve a process of reciprocal influence? That is to say that, as well as being influenced by your biology and environment, you might make choices that influence your environment and health.

Grading tip for D1

'Evaluate' means to show the value of the nature–nurture debate.

Major life events

Predictable and unpredictable events

During our life we are influenced by a range of life factors but we are also influenced by events that happen to us. Some major changes in life can be predicted and they may even be chosen. Other major changes may be unpredicted. If your life suddenly changes there is always the risk that you will feel out of control and stressed. If you have chosen to leave home, marry or retire you may feel in control of these major events. Splitting major life events into predictable and unpredictable categories involves generalisation. For example, some people have to move house because of a relationship break-up: such a move might be unpredicted and the person might feel stressed and out of control. Some people do not predict how ageing or retirement will affect them. Sometimes redundancy or divorce might be predictable. You may experience life events differently to other people.

Any major change in life may influence your development *positively* because you find positive ways of coping that may help you in the future. Alternatively, you may fail to adjust to a major change in life and this might result in stress and a loss of self-confidence in your ability to cope with change. Some major life events are set out below:

Events that are often predicted	Possible influence on development	
	Positive learning	Risk of stress
Starting school/nursery	Learning to make new friends and cope with change	Feeling unsafe – withdrawing from others. **Loss** of support from parents
Moving house	Feeling in control and able to organise change	Being overwhelmed by the amount of work and change – being out of control. **Loss** of old home
Employment	Choosing a work role and having an income from employment	Feeling pressured by new demands on time and mental energy. Finding difficulty in adapting. **Loss** of past lifestyle
Leaving home	Achieving independence – controlling personal environment	Feeling unable to cope in a new setting. Feeling pressured by all the new tasks. **Loss** of family support
Marriage	Making emotional attachments and experiencing intimacy	Feeling threatened by intimacy and sharing possessions. Possible **loss** of independence
Retirement	Controlling own life – disengaging from work	**Loss** of previous work roles. Loss of contact with work colleagues. Difficulty establishing a new lifestyle.
Ageing	Developing new lifestyles to cope with physical changes	Possible **loss** of ability. Becoming angry or depressed because of uncontrollable physical changes

Events that are often unpredicted	Possible influence on development	
	Positive learning	Risk of stress
Birth of a sibling	Learning to make new emotional attachments	Jealousy and rivalry – emotional tension because your role within the family has changed. You may **lose** attention from parents
Redundancy	Learning to adapt to changes in income and lifestyle	Refusal to accept change. Anger or depression. Failure to cope with a **loss** of income and lifestyle
Serious injury	Learning to adapt to physical change	Grief at the **loss** of good health. Anger or depression and failure to adapt
Divorce	Learning to cope with a new lifestyle	Resentment or depression. Grief at the **loss** of the relationship. Failure to adapt to a new lifestyle
Bereavement	Learning to cope with loss/new lifestyle	Grief at the **loss** of the relationship. Failure to adapt to an unwanted lifestyle
Abuse	Developing a positive view of self – to overcome emotional damage	**Loss** of self-confidence. Withdrawal, depression and anxiety. Self-destructive behaviour

Table 4.8 Predictable and unpredictable life changes

■ One loss may involve many other losses

Many life events involve loss, but loss is rarely simple and straightforward. For example, bereavement can involve a whole range of other losses and changes.

Most major changes in life involve a whole range of issues. Being seriously injured or being divorced will involve a range of losses. Even predictable and welcome changes involve a great deal of new learning and coping with a range of losses.

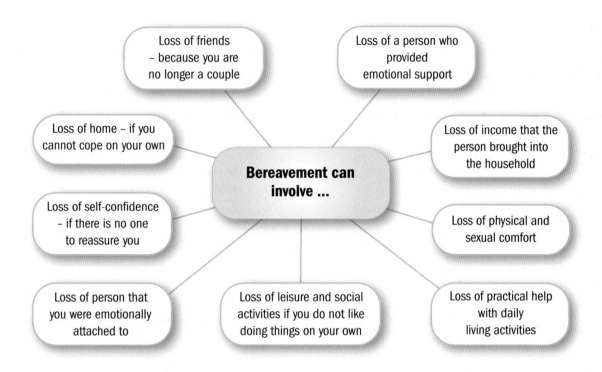

Figure 4.14 The effects of bereavement

Reflect

Look at the examples of unpredicted events in Table 4.8 on page 182 and at the effects of bereavement as set out in Figure 4.14. How many of the 'effects' above might also result from the other unpredicted events listed in Table 4.8?

Major changes in life may interact with all the life factors discussed in this section. For example, retirement, redundancy, divorce, bereavement or serious injury might all result in a loss of income or having to live on a low income. Moving home, marriage or parenthood might all involve changes in your home, or in your community and friendship networks. Major life events will change your social and economic circumstances.

Assessment activity 4.3

Describe the influences of two predictable and two unpredictable major life events on the development of the individual.

1   You should use people's life stories in order to identify two predictable and two unpredictable life events.   **P3**

Explain how major life events can influence the development of the individual.

2   You need to discuss life events and how they involve adapting to change and coping with stress. You need to be able to explore ways in which major life events interact with life factors.   **M2**

Grading tip for P3

You should use people's life stories in order to identify two predictable and two unpredictable life events. You can then describe possible ways in which these major life events influenced the lives of these people.

Grading tip for M2

'Explain' means that you must write about the ways in which life events might have influenced a person's life. You must do more than simply describe what is involved in major life events such as bereavement or ageing.

You need to discuss life events and how they involve adapting to change and coping with stress. You need to explore ways in which major life events interact with life factors.

In context   Janet's story continued …

Interviewer: You say that divorce changed you in a positive way, but most people would see it as a negative event?

Janet: Yes, it felt very negative at the time. I was very stressed and that's why I guess I never got to get the big house with the big garden and the dog! Still I learned to take control of my own life. I found the strength to be a lone parent, go to work, still be a good mother. I sorted out what I wanted from life and I think in the end my life has been happier for it.

1   Using Janet's story at the beginning of this unit (see page 152) and the information above can you identify two predictable and two unpredictable life events? How would you guess these events influenced Janet's story?

2   Can you explain how major life events like divorce might interact with life factors such as housing and income?

3   Can you explain why negative experiences such as a loss of income, the need to move home or being under emotional stress do not necessarily disrupt and permanently damage a person's life course development?

4.3 Physical changes and psychological perspectives in relation to ageing

Theories of ageing

Disengagement theory

Key terms

Disengagement theory A theory that older people will withdraw from social contact with others. Older people will disengage because of reduced physical health and loss of social opportunities.

Engagement means being involved with people or activities. Disengagement means withdrawing from involvement. In 1961 two authors called Cumming and Henry put forward a **disengagement theory** that people would naturally tend to withdraw from social involvement with others as they got older; older people would have restricted opportunities to interact with others. The issues that surround this are outlined in the table below.

Cumming (1975) argued that older people would experience a reduction in social contact as they grew older and become increasingly 'individual' (less concerned with the expectations of others). He argued that it was appropriate and healthy for older people to withdraw from others – disengagement was a natural part of ageing.

The theory of disengagement was widely accepted in the past. For example, Bromley (1974) writes: 'although some individuals fight the process all the way, disengagement of some sort is bound to come, simply because old people have neither the physical nor the mental resources they had when they were young.' The theory of disengagement fits with the 'springboard' view of life (see page 153).

Disengagement theory suggests that losing contact with other people is an inevitable consequence of biological decline and that disengagement from other people is a natural and appropriate response. But there is little statistical evidence to suggest that this is a general rule for everyone.

Zimbardo (1992) argued that 'The disengagement view of social ageing has been largely discredited for a number of reasons'. He argues that the majority of older people do remain socially involved with family and friends and that many older people become more involved with close family as they become older. It may

Problem	Explanation
Ill-health	Poor mobility or problems with hearing or vision may make interaction with other people more difficult.
Geographical mobility	Many people retire to areas away from friends and relatives. Family members may move away from older people in order to seek better housing or employment.
Retirement	Retiring from work may mean less contact with colleagues in a social setting.
Ill-health of friends and relatives	If friends or relatives have poor mobility or other disabilities they may have reduced social contact with you.
Travel and technology	Some older people do not have access to a car, the Internet or a mobile phone – this may limit opportunities for social contact.

Table 4.9 Issues that limit social interaction

▲ Figure 4.15 Health problems and isolation from friends and family might cause withdrawal and a loss of mental and physical skills

be that many older people choose to spend their time with people that they feel close to rather than seeking to make new friends. Current data from the Office for National Statistics supports the view that a majority of older people enjoy good social support networks (see pages 195). If people only interact with close friends, does this mean that they are disengaged?

Reflect

Imagine you have broken your legs – you have no access to a phone, text messages or the Internet and you can't go out. Would you begin to disengage? Now imagine the same situation but this time you have a mobile phone and an Internet-connected laptop – would technology help? Do health problems automatically cause social withdrawal or might the situation be more complicated?

When Cummings and Henry first proposed the theory of disengagement in 1961 it is worth remembering that there was no Internet or text messaging. Many older people did not have access to a car and quite a few older people would not even have had a phone in their home!

Activity theory

Key terms

Activity theory A theory which argues that older people need to stay mentally and socially active in order to limit the risks associated with disengagement.

Writing in 1966 Bromley argued that older people needed to disengage but that they needed to remain 'active' in order to prevent disengagement from going too far. Bromley argued: 'It is not sufficient merely to provide facilities for elderly people. They need to be educated to make use of them and encouraged to abandon apathetic attitudes and fixed habits.' Disengagement enabled 'the person to withdraw from those areas of life where he cannot live up to social expectations' but activity was needed to 'prevent this process from going too far in the direction of isolation, apathy and inaction'. Bromley argued that it was important to remain mentally active and maintain an interest in life and enjoy the company of others. Too much disengagement would lead to 'stagnation' and a loss of mental and physical skills.

Theory into practice

Interview some retired people who are in good health and ask them about their interests and activities. You may discover that retired people often engage in a wide range of physical and social activities.

■ Staying physically active

Many studies suggest that taking regular physical exercise can help to improve physical health in later life. Some activities that may be taken up by older people include:

- walking (the most popular form of exercise for adults)
- gardening
- yoga
- 'keep fit' activities
- swimming.

Older people who have enjoyed running, cycling, tennis and squash may continue these activities well into later life. People in day or residential care may benefit from physiotherapy and from specially designed 'keep fit' activities appropriate to individual levels of fitness and health.

■ Staying mentally active

Our brains are not muscles and mental exercise may not work in the same way as physical exercise. Some studies argue that it is physical ill-health that causes a loss of mental ability in later life and that physical activity is the most important issue. It may be that certain mental abilities become weaker (or forgotten) because nerve cell connections in the brain become weaker if these abilities are not used. It is also possible that a lack of mental activity may result in depression and that depression may cause physical inactivity. A lack of physical exercise may damage our health. Many older people choose to stay mentally active by:

- studying and taking courses (for pleasure rather than for employment reasons)
- joining community activities, such as book clubs, to engage in discussion
- taking up leisure activities that include social activities
- deliberately tackling crosswords and puzzles to practise thinking skills
- enjoying conversations and discussions with friends – perhaps in a restaurant or pub.

In day and residential care many older people join in activities such as reminiscence, where groups will discuss their own life stories together with past history.

The influence of disengagement and activity theory on health and social care provision

Provision for older people must respect the different needs of individuals. Some people accept the importance of staying active; some people may want to withdraw from certain kinds of activity.

◄ Figure 4.16 Service users have a right to choose what they do – they must not be 'made to be active'

The General Social Care Council (GSCC) code of practice for social care workers includes 'the importance of treating each person as an individual' and 'supporting service users' rights to control their lives and make informed choices about the services they receive'. Different people will make different life choices about the degree and type of social contact they wish to have with others.

Health services, residential, day and home care services will provide opportunities for physical, mental and social activities. Services will also respect the right of individuals to choose the degree of activity that they engage in.

Theory into practice

Obtain a copy of the national minimum standards for a service provided for older people. Analyse the degree to which the standards require services to provide opportunities for physical, mental or social activities. Analyse the degree to which the standards stress the importance of choice.

In context

Martha and Catherine are in their eighties and have both chosen to live in sheltered housing because they both have physical disabilities that make looking after their own home too stressful.

Martha: I enjoy living here because there is a lot to do. You see, there are always people to talk to and sometimes we get together to play cards. Now I couldn't cope where I used to live because the bungalow needed a lot of building work – I just couldn't keep it clean but I do think it's very important to have things to do. When I'm not talking to others, I like to keep my mind active by doing crosswords and sudoku. I like to get out and walk in the park as much as possible in order to stay fit.

Catherine: I enjoy living here because of the peace and quiet. I get help to do any cleaning and I get meals provided. I've had enough of working, at my time of life I just want to sit back and relax. I don't mix much with the other people here – well, why should I? I can't be bothered with all that 'chit-chat'. I look forward to seeing my children and grandchildren – that's enough for me. My daughter bought me a mobile phone but I keep it in the box – it's too difficult to learn new things.

1   How can you explain these two different views using disengagement and activity theory?

2   Do you think that Catherine has disengaged appropriately or do you think her quality of life might be improved if she was more active?

3   Why is it critically important to respect the choices that older people make with respect to their degree of social involvement?

Assessment activity 4.4

Describe two theories of ageing.

1   Arrange to talk to care workers who work with older people in order to collect some anonymous examples of situations where older people disengage and also situations where they stay active.   **P4**

Grading tip for P4

Examples of disengagement and staying active will help you to describe and write about each of the two theories.

Use examples to compare two major theories of ageing.

2   Use a number of anonymous examples of older people's behaviour so that you can compare disengagement and activity theory in a practical context.   **M3**

Grading tip for M3

'Use examples' means that you must refer to several situations where people have disengaged or been active. You cannot simply say what disengagement and activity theory are.

Evaluate the influence of two major theories of ageing on health and social care provision.

3   Use the examples you have collected as a basis for commenting on service provision. Describe how far services encourage older people to stay active or how services create barriers to remaining socially engaged with others.   **D2**

Grading tip for D2

'Evaluate' means that you must describe the value of disengagement and activity theory in influencing provision.

Your evaluation could include the vitally important issue of respecting service user choice when providing activities for older people. You might also discuss whether disengagement is an inevitable part of growing older – how far would you evaluate the theory to be correct?

Physical changes

Each person's experience of ageing is different. Some people develop serious problems associated with the ageing process in their fifties; other people have few problems even in their nineties. There is no simple process that affects everyone in the same way. Ageing can involve the physical issues summarised below.

- The skin becomes thinner, less elastic and more wrinkled.
- Bones can become more brittle and more likely to fracture.
- Joints can become stiffer and may become painful as the cartilage on the bone ends becomes thinner.
- The ligaments which reinforce joints can become looser.
- A person can lose height because the cartilage that separates vertebrae in the backbone becomes compressed. The spine may also become more rounded.

- Muscles become weaker.
- The sense of balance can become impaired.
- The ability to taste and smell can deteriorate.
- Vision can deteriorate because of a range of problems and cataracts can develop.
- Hearing can deteriorate with a failure to hear high-pitched sounds.
- A lack of skin sensitivity can lead to an increased risk of hypothermia.
- Muscles in the digestive tract can become weaker creating a risk of constipation.
- The heart is less efficient at pumping blood.
- Blood pressure can rise.
- Nutrients from food are not absorbed as well as in earlier life.
- Breathing can become less efficient because respiratory muscles are weaker.

- Gas exchange in the lungs becomes impaired as the elastic walls of the small air pockets called alveoli become damaged.
- Body metabolism is reduced due to lowered performance of the endocrine glands.

These physical changes do not come about because we 'wear out'. If you take regular exercise, you may expect to live longer and stay healthier than people who do not. The physical changes associated with ageing may come about because cells start to make damaged and imperfect copies after a genetically programmed limit of cell renewal has been reached. It seems that there is a limit to the number of times each body cell can renew itself effectively. This limit is sometimes called the 'Hayflick limit', named after the biologist who measured the limits of cell regeneration.

In context

Betty is 75 years old and she is talking about her life experience. She makes the following statements while she is talking:

- 'Food just isn't the same these days – we used to have real cheese when I was young and now you can't taste it.'
- 'I get tired so easily nowadays. If I go out shopping, I'm done for the day – but surely your age can't make you feel tired?'
- 'I do feel the cold nowadays – I mean we used to have awful winters, much worse than now – but yet I always feel cold nowadays.'

1 **Can you explain why cheese now has less taste for Betty?**

2 **What physical changes associated with ageing might explain Betty's tiredness following physical activity?**

3 **What physical changes associated with ageing might cause older people to need a higher temperature in their homes than younger people?**

Cardiovascular system

The heart pumps blood around the body. Older people may develop a narrowing of the arteries and other blood vessels due to fats such as cholesterol being laid down in the walls of the blood vessels. This process of 'clogging up' is called atherosclerosis.

Atherosclerosis can result in higher blood pressure and high blood pressure puts the person at risk of strokes (where the blood supply to the brain is blocked) and heart attacks.

The elasticity in the walls of the blood vessels can also reduce, causing the heart to work harder, increase in size and cause a rise in blood pressure. Fatty deposits can break away and cause a blockage in an artery. These blockages can result in coronary heart disease. If the coronary artery is partly blocked a person may experience breathlessness and chest pains associated with angina. Where blood flow is seriously blocked a person may experience a heart attack.

Respiratory system

When blood is not being pumped round the body efficiently breathlessness may result. The strength of the chest muscles may reduce with ageing and the efficiency of the lungs may deteriorate. Chronic diseases such as bronchitis may develop. Bronchitis involves inflammation of the airways that connect the windpipe to the lungs. Common disorders of the respiratory system include emphysema and chronic obstructive pulmonary disease (see below).

Emphysema

Emphysema is a disease in which the air sacs within the lungs (alveoli) become damaged. This causes shortness of breath and can result in respiratory or heart failure. Emphysema can be induced by smoking which causes the lungs to produce chemicals that damage the walls of the air sacs. In time, this results in a drop in the amount of oxygen in the blood.

Chronic obstructive pulmonary disease (COPD)

When there is an airflow obstruction, perhaps due to emphysema or bronchitis, the resulting condition is described as chronic obstructive pulmonary disease (COPD). This condition can create a progressively worse disruption of airflow into the lungs. Some people with COPD increase their rate of breathing in order to cope, whereas others may have a bullish appearance or might look bloated because of a lack of oxygen and a build-up of fluid in the body.

Nervous system

Ageing may involve the loss of nerve cells that activate muscles. Neurotransmitters (the chemicals released by the nerves in order to communicate and control muscles) may also function less effectively with age.

Loss of vision

After 45 years of age, the ability of the eye to focus begins to weaken and by 65 years there may be little focusing power left, making small print more difficult to read. Up to half of people over the age of 90 may have serious problems with vision.

Cataracts result from changes in the lens of the eye. As people grow older the lenses can become hard and cloudy. This process stops the lens of the eye from being able to

Intellectual activity is part of the process of ▶ staying active, fit and well in old age

change shape or transmit light appropriately. This process results in symptoms such as blurred vision. Cataracts may start to form between the ages of 50 and 60 years and often take time to develop. The majority of people over 75 years have some degree of cataract formation. Diabetes can also cause the development of cataracts.

Another problem that can affect eyesight in later life is glaucoma. Glaucoma involves an increase of fluid pressure within the eye.

Loss of hearing

Many older people experience difficulty in hearing high frequency (or high-pitched) sounds. This can happen because the sensitivity of nerve cells in the inner ear may decrease. There may also be a loss of nerve cells, which results in hearing loss. Some older people experience an increase in wax in the outer ear and this can block the transmission of sound to the sensory nerves.

Cognitive changes

Ageing can involve a loss of nerve cells in the brain and a reduction in the ability of nerves to transmit electrical signals. But this does not mean that people lose their ability to think logically or reason. Many older people do report problems with memory recall, for example, 'where did I put my glasses?' Older people often report that it takes longer to do things; there may be a feeling of slowing down. They may take longer to respond to questions. Response times might also be slower, meaning that, for example, older people need to drive more carefully in order to compensate for slower response times. Slower response times and difficulty recalling recent memories are not symptoms of dementia. Senile dementia is not part of a general ageing process, although the disease is more common among people who are over 85.

Musculoskeletal

Older people may experience the following:

- muscle thinning
- decline in mobility
- arthritis.

Ageing can result in a general reduction and shrinkage of skeletal muscles (the muscles we use to walk, lift things and move about). This loss of muscle may be due to cell death.

Arthritis involves damage to joints within the body. A substance called cartilage covers the ends of our bones and helps to 'cushion' our bones as we move. Cartilage can become thinner and less elastic with age. In osteoarthritis the bone ends can thicken and even form bony spurs which restrict movement of the joint. Many people with arthritis experience stiffness and pain when they move their hips or knees.

Osteoporosis is a major problem associated with ageing, affecting about 3 million people in the UK. Osteoporosis involves a thinning and weakening of bone, making it easier for bones to become fractured.

The role of sex hormones

Women are more at risk of osteoporosis than men because bone strength is influenced by sex hormones. Women often experience a major decrease in the hormone oestrogen following the menopause. This decrease in oestrogen is associated with osteoporosis. Some people may be more at risk of osteoporosis than others because the disorder may be influenced by genetic inheritance. Exercise is known to strengthen muscle and bone and may help to prevent osteoporosis.

Skin

As people grow older the elasticity of the skin reduces. The amount of fat stored under the skin decreases, the appearance of the skin becomes looser and it develops wrinkles.

Dementia

Dementia is more likely to occur in older people. Approximately 5 per cent of people over the age of 65 years have dementia. The Alzheimer's Society estimates that as many as 20 per cent of people over the age of 80 are affected by dementia. The majority of people who live to extreme old age will never develop dementia.

Dementia is a disorder that causes damage to the structure and chemistry of the brain. A person with dementia is likely to experience problems with understanding what is happening around them, communicating, reasoning, finding their way and remembering recent events. There are different kinds of dementia; two major types are Alzheimer's disease and dementia caused by vascular disease, which involves blood supply problems to the brain.

Motor neurone disease

Motor neurone disease is another illness that is more likely to occur in older people. It is a rare disorder that is more common among people aged 50 to 70 than in other age groups. The disease causes nerves to degenerate resulting in weakness and loss of muscle tissue. The causes of motor neurone disease are not understood but it is possible that genetic inheritance may play a role, or that exposure to toxic chemicals may increase a person's risk of developing the disease.

Psychological changes

As with physical ageing, each person's experience of psychological changes is likely to be different. Some people may disengage from social activity as argued by Cumming (1975) but many people do remain in close contact with friends and family. Another famous theorist, Erik Erikson, argued in 1963 that older people would need to develop a sense of 'ego integrity' if they were to avoid despair in later life. Ego integrity involves 'making sense of your life' – holding on to a clear and meaningful sense of who you are. In part, ego integrity involves holding on to your self-esteem. One theory is that older people need to engage in telling their life story, reminiscing or reviewing their life in order to help create self-esteem and confidence. Coleman (1994) argued that some type of reminiscence work can be useful for most people but that there are wide differences in individual needs. Joining a group to discuss past events may not be good for everybody.

Theory into practice

Interview some other students and ask them to suggest five major health problems they would expect older people to have. It is possible that some younger people may believe that dementia and incontinence are a natural outcome of getting older. Historically, older people have been negatively stereotyped as diseased and demented. Can you find evidence that these stereotypes still exist?

Figure 4.17 Some service users may choose to take part in reminiscence sessions as an important social activity

Alice Heim (1990) wrote a book about her own experiences of ageing and the experiences of 160 of her friends and colleagues. Her study showed that even within a group of people with similar cultural and life experiences, there were wide variations in how people experienced later life. Some people reported an increase in social confidence; some people appeared to become more tolerant while others became more irritable; some people appreciated the respect that they received from other people while others complained of a lack of respect. The study suggested that ageing is full of contradictions with no clear rules.

Self-confidence

Heim suggested that confidence in undertaking practical tasks decreases in old age but that social confidence increases – and that this is one of the contradictions involved in the ageing process.

Reflect

Imagine a fit, healthy 16-year-old and a frail 84-year-old person with poor eyesight who both have to cross a busy road. Which of these two people is likely to feel more confident in coping with the situation? Now imagine the same two people faced with the task of standing up at a wedding reception and making a speech. Imagine that the older person has had a lifetime of experience of public speaking. Which of the two people is now likely to feel more confident?

Physical illness may cause people to lose confidence in skills that they once had. It would be wrong, however, to assume that physical decline removes confidence in general – or in all people.

In context

Martin is 84 years old. He has a good pension, lives in a pleasant house and is supported by his wife. Martin has angina (associated with heart disease) and he is talking about his life.

Interviewer: So how would you describe your health?

Martin: Oh, it's awful! I get breathless just trying to walk upstairs. I can't go out – I can't get to the shops some days. I just feel useless.

Interviewer: Would you say that old age is a terrible thing?

Martin: No. What I would tell you is that I would like my body to be 21 again but I want to keep all the experience, memories, knowledge and self-confidence I've developed. My body doesn't work like it used to. But in nearly every other way I am content and happy.

1 **How would you describe Martin's self-esteem and self-confidence?**

2 **Can you guess at some of the life factors and life events that Martin may have experienced which have contributed to his level of confidence and self-esteem?**

3 **Does physical decline have to mean that old age is a negative experience? What makes a life stage positive or negative?**

Ageing – the positives and negatives

The majority of people over state retirement age experience reasonable health, a satisfactory social life and, in many cases a high standard of living. Only a minority of older people experience poor health, poverty and isolation. It is important to guard against the stereotype that old age is always a story of decline and isolation for everyone. Old age is like any other life stage – whether or not you lead a happy and fulfilled life depends on a large range of individual issues. Your own attitude to life will have an important influence on what you experience.

Negative perspectives	
The effects of retirement	For some people retirement could result in a loss of income, contact with work colleagues and the loss of interest in life.
Loss of partner	Bereavement may result in a range of changes and losses including role changes. Bereavement may cause temporary anxiety and depression.
Role changes	Loss of work role, loss of partner and loss of income may all result in major life changes that are difficult to cope with.
Loss of peers	Economic problems or physical disability may mean that some older people lose contact with friends. Car ownership and the ability to drive may be an important issue that influences the ability to stay in touch with friends (Arber and Ginn, 2004).
Ageism	Older people are sometimes stereotyped as being useless, diseased, demented and unable to cope. Older people may experience prejudice from younger people who see them as 'having had their lives'. Many older people fear that they will not be treated with dignity in hospital or care settings.
Financial concerns	Arber and Ginn (2004) report that some 21 per cent of people aged 65 years and over live in poverty within the UK. Most of these people will not have a private pension fund. One in five people in the UK may have concerns about paying for heating, shopping and coping financially.

Table 4.10 The negative perspectives of later life

Positive perspectives	
The effects of retirement	For many people retirement provides freedom. Retired people may be seen as 'time rich' and free from work stress.
Role changes	The majority of older people enjoy effective social networks with only one person in five experiencing a degree of isolation. Only two in every 100 older people never see friends or relatives and 79 per cent of people over 65 see a relative or friend once a week (*National Statistics*, 2004). For many people retirement provides more opportunity for contact with grandchildren and other relatives. Older people are more likely to vote than any other age group suggesting more involvement in politics, whereas younger people may be more disengaged from politics.
Learning for pleasure	Free time may enable many older people to engage in enjoyable social and mental activities such as taking new college courses, developing IT skills etc. *National Statistics* (2006) report that 51 per cent of people between 60 and 69 participate in some form of learning.
Leisure pursuits	Free time may enable many older people to engage in physical leisure activities such as walking and activity holidays. Gardening is very popular among people aged 50 to 70 (*Social Trends*, 2005).
Wealth	61 per cent of people aged 65 and over own their own home (*Social Trends*, 2004), and people over 65 have higher levels of savings in general than any other age group. Many older people enjoy a high standard of living.

Table 4.11 The positive perspectives of later life

Assessment activity 4.5

Describe physical and psychological changes due to the ageing process.

1 Talk to health and care workers about their experience of working with older people. You may be able to use their experience together with your knowledge in order to write an account of these changes. **P5**

Grading tip for P5

You need to describe physical and psychological changes; this could take the form of a list of headings with appropriate explanations following each heading.

In context Janet's story continued …

Interviewer: In 1959 you wrote that your Nan sat in a chair and did nothing. Do you think that your life will follow the same course?

Janet: Now I'm older I understand some of the reasons why she withdrew. I have arthritis and Nan did too. Now I realise that she probably found it painful to move about. But I think she also 'gave up'. The rest of the family didn't expect her to do anything and she just went along with them. My life isn't going to be like that because I have lots of things I enjoy doing – if I can't get to the shops, I'll buy what I want on the Internet – if I can't get out to meet people, I'll talk to them on the phone or the Internet. I'm not going to let health problems stop me getting the most out of life!

Interviewer: How far can you choose what happens to you in life?

Janet: Well, it's like a game of cards. You get dealt a hand of cards and everyone gets different cards from the pack. Some people are very lucky with their genetics and environment while other people aren't. But how you play your cards is what the game is all about. If you play your cards well you can make the best of a bad hand. You can be really lucky with the cards you pick up and yet you can still lose if you play them badly. I think the way you choose to live is the most important thing – although there are always things you can't control.

1 Can you describe some of the physical and psychological changes that Janet and her Nan (grandmother) may have experienced as a result of the ageing process?

2 Janet has a mobility problem that 'runs in her family'. How far will this force her to disengage from social activity?

3 How far do life factors control Janet's experience of ageing and how far is she able to control life factors? Can you use the theory of reciprocal influence to explain how nature and nurture interact in her story?

Knowledge check

1. What is puberty and how is puberty different from adolescence?

2. What is meant by emotional development?

3. What is meant by maturation?

4. Can you describe an alternative to determinist views of human development?

5. If you have a genetically inherited disease, does that mean that nothing can be done to help you?

6. If it was possible to know a newborn baby's five life factors (i.e. genetics, biological nature, environment, socio-economic status of the family and parents' lifestyle) would it be possible to accurately predict that baby's life course?

7. Describe three ways in which being made unexpectedly redundant might influence a person.

8. Some older people have difficulty with walking and moving around the home. Can you describe two possible reasons for these difficulties?

9. What is meant by disengagement?

10. Should older people be made to be more active in order to prevent excessive disengagement?

Grading criteria

To achieve a pass grade the evidence must show that the learner is able to:	To achieve a merit grade the evidence must show that, in addition to the pass criteria, the learner is able to:	To achieve a distinction grade the evidence must show that, in addition to the pass and merit criteria, the learner is able to:
P1 describe physical, intellectual, emotional and social development through the life stages **Assessment activity 4.1 page 164**		
P2 describe the potential influences of five life factors on the development of individuals **Assessment activity 4.2 page 181**	**M1** discuss the nature-nurture debate in relation to individual development **Assessment activity 4.2 page 181**	**D1** evaluate the nature-nurture debate in relation to the development of the individual **Assessment activity 4.2 page 181**
P3 describe the influences of two predictable and two unpredictable major life events on the development of the individual **Assessment activity 4.3 page 184**	**M2** explain how major life events can influence the development of the individual **Assessment activity 4.3 page 184**	
P4 describe two theories of ageing **Assessment activity 4.4 page 189**	**M3** use examples to compare two major theories of ageing. **Assessment activity 4.4 page 189**	**D2** evaluate the influence of two major theories of ageing on health and social care service provision. **Assessment activity 4.4 page 189**
P5 describe physical and psychological changes due to the ageing process. **Assessment activity 4.5 page 196**		

Preparation for assessment

1 In order to help you collect evidence for the unit outcomes you should interview an older person about their life course if at all possible. You might be able to ask a relative or a friend's relative who is in their fifties or older who would be prepared to talk to you about their life. You might even get permission to make a tape or digital recording. You should ask permission to write an outline of the person's life story after they have talked it through with you.

Talking to older service users might raise additional ethical issues. Service users are often vulnerable people. You must be confident that your questions won't make someone feel threatened or worried. It is important that they are happy to talk about their life story and that they will give you permission to use aspects of it for your work. It is vital that you maintain confidentiality and don't reveal the person's identity in your assignment.

If you listen to a person's life story, you should identify some of the physical, social and emotional development issues at different stages of the person's life. **P1**

2 When people tell you their life story it is unlikely that they will remember much about their language or intellectual development of language. If you visit a nursery, playgroup or junior school you can observe issues that will help you write about these aspects of development. Alternatively, you could talk with early years workers or teachers in order to get ideas that will help you to write about these aspects of development. **P1**

3 When you listen to a person's story you should find one example of each of the five life factors within that person's story. This will give you the evidence you need for **P2**

4 You can now think about the person's story in greater depth and work out how the nature and nurture debate might relate to the five factors you have identified. Going into greater depth would give you evidence for **M1**

5 If you have read about the nature and nurture debate, and if you have taken part in group discussions, you should write your own evaluation of the role of nature and nurture in relationship to the life story that you are studying. Don't forget to question the degree to which the person has influenced their own life (reciprocal influence theory). **D1**

6 Try to identify two predictable and also two unpredictable major life events in the life story that you have heard. **P3**

7 You should work out and explain how these events might have influenced the storyteller. **M2**

8 The person's life story may not cover theories of ageing unless you can listen to the life story of an older person, perhaps in their seventies or eighties. You could use more than one life story to help you with your assignment. Alternatively, you could talk to care workers who work in day, residential or community settings with older people. Your conversations with care workers might help you to describe theories of ageing such as activity and disengagement theory. If you can listen to (and treat as confidential) examples of people's behaviour and the services provided for older people, you may have the examples you need to compare theories of ageing. **P4** **M3**

9 Your conversations will be vital in helping you to evaluate the role of activity and disengagement theory in relationship to care service provision. **D2**

10 You might be able to use life-story work or discussions with care workers to help you describe some of the physical and psychological changes associated with ageing. **P5**

Resources and further reading

Acheson, D. (1998) *Independent Inquiry into Inequalities in Health* London: HMSO

Ainsworth, M.D.S., Blehar, M. C., Walter, E., Wall, S. (1978) *Patterns of Attachment: A Psychological Study of the Strange Situation* New Jersey: Lawrence Erlbaum Associates Inc.

Arber, S., Ginn, J. (2004) 'Ageing and Gender: Diversity and Change' in *Social Trends,* Vol. 34 (2004) London: HMSO

Berryman, J.C., Hargreaves, D., Herbert, M., Taylor, A. (1991) *Developmental Psychology and You* London: Routledge

Bowlby, J. (1953) *Childcare and the Growth of Love* Harmondsworth: Pelican

Bromley, D.B. (1966) *The Psychology of Human Ageing* Harmondsworth: Penguin

Bromley, D.B. (1974) *The Psychology of Human Ageing*, second ed. Harmondsworth: Penguin

Chomsky, N. (1959) Review of Skinner's V*erbal Behaviour, Language*, 35, 26-58.

Coleman, P. (1994) 'Reminiscence within the study of ageing: the social significance of story', in Bornat, J. (1994) *Reminiscence Reviewed* Buckingham: OU Press

Cumming, E. (1975) 'Engagement with an old theory' *International Journal of Ageing and Human Development*, 6, 187-191

Cumming, E., Henry, W.E. (1961) *Growing Old* New York: Basic Books

Erikson, E.H. (1963) *Childhood and Society*, second ed. New York: Norton.

Havighurst, R.J. (1972) *Developmental Tasks and Education*, third ed. New York: David MaKay

Heim, A. (1990) *Where Did I Put my Spectacles?* Cambridge: Allborough Press

Levinson, D.J., Darrow, D.N., Klein, E.B., Levinson, M.H., McKee, B. (1978) *The Seasons of a Man's Life* New York: A. A. Knopf

Marris, P. (1996) *The Politics of Uncertainty* London: Routledge.

Paxton, W., Dixon, M. (2004) *The State of the Nation – an Audit of Injustice in the UK* London: Institute for Policy Research

Pinker, S. (1994) *The Language Instinct* London: Penguin

Sugarman, L. (1986) *Life-Span Development* London & New York: Methuen

Social Trends, Vol. 34 (2004) London: HMSO

Social Trends, Vol. 35 (2005) London: HMSO

Social Trends, Vol. 36 (2006) London: HMSO

Zimbardo, P.G. (1992) *Psychology and Life* London: HarperCollins

Useful websites

Institute for Public Policy Research
www.ippr.org

National Statistics
www.statistics.gov.uk

Fundamentals of anatomy and physiology

Introduction

This unit aims to provide learners with a clear understanding of fundamental aspects of the anatomy and physiology of human body systems. Learners will gain an overview of the gross anatomy and functions of all human body systems before investigating selected body systems in greater depth.

The unit introduces core knowledge of cellular structure and function and the organisation of the body as a whole. It then builds on this to develop a more detailed knowledge of the fine anatomy and physiology of the systems involved in energy metabolism.

Learners will also examine the homeostatic mechanisms involved in the regulation of these systems, for the maintenance of health. Practical activity will require learners to take measurements of the cardiovascular and respiratory systems and of body temperature using non-invasive techniques to investigate normal responses to routine variations in body functioning.

This unit provides the core understanding of human physiology that underpins the study of the specialist physiology units within this programme. The unit also provides an overview of body functioning that is valuable for anyone working in a field related to health and social care.

How you will be assessed

This unit is internally assessed by your tutor. A variety of activities, exercises and scenarios have been included to assist you with studying different aspects of anatomy and physiology and in preparation for assessment.

Thinking points

Physiology is the study of the functions of living organisms and living matter.

You will have studied physiology in science, but it might not have been called physiology. You probably already know more than you think you do!

Anatomy is learning about the structures of the body. Anatomy of the heart is learning about the different chambers and blood vessels and the type of muscle making up the bulk of the heart. Physiology of the heart is studying how the heart works to drive blood onwards through the circulation and how the action of the heart muscle is co-ordinated in one heartbeat, known as the cardiac cycle.

Make a list of the human body systems that you already know and the organs associated with each system.

Using your list, write down all the functions of the systems that you know.

After completing this unit you should be able to achieve the following outcomes:

- Understand the organisation of the human body
- Understand the functioning of the body systems associated with energy metabolism
- Understand how homoeostatic mechanisms operate in the maintenance of an internal environment
- Be able to interpret data obtained from monitoring routine variations in the functioning of healthy body systems.

Every individual is composed of billions of microscopic units called cells. The cells carry out vast numbers of chemical reactions and processes that make up the essence of life itself.

Cells rarely exist in isolation; they are usually grouped together with other similar cells carrying out particular tasks. Groups of cells are known as tissues.

Different types of tissues are commonly grouped together to form a body which carries out a particular function. Such bodies are called organs.

Finally, groups of organs responsible for main tasks or functions in the body are called organ systems or sometimes body systems.

Electron microscopes are necessary to see the detail of cell contents and as these are highly expensive instruments requiring trained operators to prepare the specimens and interpret the organisation inside cells, we use diagrams and **photomicrographs** instead.

Key term

Photomicrograph A photograph taken of an object magnified under a microscope. Electromicrography may be used for photographs taken with electron microscopes.

Details of the interior of a cell are often referred to as the ultrastructure of the cell where 'ultra' means beyond what is considered normal. This is because they can only be seen with immense magnification. Before the electron microscope was invented and developed, the interior of a cell was considered to be a granular sort of 'soup' but now we know that the ultrastructure is highly organised and composed of many different bodies carrying out their own functions.

Theory into practice

Classify the following into cells, tissues, organs and systems:

- heart
- blood
- red blood cell (or erythrocyte)
- nervous system
- brain
- skin
- muscle cell
- muscle
- bone
- skeleton
- cartilage
- kidney
- digestive system
- bladder
- renal system.

Remember!

Do you remember the definition of an organ? The very tiny bodies inside a cell are collectively known as organelles because they have different physical (and chemical) compositions and carry out their own functions.

Cells

The largest cell in the human body is the female ovum which can just be seen with the naked eye. Most cells are much smaller than this and microscopes are required to view them. Ordinary light microscopes, such as those found in school or college laboratories, are quite good for viewing tissues and organs, but not very useful for viewing the interior of individual human cells.

Although you will learn about a typical human cell, there are lots of different types of cells each with their own characteristics and the typical cell exists only for study purposes and has no specialisation; you must then adapt your knowledge to the specific type of cell being considered. For example, a mature red blood cell does not have a nucleus, so any description of the ultrastructure of a red blood cell would not include the nucleus.

Living material making up a whole cell is called **protoplasm** and this subdivides into the **cytoplasm** and **nucleus**.

Key terms

Protoplasm The word means 'first material' and protoplasm is anything inside the cell boundary. Cell or plasma membrane surrounds the protoplasm.

Cytoplasm The word means 'cell material' and cytoplasm is anything inside the cell boundary and outside the nucleus.

Nucleus This is the central part of the cell.

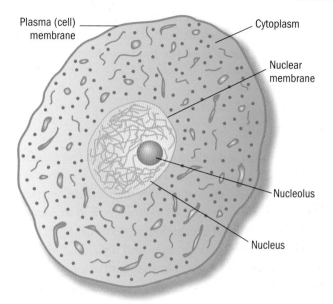

Figure 5.1 Diagram of a cell viewed under a light microscope (x 300)

Under the light microscope, cytoplasm appears granular with no distinct features. This is the site of most complex chemical reactions, mainly directed by the nucleus, which is also responsible for inherited characteristics. The nucleus is a dark body, usually centrally placed; a smaller, darker spot, the nucleolus, is often visible. Both the whole cell and the nucleus are surrounded by a membrane which appears as a single line (see Figure 5.1).

Cell ultrastructure is so complex and highly organised that a separate branch of science has arisen – cytology, the study of cells. You will learn about the structure and functions of the cell membrane, the organelles in the cytoplasm, and the nucleus.

Cell (or plasma) membrane

The electron microscope shows the cell membrane to be a lipid-protein sandwich. The lipids are small, fatty molecules in two layers (bi-layer) with larger protein molecules inserted at intervals partly or completely through the bi-layer. The lipid molecules are phospholipids; the phosphate head is water soluble and two lipid chains are insoluble in water; this is why the two layers align themselves with the lipid chains facing one another. The fluid surrounding cells (called tissue fluid) and the cytoplasm are both watery environments adjacent to the phosphate heads (see Figure 5.2).

Protein molecules often form channels through the membrane for substances to pass to and from the cell and also act as

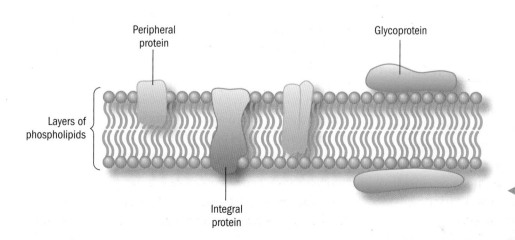

Figure 5.2 Model of the structure of the cell membrane magnified several thousand times

identity markers or reception sites for other molecules such as hormones important to those cells. This structure is often termed the 'fluid mosaic model' of the cell membrane.

Cytoplasm

Cytoplasm is a semi-fluid material likened to a gel and capable of flowing slowly. Many chemical reactions are carried out here. The collective term for these reactions is metabolism and you will find this term in frequent use in physiological and biological texts. Complex storage sugars such as glycogen and melanin, the dark pigment responsible for skin and hair colour, are found in cytoplasm.

Nucleus

This is usually the largest structure inside the cell and as it takes up dyes or stains very easily it stands out as a dark shape. Most cells have a single, central spherical nucleus but there are many variations. Some muscle cells have many nuclei and are called multinucleate, some red blood cells have lost the nucleus during development and are said to be anucleate while some white blood cells have distinct lobed nuclei. Apart from red blood cells, which cannot reproduce and have a limited life span, most cells separated from their nuclei will die.

The nuclear membrane has a structure similar to that of the cell membrane but contains gaps or pores through which proteins and nucleic acids pass. When a cell is not dividing (known as resting) the nuclear material appears like a thick, tangled mass and is called the **chromatin network**. A smaller, darker sphere is often visible, the nucleolus, and this is a source of **ribonucleic acid** (RNA), one of the nucleic acids. There may be more than one nucleolus present in some cells. When a cell is in the process of dividing, the chromatin network separates into distinct black threads known as **chromosomes**. There are 23 pairs of chromosomes in a human cell containing specific sequences of **DNA** (another nucleic acid) responsible for all our inherited characteristics such as hair and eye colour. The sequences of DNA are our genes.

Key terms

Chromatin network The dark tangled mass seen in the nucleus of a resting cell.

Ribonucleic acid (RNA) A nucleic acid found in both the cell and the nucleus, responsible for the manufacture of cell proteins such as pigments, enzymes and hormones.

Chromosomes Long threads of DNA and protein seen in a dividing cell. They contain the genetic material or genes responsible for transmitting inherited characteristics.

Deoxyribonucleic acid (DNA) A nucleic acid found only in the chromatin network and chromosomes of the nucleus. DNA is responsible for the control and passing on of inherited characteristics and instructions to the cell.

The nucleus of the cell controls nearly all the activities of the cell and has been likened to the architectural drawing or blueprint from which the cell operates.

Cell organelles

Organelles are various components of a cell with a distinct structure and functions and are likened to miniature organs (hence the term 'organelles').

Organelles include:

- mitochondria
- the endoplasmic reticulum
- the Golgi apparatus
- lysosomes.

Before looking at the organelles in detail, you will see in Figure 5.3 a diagram of a typical cell that might be seen under the electron microscope; refer to the diagram as you learn about the organelles. Note that the magnification is still not sufficient to make out the full structure of the cell and nuclear membranes.

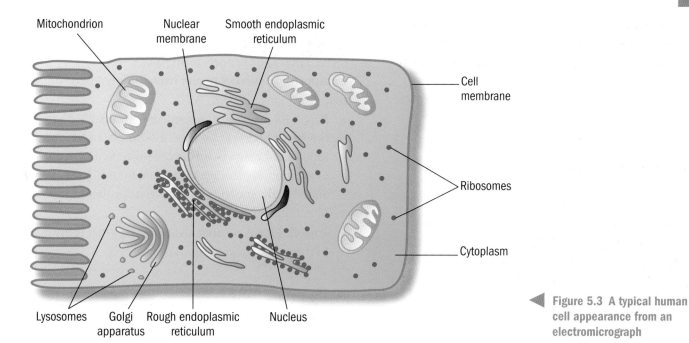

Mitochondrion Nuclear membrane Smooth endoplasmic reticulum

Cell membrane

Ribosomes

Cytoplasm

Lysosomes Golgi apparatus Rough endoplasmic reticulum Nucleus

Figure 5.3 A typical human cell appearance from an electromicrograph

Theory into practice

You may be feeling somewhat bewildered by these difficult terms that are also hard to spell. Don't be disheartened! It really is surprising how quickly you will learn them if you keep repeating them over and over and pointing them out in electromicrographs. When you feel confident about recognising their shapes, try adding their functions too, such as 'these are mitochondria and they are involved in releasing energy'. Your tutor will be able to find different copies of electromicrographs for practice and one is included on page 206.

■ Mitochondria

Every cell in the body has at least 1000 of these rod-shaped or spherical bodies, and very energy-active cells like muscle and liver cells will have many more. **Mitochondria** are concerned with energy release. Each mitochondrion (singular) has a double-layered membrane like the cell membrane but the inner layer is folded at intervals producing a series of 'shelves' or ridges known as **cristae**. The enzymes responsible for the terminal stages of glucose oxidation are located on

the cristae. The energy released is trapped and stored until required by a 'chemical battery' called **ATP**. When energy is required for building complex molecules, movement and secretion, the ATP breaks down to **ADP** plus energy. The ADP is then recycled to be built up once more in the mitochondria to ATP.

Key terms

Mitochondria Spherical or rod-shaped bodies scattered in the cytoplasm and concerned with energy release.

Cristae Folds of the inner layer of mitochondrial membrane on which the enzymes responsible for the oxidation of glucose are situated.

ATP Adenosine triphosphate is a chemical in mitochondria which is capable of trapping lots of energy in the last chemical bond, for example, A-P-P~P where P is a phosphate group – an ordinary chemical bond – and ~ is a high energy bond.

ADP Adenosine diphosphate, a chemical left after ATP has released its stored energy to do work. For example, A-P-P, ADP is then recycled in the mitochondria to ATP.

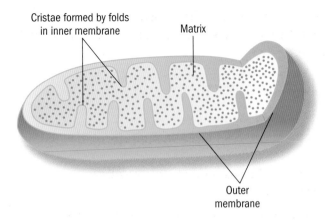

Cristae formed by folds
in inner membrane

Matrix

Outer
membrane

▲ **Figure 5.4 Structure of a single mitochondrion**

*Oxidation of glucose → Starts in the cytoplasm→
Mitochondria, energy released → ADP converted into
ATP.*

*Energy required for cells to do work→ATP converted to
ADP.*

■ Endoplasmic reticulum

This can be shortened to ER. There are two variations,
called rough and smooth ER. Endo- means 'within'
and reticulum is a technical term for a network. ER is
a branching network which fills the cell interior. The

membrane of the channels is similar in structure to
the cell membrane and continuous with the nuclear
membrane. The channels form passageways for
transporting materials to and from different parts of the
cell.

- *Rough ER* is so-called because it is studded with
  tiny black bodies known as ribosomes and has the
  function of manufacturing cell proteins and acting
  as a temporary storage area. Sometimes sugars are
  added to the proteins to make glycoproteins in
  secretions such as mucus.

- *Smooth ER* has no attached ribosomes and is involved
  in the metabolism of lipids or fats.

■ Golgi apparatus

This appears as a series of flattened fluid-filled sacs
stacked like pancakes. Many tiny fluid-filled globules
or bags lie close to the main stack and these are often
termed vesicles. Golgi was a famous Italian scientist
specialising in cells and tissues in the nineteenth and
twentieth centuries and this organelle takes his name. It
is believed that the Golgi apparatus, or body, packages
proteins for delivery to other organelles or outwards
from the cell in secretions. The Golgi apparatus is also
responsible for producing lysosomes.

■ Lysosomes

Lysosomes can be found in all
parts of the cell cytoplasm and
are also small vesicles produced
by part of the Golgi apparatus.
They contain powerful enzymes
capable of digesting all major
chemical components of living
cells and have been called
'suicide bags'. Lysosomes can
travel freely throughout the cell
and by releasing their contents
can destroy old or damaged
organelles and even entire cells.
Another function is to destroy

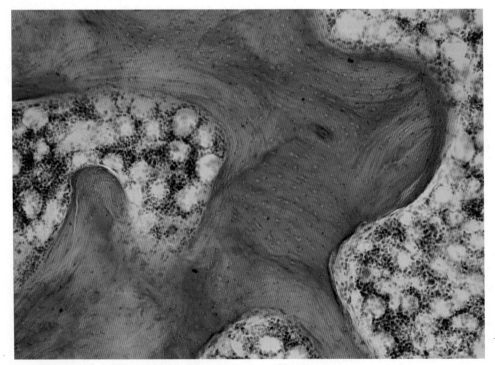

◄ **Figure 5.5 Electromicrograph of
bone cells**

bacteria and other foreign materials such as carbon particles that enter the cell. They do this by taking the foreign matter into their vesicles and, after destruction, releasing the digested material outside the cell.

Some types of white blood cells (phagocytes – literally 'eating cells' – and monocytes) and tissue cells known as macrophages (meaning 'large eaters') are loaded with lysosomes because their function is to destroy bacteria, viruses and foreign material entering the body cells and tissues.

Many disease-causing agents are thought to be capable of damaging lysosome membranes, bringing about internal cell destruction.

When you feel that your learning is complete, try the activity below. You can improve your work if you are not satisfied with it.

Assessment activity 5.1

P1 Describe the functions of the main cell components.

1   What are the main activities carried out by the mitochondria, lysosomes, Golgi apparatus and endoplasmic reticula (both rough and smooth)?

Reflect

The electron microscope enables you to see extremely small objects to identify their structure but it does not tell you what the structures actually do. Many researchers with a range of expertise e.g. chemists, physicists and biochemists must separate out the different structures and carry out many tests to identify their functions.

Grading tip for P1

This is an overview of the cell structure and function and should not be in any more detail than is included in the text. Although you are not obliged to include images of cell structure, clearly your work will be more coherent if you include labelled images. If you download material from the Internet you must show clearly how you have adapted it to show your learning, as well as providing a detailed reference and acknowledgement. It would be acceptable to obtain an image and label it carefully yourself to show the relevant parts.

You could annotate the image with text to describe the functions of the parts or attach a report describing the functions *in your own words*.

Theory into practice

Using a copy of the electromicrograph in Figure 5.5 and/or similar material from your tutor and the labelled diagram in Figure 5.3, match the different parts of a cell and the organelles. You will realise that interpreting photographs of real cells is more difficult than it appears. As you carry out this exercise, describe the appearance and the function of each part. Although you can carry out this activity on your own, you can learn more with a 'study buddy' as you can check each other's learning and interpretation of the cell parts. After each 'journey' through the cell parts, check your recall against this text and any class notes you may have.

Tissues

Tissues are groups of similar cells carrying out specific functions. You will learn about the following tissues:

●   epithelial
●   connective
●   muscle
●   nervous.

Epithelia are the linings of internal and external surfaces and body cavities, including ducts (tubes or channels) carrying secretions from glands. They may be composed of several layers of cells called compound epithelia or just a single layer known as simple epithelia. The lowest or bottom layer of cells are attached to a basement membrane for support and connection. The basement membrane is secreted by the epithelial cells. There are nerve supplies to epithelia but they are supplied with oxygen and nutrients from deeper tissues by diffusion. As they are surface tissues and exposed to friction, their capacity for growth and repair is greater than other tissues and usually occurs during sleep.

■ Simple epithelia

Squamous epithelium

These cells are very flat with each nucleus forming a lump in the centre. The word squamous means scaly to signify the 'flatness'. The cells fit closely together rather like crazy paving. Clearly such delicate thin cells cannot offer much protection and their chief function is to allow materials to pass through via **diffusion** and **osmosis**. Simple squamous epithelium is found in the walls of:

- lung alveoli
- blood capillaries
- Bowman's capsule of nephrons.

Key terms

Diffusion This is the passage of molecules from a high concentration to a low concentration.

Osmosis This is the passage of water molecules from a region of high concentration (of water molecules) to one of low concentration through a partially permeable membrane such as the cell membranes of simple epithelial cells.

Cuboidal epithelium

As their name suggests, these are cube-shaped with spherical nuclei. They often line ducts and tubes and can allow materials to pass through in a way similar to squamous epithelia. They are often found in glandular tissues making secretions.

They can be found in:

- kidney tubules
- sweat ducts
- glands like the thyroid gland and breast tissue.

Columnar epithelium

These cells are much taller with slightly oval nuclei. They are often associated with microscopic filaments known as cilia. Cilia move in wave-like motions beating towards the orifices and are commonly found associated

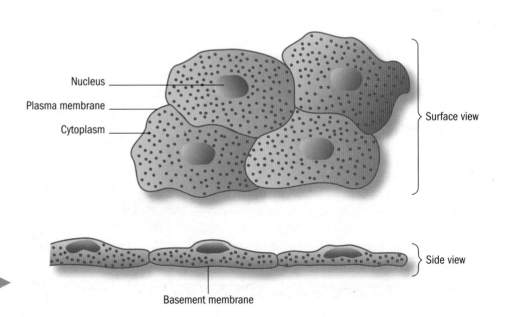

Nucleus
Plasma membrane
Cytoplasm

Surface view

Side view

Basement membrane

Figure 5.6 Simple squamous epithelium ▶

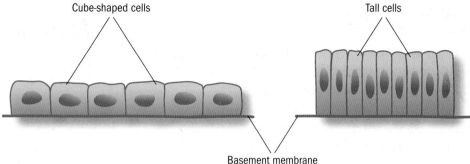

Figure 5.7 Cuboidal and columnar ▶ epithelia

Cube-shaped cells

Tall cells

Basement membrane

with goblet cells, which secrete mucus in the respiratory and alimentary tracts. The mucus traps unwanted particles like carbon and the cilia transports the flow of 'dirty' mucus towards the exterior.

Columnar cells are found lining:

- the trachea and bronchi
- villi in the small intestine.

■ Compound epithelia

The principal function of compound epithelia is to protect deeper structures. Multiple layers of cells hamper the passage of materials which is often so characteristic of the simple epithelia. The vagina, mouth, tongue and oesophagus are lined by stratified epithelia (simple) consisting of layers of squamous, cuboidal or columnar cells which gradually become flattened by pressure from below as they reach the surface. The lowest layer of cells on the basement membrane actively divides and the older cells are pushed upwards. This type of epithelia is usually a pink colour and often termed mucous membrane.

The skin has an outer layer of epithelium similar in structure to the stratified epithelium but with the important addition of a layer of flattened dead cells on the outside. This is known as the epidermis. As the cells advance from the basement membrane, they gradually become filled with a protein called keratin and are said to be keratinised or cornified. This layer is vital in keeping microorganisms from invading deeper structures and has a waterproofing effect on the skin. Skin can be variously coloured with pigment produced by pigment cells in the lowest layer. The pigment melanin darkens under the influence of the sun. The numbers of pigment cells in the skin is genetically inherited although they are capable of dividing during exposure to sunshine.

The structure of the skin epidermis can be seen in Figure 5.43 on page 249.

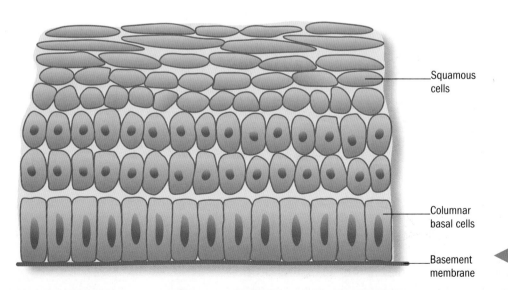

Squamous cells

Columnar basal cells

Basement membrane

◀ Figure 5.8 Section through stratified epithelium

These tissues are the most widely distributed in the body and lie beneath the epithelial tissues, connecting different parts of the internal structure.

Various types of cells lie in a background material known as a **matrix**. The matrix may be liquid as in blood, jelly-like as in areolar tissue, firm as in cartilage or hard as in bone. The matrix of a tissue is usually secreted by the connective tissue cells.

The functions of these tissues are to transport materials (as in blood), give support (as in areolar tissue and cartilage) and strengthen and protect (as in bone). Many tissues contain different fibres secreted by the cells to provide special characteristics.

You will learn about the connective tissues of:

- blood
- cartilage
- bone
- areolar tissue
- adipose tissue (fatty tissue).

Key term

Matrix Background material in which various types of cells lie.

■ Blood

Blood consists of straw-coloured plasma (the matrix) in which several types of blood cells are carried. Plasma is mainly water in which various substances are carried, such as dissolved gases like oxygen and carbon dioxide, nutrients like glucose and amino acids, salts, enzymes and hormones. There is also a combination of important proteins, collectively known as the plasma proteins, which have roles in blood clotting, transport, defence and osmotic regulation.

The most common cells by far in the plasma are red blood cells, also known as erythrocytes. These are very small cells with a bi-concave shape and elastic membrane. The elastic membrane is important as they

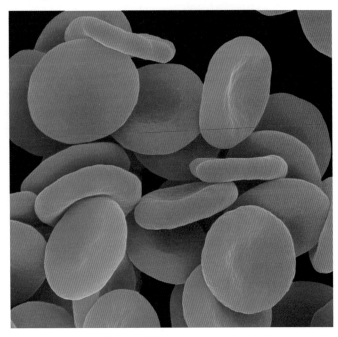

Figure 5.9 Human blood

often have to distort to travel through the smallest capillaries. Erythrocytes have no nucleus in their mature state (the loss produces a depression in the top and bottom of the cell, hence their shape) to provide a larger surface area for exposure to oxygen. They are packed with haemoglobin which gives them a red colour – this is why blood is red. In oxygenated blood (**arterial blood**), the oxyhaemoglobin is bright red but, in deoxygenated blood (**venous blood**), after the dissolved oxygen is delivered to body cells, the reduced haemoglobin is dark red in colour.

Key terms

Arterial blood Blood flowing through arteries which are blood vessels coming from the heart, usually carrying oxygenated blood to the tissues.

Venous blood Blood flowing through veins which are blood vessels, returning blood to the heart from the tissues; the blood has left considerable amounts of oxygen behind to supply the cells and is known as deoxygenated blood.

See also pages 229–231.

Due to the absence of nuclei, erythrocytes cannot divide and have a limited lifespan of around 120 days.

White blood cells or leucocytes are larger, nucleated and less numerous. There are several types but the most numerous are the granulocytes (also termed polymorphs, neutrophils and phagocytes). They are called granulocytes because they contain granules in their cytoplasm as well as lobed nuclei. They are capable of changing their shape and engulfing foreign material such as bacteria and carbon particles. This process is known as phagocytosis. A granulocyte acts rather like an amoeba and is sometimes said to be amoeboid. Granulocytes, because of their ability to engulf microbes and foreign material, are very important in the defence of the body. The number of granulocytes rises significantly in infections, so a blood count can often be a valuable pointer to an infection in an undiagnosed illness.

Lymphocytes are smaller white blood cells with round nuclei and clear cytoplasm – they assist in the production of antibodies. Antigens are found on the surface coats of disease-causing microbes or pathogens and act as identity markers for different types of pathogens (rather like name tags on school uniform).

Antibodies neutralise antigens and prevent the microbes from multiplying. They can then be phagocytosed by granulocytes and monocytes. Antibodies are chemically globulins, types of plasma protein carried in the plasma.

In a completely different way from granulocytes, lymphocytes also contribute to the defence of the body because of their role in the production of antibodies.

Monocytes are another type of white blood cell, larger than lymphocytes. They also have large round nuclei and clear cytoplasm. They are very efficient at phagocytosis of foreign material and, like granulocytes, can leave the circulatory blood vessels to travel to the site of an infection and begin phagocytosing pathogens very rapidly.

Thrombocytes are not true cells but are usually classed with the white blood cells. They are more commonly called platelets. They are products of much larger cells which have broken up and they have an important role in blood clotting.

■ Cartilage

This is the smooth, translucent firm substance that protects bone ends from friction during movement, and

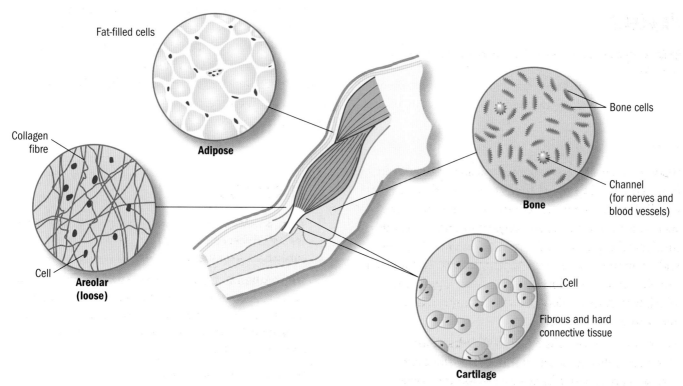

Fat-filled cells

Adipose

Collagen fibre

Cell

Areolar (loose)

Bone cells

Channel (for nerves and blood vessels)

Bone

Cell

Fibrous and hard connective tissue

Cartilage

▲ **Figure 5.10 Other types of connective tissue**

forms the major part of the nose and the external ear flaps, called pinnae. The matrix is secreted by cartilage cells called **chondro**cytes and is a firm but flexible glass-like material of chondrin. The cells become trapped in the matrix and sometimes divide into two or four cells giving a very characteristic appearance. It does not contain blood vessels and is nourished by diffusion from underlying bone.

Key term

Chondro- A prefix associated with cartilage.

■ Bone

Bone is a much harder substance than cartilage but it can be worn away by friction. The rigid matrix has two major components:

- calcium salts, which form around collagen fibres and give bone its hardness
- **collagen** fibres, which offer some ability to bend under strain and prevent bone from being too brittle and therefore being very likely to fracture.

Osteocytes or bone cells are trapped in the hard matrix on concentric rings called lamellae. A system of these rings is known as a Haversian system or osteone. Blood vessels and nerves pass through the hollow centre of each osteone.

Key terms

Collagen Fibrous structural protein, generally in the form of fibres for added strength.

Osteo- A prefix associated with bone.

Bone is designed to bear weight and the limb bones are hollow, like girders (the strongest mechanical structures). Bone is also used to protect vital weaker tissues such as the brain, lungs and heart.

■ Areolar tissue

This is the most common tissue in the body and you have probably never heard of it before! If you eat meat, you will have seen it many, many times. It is the sticky, white material that binds muscle groups, blood vessels and nerves together. The matrix is semi-fluid and it contains collagen fibres and elastic fibres secreted by the cell types found in this loose connective tissue. Elastic fibres provide flexibility to the tissue, which is located around more mobile structures. The deeper skin layer known as the dermis is a more dense type of areolar tissue with extra fibres and cells. Areolar tissue offers a degree of support to the tissues which it surrounds.

■ Adipose tissue

Adipose is a technical term for fatty tissue and it is a variation of areolar tissue in which the adipose or fat cells have multiplied to obscure other cells and fibres. When mature, an adipose cell becomes so loaded with fat that the nucleus is pushed to one side and as fat is translucent the cell takes on a distinctive 'signet ring' appearance. Adipose tissue is common under the skin and around organs such as the heart, kidneys and parts of the digestive tract. It helps to insulate against changes of external temperature, acts as a hydraulic shock absorber to protect against injury and is a high-energy storage depot.

Muscle tissue

Muscle is an excitable tissue because it is capable of responding to stimuli. There are three different types of muscle in the human body:

- striated
- non-striated
- cardiac.

Each is composed of muscle fibres capable of shortening or contracting and returning to their original state known as relaxation. Contraction causes movement of the skeleton, soft tissue, blood or specific material such as urine, food and faeces. Muscle has both blood and nerve supplies.

Muscle activity generates heat and contributes to maintaining the body temperature.

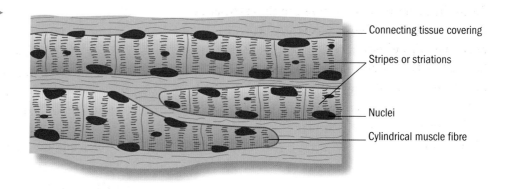

Figure 5.11 Microscopic appearance of striated muscle

Connecting tissue covering

Stripes or striations

Nuclei

Cylindrical muscle fibre

Striated muscle

Most striated muscle (also called voluntary, skeletal or striped muscle) is attached to the bones of the skeleton although some facial muscles are attached to skin. It makes up the familiar animal meat seen in the butchers. Striated muscle will contract on receipt of nerve impulses controlled by conscious thought from the **central nervous system**, hence the alternative name of voluntary muscle. The name striated means striped; each individual fibre shows alternate dark and light banding from the muscle protein filaments from which it is made.

Non-striated muscle

Although this type of muscle tissue (also called involuntary, smooth or plain muscle) still contains the protein filaments, they do not lie in an ordered pattern and therefore do not produce the banding characteristic of striated muscle. The muscle fibres are spindle- or cigar-shaped with single central nuclei, and dovetail with each other. This type of muscle tends to form sheets and although still requiring nervous stimulation to effect contraction, this is not under conscious thought, but supplied by the **autonomic nervous system** (hence the name involuntary muscle). This type of muscle is found around hollow internal organs such as the stomach, intestines, iris of the eye, bladder and uterus; it is not attached to bones.

Key term

Central nervous system The brain and spinal cord.

Key term

Autonomic nervous system Part of the nervous system responsible for controlling the internal organs.

Each fibre is cylindrical and multinucleate, lying parallel to its neighbours. There may be hundreds or thousands of fibres in a muscle depending on its size. Some fibres are 0.3 m long and one hundredth of a millimetre wide. Muscle fibres contain many thousands of mitochondria to supply ATP for the energy used in of contraction.

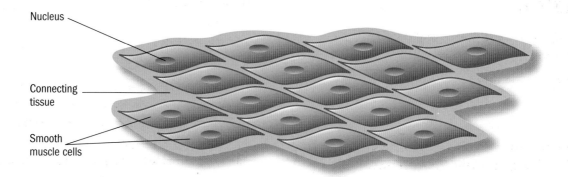

Nucleus

Connecting tissue

Smooth muscle cells

Figure 5.12 Non-striated muscle tissue

Non-striated muscle frequently occurs in two sheets running in different directions. In the digestive tract, one sheet runs circularly around the intestines while another outer sheet runs down the length. The two sheets are said to work **antagonistically** to propel the food contents down the tract. This is known as peristalsis (see page 240).

Key term

Antagonistic muscles One muscle or sheet of muscle contracts while an opposite muscle or sheet relaxes.

In the iris of the eye, one set of muscle runs radially like the spokes of a wheel while the other set runs circularly around the central pupil. This arrangement allows for the control of light entering the eye and the pupil is said to be dilated (open) or constricted (narrowed).

■ Cardiac muscle

This muscle is found only in the four chambers (atria and ventricles) of the heart. It is said to be myogenic because it is capable of rhythmically contracting without receiving any nervous stimuli and in this it differs from other muscle. The muscle cells branch repeatedly to form a network through which contraction spreads rapidly. Each cell has a central nucleus and is both horizontally and vertically striped. The divisions between cells are known as intercalated discs and are specially adapted for transmission of impulses. Under normal healthy circumstances, cardiac muscle is not allowed to contract myogenically because the atrial or upper chamber muscle has a different contraction rate to that of the lower ventricular muscle and this would lead to inefficient and unco-ordinated heart action. The autonomic nervous system controls the rate

of contraction in order to adapt the flow of blood to specific circumstances such as rest and exercise.

Nervous tissue

Nervous tissue is only found in the nervous system and consists of the brain, spinal cord and nerves. Receiving stimuli from both external and internal sources, it serves to create consistency (particularly in respect of **homeostasis**), co-ordination and communication between different parts of the body. The nervous system interprets stimuli from the sense organs so that vision, hearing, smell etc become apparent.

Key term

Homeostasis The process of maintaining a constant internal environment despite changing circumstances. For example, this means that pH, temperature, concentrations of certain chemicals, water content etc in the fluid surrounding body cells (the internal environment) must be kept within a narrow range even when you are consuming acids (vinegar, lemon juice), are in a freezing climate, or are doing vigorous exercise etc.

Nervous tissue is composed of:

- **neurones** – highly specialised nerve cells which transmit nervous impulses. They are present only in the brain and spinal cord, but their long processes form the nerves

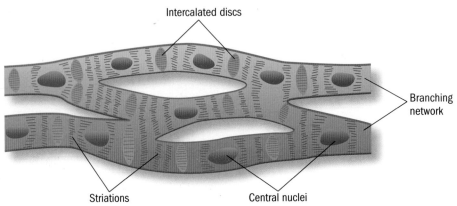

Figure 5.13 Cardiac muscle tissue ▶

Intercalated discs

Branching network

Striations

Central nuclei

Figure 5.14 General features of a ▶
neurone

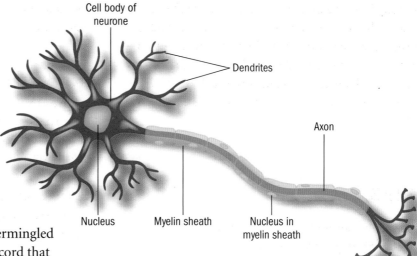

Cell body of
neurone

Dendrites

Axon

Nucleus   Myelin sheath   Nucleus in
myelin sheath

- **neuroglia** – connective tissue cells intermingled with neurones in the brain and spinal cord that offer support and protection.

Assessment activity 5.2

Describe the structure of the main tissues of the body and their role in the functioning of two named body organs. **P2**

1 The stomach has three layers of non-striated muscle in its wall and an inner lining of columnar epithelium with goblet cells. The tissue connecting the lining with the muscular coat is areolar tissue. Describe these three tissues and their roles in the functioning of the stomach.

2 Skin has an outer layer of keratinised stratified epithelium and a deeper layer of areolar tissue overlying adipose tissue and skeletal muscle. Describe keratinised stratified epithelium, adipose tissue and

non-striated muscle and their roles in the functioning of the skin.

Grading tip for P2

You could carry out these tasks using large annotated diagrams of the named organs or you may prefer to provide illustrated accounts. Ensure that the functions you describe are specific to the named organs and are not general. This demonstrates how you have applied your knowledge and understanding.

Body organ	Associated body system	Location description
Heart	Cardiovascular	Middle of the chest between the lungs, with apex lying to the left.
Lungs (2)	Respiratory	Each lies to one side of the heart, filling the **chest** or **thorax**.
Brain	Nervous	Within the skull of the head.
Stomach	Digestive	Abdominal organ lying just beneath the **diaphragm** on the left side.
Liver		Beneath the diaphragm, mainly on the right side but also overlapping part of the stomach.
Pancreas		Lies just below the stomach in a curve of the duodenum.
Duodenum		C-shaped part of the small intestine immediately beyond the stomach.
Ileum		Long coiled tube which follows the duodenum in the **abdomen**.
Colon		Begins after the ileum in the right **pelvis** area, runs up the right side to the liver, sweeps across under the stomach and down the left side of the abdomen to end at the rectum in the lower central pelvic area.
Kidneys (2)	Renal	One on each side of the posterior wall of the abdomen. The upper poles of the kidneys lie just inside the ribs. The left kidney is slightly higher than the right due to the bulk of the liver.
Bladder		Lies centrally in the lower pelvis at the front.
Ovaries (2)	Reproductive	One on each side of the posterior wall of the pelvis, below the kidneys.
Testes (2)		One on each side of the penis in a skin sac called the scrotum – outside the body cavities.
Uterus		Lies centrally in the pelvis with the ovaries on either side connected by oviducts.

Table 5.1 The major organs and where they can be found

Body organs

You are required to know the locations of major body organs; most of these will be illustrated in detail later in the unit. A quick reference can be found in Table 5.1.

Remember!

An organ is a collection of different tissues working together to carry out specific functions.

The structure and functions of the skin will be described on pages 248–250.

Key terms

The human trunk is divided into three body cavities. The upper **chest** or **thorax** is separated from the larger **abdomen** (often called inaccurately the stomach or 'tummy') by a fibro-muscular sheet known as the **diaphragm**. Only the oesophagus or gullet, and the chief artery and vein (aorta and vena cava), penetrate the diaphragm. The lower, narrower part below the abdomen is the **pelvis**. There is no physical separation like the diaphragm between the abdomen and the pelvis.

Systems

You are required to learn the gross structure of 10 body systems. Some systems will be considered in much greater detail later in the chapter. You will find the gross structure of the cardiovascular system included on pages 224–232. The gross structure of the respiratory system is included on pages 232–236 and that of the digestive system on pages 236–242. Remember, gross structure is only what the eye can see.

Remember!

A body system is a collection of organs with specific functions in the body.

The renal system

The renal system consists of two kidneys with emerging tubes called the ureters running down the posterior abdominal wall to a single pelvic collecting organ, the bladder. The passage from the bladder to the exterior is via the urethra and the flow of urine is controlled by a sphincter muscle located just below the bladder. The kidneys are supplied by short renal arteries coming off the main **artery** of the body, the aorta. Renal **veins** take the blood from the kidneys straight into the vena cava, the main vein of the body.

Key terms

Artery A blood vessel coming from the heart usually carrying oxygenated blood to the tissues.

Vein A blood vessel returning blood to the heart from the tissues; the blood has left considerable amounts of oxygen behind to supply the cells and is known as deoxygenated blood.

See also pages 229–231.

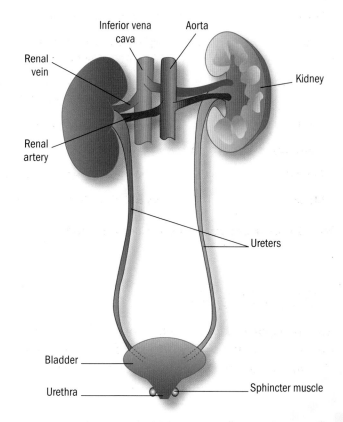

▲ Figure 5.15 Gross structure of the renal system

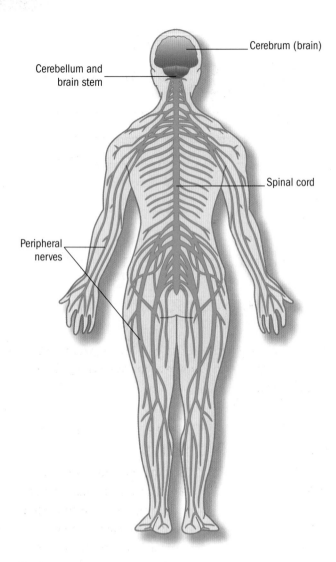

Figure 5.16 Gross structure of the nervous system

The nervous system

The nervous system comprises the central nervous system, the brain and spinal cord and the peripheral nervous system, the nerves running to and from the brain (cranial nerves) and spinal cord (spinal nerves). A chain of ganglia runs close to the spinal cord and is associated with the autonomic nervous system which controls internal organs. Autonomic nerve fibres are also contained within the peripheral nerves.

The endocrine system

This is a collection of ductless glands scattered throughout the body. Endocrine glands pass their secretions directly into the bloodstream so are always adjacent to blood vessels.

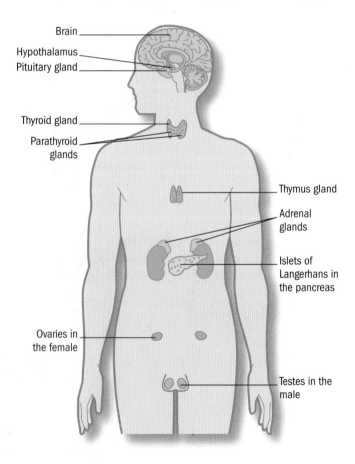

Figure 5.17 Gross structure of the endocrine system

Figure 5.18 Gross structure of the female reproductive system ▶

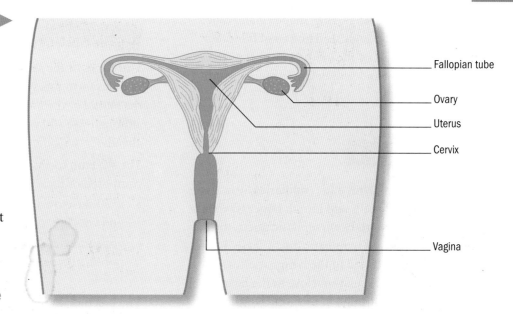

Fallopian tube

Ovary

Uterus

Cervix

Vagina

The reproductive system

Males and females have different reproductive organs as these serve different purposes.

■ Female reproductive system

This system comprises two ovaries each with an emerging oviduct or fallopian tube connecting to the uterus or womb. The neck of the uterus protrudes into the muscular vagina and this opens to the exterior at the vulva. Two fleshy folds known as the labia conceal the vaginal orifice.

■ Male reproductive system

Two testes hang in a skin sac called the scrotum just outside the abdomen and are connected by long tubes each known as the vas deferens to the urethra. The urethra is much longer than that of the female and enclosed in an organ called the penis. Two columns of erectile tissue lie alongside the urethra in the penis. Two pairs of glands, the seminal vesicles and Cowper's glands pour their secretions into the vasa deferentia (plural)

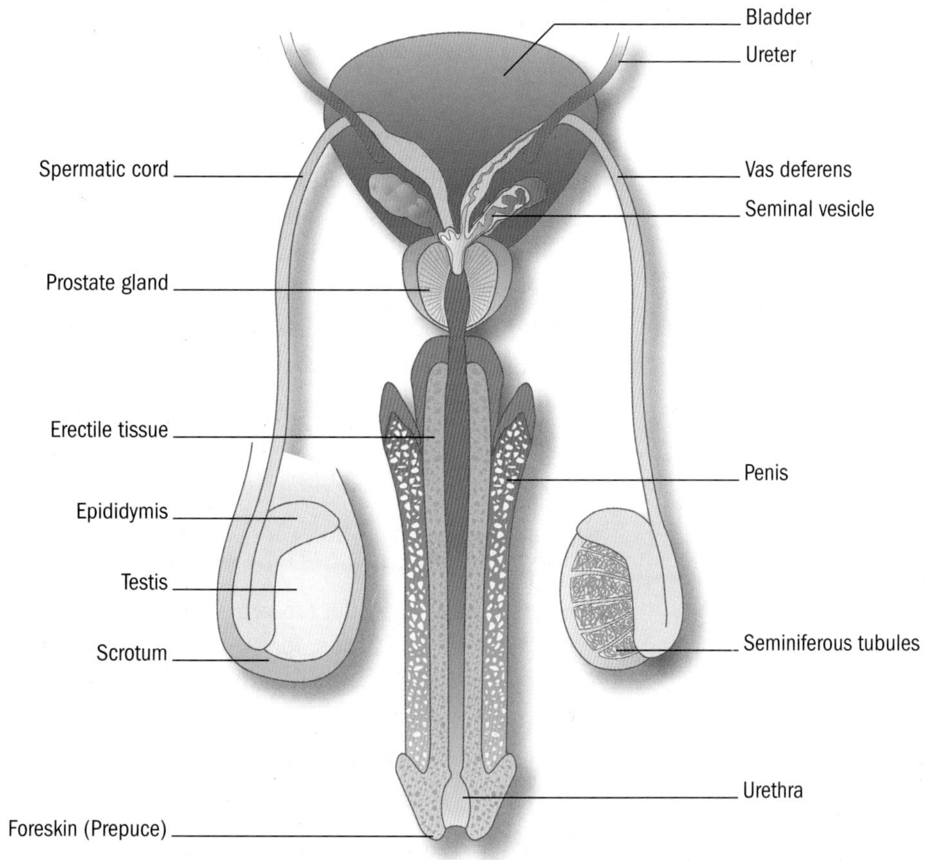

Bladder

Ureter

Spermatic cord

Vas deferens

Seminal vesicle

Prostate gland

Erectile tissue

Penis

Epididymis

Testis

Scrotum

Seminiferous tubules

Urethra

Foreskin (Prepuce)

Figure 5.19 Gross structure of the male reproductive system

close to the bladder. A single ring-shaped gland called the prostate gland also adds secretions and is located around the upper part of the urethra, just below the bladder. The urethra and vasa deferentia unite within the prostate gland.

Minute blind-ending lymphatic capillaries lie in tissue spaces between body cells and join to larger lymphatic vessels and eventually to two lymphatic ducts, the thoracic duct and right lymphatic duct. These ducts transfer the fluid collected in the lymphatic vessels back into the blood circulation close to the heart. Each lymph vessel passes through at least one lymph node (sometimes mistakenly called 'glands') and usually more than one. There are hundreds of lymph nodes all over the body often associated in groups. Lymphoid tissue also occurs in specialised areas more associated with potential sources of infection, such as the tonsils, adenoids, small intestine, spleen and thymus gland. Tiny lymphatic vessels called lacteals are present in the villi of the small intestine (see Figure 5.35, page 238) and are associated with the absorption of lipids from the digestive tract.

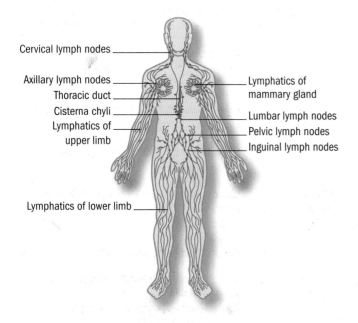

Figure 5.20 The lymphatic system

The musculo-skeletal system

The bones of the skeleton and their attached striated muscles form this system. You are not required to learn the names of the muscles or the individual bones, although you will probably know some of these already.

The skeleton forms the framework of the body and is composed of the:

- axial skeleton, in the midline of the body – the skull and vertebral column or spine
- appendicular skeleton, comprising the limb bones and their girdles, which attach them to the trunk.

The meeting place of two or more bones is known as a joint and joints may be:

- fixed by fibrous tissue and therefore immoveable; this type occurs between several bones of the skull
- slightly moveable because the bones are joined by a pad of cartilage; this type is found in between the vertebra and joining the two halves of the pelvic girdle together
- freely moveable with a more complex structure known as synovial joints; examples of synovial joints are found at the shoulder, elbow, knee, hip, fingers and toes.

Striated muscle fibres are bound together to form muscles that pull bones into different positions by contracting. Muscles never push so an 'opposite' muscle is required to return the bones to their original positions. As well as individual names such as biceps and triceps, muscles are often given names like **flexors** and **extensors** which describe the action of the muscle.

Key terms

Flexors These carry out flexion, which decreases the angle between two bones, for example, the biceps (a flexor) raises the forearm.

Extensors These carry out extension, which increases the angle between two bones, for example, the triceps (an extensor) straightens the forearm after flexion.

Theory into practice

Try bending and straightening your forearm and feel the muscles which increase in firmness as you carry out this action. Identify the biceps and triceps muscles. Repeat the action but this time raising and straightening your leg. Identify where the flexors and extensors are located.

The immune system

The immune system is more scattered than most other systems and is often not included as a major system in text books. It is a collection of cells, tissues and proteins which protects the body from invasion by harmful microorganisms. The diagram below illustrates the main components of the immune system.

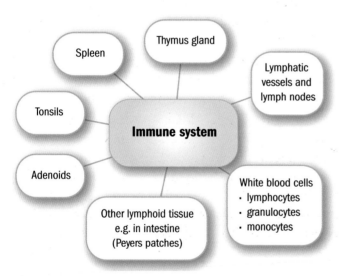

▲ Figure 5.21 The major components of the immune system

Main functions of systems

Interactions of different structures within each system

You will find this information in each section detailing the different systems.

Name of system	Main functions
Cardiovascular system	• Major transport of materials to and from cells • Distributes heat around the body and assists in temperature regulation • Defence of the body • Water regulation
Respiratory system	• Maintains oxygen supply to cells • Removes carbon dioxide and water from body
Digestive system	• Reduces complex food molecules to simple substances capable of being absorbed and delivered to cells • Removes undigested waste at intervals • The liver is the main producer of important chemicals
Renal system	• Removes excess water and salts • Eliminates nitrogen-containing waste in the form of urea • Assists in the production of new red blood cells • Involved in the maintenance of blood pressure
Nervous system	• Receives and interprets information from the environment • Controls and co-ordinates the internal organs • Associated with the endocrine system • Reflex actions protect the body from injury
Endocrine system	• Controls and co-ordinates organs • Maintains blood glucose, water and salt levels • Assists in reproduction and growth
Reproductive system	• Produces gametes which can create new life when united with a gamete from the opposite sex • Assists in growth • Responsible for secondary sexual characteristics
Lymphatic system	• Removes excess tissue fluid and proteins from spaces between cells • Defence of the body • Transports fatty acids from the digestive system
Musculo-skeletal system	• Effects movement (with the nervous system) • Stores calcium • Protects vital organs • Supports organs • Manufactures many blood cells
Immune system	• Defends against invasion by microorganisms • Anti-cancer role • Rejects material perceived as 'foreign'

Table 5.2 The main functions of the 10 body systems

Assessment activity 5.3

Describe the gross structure and main functions of all major body systems.

1 On large sheets of A3 paper, draw your own version of the gross structure of the body systems listed below, labelling each part with its name and adding a short description of the function of the part. **P3**

Body systems:

- cardiovascular
- respiratory
- digestive
- renal
- nervous
- endocrine
- reproductive – male and female
- lymphatic
- musculo-skeletal
- immune.

2 Download images of the more complicated systems from the Internet. Delete any prepared text and make the images your own by inserting labels and functions as in question 1 above.

Grading tip for P3

You need not include any details of microscopic structures such as alveoli or nephrons as these are not part of the gross structure.

Make sure the image for downloading is of good quality and clear enough to label.

The renal and endocrine systems are particularly suitable for your own diagrams as they are less complex than others.

You may find it suitable to describe the immune system in words rather than attempt to use an image as it is rather diffuse.

5.2 Functioning of body systems associated with energy metabolism

The role of energy within the cell, respiratory, cardiovascular and digestive systems has been discussed, but these were brief overviews and this section will investigate the concept of energy in more detail.

Laws of energy

Energy can be defined easily as the capacity to do work – but energy doesn't just appear, it must come from somewhere!

The first law of thermodynamics, sometimes known as the conservation of energy, states that:

Energy can neither be created nor destroyed only converted from one form to another.

The last part of this law refers to the transformation of energy from one form into another. The second form may not be of use or be capable of being measured.

Forms of energy

Energy can exist in several forms and chemical energy is the most common. The energy is in the chemical bond which unites atoms or molecules to each other. When a new bond is made between two atoms, energy is required for its formation and is usually in the form of heat although light and electrical energy can be used. When a bond is broken and atoms are released so is the energy in the bond. Heat, light, sound, electrical and nuclear are other forms of energy.

Reflect

Placing a lump of coal or wood on a fire illustrates the energy laws. As the coal burns, the chemical energy contained within it is released and transformed into heat, light and sometimes sound (crackling). The chemical energy in the wood or coal has come from the sun and the tree has converted this into stored glucose by means of photosynthesis.

Energy metabolism

Metabolism is the sum of all the chemical reactions occurring in human physiology and these will involve using or releasing energy from chemical substances.

Role of energy in the body

At this stage, you may be wondering why there is so much emphasis on energy and be thinking that it is only concerned with muscular activity and movement. However, energy is also necessary to circulate blood, lymph and tissue fluid throughout the body; it is necessary for breathing and taking in oxygen; it is necessary for making new cells for carrying out growth and repair; it is used to transmit nerve impulses so that we can respond to changes in the environment; and it is needed to build different complex molecules such as enzymes and hormones from the simple molecules produced after digestion of food.

Remember!

Energy is contained in the chemical bonds uniting the atoms of molecules.

Anabolism and catabolism

You have already learned about metabolism and how some chemical reactions involve breaking down molecules and releasing energy – these are catabolic reactions. The oxidation of glucose inside cells is a

In context

John was sliding down a rope to get down a slope. He was wearing a T-shirt and shorts and later on that day the skin on his hands and inner legs became red, swollen and painful. John had friction burns from the rope. The kinetic (motion) energy had been partly converted into heat energy, which had caused the burn. Friction is the resistance to motion when two bodies are in contact. This was neither useful nor measurable!

1 Which two bodies were in contact to cause the friction burn?
2 Name the two forms of energy and the relationship between them.
3 What is the name given to the law associated with this example?

catabolic reaction and there are many more. The opposite process is building complex molecules from simple substances and using energy – these are anabolic reactions.

Reflect

If you are interested in world sports, you will often have read about sportsmen and sportswomen who have been banned as a consequence of taking drugs. The most commonly banned substances are called anabolic steroids as these build up muscle tissue and in theory enable sportspeople to compete unfairly with an enhanced performance. This will remind you that anabolic means 'building up' so catabolic must mean 'breaking down'.

Metabolism = catabolism and anabolism

Energy supply to the cells

The activities involved in energy supply include the roles of the cardiovascular, respiratory and digestive systems.

You will learn about these systems in more detail in the sections which follow but first, here is an overall view.

The digestive system is responsible for taking in food and water and, using enzymes, breaking up complex molecules into the simple soluble materials capable of passing into the adjacent capillaries of the cardiovascular system. The cardiovascular system transports these simple materials to the liver and body cells via the bloodstream, driven by the pumping action of the heart. At the same time, the respiratory system constantly refreshes lung oxygen and disposes of waste products such as carbon dioxide and water through the process of breathing. Dissolved oxygen passes through the thin alveolar walls into the bloodstream and is transported to cells. Body cells thus have a constant delivery of raw materials such as glucose and other nutrients and

dissolved oxygen so that the breakdown (catabolic) process of glucose oxidation can take place and release energy to do work. This takes place initially in the cytoplasm and is completed in the mitochondria.

The released energy is trapped as chemical energy in ATP (see 'Mitochondria' on page 205).

Remember!

Very active cells or tissues have great numbers of mitochondria to supply ATP for their activities. Muscle tissue is a good example of this.

Cardiovascular system

The heart is a muscular pump which forces blood around the body through a system of blood vessels, namely arteries, veins and capillaries. Blood carries dissolved oxygen to the body cells and at the same time removes the waste products of respiration, carbon dioxide and water. However, blood is also important in distributing heat around the body, along with hormones, nutrients, salts, enzymes and urea.

The structure of the heart

The adult heart is the size of a closed fist located in the thoracic cavity between the lungs and protected by the rib cage. It is surrounded by a tough membrane, the pericardium, which contains a thin film of fluid to prevent friction.

The heart is a double pump, each side consisting of an upper chamber (the atrium) and a lower chamber (the ventricle). The right side of the heart pumps deoxygenated blood from the veins to the lungs for oxygenation. The left side pumps oxygenated blood from the lungs to the body and the two sides are completely separated by a septum. The blood passes twice through the heart in any one cycle and this is often termed a double circulation.

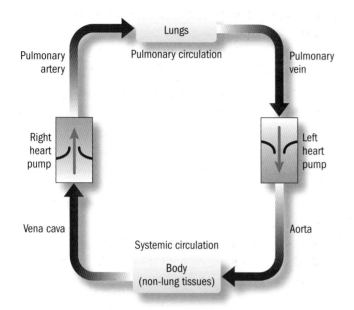

▲ Figure 5.22 The double circulation of the heart

Remember!

Atria have veins entering and ventricles have arteries leaving. A and V for each chamber – NEVER two As or two Vs.

A schematic diagram showing the double circulation with the heart artificially separated is shown in Figure 5.22.

Each of the four heart chambers has a major blood vessel entering or leaving it. Veins enter the atria and arteries leave the ventricles.

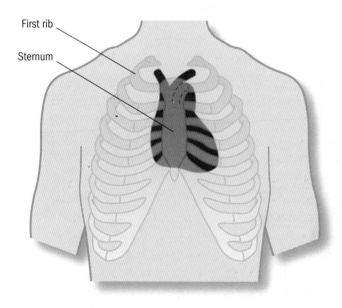

▲ Figure 5.23 The location of the heart

The circulation to and from the lungs is known as the pulmonary circulation and that around the body is the systemic circulation.

Arteries are blood vessels that leave the heart while veins take blood towards the heart.

In the pulmonary circulation, the pulmonary artery carrying deoxygenated blood leaves the right ventricle to go to the lungs – you will realise that it must divide fairly soon after leaving the heart because there are two lungs to be supplied – hence the right and left pulmonary arteries. The pulmonary veins (there are four of them), now carrying oxygenated blood, must enter the left atrium.

The main artery to the body leaving the left ventricle is the aorta and the main vein bringing blood back to the heart from the body enters the right atrium and is the vena cava. The vena cava has two branches, the superior vena cava returning blood from the head and neck and the inferior vena cava returning blood from the rest of the body. In many diagrams of the heart, these are treated as one vessel.

It is important that the blood flows in only one direction through the heart so it is supplied with special valves to ensure that this happens. There are two sets of valves between the atria and the ventricles, one on each side. Sometimes these are called the right and left atrio-ventricular valves but the older names are also used – the bicuspid, or mitral (left side), and tricuspid (right side) valves. These names refer to the number of 'flaps' known as cusps that make up the valve, the bicuspid having two cusps and the tricuspid having three cusps. Each cusp is fairly thin so, to prevent them turning inside out with the force of the blood flowing by, they have tendinous cords attached to their free ends and these are tethered to the heart muscles of the ventricles by small papillary muscles. The papillary muscles tense just before the full force of the muscle in the ventricles contracts so the tendinous cords act like guy ropes holding the valves in place.

The two large arteries, the pulmonary and the aorta, also have exits guarded by valves called semi-lunar valves (so-called because the three cusps forming each valve are half-moon shaped); when the blood has been forced into the arteries by the ventricular muscle contractions, the blood must not be allowed to fall back into the ventricles when they relax. These valves are also called the pulmonary and aortic valves.

■ How to work out the left and right sides of the heart

Sometimes learners are confused about the correct labels for the heart chambers. When you look at an image in front of you, it is like a mirror image so the left side of the image is opposite your right hand and vice versa. A paper-based image can be placed facing outwards on the front of your chest to make the sides the same as your left and right hands. You do need to know which is your right and left hand though!

Remember!

It is easy to recall which side each valve is on if you think that the TRIcuspid is on the RIghT side, a rearrangement of the letters TRI, so the bicuspid must be on the left!

Reflect

Using a stethoscope over the heart area and either on your own or with a partner, listen for the heart sounds.

These have been likened to lubb-dup, each separated by a very short interval. Valves, like hands clapping, make sounds when closing not opening. Lubb represents the atrio-ventricular valves closing while dup is the sound made by the semi-lunar valves closing. In some people, swishing sounds can be heard between heart sounds and these are called murmurs. All murmurs should be investigated but most are not related to disease. Murmurs are the result of disturbed blood flow.

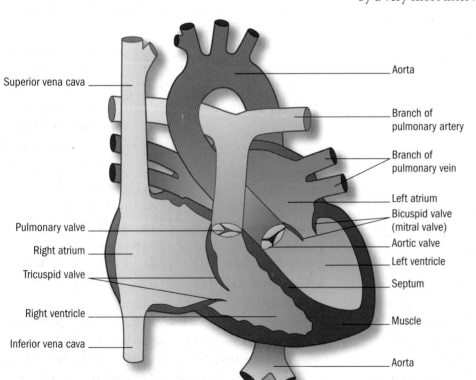

Superior vena cava

Pulmonary valve

Right atrium

Tricuspid valve

Right ventricle

Inferior vena cava

Aorta

Branch of pulmonary artery

Branch of pulmonary vein

Left atrium

Bicuspid valve (mitral valve)

Aortic valve

Left ventricle

Septum

Muscle

Aorta

Figure 5.24 Section through the heart

Heart muscle, as you learned on page 214, is cardiac muscle, composed of partially striped interlocking, branched cells. It is myogenic, which means capable of rhythmic contractions without a nerve supply. However, the atrial muscle beats at a different pace to the ventricular muscle so it needs a nerve supply to organise and co-ordinate the contractions so that the heart is an efficient pump. The heart muscle has its own blood supply, the coronary arteries and veins.

The muscular walls of the atria are much thinner than the ventricular walls as the flow of blood is aided by gravity and the distance travelled is merely from the atria to the ventricles. The ventricles are much thicker than the atria but they also differ from each other. The right ventricle is about one-third the thickness of the left ventricle because this has to drive oxygenated blood around the whole of the body including the head and neck, which is against the force of gravity. The right ventricle only has to deliver blood a short distance to the lungs on either side of the heart.

Theory into practice

With a partner, measure the distance from your heart to one of your big toes and compare this with the distance from your heart to one lung. Now you really know the reason for the much thicker muscle of the left ventricle.

The cardiac cycle

The cardiac cycle comprises the events taking place in the heart during one heart beat. Taking the average number of beats in a minute or 60 seconds at rest to be 70, then the time for one beat or one cardiac cycle is 60 divided by 70 seconds, which works out at 0.8 seconds. You must remember that this is based on an average resting heart rate. When the heart rate rises to say 120 beats during moderate activity, the cardiac cycle will reduce to 0.5 seconds. As we can see, the higher the heart rate, the shorter the cardiac cycle until a limit is reached when the heart would not have time to fill between successive cycles.

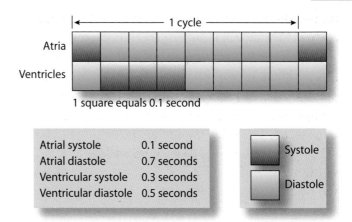

1 square equals 0.1 second

Atrial systole	0.1 second
Atrial diastole	0.7 seconds
Ventricular systole	0.3 seconds
Ventricular diastole	0.5 seconds

Systole / Diastole

Figure 5.25 The timing of events in the cardiac cycle

The cardiac cycle is shown in Figure 5.25 as a series of boxes representing 0.1 second each, to study the events occurring in the heart; red boxes signify when contraction is occurring and green boxes signify relaxation time. The technical term for contraction is systole and the term for relaxation is diastole. The activity of the atria is shown on the top line and the ventricles at the bottom.

The events in the cardiac cycle can be described in stages as follows:

1 Both atria contract forcing blood under pressure into the ventricles.
2 Ventricles are bulging with blood and the increased pressure forces the atrio-ventricular valves shut (giving rise to the first heart sound – lubb).
3 Muscle in the ventricular walls begins to contract, pressure on blood inside rises and forces open the semi-lunar valves in the aorta and pulmonary artery.
4 Ventricular systole forces blood into the aorta (left side) and pulmonary artery (right side). These arteries have elastic walls and begin to expand.
5 As the blood leaves the ventricles, the muscle starts to relax. For a fraction of a second blood falls backwards, catching the pockets of the semi-lunar valves and making them close (the second heart sound – dup).
6 With the ventricles in diastole, the atrio-ventricular valves are pushed open with the blood that has been filling the atria. When the ventricles are about 70 per cent full, the atria contract to push the remaining blood in rapidly and the next cycle has begun.

You can see that when the chambers are in diastole and relaxed, they are still filling. The heart is never empty of blood. The cycle is continuous and with a high heart rate it is the filling time which has shortened.

Theory into practice

Construct another set of boxes similar to those in Figure 5.25 and discover how much time the atria and ventricles have to fill when the heart rate is 120 beats per minute. Remember the cardiac cycle is now lasting only 0.5 seconds (60/120). On your chart, mark clearly the places where the heart sounds will be heard.

Remember!

Both atria and both ventricles contract at the same time.

Heart rate and stroke volume

The cardiac output is the quantity of blood expelled from the heart in one minute. To calculate this, you need to know the quantity of blood expelled from the left ventricle in one beat (known as the stroke volume) and the number of beats in one minute (or the heart rate). The average individual has a stroke volume of 70cm³ and a heart rate between 60 and 80 beats per minute. An individual who trains regularly might have a lower heart rate but a higher stroke volume.

Control of the cardiac cycle

The heart is controlled by the autonomic nervous system which has two branches – the sympathetic nervous system and the parasympathetic nervous system. These

Theory into practice

Tamsin is a sprinter and has trained every day since she entered her teens, while Vicky enjoys watching TV and only occasionally goes clubbing. Explain the figures in the table below with respect to their lifestyle and calculate their cardiac outputs.

Heart statistics	Tamsin	Vicky
Stroke volume (cm³)	95	72
Resting heart rate (beats/minute)	62	72
Cardiac output (cm³/min)		

two systems act rather like an accelerator and a brake on the heart. The sympathetic nervous system (NS) is active during muscular work, fear and stress, causing each heartbeat to be increased in strength and an increased heart rate. The parasympathetic NS calms the heart output and is active during peace and contentment.

The sympathetic NS is boosted by the hormone adrenaline during periods of fright, flight and fight!

Blood pressure

The force blood exerts on the walls of the blood vessels it is passing through is known as the blood pressure (BP). It can be measured using a special piece of equipment called a sphygmomanometer, often abbreviated to 'sphygmo' (pronounced *sfigmo*).

Systolic blood pressure corresponds to the pressure of the blood when the ventricles are contracting. Diastolic BP represents blood pressure when the ventricles are relaxed and filling. BP is usually written as systolic/diastolic, for example, 120/80, and the units are still mm Hg or millimetres of mercury. Newer SI (International System of Units) units are kPa or kiloPascals but few establishments have converted.

The standard BP for a young healthy adult is taken as 120/80 mm Hg (or 15.79/10.53 kPa).

BP is highest in blood vessels nearer the heart like the aorta and the large arteries. BP drops rapidly as blood is forced through the medium-sized arteries and the arterioles as these vessels present a considerable

In context

Paul is in a Guards regiment and was very embarrassed when he fainted during an important parade on a hot day. He had been required to stand to attention for a very long time. As the parade had lasted several hours he had suffered from a lack of circulating blood to his brain which had caused him to faint. His muscles were inactive for a lengthy period, the blood had pooled in his leg veins causing him to faint and he had also lost a lot of body water through sweating in his thick uniform.

1   **Can you suggest a way of avoiding such a disaster?**

2   **Describe the effect on Paul's legs.**

3   **Why is fainting an effective way of managing a lack of circulating blood to the brain?**

resistance. BP in the capillaries is very low and blood in the veins has to be assisted back to the heart by a so-called 'muscle pump'. Veins in the limbs are located between muscle groups and as they have thinner walls than arteries and possess valves at intervals, muscle action 'squeezes' the blood upwards in columns and the valves prevent backflow. The slightly negative pressure in the chest during breathing also tends to 'suck' blood back towards the heart.

Blood vessels

■ Arteries and arterioles

Arteries leave the heart and supply smaller vessels known as arterioles which, in turn, supply the smallest blood vessels, the capillaries. Arteries usually carry oxygenated blood. The exceptions are the pulmonary and umbilical arteries carrying, respectively, blood to the lungs and placenta in pregnancy for oxygenation. The arterioles provide an extensive network to supply the capillaries and, in overcoming the resistance of these muscular vessels, BP drops significantly at this stage. Arteries and arterioles are lined by endothelium (see simple squamous epithelium on page 208) and have a thick muscular coat. The lumen or central hole is round.

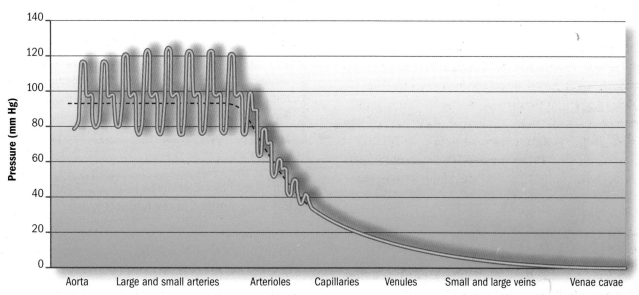

Figure 5.26 Graph to show the fall in blood pressure as blood moves through the circulation

An artery

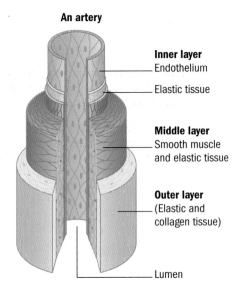

Inner layer
Endothelium

Elastic tissue

Middle layer
Smooth muscle
and elastic tissue

Outer layer
(Elastic and
collagen tissue)

Lumen

A vein

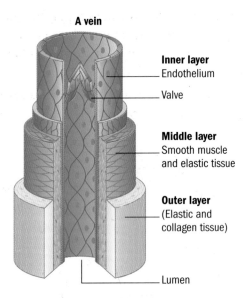

Inner layer
Endothelium

Valve

Middle layer
Smooth muscle
and elastic tissue

Outer layer
(Elastic and
collagen tissue)

Lumen

A capillary

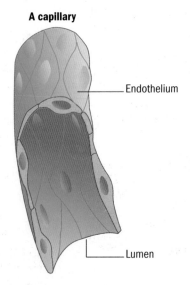

Endothelium

Lumen

■ Capillaries

These single-cell walled vessels are supplied with blood by the arterioles (see 'Simple squamous epithelium' on page 208). Body cells are never very far from a capillary on which they rely for nutrients and oxygen. A protein-free plasma filtrate is driven out of the arterial ends of capillaries to supply the cells with oxygen and nutrients. This is called tissue or interstitial fluid. Tissue fluid re-enters the venous ends of the capillaries, bringing the waste products of the metabolic activities of the body cells (such as dissolved carbon dioxide and water).

■ Venules and veins

Venules are small veins which are supplied by capillaries and feed into veins. The largest vein is the vena cava which enters the right atrium of the heart. Limb veins contain valves to assist the flow of blood back to the heart because of the low BP in the veins. Veins have a much thinner muscular coat than arteries, more fibrous tissue and an oval lumen. BP is low in veins and venules. Generally, veins carry deoxygenated blood with the exceptions of the pulmonary and umbilical arteries bringing blood back from the lungs and placenta respectively.

Remember!

A first aider learns that arterial bleeding is bright red and spurts out in time with the heart beat; capillary bleeding oozes from a wound and is most common, while venous bleeding is dark red (less oxygen) and flows at a low pressure.

Each type of blood vessel has structural and functional differences outlined in the table opposite.

◀ Figure 5.27 Arteries, veins and capillaries

Arteries	Veins	Capillaries
Carry blood away from heart to organs	Carry blood to heart from the organs	Connects arteries to veins
Carry blood under high pressure Thick, muscular walls Round lumen	Carry blood under low pressure Thin, muscular walls Oval lumen	Arterioles and capillaries cause greatest drop in pressure due to overcoming the friction of blood passing through small vessels
Usually contain blood high in oxygen, low in carbon dioxide and water	Usually contain blood low in oxygen, high in carbon dioxide and water	Delivers protein-free plasma filtrate high in oxygen to cells and collects respiratory waste products of carbon dioxide and water
Large elastic arteries close to the heart help the intermittent flow from the ventricles become a continuous flow through the circulation	Veins in limbs contain valves at regular intervals and are sandwiched between muscle groups to help blood travel against gravity	Walls are formed from a single layer of epithelium cells

▲ Table 5.3 The functional differences of blood vessels

Pulmonary and systemic circulations

The circulation of blood to and from the lungs is known as the pulmonary circulation and that around the body is the systemic circulation.

The pulmonary circulation comprises the pulmonary arteries supplying the lungs with deoxygenated blood from the right ventricle and the pulmonary veins carrying oxygenated blood back to the left atrium of the heart.

Each organ has an arterial and venous supply bringing blood to the organ tissues and draining blood away respectively. The link vessels supplying the cells of the organ tissues are the capillaries.

The systemic circulation comprises all the blood vessels not involved in the pulmonary circulation.

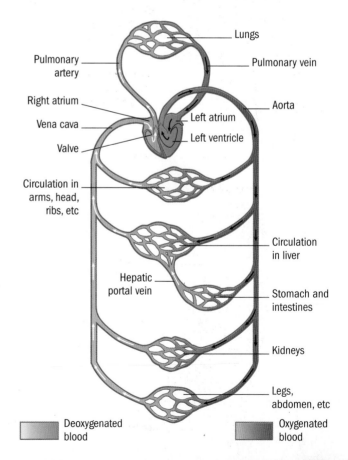

Figure 5.28 Simplified diagram to show human circulation ▶

Structure and functions of blood

You have already learned about blood in the section on tissues on pages 210–211. You might like to read this section again before reading on about haemoglobin.

Erythrocytes contain haemoglobin, a very important respiratory pigment essential for human life.

Haemoglobin is a very special iron-containing protein because:

- in an environment containing a high concentration of oxygen, the *haem* part of the molecule forms a strong chemical bond with oxygen, becoming oxyhaemoglobin. Oxyhaemoglobin is formed in the blood of the lung capillaries and carries oxygen to tissue cells

- in an environment containing a low concentration of oxygen, the oxygen is released to pass down a concentration gradient to body cells. Haemoglobin is now said to be reduced haemoglobin.

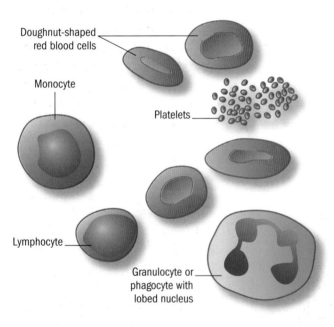

Doughnut-shaped red blood cells

Monocyte

Platelets

Lymphocyte

Granulocyte or phagocyte with lobed nucleus

▲ Figure 5.29 Different types of blood cell

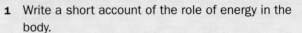

Assessment activity 5.4

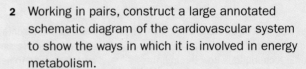

Describe the role of energy in the body and the physiology of three named body systems in relation to energy metabolism. **P4**

1 Write a short account of the role of energy in the body.

2 Working in pairs, construct a large annotated schematic diagram of the cardiovascular system to show the ways in which it is involved in energy metabolism.

You will be able to use this as a basis for your individual account for the P4 assessment.

Grading tip for P4

You will need to describe why the body needs energy and what it is used for.

A schematic diagram is one in which you will not actually draw the heart, for example, but write 'heart' inside a box.

You will be interrelating the cardiovascular system with the respiratory and digestive systems to complete P4, so you need to remember that the blood circulation is the main transport system of the body and include in your account all the raw materials and waste products involved in energy metabolism that are transported to and from body cells.

The respiratory system

Respiration can be artificially subdivided into four sections to facilitate study. These are:

A External respiration comprising:

- breathing
- gaseous exchange
- blood transport.

B Internal or tissue respiration carried out inside body cells.

Breathing

The thorax, better known as the chest, is an airtight box containing the lungs and their associated tubes, the bronchi and the heart.

Air can enter the thorax via the nose or the mouth; the former is specially adapted for the entry of air in breathing and is the recommended route.

■ Role of the air passages in the nose

The nose contains fine bones on its side walls which are curled like scrolls and covered with moist ciliated mucous membrane, rich in blood capillaries. This arrangement produces a large surface area over which incoming air flows. During the passage through the nose, the air is warmed and moistened by the close contact with the mucous membrane and filtered by the ciliated cells. By the time the air reaches the throat, it is warmed to almost body temperature, moistened to almost saturation point and most foreign materials such as dust, carbon particles and many pathogens have been filtered out.

■ Structure and function of the trachea and bronchi

The trachea commences at the back of the throat, or pharynx, and divides into two main bronchi, each serving one lung on each side of the heart. The first part of the trachea is specially adapted to produce sound and is called the larynx, or voice box. It is protected by a moveable cartilage flap, the epiglottis, which prevents food entering during swallowing.

When any material, such as a crumb, manages to pass by the epiglottis it invokes an intense bout of coughing by reflex action to expel the foreign body.

The trachea (or windpipe) and the bronchi have rings of cartilage to prevent them collapsing; those in the trachea are C-shaped with the gap at the back against the main food tube, the oesophagus. This is because when food is chewed in the mouth, it is made into a ball shape (called a bolus) before swallowing. The bolus stretches the oesophagus as it passes down to the stomach and whole rings of cartilage in the trachea would hamper its progress. The gap is filled with soft muscle which stretches easily, allowing the bolus to pass down the oesophagus.

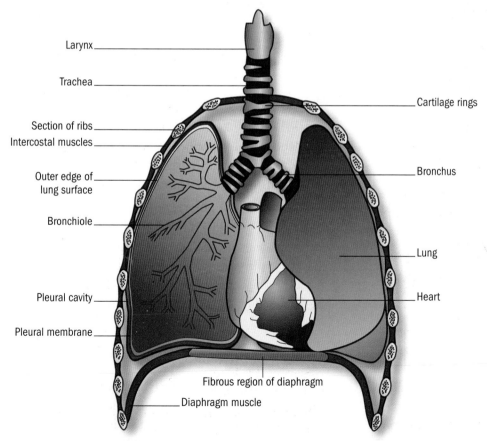

Larynx
Trachea
Section of ribs
Intercostal muscles
Outer edge of lung surface
Bronchiole
Pleural cavity
Pleural membrane
Cartilage rings
Bronchus
Lung
Heart
Fibrous region of diaphragm
Diaphragm muscle

Remember!

It is not possible to breathe and swallow at the same time so when assisting a service user to take food, you must allow time for breathing between mouthfuls of food.

◀ Figure 5.30 Section through the thorax to show the respiratory organs

On entering the lung, each bronchus divides and sub-divides repeatedly, spreading to each part of the lung. The tiniest sub-divisions, supplying oxygen to air sacs in the lung, are called bronchioles, and even these are held open by minute areas of cartilage. This branching arrangement is often called the bronchial tree.

The inner lining of the trachea and bronchi is composed of mucus-secreting and ciliated, columnar epithelium cells. Mucus is the sticky white gel which traps dust particles that may cause infection.

■ Structure and function of the lungs

Each lung is a pale pink smooth structure closely mimicking the interior of half the chest in shape. Each is divided into a few lobes with a hilum, or root, that marks the entry of the bronchus, blood vessels and nerves on the inner side.

The lungs themselves have a spongy feel to them and are lined on the outside by a thin, moist membrane known as the pleura. The pleura continues around the inner thoracic cavity so that the two pleural layers slide over one another with ease and without friction. The **surface tension** of the thin film of moisture does not allow the two layers to pull apart but does allow them to slide. This means that when the chest wall moves in breathing, the lungs move with it.

Key term

Surface tension The downward pull of water molecules so that the surface of the liquid occupies the least area.

Each bronchus after repeatedly dividing ends in a group of single-layered globe-shaped structures called alveoli, rather like a bunch of grapes on a stem. The walls of the alveoli consist of very thin, flat simple squamous epithelium, and each alveolus is surrounded by the smallest blood vessels known as capillaries. The walls of the capillaries are also composed of simple squamous epithelium, in a single layer. This means that the air entering the alveoli during breathing is separated from the blood by only two single-layered, very thin walls.

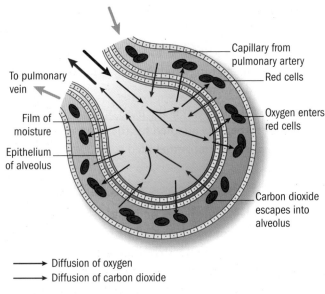

To pulmonary vein

Film of moisture

Epithelium of alveolus

Capillary from pulmonary artery

Red cells

Oxygen enters red cells

Carbon dioxide escapes into alveolus

→ Diffusion of oxygen
→ Diffusion of carbon dioxide

▲ Figure 5.31 Gaseous exchange in the alveolus

There are elastic fibres round the alveoli enabling them to expand and recoil with inspiration and expiration respectively. A film of moisture lines the inside of each alveolus to enable the air gases to pass into solution. As the two layers of epithelium are very thin and semi-permeable, the dissolved gases can easily and rapidly pass through, in the process called gaseous exchange.

■ Ventilation, or breathing, and the respiratory muscles

Ventilation is the movement of air in and out of the thorax to replenish the oxygen supply and remove surplus waste products (carbon dioxide and water).

Ventilation has two phases, namely inspiration (or inhalation) and expiration (or exhalation).

The movements are effected by respiratory muscles attached to the skeleton. Two sets of intercostal muscles run obliquely at right angles to each other between the ribs, and the diaphragm is a dome-shaped muscle attached to the lower ribs and separating the thorax from the abdomen.

■ Inspiration

When the intercostal muscles contract, the ribs move upwards and outwards and at the same time the contraction of the diaphragm causes it to flatten. All these movements serve to increase the volume of the

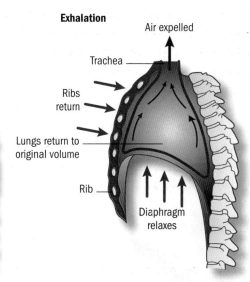

Figure 5.32 Changes in the thorax during inspiration and expiration

Inhalation

Air drawn in
Trachea
Ribs raised
Lungs expand
Rib
Diaphragm pulled down

Exhalation

Air expelled
Trachea
Ribs return
Lungs return to original volume
Rib
Diaphragm relaxes

thorax and the lungs and thus reduce the pressure inside the lungs, causing air to rush in from the environment. This is known as inspired, or inhaled, air.

■ Expiration

The main force in expiration during quiet breathing is the elastic recoil of the fibres around the alveoli and the relaxation of the diaphragm. However, during exertion, more forcible expiration can occur with the assistance of the other set of intercostal muscles contracting to move the ribs downwards and inwards. The volume of the thorax decreases, the pressure increases above that of the environmental air and air rushes out.

Nervous impulses from the brain cause the diaphragm and intercostal muscles to contract

Diaphragm flattens and the intercostal muscles cause the ribs to move upwards and outwards

Volume of the chest increases, so the pressure inside the chest must decrease

Surface tension between the pleura drags the lungs with the chest wall. As they expand, they fill with air

Air containing oxygen rushes down the trachea and bronchi to equalise the pressure with the external environment – *inhalation*

After a few seconds, the nervous impulses stop arriving and the elastic tissue in the lung causes recoil: the diaphragm rises and the ribs lower

Volume of the chest decreases, so pressure increases, causing air to rush out of the trachea – *exhalation*

The cycle repeats after a few minutes because the respiratory control centre becomes active again, sending more nervous impulses

▲ Figure 5.33 The process of breathing

Normal ventilation rate is from 16 to 20 breaths per minute but this rises significantly during exertion.

Gaseous exchange

The composition of inspired air, which is the air around us, and that of expired air is shown in the table below:

Component	Inspired air	Expired air
Oxygen	20%	16%
Nitrogen	80%	80%
Carbon dioxide	Virtually 0% (0.04)%	4%
Water vapour	Depends on climate	Saturated

Table 5.3 The composition of inspired and expired air

Reflect

Study the table above and write down the differences that you can see. These changes must have happened in the lungs through gaseous exchange.

Although the largest component of air is nitrogen and this too passes into solution, it takes no part in the process of respiration.

Breathing in fresh air replenishes the high concentration of dissolved oxygen molecules in the lung alveoli, and the removal of diffused oxygen by the bloodstream maintains the low concentration. With carbon dioxide, the situation is reversed – the high concentration is in the blood and the low concentration is in the refreshed air, so diffusion (see below) removes dissolved carbon dioxide from the blood into the expired air from the lungs. Carbon dioxide and water are waste products from internal respiration in cells.

Diffusion

Diffusion occurs in liquids or gases because the molecules are in constant random motion, and diffusion is an overall 'equalling up' of a situation where you have a lot of molecules meeting a few molecules. Diffusion will stop in time, as the numbers of molecules become more evenly distributed. This is said to be equilibrium. (Note that this does not mean the molecules stop moving, only that there are now equal numbers of molecules passing in all directions.)

Key term

Diffusion The movement of molecules of a gas or a liquid from a region of high concentration to a region of low concentration.

In the human body, where diffusion is a common method of transport, the state of equilibrium is not desirable as it means overall transport would cease. To prevent equilibrium being attained, the high concentration must be continually kept high and the low concentration must also be maintained.

Diffusion can only occur where there is no barrier at all to the molecules or where the barrier (in gaseous exchange, this is cell membranes) is thin. The rate of diffusion is enhanced with an increased surface area – usually by folds or similar structures to alveoli, and with temperature, since warmth increases the random motion of molecules.

Assessment activity 5.5

Describe the role of energy in the body and the physiology of three named body systems in relation to energy metabolism.

1 Working in pairs and using the annotated diagram you constructed for the cardiovascular system, add notes on the processes occurring in respiration that are concerned with energy metabolism. **P4**

Grading tip for P4

Using a different colour from the one you used in Assessment activity 5.4, draw interconnecting lines to boxes depicting parts of the respiratory systems such as alveoli, ribs and diaphragm etc. You should end up with a display showing how the two systems interrelate in relation to energy metabolism.

Do not worry if your display looks untidy, it will form a memory aid for your assessment.

The digestive system

The alimentary canal

The alimentary canal is a tube that extends from the mouth to the anus. It is dilated, folded and puckered in various places along its length. You will need to know the names of the various regions, their main purpose and the outcomes of their activities. Many glands are associated with the alimentary canal, and have important roles to play in digestion.

See Table 5.1 on page 216. When food is taken into the mouth it is mixed with saliva, chewed or masticated by the action of the tongue and teeth, rolled into a small ball known as a bolus, and swallowed. This process is called mechanical digestion and is an important part of physically breaking the food down at an early stage.

■ The salivary glands

Three pairs of salivary glands pour their secretions known as saliva into the mouth.

Saliva, a digestive juice, contains an **enzyme** known as salivary amylase, which begins the digestion of carbohydrates as well as lubricating the mouth and helping bolus formation.

Key term

Enzymes These are biological catalysts which alter the rates of chemical reaction (usually speeding them up) but which are themselves unchanged at the end of the reactions.

Read more on enzymes on pages 240–241.

■ The oesophagus

The oesophagus or gullet transports the food bolus from the back of the mouth (the pharynx) to the stomach in the abdomen. The swallowed bolus is in the oesophagus for a few seconds only and no enzymes are secreted here, although salivary amylase will continue to act during this brief journey. The oesophagus is mainly a transit for food boluses which it moves by muscular contractions known as peristalsis (see page 240).

■ The stomach

The stomach is the widest part of the alimentary canal, tucked mainly behind the rib cage under the diaphragm on the left side and receiving food from the mouth by way of the oesophagus. Food can stay in the stomach for up to three hours, with a protein meal remaining the longest and food not containing protein passing through relatively quickly. During this time, the strong stomach walls roll and churn the food around and pour on secretions from the gastric glands. The resulting paste-like material is called chyme.

Gastric glands produce gastric juice that contains gastric protease and hydrochloric acid. The gastric juice works on proteins. In babies, another enzyme, rennin, solidifies and digests milk protein. The pH of the stomach is 1–2; this is strongly acidic. The epithelial lining of the stomach contains goblet cells which produce thick mucus to protect the lining from acid erosion.

The stomach empties the chyme in spurts into the duodenum through the pyloric sphincter, a thick ring of muscle which alternately contracts and relaxes.

■ The duodenum

The next part of the alimentary canal is the small intestine, so-called because of its small diameter – certainly not its length, for it is around six meters long! The first C-shaped part, and the shortest, is called the duodenum; it is mainly concerned with digestion and is helped by two large glands, the liver and the pancreas, that pour their secretions or juices into this area. The duodenal wall also contains glands which secrete enzyme-rich juices (called succus entericus) that continue the digestive process on proteins, carbohydrates and lipids, or fats. These work either on the surface or inside the epithelial lining cells.

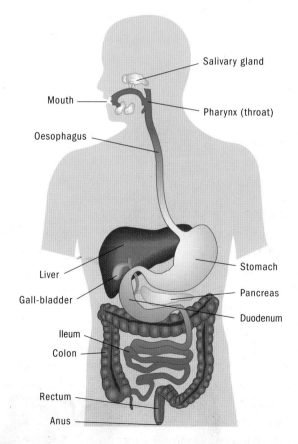

Salivary gland
Mouth
Pharynx (throat)
Oesophagus
Liver
Gall-bladder
Stomach
Pancreas
Duodenum
Ileum
Colon
Rectum
Anus

▲ **Figure 5.34 The alimentary canal**

■ The ileum

The remainder of the small intestine, known as the ileum, is mainly concerned with the absorption of the now fully digested food. It is specially adapted for this by:

- long length
- folded interior
- lining covered in many thousands of tiny projections called villi
- epithelial cells of villi covered in microvilli, projections so small that they can only be detected using an electron microscope.

These adaptations increase the surface area for absorption of nutrients from digested food to enormous proportions.

Each villus is lined by columnar cells and goblet cells only one-cell thick with an internal extensive capillary network and a blind-ended branch of the lymphatic system called a lacteal.

The chief products of protein and carbohydrate digestion pass into the capillary network which drains to the liver by the hepatic portal vein. Products of fat digestion pass into the lacteal and eventually they pass via the lymphatic system into the general circulation.

■ The colon

In the right hand lower corner of the abdomen, the small intestine meets the large intestine; there are two biological remnants at this point, the caecum and the appendix. In grass-eating animals the caecum is a large structure with the worm-like appendix at the end. They are known as biological or evolutionary remnants because in the human species, neither the caecum nor the appendix has any function. The appendix can become inflamed or pustulous and threaten life – a condition known as appendicitis. As well as the caecum and appendix, the large intestine consists of the colon

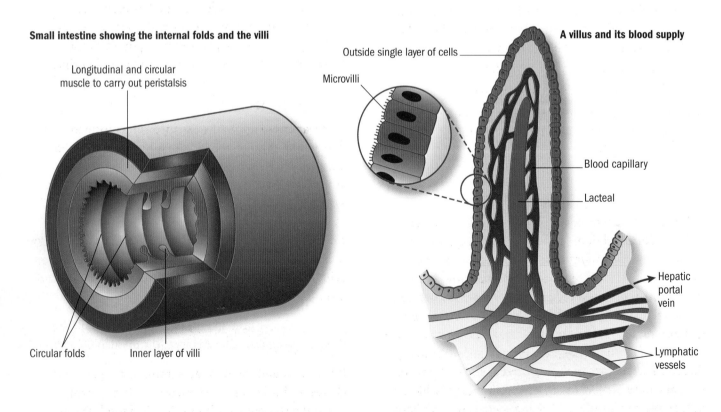

Small intestine showing the internal folds and the villi

Longitudinal and circular muscle to carry out peristalsis

Circular folds

Inner layer of villi

A villus and its blood supply

Outside single layer of cells

Microvilli

Blood capillary

Lacteal

Hepatic portal vein

Lymphatic vessels

▲ Figure 5.35 Small intestine and villi of the ileum

and rectum, ending in the sphincter (the anus) for the elimination of faeces.

The colon runs up the right side of the abdomen and turns to travel across to the left side before ending at the anus. There are no enzymic juices in the large intestine.

The colon has a puckered appearance because the outer longitudinal muscle coat splits into three bands and the circular muscle bulges out between the bands. During the journey down the alimentary canal, many glands have poured watery juices onto the chyme. The body cannot afford to lose so much water and the purpose of the large intestine is to slow down the passage of food waste. (Food waste is all that is left at this stage because all the absorption of nutrients occurred in the small intestine). This means that water can be reabsorbed and the motion, or faeces, becomes semi-solid. It can then be eliminated by muscular action of the rectum and relaxation of the anus at a convenient time.

Faeces contain:

- cellulose (fibre or roughage) from plant cell walls from fruit and vegetables
- dead bacteria, including the usually harmless bacteria living in the large intestine which have died a natural death, and other bacteria, which are often killed by the hydrochloric acid in the stomach
- scraped-off cells from the gut lining.

The colour of faeces is due to bile pigments.

Mucus is secreted by enormous numbers of goblet cells in the gut lining to reduce friction as chyme and waste are moved along by peristalsis.

■ The liver

The liver is a large dark-red organ occupying the top right half of the abdomen and partly overlapping the stomach. It has a multitude of vital functions in the body, one of which is to produce bile. Bile flows down the bile duct into the duodenum after temporary storage in the gall bladder on the undersurface of the liver. Bile contains no enzymes at all, but it provides important bile salts that cause the **emulsification** of fats (lipids) in the duodenum. You will recall that protein and carbohydrate have already experienced enzymic action. Lipids, like all fats, do not mix readily with water, so the enzymes have only a small water/lipid surface on which to work.

The emulsification results in the fats forming millions of tiny globules, each with a water/lipid surface so that enzymes can work efficiently over a massively enlarged surface area. Bile also contains bile pigments – bilirubin and biliverdin. These are the waste products of degraded haemoglobin from old, broken red blood cells. They give the brown colour to faeces. Bile is secreted continuously by the liver and temporarily stored in a sac called the gall bladder. When a lipid-rich meal arrives, the gall bladder releases bile into the small intestine.

Key term

Emulsification This occurs when an emulsifier causes oil or lipids to be suspended as a large number of tiny globules in water.

The liver also removes glucose and other sugars from the blood coming from the small intestine and converts them into glycogen for storage. Surplus amino acids not required for manufacturing cell proteins are broken down in the liver to form glycogen and urea – a nitrogenous waste product transported by the bloodstream to the kidneys for elimination in urine.

■ The pancreas

The pancreas is a slim, leaf-shaped gland, located between the intestines and the stomach, close to the duodenum. It secretes enzyme-rich pancreatic juice as well as alkaline salts needed to neutralise the acidic secretions from the stomach. Pancreatic enzymes go to work on all three macronutrients (protein, fat and carbohydrate) and are important agents for the complete breakdown of the complex food molecules into amino acids, glucose and similar simple sugars, fatty acids and glycerol.

Breakdown and absorption of food materials

It is vital to understand that, without the organs and glands of the digestive system, we would be unable to use the substances collectively called food. Taking food in through the mouth (what we would call 'eating') is known technically as **ingestion**. Food is generally composed of large complex molecules of protein, carbohydrate and lipids (or fats) that would be unable to pass through the lining of the alimentary canal. Converting these complex molecules into simple soluble molecules enables their **absorption** into the bloodstream and onward transit for metabolic processes. Waste material that has not been capable of absorption is passed out through the anus periodically: the technical term for this is **egestion.**

■ Peristalsis

Food and chyme move down the alimentary canal by a process known as peristalsis. Note that in Figure 5.36 there are two sheets of muscle surrounding the tube – one sheet runs in a circular fashion around the tube

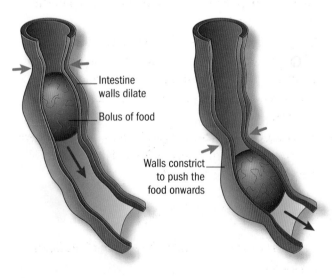

Intestine walls dilate

Bolus of food

Walls constrict to push the food onwards

▲ **Figure 5.36 Muscular coats involved in peristalsis**

while the other runs down the tube. Behind the bolus or chyme the inner circular muscle contracts (and the longitudinal muscle relaxes) pushing material in front of it. This is rather like your fingers pushing toothpaste up the tube. In front of the material, the circular muscle relaxes and the longitudinal muscle contracts to hold the tube open to receive the food. Two sets of muscles acting in this way are said to be antagonistic.

Even if you stand on your head, peristalsis will still push your food down your alimentary canal!

Strong peristaltic waves will cause abdominal pain, usually called colic, and the food is hurried down the intestines.

The role of enzymes in digestion

To break down large complex molecules in the laboratory we would use heat (as in cooking) or the addition of chemicals such as acids or alkalis. These processes are not possible in the human body, since cell and tissue structures would be destroyed or severely damaged.

Body cells are able to produce 'magical' substances called enzymes that can alter the rate of chemical reactions to build up or break down other molecules without using heat or harmful chemicals.

Enzymes are biological catalysts – in simpler terms, substances that can act within living organisms to enable the breakdown or building-up of other chemicals, the enzymes themselves being unchanged at the end of the reactions or tasks.

Enzymes are specific to the material on which they act (called a substrate). For example, a protease only acts on protein and a lipase only acts on lipids or fats. You may have noted that adding –*ase* at the end of the substrate name signifies that it is an enzyme. Not all enzymes are named in this way, but most are.

The main bulk of the human diet consists of protein, fat and carbohydrate so these are called macronutrients. They provide calories or joules of heat energy. Vitamins and mineral salts are only required in tiny amounts and are called micronutrients. They do not provide energy but are often important in energy release processes, oxygen carriage, metabolic rate, red blood cell formation and so on.

Enzyme reactions have some special features:

- Enzymes are sensitive to temperature. At low temperatures they work very slowly, or stop working; at high temperatures, they become distorted (denatured) and permanently stop working. Enzymes work best, or optimally, at body temperature.

- Enzymes are sensitive to the acidity or alkalinity of their surroundings, known as pH. Some digestive enzymes like pepsin (also known as gastric protease) work best in an acid environment. The stomach lining secretes gastric protease and hydrochloric acid for maximum efficiency in breaking down proteins. Lipase prefers alkaline conditions and the pancreas secretes alkaline salts, such as sodium hydrogen carbonate, to provide optimal conditions. Salivary amylase prefers neutral or pH7 conditions. (Amylum is the Latin name for starch, so amylase works on starch.)

- Relatively few molecules of enzymes are required to break down lots of large food molecules because they are catalysts.

- Amylases work on cooked starch substrates (bread, rice, potatoes etc), converting the molecules to simple sugars like glucose.

- Proteases act on proteins, breaking them down into amino acids and peptides (two amino acids joined together chemically).

- Lipases convert lipids to fatty acids and glycerol.

Table 5.3 on page 242 summarises the sites of enzyme secretion and their role in digestion.

Major products of digestion

Roles in the body, storage and deamination

- **Peptides and amino acids** are nitrogenous compounds; they travel via the bloodstream to areas of need in body cells. They are important in making enzymes, some hormones, plasma proteins, new cells (growth) and in repair processes. Surplus amino acids are broken down in the liver as they cannot be stored. Some parts of the molecules are used for energy but the nitrogen-containing part is converted into urea in the liver by a process called deamination and excreted by the kidneys in urine.

- **Sugars**, the chief one being glucose, are either transported to cells to be broken down in internal respiration to release energy, stored in liver and muscles as glycogen or converted into fat to be stored around organs or under the skin. Glycogen is converted back to glucose when energy is required to top up the blood glucose supply to cells or for muscle contraction. End products of internal respiration are carbon dioxide and water removed by the respiratory and renal systems.

- **Glycerol and fatty acids** – glycerol is used for energy or reconverting fatty acids into a form of fat which can be stored. Fatty acids travel from the lacteals, through the lymphatic system into the main veins of the neck; this circuitous route enables smaller quantities of potentially harmful lipids to enter the circulation gradually.

- **Fatty acids** are also used in internal respiration to release energy to drive metabolic processes. End products of internal respiration are carbon dioxide and water removed by the respiratory and renal systems.

- **Fat** is stored under the skin and around organs where it forms a long-term energy store to be used after glycogen stores are depleted.

Absorption of food

This topic is to be found under the heading 'The ileum' on page 238.

Location	Gland and juice	Contents	Substrate	End product	Other comments
Mouth	Salivary glands/saliva	Salivary amylase	Carbohydrate: starch	Disaccharides: 'double' sugar molecules	Salivary amylase is mixed with food during mechanical digestion. Requires a neutral pH to function efficiently.
Oesophagus	None	None	None	None	Salivary amylase still acting on short journey.
Stomach	Gastric glands/gastric juice	• Gastric protease * • Hydrochloric acid • Rennin in babies	Protein	Amino acids and peptides (like double amino acids)	The pH of gastric juice must be acid for pepsin to work. Food is churned into chyme. Bacteria in raw food is killed by acid.
Small intestine a) Duodenum	Intestinal glands/ intestinal juice (succus entericus)	• Peptidase • Various carbohydrases	• Peptides • Disaccharides: 'double' sugar molecules	• Amino acids • Glucose and other simple soluble sugars	Alkaline medium (pH8).
b) Liver, an associated gland (not part of the alimentary canal)	Liver/bile	• No enzymes • Bile salts • Bile pigments	None	None	Bile salts are important in emulsifying lipids or fats. Converts small intestine contents from acid to alkaline.
c) Pancreas, an associated gland (not part of the alimentary canal)	Pancreas/pancreatic juice	• Lipase • Pancreatic amylase • Pancreatic protease * (formerly called trypsin) • Alkaline salts	• Lipids or fats • Carbohydrates • Proteins and peptides	• Glycerol and fatty acids • Glucose • Amino acids	An important digestive gland. Salts convert acid stomach secretions to alkaline so that enzymes work optimally.
d) Ileum	None	None	None	None	Main area for absorption of the end-products of digestion through millions of villi.
Large intestine a) Colon	None	None	None	None	Main area for reabsorption of water.
b) Rectum	None	None	None	None	Muscular walls expel semi-solid faeces through anus at periodic intervals.

*Gastric protease and pancreatic protease are secreted as inactive precursors; they become activated by other substances once they are mixed with chyme in the lumen (hole) of the tube.

Table 5.4 The main digestive processes, locations and outcomes

Assessment activity 5.6

Describe the role of energy in the body and the physiology of three named body systems in relation to energy metabolism.

1 Describe how you might obtain energy from the digestion of your favourite meal.

Explain the physiology of three named body systems in relation to energy metabolism.

2 Write a detailed, reasoned explanation of the physiology of three systems (cardiovascular, respiratory and digestive) in relation to energy metabolism.

Use examples to explain how body systems interrelate with each other.

3 Use examples to explain how these body systems interrelate with each other.

Grading tip for P4

You need only consider the three major macronutrients present: protein, carbohydrate and lipids.

Start with mechanical digestion in the mouth and explain what happens in each part of the alimentary canal. You need not go beyond the ileum but need to include absorption and the fate of the end-products of digestion where this is associated with energy metabolism.

Grading tip for M1

At pass level a description might involve 'telling the story' of how the heart pumps blood to the lungs via the pulmonary artery to take up oxygen from the inspired air and at the same time releasing the waste product of carbon dioxide. For a merit, an explanation would incorporate details of ventilation, the cardiac cycle and the role of haemoglobin in the erythrocytes as well as the above.

Grading tip for D1

As you explain your work, you will naturally make links, for instance the regulation of plasma glucose by the endocrine system or the way in which the nervous system is involved in the regulation of the cardiac cycle. This will lead you towards a distinction. Try to make at least five substantial links of this nature. It might be advisable to draw attention to such links by the use of headings.

You have learned how tissue fluid bathes body cells and is a protein-free plasma filtrate driven out of leaky capillaries by blood pressure and how (digestive) enzymes are sensitive to pH and body temperature. It will not be surprising therefore to extend this by realising that blood and tissue fluid and consequently cell contents require stability in their chemical and physical makeup. All metabolic processes are governed by enzyme actions subject to the same characteristics as digestive enzymes.

Homeostasis

Homeostasis is the technical term for the process of maintaining a constant internal environment despite external changes.

'The internal environment' in this context comprises blood, tissue fluid, body cell contents and all the metabolic processes taking place.

It is important to realise that the use of the term 'constant' in this context is not absolute and fixed – it is more flexible and dynamic and refers to the physical and chemical composition being kept within a limited range of variables for maximum efficiency, well-being of the whole body and indeed the maintenance of life itself. This limited range of variables is said to be regulated.

Key term

Homeostasis The process of maintaining a constant internal environment despite external changes.

Negative feedback as a regulatory feedback

Negative feedback occurs when an important variable, sometimes known as a key variable, such as the pH of blood and tissue fluid deviates from the accepted range or limits and triggers responses that return the variable to within the normal range. In other words, deviation produces a negative response to counteract or nullify the deviation. It is a 'feeding back' of the disturbance to the status quo. During your study of the liver as part of the digestive system, you learned that when blood glucose levels fall, the liver glycogen is converted into glucose to top up those crucial energy levels in cells. This is an example of a negative feedback system and we shall study this further in due course.

The brain and nervous system play a vital role in controlling homeostatic mechanisms but it also helps us to anticipate when key variables might rise or fall beyond the accepted range. For example, if it is several hours since your last meal and you are beginning to feel tired and cold, you will try to eat a warm energy-giving meal to counteract these feelings. This can be termed feedforward rather than feedback as you are taking steps to avoid a low energy state before it has happened.

Negative feedback systems require:

- receptors to detect change
- a control centre to receive the information and process the response
- effectors to reverse the change and re-establish the original state.

Most control centres are located in the brain.

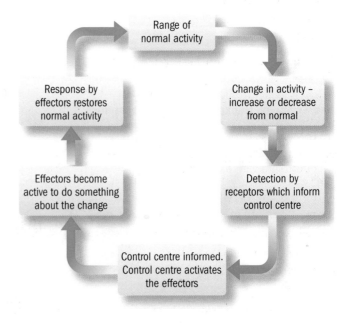

▲ Figure 5.37 Feedback control systems

Reflect

Can you think of other examples of times when when your brain might be suggesting feedforward strategies?

Homeostatic mechanisms for regulation of heart rate

First we will learn how the heart beat is regulated.

Let's begin by looking at the control of the cardiac cycle and the role of the autonomic, parasympathetic and sympathetic nervous systems.

The heart is controlled by the autonomic nervous system which has two branches, namely the sympathetic nervous system and the parasympathetic nervous system. These two systems act rather like an accelerator and a brake on the heart. The sympathetic nervous system is active when the body is undergoing muscular work, fear or stress. It causes each heartbeat to increase in strength as well as an increase in heart rate. The parasympathetic nervous system calms the heart output and is active during resting, peace and contentment. The main parasympathetic nerve is the vagus nerve and if this is severed the heart beats faster.

The sympathetic nervous system is boosted by the hormone adrenaline during periods of fright, flight and fight! Its nerves are the cardiac nerves.

The sympathetic and parasympathetic nervous systems supply a special cluster of excitable cells in the upper part of the right atrium. This is called the sino-atrial node (S-A node) or in general terms 'the pacemaker'.

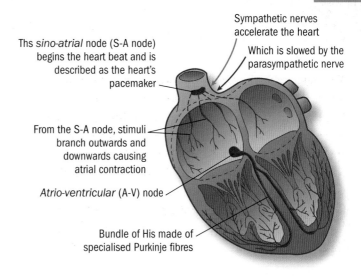

Ths *sino-atrial* node (S-A node) begins the heart beat and is described as the heart's pacemaker

Sympathetic nerves accelerate the heart

Which is slowed by the parasympathetic nerve

From the S-A node, stimuli branch outwards and downwards causing atrial contraction

Atrio-ventricular (A-V) node

Bundle of His made of specialised Purkinje fibres

▲ **Figure 5.39 Control of the cardiac cycle by the conduction system**

An interplay of impulses from the sympathetic and parasympathetic nerves acting on the S-A node regulates the activity of the heart to suit circumstances from minute to minute, hour to hour and day to day.

Every few seconds, the S-A node sends out a cluster of nerve impulses across the branching network of atrial muscle fibres to cause contraction. The impulses are caught by another group of cells forming the atrio-ventricular node (A-V node) and relayed to a band of

◄ **Figure 5.38 Sympathetic and parasympathetic control of the heart**

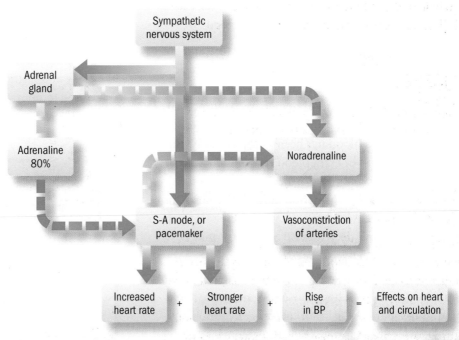

Sympathetic nervous system

Adrenal gland

Adrenaline 80%

Noradrenaline

S-A node, or pacemaker

Vasoconstriction of arteries

Increased heart rate + Stronger heart rate + Rise in BP = Effects on heart and circulation

conducting tissue made of large, modified muscle cells called Purkinje fibres.

The transmission of impulses is delayed slightly in the A-V node to enable the atria to complete their contractions and the atrio-ventricular valves to start to close.

Heart valves are located on a fibrous figure of eight between the atrial and ventricular muscle masses, and the first part of the conducting tissue (the bundle of His) enables the excitatory impulses to cross to the ventricles. The bundle of His then splits into the right and left bundle branches which run down either side of the ventricular septum before spreading out into the ventricular muscle masses.

Impulses now pass very rapidly so that the two ventricles contract together forcing blood around the body organs.

Cardiac centres

The medulla of the brain is the lowest part located just above the spinal cord and often known as the 'brain stem'. Two important centres for control of the heart rate are located here. The cardio-inhibitory centre is responsible for the origins of the parasympathetic fibres of the vagus nerve reaching the S-A node while the sympathetic fibres descend through the spinal cord from the vasomotor centre.

Role of internal receptors

Baroreceptors detect changes in blood pressure and are found in the walls of the aorta and part of the carotid arteries delivering blood to the head and neck and labelled the aortic and carotid bodies (see Figure 5.40). A small upward change in BP in these arteries often indicates that extra blood has been pumped out by the ventricles as a result of extra blood entering the heart on the venous or right side. Baroreceptors detect the change and relay the information in nerve impulses to the cardiac centres. Activity in the vagus nerve slows the heart rate down and decreases BP back to normal.

Receptors sensitive to temperature are known as thermoreceptors and these are present in the skin and deep inside the body. They relay information via nerve impulses to a part of the brain called the hypothalamus which activates appropriate feedback systems.

Effects of adrenaline on heart rate

Circulating adrenaline, a hormone from the adrenal gland released during fear, stress and exertion, stimulates the S-A node to beat faster thus boosting the effect of the sympathetic nervous system.

Effect of increased body temperature on heart rate

Thermoreceptors indicating a rise in body temperature to the brain cause the hypothalamus to activate the sympathetic nervous system. This in turn causes the heart rate to increase.

Homeostatic mechanisms for regulation of breathing rate

Mainly we are on 'automatic pilot' for the rate of ventilation and do not notice minor variations that are the result of homeostatic regulations. Only when taking deep breaths, speaking or holding a breath are we voluntarily controlling our breathing. When metabolism produces extra carbon dioxide, for example, breathing rates will increase slightly until this surplus is 'blown off' in expiration. Similarly a period of forced ventilation such as gasping will lower the carbon dioxide levels in the body and homeostatic mechanisms will slow or stop breathing temporarily until levels return to normal.

Theory into practice

Count your own or a partner's quiet breathing rate over several minutes and then breathe (voluntarily) rapidly for 2 minutes. Immediately afterwards count the breathing rate for the next 3 minutes. Compare the rates before and after the forced ventilation to demonstrate homeostatic regulation.

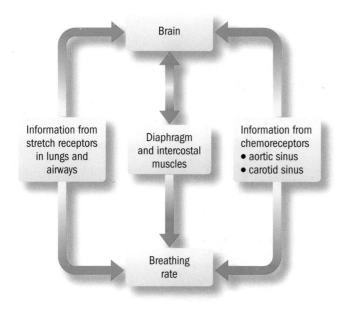

▲ **Figure 5.40 The role of internal receptors**

Roles of internal receptors

Internal receptors can be stretch receptors in muscles and tissues that relay nervous impulses to the brain about the status of ventilation from the degree of stretch of muscles and other tissues. The intercostal muscles are the site of many stretch receptors.

Chemoreceptors detect changes in chemical stimuli such as H^+ ions and oxygen levels and supply the brain with this information. There are central and peripheral chemoreceptors. The central chemoreceptors monitoring H^+ ion concentration are located in the medulla of the brain; an increase in H^+ ion concentration results in increased ventilation rate. Peripheral receptors, monitoring changes in oxygen concentration, increase ventilation when oxygen levels decrease. Peripheral chemoreceptors are scattered around the aorta and carotid arteries in groups labelled the aortic and carotid sinuses (see Figure 5.40).

Autonomic nervous system: parasympathetic and sympathetic branches

Most internal organs have a dual autonomic supply and the respiratory system is no exception. What can be

different, however, is the way they act. It would be easy to say that the sympathetic always causes contraction and the parasympathetic causes relaxation of muscle coats – but unfortunately this is not so. In the case of bronchial muscle, the sympathetic causes it to relax and the parasympathetic causes contraction resulting in narrowing of the bronchi. Most of these fibres run in the vagus nerve (which you have already met) in serving the heart. The vagus nerve is so called because it wanders all over supplying internal organs; vagus means 'a wanderer' – like a vagrant! Sympathetic nerves emerge from a chain of ganglia (places where nerves interconnect) to run to the bronchi.

Remember!

The parasympathetic is active during rest, peace and contentment and the sympathetic during emergencies. A useful way to work out the actions is to imagine yourself in a life-threatening emergency – let's say you are crossing a field when you see an angry bull preparing to charge towards you. What would you like to happen physiologically to your body? You would need plenty of oxygen and glucose delivered fast to your skeletal muscles – so, heart and breathing rates would increase, stroke volume would rise, bronchi would relax/dilate, glycogen would be converted to glucose, muscle arterioles would relax/dilate, pupils would widen and eyelids open further etc. It would not be the time for digesting food or controlling skin temperature as most blood would be needed by muscles, so blood flow to the skin and digestive organs would be reduced and vessels narrowed – the skin would be pale but clammy with sweat to make the body slippery to catch (a very primitive response) and you might feel nauseous afterwards. In this way, thinking logically, you can work out the actions of the autonomic system.

Respiratory centre, diaphragm and intercostal muscles

The brain area responsible for voluntary control of breathing is in the upper part of the brain known as the cerebral cortex. The involuntary centre known as the respiratory centre is in the medulla and the area just above, known as the pons. These are both at the base of the brain.

Each centre gets information from internal receptors regarding the state of ventilation.

The respiratory centre is similar to a respiratory 'pacemaker'. There are two groups of nerve cells known as the inspiratory and expiratory centres and when one is active the other is inhibited. Clearly, the inspiratory centre is actively sending nerve impulses to the nerve to the diaphragm – the phrenic nerve – and the thoracic nerves are sending impulses to the intercostal muscles to cause contraction resulting in inspiration. Inspiration ceases when the stretch receptors send bursts of impulses to the inspiratory centre saying that the chest and lungs are fully expanded, and the flow of impulses subsides, releasing the expiratory centre from inhibition. This centre then sends nerve impulses to the respiratory muscles causing relaxation and expiration. This cycle of activity is monitored and modified by the information emanating from the other internal receptors such as the chemoreceptors effecting homeostatic regulation.

Before exercise commences, the body predicts the changes because the sympathetic nervous system is stimulated and adrenaline released to increase cardiac output and stroke volume; BP rises because arterioles

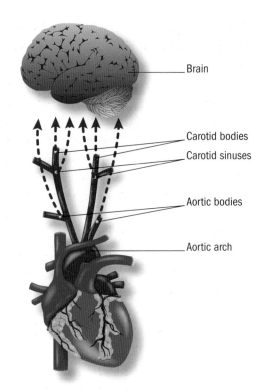

▲ Figure 5.42 Location of internal chemoreceptors

narrow, except for those in muscle, which relax. The extra demands for oxygen and glucose are met by increased blood flow and ventilation rate, the latter caused by enhanced chemoreceptor activity on the medullary brain centres.

Structure and functions of skin

The skin covers the outer surface of the body and surprisingly forms the largest organ. New cells are continually forming to replace those shed from the surface layers. The skin is a significant part of our in-built or innate immunity and forms not only a waterproof layer but also a microbe-proof covering. It plays an important part in the homeostatic regulation of body temperature and is considered to be part of our nervous system because of its sensitivity.

The skin varies in thickness throughout the body, being thinnest over the eyelids and lips and thickest on the soles of the feet. For study purposes, it is divided into

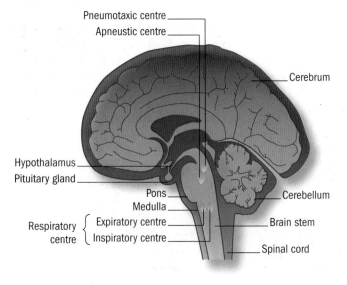

▲ Figure 5.41 The brain showing respiratory centres

an outer thinner layer, the epidermis and a deeper layer called the dermis. The dermis covers adipose, areolar, striated muscle, some cartilage and bone. You have already learned about the structure of the epidermis as a tissue on page 209 and the keratinisation of its cells. Hair follicles are also extensions of the epidermis which run down into the dermis and produce hairs made of keratin. Attached to these are the sebaceous or oil glands that coat the surface in hairy parts, assisting the water-proofing. Sweat ducts penetrate the epidermis as they emerge from the actual sweat gland in the dermis. In the basal layer, there are collections of pigment cells known as melanocytes that produce skin colour. The pigment melanin protects against damage to deeper structures from ultra-violet light radiation.

The dermis is connective tissue, mainly areolar, in which blood vessels, nerves, sweat glands, elastic and collagen fibres intermingle.

Nerve endings form specialised receptors for temperature changes, pain, touch and pressure.

Hair erector muscles have their origins low down on the hair follicles and their attachments to the basal layer of the epidermis. When hair erector muscles contract (usually from fear or the sensation of coldness) the hair becomes more erect, making the skin surface lumpy (known as 'goose bumps').

Reflect

When you experience 'goose bumps', the hair erector muscles have contracted and the effect is a small bump at the base of the hair. In hairy animals, this traps a layer of warm air around the body for extra warmth and makes the animal look larger in a threatening situation. In humans however, neither effect is much use! We rely on clothing, muscular activity, fat layers and shelter to keep us warm.

The major functions of skin are:

• to protect the underlying tissues against friction damage

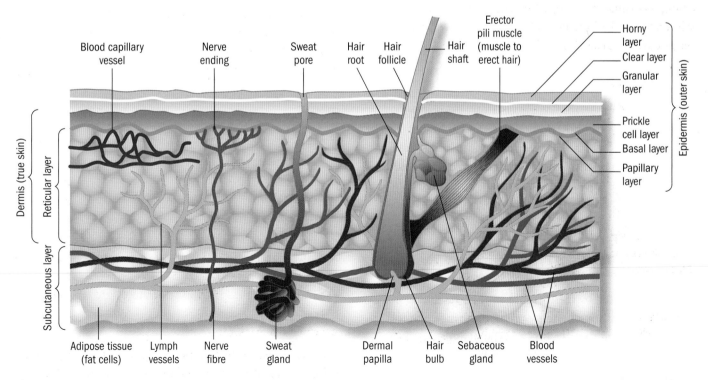

Figure 5.43 The structure of skin

- to waterproof the skin
- to protect deeper structures from invasion by microorganisms
- to protect against ultra-violet radiation
- thermo-regulation (control of body temperature)
- to relay nerve impulses generated from the specialised skin sensory receptors for heat, cold, touch, pain and pressure, thus informing the brain of changes in the environment
- the synthesis of vitamin D from sunlight acting on the adipose layers.

Homeostatic mechanism for regulation of body temperature

Human beings are the only animals that can survive in both tropical and polar regions of the earth. This is largely due to efficient thermo-regulatory homeostatic processes and the use of intelligence (for shelter and clothing), and means that body temperature varies only minimally.

The fundamental precept is to keep the inner core of the body (containing the vital organs) at normal temperatures while allowing the periphery (skin, limbs etc) to adapt to changing conditions of external temperature.

At very low temperatures such as –30°C, the water component of the body would freeze and at high temperatures such as +50°C, enzymes and body proteins would be permanently altered or denatured; life would not be possible under these conditions so homeostatic regulation of body temperature or thermo-regulation is vital.

Production of heat by the body

Heat is generated by the metabolic processes taking place in the body. Although energy released during chemical reactions is used to drive processes such as muscle contraction (heart pump, breathing, movement, nerve impulses etc) some is always released as heat. Hundreds of chemical reactions take place in the liver, for example,

every day and the liver is a massive generator of body heat. It doesn't feel hot because the blood distributes this heat around the body, particularly the extremities. Some heat is also gained from hot food and drinks and under some circumstances from the sun's rays.

Loss of heat from the body

Skin capillaries form networks just below the outer layer or epidermis. When you are hot, you need to lose heat from the skin surface to cool yourself down. There are four ways of losing heat from the skin:

- **Conduction** – warming up anything that you are in contact with, like clothes and seats – even a pen becomes warm from your hand when you are writing!
- **Convection** – this is when you warm up the layer of air next to your skin and it moves upwards (because hot air is less dense and rises) to be replaced by colder air from the ground.
- **Radiation** – you can think of this as rather like diffusion but of heat temperature. In other words, heat will pass from your skin to warm up any colder

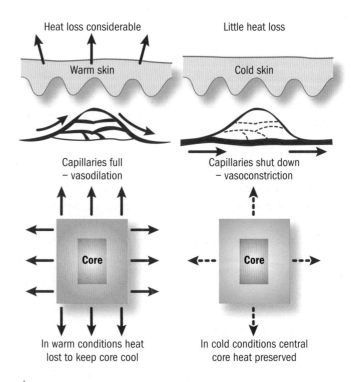

Figure 5.44 Changes in skin radiation

objects around you and, conversely, you will warm up by radiation from any object hotter than yourself like a fire or the sun.

- **Evaporation of sweat** – when liquid water is converted into water vapour (the technical term is evaporation), it requires heat energy to do so. When you are hot, sweating will only cool the skin if it can take heat energy from the skin surface to convert to water vapour and evaporate.

Reflect

If you have had a bath or a swim and allowed yourself to dry naturally rather than rubbing down with a towel, you might have noticed how cold you become afterwards, even if it is a warm, sunny day. This is because the water has evaporated from your skin using the heat energy in the skin and made the skin cold.

Although conduction and convection take place, they cannot be changed significantly to alter body temperature. The main methods of regulating temperature are by changing radiation and sweat-evaporation processes.

Reflect

During the monsoon seasons in some parts of the world, the environmental air is saturated with water vapour and sweat cannot evaporate and cool the skin. People tend to avoid travelling or working hard during monsoons because it is so uncomfortable.

Role of the hypothalamus

The receptors for temperature, both heat and cold, are located in the peripheral skin and around internal

organs. These are specially adapted cells with nerve fibres that run up the spinal cord to the temperature control centre in the hypothalamus of the brain (see Figure 5.45). The hypothalamus sends nerve impulses to muscles, sweat glands and skin blood vessels to cause changes that counteract the external changes. You can see the precise effects of a rising and falling external temperature in the flow charts in Figures 5.45 and 5.46.

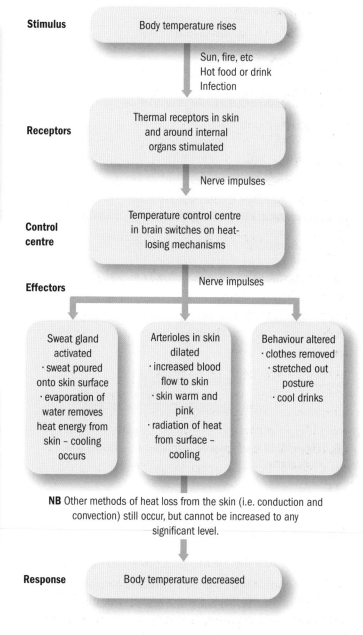

▲ Figure 5.45 Homeostatic regulation of an increasing body temperature

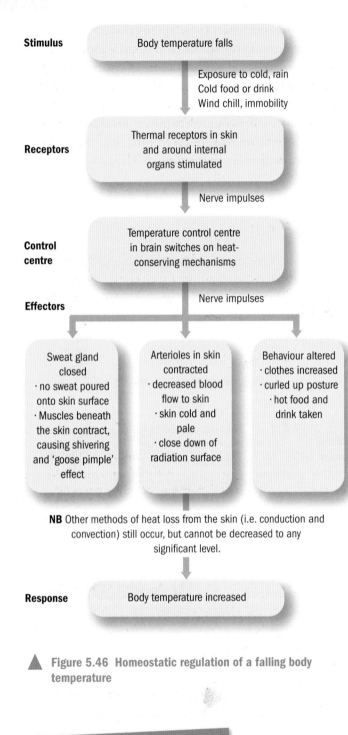

Stimulus	Body temperature falls

Exposure to cold, rain
Cold food or drink
Wind chill, immobility

Receptors	Thermal receptors in skin and around internal organs stimulated

Nerve impulses

Control centre	Temperature control centre in brain switches on heat-conserving mechanisms

Nerve impulses

Effectors

Sweat gland closed	Arterioles in skin contracted	Behaviour altered
· no sweat poured onto skin surface · Muscles beneath the skin contract, causing shivering and 'goose pimple' effect	· decreased blood flow to skin · skin cold and pale · close down of radiation surface	· clothes increased · curled up posture · hot food and drink taken

NB Other methods of heat loss from the skin (i.e. conduction and convection) still occur, but cannot be decreased to any significant level.

Response	Body temperature increased

▲ Figure 5.46 Homeostatic regulation of a falling body temperature

Roles of the parasympathetic and sympathetic nerves

The parasympathetic has no significant role in thermo-regulation although it helps the unstriated muscle coats of the skin arterioles to relax, but the sympathetic nervous system controls both sweat glands and the calibre of the arterioles.

Roles of arterioles and sweat glands

As thermoreceptors tell the hypothalamus in the brain that temperature is rising, sweat glands are activated by the sympathetic nerves, and arterioles are dilated to let more heat to the surface of the skin, thus increasing heat loss by radiation and evaporation of sweat. Conversely, if the core temperature is cooling, the sympathetic is active in causing constriction of the arterioles but sweating is 'turned off'. This reduces heat loss, makes the skin colder to touch and thus preserves the core temperature.

Reflect

Can you explain why a hot cup of tea is more effective at cooling the body than an ice cream when the weather is hot?

The reason is that core temperature overrides the peripheral skin thermoreceptors when conflicting information is received. Think about what happens when a hot volume of fluid reaches the core and compare this with a mass of freezing food.

Effects of shivering

Rhythmic involuntary contractions of the skeletal muscles are known as shivering. Muscular activity generates heat so in a cold environment we may stamp our feet, swing our arms, rub our face, hands and feet and also shiver. This is a very effective way to generate heat as it is all available to warm the body up.

Implications of surface area to volume ratio and the care of babies

Babies have a larger surface area to volume ratio than adults and cannot effect changes to gain or lose heat for themselves; this means that they are at risk of developing **hyperthermia** or **hypothermia**.

Key terms

Hyperthermia Increased body temperature above the normal range of values

Hypothermia Decreased body temperature below the normal range of values.

Theory into practice

Although we may not have learned about surface area to volume ratio, we are all subconsciously aware of the implications of this. In hot weather, we might lie on a beach stretched out, wearing only a few clothes to expose as much skin surface as we can to lose heat by. In winter conditions, we wear more clothing and, particularly in bed at night, curl up in a ball to reduce surface area to conserve heat. Body volume cannot change much but the proportion of exposed surface area to volume can be made to work best for different conditions.

1 Explain the main way that heat is lost by increasing the surface area to volume ratio in hot weather.

2 Adolescents commonly go out in very cold weather wearing skimpy clothing without feeling cold. Explain why this might be dangerous for older people.

3 Explain why babies need to wear hats in colder weather.

Babies do not sweat much and newborn babies do not shiver. Therefore, it is important in cold weather to wrap babies warmly including the extremities and the head and to guard against over-heating in hot weather.

Fever

Fever is one type of hyperthermia and is most usually caused by infection; other types are heat stroke and heat exhaustion – all can be life-threatening. Factors released as a result of disease act on thermoreceptors in the hypothalamus, raising the upper **set point**. Consequently the sufferer feels cold, curls up, pulls on covers, looks pale due to vasoconstriction (narrowing of the arterioles) and even experiences intense shivering known as rigors. It is not until the new set point has been reached (often called 'the crisis') that sweating and other heat loss mechanisms begin. When the infection has subsided the set point is reset at a lower level.

Key term

Set point The temperature of the 'hypothalamic thermostat' when autonomic thermo-regulatory mechanisms start to act to reverse the rise or fall and restore normal temperature.

Remember!

Customary practice to reduce temperature of a fever is to bathe with tepid water, blow cold air from a fan over exposed skin and/or use appropriate medication.

Homeostatic mechanisms for regulation of blood glucose levels

Role of the pancreas, liver, insulin and glucagon

You have learned how carbohydrates are broken down by digestive enzymes to produce simple soluble sugars, mainly glucose. After a meal rich in carbohydrates such as rice, bread, pasta and certain vegetables, blood glucose will start to rise. This increased level of glucose stimulates the production of the hormone insulin from the beta cells in the islets of Langerhans in the pancreas. Insulin has two main functions:

- to regulate the concentration of glucose in the blood
- to increase the passage of glucose into actively respiring body cells by active absorption.

In the absence of insulin, very little glucose is able to pass through cell membranes (with the exception of liver cells) and so the plasma level of glucose rises. Individuals with untreated diabetes mellitus (caused by a lack of insulin secretion) have high plasma glucose levels and this leads to other biochemical disturbances. In healthy people, the plasma glucose varies hardly at all because liver cells, under the control of insulin, convert glucose into liver (and muscle) glycogen for storage. When blood glucose starts to fall as a result of fasting or utilisation by respiring cells, another hormone, glucagon, from the alpha cells in the islets of Langerhans, is secreted and this converts liver glycogen back into glucose for release into the bloodstream. These two hormones regulate the amount of glucose in the blood plasma by negative feedback mechanisms. Both have receptors attached to their islet cells to identify rising and falling plasma glucose levels.

Insulin also promotes the conversion of glucose into fat (once again removing surplus glucose from the circulation) and delays the conversion of amino acids into energy (see 'Roles in the body' on page 241).

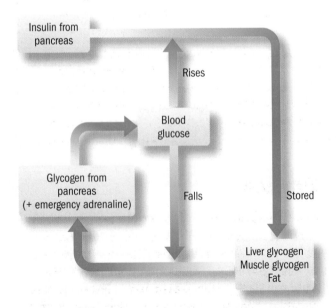

▲ Figure 5.47 Negative feedback mechanism to maintain plasma glucose concentration in blood

Theory into practice

Explain what will happen to your plasma glucose if you go for a jog before breakfast and eat nothing but a slimming-type of cereal bar (low sugar, low fat) until lunch. Describe the homeostatic mechanism for restoring plasma glucose levels to normal.

Remember that:

- muscular activity requires energy
- energy stores are in the liver and in fat deposits
- hormonal action is necessary to release stored energy.

Take it further

Diabetes mellitus (sugar diabetes) is caused by insufficient insulin, a hormone produced by the pancreas. Insulin helps glucose to move through cell membranes for internal respiration. When insulin is lacking, body fluids become loaded with surplus glucose. When blood glucose is abnormally high, the first renal tubule cannot reabsorb it all, so urine becomes loaded with surplus glucose. There is no glucose in normal urine. The glucose is an osmotically-active substance and consequently attracts water with it. An untreated diabetic will produce lots of urine (polyuria), loaded with glucose (glycosuria) and be constantly thirsty (polydipsia).

Research other signs and symptoms of diabetes mellitus (Type 1) and try to explain them using the information supplied above.

It is also necessary to identify the role of another hormone, adrenaline, in the homeostasis of glucose. Adrenaline, released by the adrenal glands when the sympathetic nervous system is active under stressful conditions, acts antagonistically to insulin and overrides it to convert glycogen in the liver to glucose. This outpouring of glucose provides energy for muscles to become active under emergency conditions. In addition, adrenaline converts fats to fatty acids for muscle contraction. When the emergency is over, insulin will once more become active and store any surplus as before.

In this section you will be required to obtain data by measuring the temperature, pulse and breathing rates of a healthy individual at rest and at intervals during recovery from a standard exercise test. You will need to know:

- how to take the measurements using safe practice
- the range of normal values
- the factors which affect the reliability of the data you obtain.

You will need to interpret and analyse your data and demonstrate how homeostatic mechanisms respond to exercise.

Measurements

You will now learn best practice in taking routine measurements.

Pulse rate measurements, normal values and range

A pulse can be detected when an artery is close to the surface of the body and runs over a firm structure such as bone. The pulse is the elastic expansion and recoil of an artery caused by the left ventricle of the heart contracting to drive blood around the body. You are feeling the 'shock' wave of the contraction as it travels rapidly down the arteries.

■ Factors affecting reliability of pulse rate measurements

As well as the pulse rate, professional health care workers will also monitor the rhythm of the pulse noting any irregularities and the quality of the pulse – terms used are full, bounding, normal, weak or thready. They will also take note of the character of the blood vessel; in a young person it feels straight, flexible and elastic but, in an elderly person, it might feel much firmer, even hard and take a winding course due to arteriosclerosis. This condition might mean that the pulse is harder to count.

Theory into practice

You will need a watch with a second hand or a stopclock that can measure in seconds.

- Wash your hands to prevent cross-infection.
- Explain what you are going to do to the person on whom you are carrying out the measurement and obtain their consent.
- Make sure that the person is comfortable and relaxed as this will help you to achieve an accurate measurement. Observe the individual while taking the measurement (this takes practice) so that you can stop if there are any signs of distress or anxiety.
- Find the radial artery, preferably on the arm that is free from any restrictions such as a watch strap. You will find the artery on the wrist, just below the base of the thumb.
- Place the first and second fingers lightly on the artery – get used to the feel of the pulse before you start counting for 60 seconds. Record the measurement with the date and the time. Wash your hands.

You may wish to repeat the measurement twice more as this is a practical exercise and a **mean pulse** is more useful for recording as either you or the individual might be a little apprehensive at first.

An average resting pulse in a healthy individual ranges from 60–80 beats per minute. Increases in pulse rates during vigorous exercise vary depending on the fitness of the individual and the intensity of the exercise but can rise to 190–200 beats per minute.

Key term

Mean pulse The mean of a set of numbers is calculated by adding the numbers and dividing by the number of numbers. If an individual's pulse rates were 70, 68 and 65 beats per minute then the mean would be 70, 68 and 64 ÷ 3 = 67 to the nearest whole number. As this calculation has considered three readings it is a more accurate reflection than taking the first reading only.

A pulse taken in babies or young children is much faster than in adults. Exercise, or even just moving about before or during the pulse-taking, will cause an increase in rate as will an increased body temperature. Hypothermia will produce a slow pulse rate.

Many carers measure the pulse rate for 10- or 15-second periods and multiply by 6 or 4 respectively to gain the pulse rate per minute. Any error in counting will thus be magnified six- or four-fold. However, a single error is still unlikely to be significant in terms of results for monitoring purposes. Counting for the whole 60 seconds is not a long time and reduces these errors.

Irregular pulses (found in patients with heart disease or ectopic beats) and fast pulses (tachycardia or in babies and young children) can prove difficult to count. Arteriosclerotic arteries are also more difficult to count. Multiple counting errors are more likely to occur and when multiplied these could be **significant**.

Key term

Significant A simple explanation of the term 'significant' in this context would be whether the error was meaningful and likely to distort any conclusions drawn. 'Not significant' means that the error can be ignored.

Many establishments use electronic digital recorders for measuring pulse rates, blood pressure, body temperature and other physiological features.

You should be familiar with the manufacturer's instructions for safe practice, potential risks and levels of accuracy. In addition, you must be trained by an appropriately qualified person to use this type of equipment. Different pieces of equipment may operate in different ways.

All items of electrical equipment are potentially hazardous both to the client and the carer operating the devices. The major hazards are burns and electric shock. You should be constantly on the look-out for:

- malfunction of the equipment
- frayed electric flexes and trapped wires
- loose connections, plugs and sockets.

Any fault must be reported immediately – verbally and in writing: most establishments have standard forms for reporting faults or damaged equipment. The device must be clearly identified with a notice 'Faulty, Do Not Use' and taken out of use. No one should be asked to use faulty equipment in their job role. Only suitably qualified personnel should investigate, modify, repair or scrap equipment belonging to the establishment.

Reflect

You used a pulse meter to measure the pulse rates of a peer and found the mean to be 80 beats per minute. The manufacturer's instructions quote accuracy at + or –2.5%. This means that the rate might range from 78 to 82 beats per minute.

Explanation: (80 x 5) ÷ 200 (N.B. 2.5% = 5/200ths). This works out at 2 so the range is from 80–2 to 80+2 or 78–82.

Once you have familiarised yourself with taking pulse rate measurments at rest, practise taking them at different levels of activity on, for example, one of your peers.

Reflect

Think about the different activities that you might use and at this point make your practice measurements fit the individual on whom you will do the assessment task.

You might take the pulse rate after light, medium or intense exercise of your own design or use the Harvard step test described on page 260.

■ Safe practice in taking pulse measurements

You must not compress the artery over the bone when taking measurements or you may stop the blood flow to part of the hand, causing pain and cramp. This is more likely to occur in babies and older people when the pulse is more difficult to detect and count.

Ensure that the person under assessment is suitably healthy to undertake physical exercise: for example, you would not ask your grandmother to run up and down the stairs several times or do a 'step test' – this might trigger angina or a heart attack. The person must be used to participating in, and happy to carry out, the type of exercise you devise. There must be no risk to health in carrying out the activities.

Ensure that you wash your hands before and after the procedure to prevent cross-infection.

Remember!

The radial pulse is difficult to detect in a baby so the preferred location is the brachial artery on the inner side of the upper arm.

Breathing rate measurements, normal values and range

You will need to observe the rise and fall of the person's chest in order to count the respiratory rate. It is best to do this after pulse-taking. The problem you may find is that, as soon as the person is aware of the count, voluntary control takes over and the rate may alter. Many carers continue to keep their fingers on the pulse for an extra 60 seconds to distract the individual while counting the respirations. One rise and one fall counts as one respiration. You can then record both rates. Normal respiratory rate is said to be 12–20 breaths per minute – during exercise, breathing rate can rise to 30–40 breaths per minute.

■ Factors affecting reliability of breathing rate measurements

You should be alert for any changes in chest movement as the individual may have become aware of the

measuring and alter the pattern of breathing. When you are taking a resting breathing rate measurement, ensure that the person is not disturbed or anxious and has been resting for at least 10 minutes or you might get a false reading. The individual should not have smoked recently as this too will produce a false reading.

Sometimes the rise and fall of the chest is slight and it is easy to miss and to miscount when you are registering two movements as one count.

■ Safe practice in taking breathing rates

As you are observing a phenomenon rather than actually doing something, the risks are small. However clothing may need to be adjusted and washing hands before and after the procedure is important to prevent cross-infection.

Body temperature measurements, normal values and range

Body temperature must be kept within a narrow range in order for the physiological processes of the body to function at their maximum efficiency.

However, body temperature varies between individuals even when they are in the same environment. They can vary in the same person, at different times of the day, during different activity levels and depending on whether food and drink has been consumed or not. In women, body temperature is affected by the stages of the menstrual cycle – being highest at ovulation and lowest during actual menstruation. Most people experience their lowest temperature around 3 a.m. and their highest around 6 p.m.

Reflect

No one knows exactly the range of temperature compatible with life, but it is thought that the upper limit is around 44°C and the lower 27°C. Clearly an individual will be seriously ill long before these limits are reached.

In addition to all these influences, body temperature varies according to the location of the measurement, for example, mouth, axilla (armpit), ear canal and rectum. The latter is only used when the other sites are unavailable and in patients who are unconscious and/or very seriously ill as the procedure causes raised anxiety and stress levels. Rectal temperatures are nearer to actual body core temperatures but are slower to change. Mouth or oral temperatures are about ½°C higher than axillary temperatures.

Normal body temperatures range from 36.5 to 37.2°C. Most people will quote 37°C as normal body temperature but, given the range of influencing factors, this is rather too precise.

Temperatures are often taken once or twice daily as a routine but the frequency can be varied according to need. A patient suffering from (or at risk of developing) an infection, or who is recovering from hypothermia or who is post-operative, may have their temperature taken hourly or every four hours.

Since mercury-filled thermometers were banned in care establishments, several types of non-mercury thermometers are now available. These are:

- disposable thermometers
- calibrated electronic probes
- tympanic (ear canal) thermometers.

Theory into practice

You are most likely to take temperatures in the axilla (armpit).

- Wash your hands first to prevent cross-infection.
- Explain what you are going to do to the individual and obtain their consent and co-operation.
- Make sure that the individual is sitting or lying comfortably and can keep that position for a few minutes.
- Respect privacy and help to remove clothing from one axilla.
- Dry the axilla with a disposable tissue.
- Place the temperature probe in the axilla so that it is surrounded by skin.
- Observe the individual throughout the process to check for signs of distress.
- Ask the individual to hold their arm across their chest to hold the probe in position.
- Leave for the correct time (as per the manufacturer's instructions).
- Stay with the individual to ensure the position is maintained.
- After the appropriate time has elapsed, remove the thermometer, read and record the temperature along with the date and time.
- Safely dispose of or clean and store the thermometer as appropriate for the establishment. Wash your hands again.
- Check that the individual is still comfortable and, if relevant, compare with previous readings.

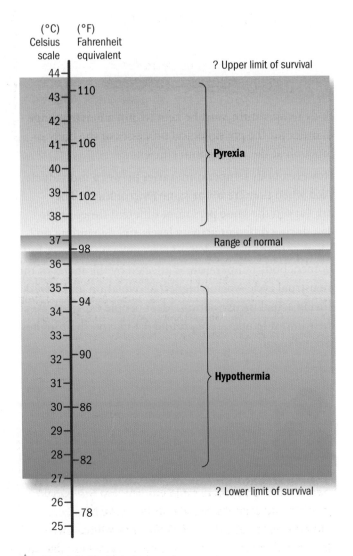

▲ Figure 5.48 Body temperature range

However, you must remember that in many private homes in the country, mercury-filled, clinical thermometers are still in use.

Temperatures were once measured in degrees Fahrenheit but now degrees Celsius are used. If you are using an old thermometer, you will need to look at it very closely to see the measuring scale.

The procedure outlined above can be adapted to any type of axillary thermometer.

Disposable oral and oral probe thermometers should be placed under the tongue. There are right and left pouches on either side of the fold of membrane (the frenulum) on the underside of the tongue and either one of these is a suitable place for the thermometer. The individual should not bite or chew on the probe but should close their lips around it for the prescribed length of time. The rest of the procedure is the same as for axillary temperature-taking.

Rectal thermometry should not be carried out by unqualified individuals and so it will not be described here.

Tympanic thermometers measure the temperature of the ear drum (tympanic membrane) and this is very near to the body core temperature. A probe with a disposable cover is inserted into the ear canal while gently pulling the ear lobe downwards. When the ear drum can no longer be seen (because it is obscured by the probe),

hold the thermometer still and take the recording. Remove the probe and dispose of the cover before storing the equipment safely. Otherwise, use the same procedure as for axillary recordings. This is the preferred method for taking temperatures in children as it is fast and well-tolerated.

LCD (liquid crystal display) thermometers are cheap, disposable, safe and easy to use. They are also available in high street pharmacies, and parents of young children are encouraged to keep a supply at home. They are single-use only and the manufacturer's instructions must be followed to obtain correct results.

Theory into practice

Purchase an LCD strip thermometer and try it out for yourself. If you can, immediately take your temperature with another type of thermometer and compare the results.

■ Safe practice in taking body temperatures

See the information on dealing with electrical equipment on page 256.

Oral temperatures should only be used with attentive, co-operative adults to ensure that the probe is not bitten or chewed, with the accompanying risks to safety. All equipment should have disposable covers or sheaths or be thoroughly cleaned after use to prevent cross-infection.

Even with the use of disposable covers, tympanic thermometers have been found to transmit ear infections (often with drug-resistant bacteria) between individuals. Extra care should be taken with personal and equipment hygiene.

Mercury and glass thermometers are now considered obsolete and even domestic settings should be encouraged to substitute LCD thermometers. The danger is from mercury poisoning and glass inhalation or ingestion.

Figure 5.49 Taking a tympanic temperature

■ Factors affecting reliability of body temperature measurements

Several factors are discussed under normal values and range.

Ensure that you fully understand the operation of the temperature measuring device and know both the correct location of the sensitive probe, strip or bulb and the length of time needed for measuring. Failure to comply with the manufacturer's instructions may lead to inaccurate readings and errors.

Reflect

Has your client had a hot or cold drink in the last few minutes, had a hot bath or shower, or been engaged in a form of exercise?

If so, you should delay the temperature recording unless it is required for study purposes such as for this unit assessment.

Prepare the equipment correctly and make sure that it is calibrated where this is appropriate.

The accuracy of a thermometer depends on fully-functioning equipment and your skill in carrying out the measurements. When taking oral temperatures do not ask the individual questions or allow them to talk as the colder air flowing over the thermometer will cause inaccuracies.

There have been several studies relating to the accuracy of temperatures taken with tympanic thermometers but, over time, carers are becoming more experienced at using these devices.

LCD strips, while valuable in domestic and community settings, are not absolutely accurate but they do provide useful guidance when the temperature is raised.

Consult the manufacturer's instructions for accuracy levels.

Normal variations measured at rest and following exercise

In this section you will be required to obtain data by measuring temperature, pulse and breathing rates of a healthy individual at rest and at intervals during recovery from a standard exercise test. You will need to know:

- how to take the measurements using safe practice
- the range of normal values
- the factors which affect the reliability of the data you obtain.

You will need to interpret and analyse your data and demonstrate how homeostatic mechanisms respond to exercise.

You can use a standard exercise test of your own choosing, subject to your tutor's approval, but a useful resource is the Harvard step test described here.

Theory into practice

You can practise assessments on yourself once you are competent with making routine measurements. The procedure that might be used is outlined below.

Harvard step test

You will need:
- a safe step about 50 cm high
- a stop clock or watch.

Procedure:

1   The subject being tested steps up and down (one foot, then both feet) at a rate of 30 steps per minute for 5 minutes.

Note: if the stepping cannot be maintained for 15 seconds at any time, this is deemed to be exhaustion and the test is stopped at that point and the precise time noted.

2 The individual sits down after the test and the measurements are taken as below. You will need to start the stopwatch again immediately after the subject has stopped the test.

Taking results:

3 Count the rate of pulse or breathing or take the temperature at 1–1.5, 2–2.5 and 3–3.5 minutes after the test.

Note: it is a good idea to draw up relevant chart/s for the recording of results before you start. An example is provided in Table 5.5.

Harvard step test results				
Subject name or code for confidentiality		**Date/s of test**		**Tester's name**
Measurement	Rest	1–1.5 mins	2–2.5 mins	3–3.5 mins
Pulse/ heart rate beats/minute				
Breathing rate breaths/minute				
Temperature °C				
Duration of test if not 5 minutes		Test 1	Test 2	Test 3

Table 5.5 Recording the results of a Harvard step test

It is worth noting that taller individuals have a mechanical advantage in this type of test.

Note: you may need to repeat the test more than once as it might be difficult for you to take more than one measurement accurately per test.

The Harvard step test is commonly used for assessing cardiovascular fitness and a scoring system has been devised for this. You might wish to use this or leave the results in beats per minute.

Theory into practice

To use the scoring system for cardiovascular fitness with the Harvard step test, use the following method:

1 Calculate, in seconds, the duration of the test as it was carried out by the subject. If the subject did not become exhausted and finished the test before the due time, this will be 5 x 60 = 300 seconds. This figure will be represented by T.

2 Add together the number of pulse beats recorded in the three time periods. This figure will be represented by B.

3 Substitute your data for T and B in the following equation:
100 x T ÷ 2 x B

4 The product for this equation can be interpreted from the following table indicating cardiovascular fitness.

Excellent	>90
Good	80–89
High average	65–79
Low average	55–64
Poor	<55

Example: Chris completed only 4 minutes 35 seconds of the test before he was exhausted. His heart rates for the three time periods were 108, 92 and 75. His assessment on this scoring was 100 x 275 ÷ 2 x 275 = 50. Chris has a poor cardiovascular rating.

Data presentation and interpretation

Graphs and charts

Ensure that the data you have obtained is clear in content by drawing up charts for recording your results – do this before you start the exercise tests. It is depressing and frustrating to find that you are unable to remember the details of the work afterwards because you just noted figures haphazardly during the tests. You are most likely to be analysing and presenting your data on a different day to the one when you carry out the tests.

Charts should have each column headed with a title and the units of measurement. There should be clear indications of the time the measurements are taken, their frequency and the date.

Graphs can be an effective way to display data and trends as they are generally easier to interpret than columns of figures.

Each graph should have:

- a title such as: *Graph to show how pulse measurements vary with exercise*
- labels on both axes denoting what is being measured and the units of the measurement
- the vertical axis should be the unknown variable – in this case, it will be pulse rate, breathing rate or body temperature
- the horizontal axis should be the known variable – in this case it will be time.
- clear marks and values on the axes denoting the scales being used
- a key, if more than one trend is shown
- points plotted as accurately and finely as possible
- fine lines linking the plotted points.

Your graph will also need the period of exercise to be defined and labelled after the resting period. You might wish to lightly shade or hatch this area.

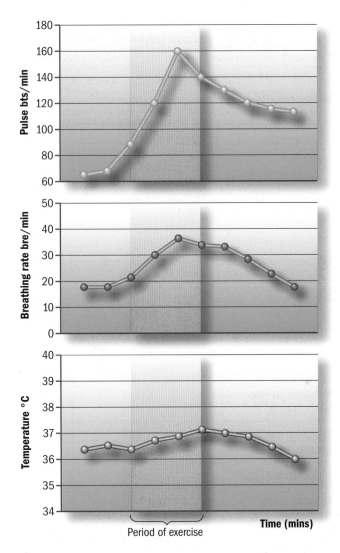

▲ Figure 5.50 How pulse, breathing rates and body temperature vary with exercise

Assessment activity 5.7

Describe the concept of homeostasis and the homeostatic mechanisms that regulate heart rate, breathing rate, body temperature and blood glucose levels.

1 What are the general features of homeostatic systems and how do they stop heart rate, breathing rate, body temperature and blood glucose levels rising or falling to dangerous levels? **P5**

Explain the probable homeostatic responses to changes in the internal environment during exercise.

2 When you start to run, your muscles need a lot more oxygen and glucose. How is this accomplished? What prevents the cardiovascular, respiratory and endocrine systems from over-compensating during exercise?

3 Muscular activity generates heat. How does the body resist over-heating? **M2**

Explain the importance of homeostasis in maintaining the healthy functioning of the body.

4 What might happen if body temperature and blood glucose fall below or rise above their normal ranges?

5 What might be the consequences of having a very slow or very rapid heart and breathing rate? **D2**

Grading tip for P5

You will need to describe the general features of homeostasis and homeostatic mechanisms first and then show how these are applied to the relevant systems.

Grading tip for M2

You will need to consider a falling glucose level as energy is being utilised for muscular activity, an increased demand for oxygen and the need to eliminate more carbon dioxide (cardiovascular and respiratory mechanisms) and an increased body temperature from working muscles.

Annotated diagrams will save you from a great deal of writing and are acceptable.

Grading tip for D2

You will need to show the importance of keeping to a narrow range of variables and what can happen if this is not carried out.

Supporting explanations of collated data

Presenting a chart of results and a graph is not sufficient for your practical assessment; you will need to describe details of the equipment you used and say how you used it – in other words, the method. An account of the way you organised the resting and exercise periods in conjunction with the measurement of the data needs to be clear, accurate and complete. The reader should understand exactly how you have conducted the assessment.

After displaying the results, chart and graphs, you will need to identify the trends shown by the figures and graphs and from your knowledge of homeostatic mechanisms, attempt an explanation for each rise or fall.

For example:

The readings immediately after the exercise ceased showed a marked rise above resting levels in both pulse and breathing rates. This is because muscular activity demands a massive increase in oxygen and glucose. As the muscles use up oxygen and produce extra carbon dioxide, chemoreceptors are stimulated and these act on the cardiac and respiratory centres in the brain …

You can also comment on the reliability and validity of your data.

Remember!

Reliability relates to the extent to which a set of results can be replicated by repeating the test.

Validity relates to the quantity of the test results to tackle the study in question. Validity means true, sound or well-grounded.

Assessment activity 5.8

Measure body temperature, heart and breathing rate before and after a standard period of exercise, interpret the data and comment on its validity.

1   How will you interpret the findings from measuring body temperature, heart and breathing rates, before and after a set period of exercise?

Grading tip for P6

You can follow the guidelines on pages 255–260 for the measurements you have to take. Have a pre-prepared chart for recording your results.

You will be able to interpret your results more easily if you produce graphical displays. Indicate on your graphs, the period of the exercise and describe how the measurements vary with regard to the exercise.

Body temperature may vary very little over the period of time of the exercise and a graph may not be useful.

Comments on validity will refer to how many measurements you have taken to arrive at your conclusions and whether they are a true reflection of how the heart and breathing rates have changed over the period of time.

Analyse the data obtained to show how homeostatic mechanisms control the internal environment during exercise.

Grading tip for M3

Link the variations in heart and breathing rates (and body temperature if you have much variation) to the regulation of heart rate and breathing rate that you have already learned about. You will find that rates rise initially quite sharply to a peak and then fall more slowly as the regulatory mechanisms 'kick in' to effect control. Make multiple references to the data obtained.

Knowledge check

1 Complete the table below to outline the functions of the named organelles:

Name of organelle	Main function
Lysosome	
	Energy release
	Contains DNA
Rough endoplasmic reticulum	
Cell membrane	

2 Explain one location of the type of tissues given below:
  a simple squamous epithelium
  b ciliated columnar epithelium
  c keratinised epithelium.

3 Describe the difference in the nature of the matrix of blood, cartilage and bone.

4 Starting at the mouth, list the glands and organs making up the digestive system in descending order.

5 State the law of conservation of energy.

6 Describe three structural and functional differences between arteries and veins.

7 How is tissue fluid formed? Why is tissue fluid important in the sphere of energy metabolism?

8 Explain how the heart rate is controlled by the sino-atrial node.

9 Define diffusion and explain how this process is important in energy metabolism.

10 Describe the characteristics of enzymes.

11 Explain the role of baroreceptors in the homeostatic mechanisms controlling heart rate.

12 Why is it difficult to stay cool in a tropical humid atmosphere?

13 Describe the effects of sympathetic stimulation on the heart rate in an emergency.

14 State the normal range of values for heart and breathing rates at rest.

15 Explain how plasma glucose is regulated by hormones.

Grading criteria

To achieve a pass grade the evidence must show that the learner is able to:	To achieve a merit grade the evidence must show that, in addition to the pass criteria, the learner is able to:	To achieve a distinction grade the evidence must show that, in addition to the pass and merit criteria, the learner is able to:
P1 describe the functions of the main cell components **Assessment activity 5.1 page 207**		
P2 describe the structure of the main tissues of the body and their role in the functioning of two named body organs **Assessment activity 5.2 page 215**		
P3 describe the gross structure and main functions of all major body systems **Assessment activity 5.3 page 222**		
P4 describe the role of energy in the body and the physiology of three named body systems in relation to energy metabolism **Assessment activity 5.4 page 232, 5.5 page 236, 5.6 page 243**	**M1** explain the physiology of three named body systems in relation to energy metabolism **Assessment activity 5.6 page 243**	**D1** use examples to explain how body systems interrelate with each other **Assessment activity 5.6 page 243**
P5 describe the concept of homeostasis and the homeostatic mechanisms that regulate heart rate, breathing rate, body temperature and blood glucose levels **Assessment activity 5.7 page 263**	**M2** explain the probable homeostatic responses to changes in the internal environment during exercise **Assessment activity 5.7 page 263**	**D2** explain the importance of homeostasis in maintaining the healthy functioning of the body. **Assessment activity 5.7 page 263**
P6 measure body temperature, heart rate and breathing rate before and after a standard period of exercise, interpret the data and comment on its validity. **Assessment activity 5.8 page 264**	**M3** analyse data obtained to show how homeostatic mechanisms control the internal environment during exercise. **Assessment activity 5.8 page 264**	

Preparation for assessment

This unit is internally assessed by your tutor on the evidence you present in your portfolio. The evidence must be entirely your own work. Due to the nature of this unit, you will probably use many images, which can be your own diagrams (or photographs), professional images from reference texts, leaflets and websites. Work that is not your original creation must be appropriately referenced to the source and adapted by you to demonstrate the scope of your knowledge and understanding. It is not acceptable to download or copy images that you have not referenced, explained, adapted or annotated in any way.

1 **P1** could be achieved by annotating a large diagram of the ultrastructure of a cell with a short description of each organelle and details of its functions.

2 For **P2**, you will not be able to find two named organs containing all the main tissues listed in the specification so you will need to choose two diverse organs and include some supplementary material to provide the rest. An example might be the skin, showing cuboidal epithelium of sweat glands, keratinised, compound epithelium of the epidermis, capillary networks of simple squamous epithelium, adipose and areolar tissues, sensory nerve endings (though not neurones), striated muscle underneath and non-striated muscle around the arterioles. You could have a large labelled diagram of a section through the skin and expanded tissue diagrams leading from this by label lines with annotations of their functions.

3 Diagrams and annotations should be appropriate for **P3** .

4 For **P4**, briefly describe the role of energy in the body and provide examples of how energy is used. Describe the physiology of the cardiovascular, respiratory and digestive systems in providing and transporting raw materials such as food materials and oxygen to the body cells.

5 For **M1**, you will need to provide a more detailed explanation in your own words of these three systems and their structure and functions within the body relevant to energy metabolism. In P4, you are only asked to describe but in M1 you must explain; this is a higher demand because you must supply reasons and extra details.

6 For **D1**, with reference to nervous and endocrine systems as well, you must be able to illustrate how these three systems work together with appropriate examples. This may involve, say, the maintenance of oxygen supplies, or glucose levels in the blood.

7 For **P5**, you will need to produce annotated diagrams or flow charts with supportive descriptions of the homeostatic mechanisms with an explanation of your understanding of the overall concept of homeostasis.

8 **M2** requires you to extend P5 by considering how the internal environment might change during exercise, for example, if more heat is generated, more oxygen is used up and more carbon dioxide is produced, and the likely homeostatic responses to such changes. This can be linked to **M3**.

9 For **P6** you are measuring and interpreting data, and commenting on its validity; for **M3**, you need to analyse the data to show how homeostatic mechanisms control the internal environment during exercise.

10 **D2** requires an explanation of the importance of homeostasis in maintaining the healthy functioning of the body. The requirement is for a detailed, accurate account of the need to maintain the internal environment variables within a narrow range and of the consequences of failure.

For example, you might choose to explain how an increase in body temperature will affect the functioning of enzymes (in body cells controlling internal respiration and/or in the digestive processes). Consequences of failure of the former must be life-threatening as energy will cease to be released to maintain breathing and heart function. Failure of the latter means that food will not be properly digested and when existing energy stores are depleted, life will once again be threatened. This of course would not happen as death from intracellular failure would occur first.

References and further reading

Baker, M. et al (2001) *Further Studies in Human Biology (AQA)* London: Hodder Murray

Boyle, M. et al (2002) *Human Biology* London: Collins Educational

Givens, P., Reiss, M. (2002) *Human Biology and Health Studies* Cheltenham: Nelson Thornes

Indge, B. et al (2000) *A New Introduction to Human Biology* (AQA) London: Hodder Murray

Jones, M., Jones, G. (2004) *Human Biology for AS Level* Cambridge: Cambridge University Press

Moonie, N. et al (2000) *Advanced Health and Social Care* Oxford: Heinemann

Pickering, W.R. (2001) *Advanced Human Biology through Diagrams* Oxford: Oxford University Press

Saffrey, J. et al (1972) *Maintaining the Whole* Milton Keynes: The Open University

Vander, A.J. (2003) *Human Physiology: The Mechanisms of Body Function* London: McGraw Hill

Wright, D. (2000) *Human Physiology and Health for GCSE* Oxford: Heinemann

Useful websites

www.bbc.co.uk/science/humanbody

www.bhf.co.uk

www.netdoctor.co.uk

www.nhsdirect

www.webschoolsolutions.com/patts/systems

Personal and professional development

Introduction

This unit is mainly about you. You will explore how people learn from everyday experience and review your own knowledge, skills and experiences at the start of the course. Using understanding of your own learning, self-assessment and your work placement experiences, you will make a plan for your development during the course and for a career in health and social care. The unit is different from the others because it is a large unit, it requires you to attend work experience placements and because you will need to work on the unit over the whole length of the course.

You will implement your personal development plan and review your learning and progress against it regularly throughout the course. You will also need to investigate a health or social care setting and assess how it contributes to the provision of services nationally.

How you will be assessed

This unit is internally assessed and a minimum of 100 hours of work experience is essential for achievement. Assessment later in the programme will depend on the self-assessment you make at the start. You will reflect on a portfolio of evidence of your development which will be collected from assignments and placement experience.

After completing this unit you should be able to achieve the following outcomes:

- Understand the learning process
- Be able to plan for, monitor and reflect on your own development
- Understand service provision in health or social care sectors.

Thinking points

This unit will help you to explore how you learn by reflecting on your experiences of study and work placements. It will support your achievement on the course and help you to make informed decisions about your career in health or care.

Most people experience some sort of health and/or social care from a very early age. So it is likely that you will have experience of being a service user, either as a patient when you have visited your doctor's or dentist's surgery, or as a child attending a childminder or day nursery.

Think about your different experiences as a service user and, in particular, the health and social care workers with whom you have interacted in some way.

- As a service user, what did you expect of the different workers, whether they were professionals or support workers?
- What skills and knowledge did the workers use?
- At the time, did you feel that the service(s) met your needs? If not, why not?
- What would you like to have been done differently?

Asking yourself questions like these, and seeking answers to them, is one way of reflecting on your experiences – you will explore this more in this unit. Awareness of your own experiences as a service user is important as this can influence you in your care work. Being aware of other people's perspectives and not just your own viewpoint is important when working professionally in health and social care, education or other work where the focus is on people.

The NMC Code of professional conduct: standards for conduct, performance and ethics

As a registered nurse, midwife or specialist community public health nurse, you are personally accountable for your practice. In caring for your patients and clients, you must:

▶ respect the patient or client as an individual

▶ obtain consent before you give any treatment or care

▶ protect confidential information

▶ co-operate with others in the team

▶ maintain your professional knowledge and competence

▶ be trustworthy

▶ act to identify and minimise risk to patients and clients.

These are the shared values of all the United Kingdom health care regulatory bodies.

▲ The Nursing and Midwifery Council Code of Professional Conduct

An overview of learning

Learning is a process by which we acquire knowledge, skills and an understanding of abstract concepts. Learning starts with early experiences as an infant and continues through formal schooling and academic study or training. You will need to complete specialist training to acquire the knowledge and skills for work in health or care as a care assistant, nurse or social worker. Learning also continues informally throughout life and most health and social care workers expect to support the learning of other staff as a routine aspect of their work. Workers may also need to support service users to learn new information or skills.

Workers in health or social care are expected to *take active steps* to develop their own learning appropriately for the specific care they do. This unit will help you to:

- understand how *you* learn
- understand *what* you have learnt from your formal study and experiences to date
- *plan* your learning in advance to develop your knowledge, skills and abilities for your studies and work placements
- *implement* your plan for your personal development
- check, or *monitor* your progress against the plan, amending it as learning proceeds

Theory into practice

When they have qualified, workers in health or care continue to learn from their experiences and through courses of study.

Why do you think it is necessary for health and care workers to continue to learn after qualifying?

Draw a spidergram to show all the reasons you can think of and then share your ideas with a friend. See whether, together, you have more reasons to add to your spidergram.

- *reflect* on the progress of your learning and development on the national programme, especially with regard to your career aspirations.

Before you qualify as a professional, learning from experience is called **personal and professional development (PPD)** but learning *after* qualifying is called **continuing professional development (CPD)**. You will come across both terms in this unit.

Key term

Personal and Professional Development (PPD) This is learning you will acquire from experience before you qualify as a professional.

Continuing Professional Development (CPD) This is learning that you will acquire after qualifying as a professional.

As an older adolescent or adult you will learn from formal study but you will also learn from your experience of daily life (jobs you have had, your home life etc). You will have innate abilities (ones that you are born with) – perhaps you are musical (and can play several instruments) or you will acquire specific new skills through practice. Often learning blends skills with theory – driving a car involves practical skills and knowledge of the Highway Code. Figure 6.1 shows how these three different areas overlap. As you go through the

Remember!

This unit explores learning from experiences in *adult* life i.e. from mid-adolescence onwards. Theories relating to the learning and development of young children and younger adolescents are different and are addressed elsewhere in this book (see Unit 4: Development through the life stages).

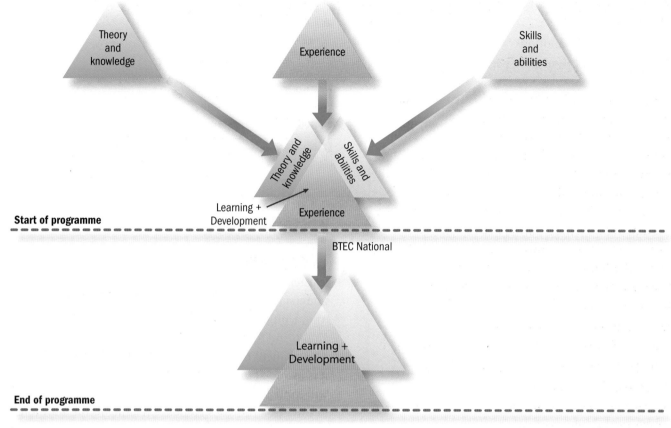

▲ **Figure 6.1 A model to show personal and professional development**

course, you will develop your abilities in all three areas as preparation for qualifying to work in health or social care.

Organising yourself – your portfolio

You will develop a PPD portfolio as part of this unit. You will store evidence of your development through the course in this portfolio. More advice on presenting your portfolio is given at the end of Section 2 on pages 309–312.

Keeping your personal journal

You will be working on this unit throughout your course and learning from your college studies, work placements and wider life. This means you will need to be organised and keep careful records of your experiences so that you can refer back to them later in your study. A practical

way of doing this is to buy a bound notebook, either A5 or A4 size. Ideally it should have a firm cover for protection and so you can write on it on your lap if necessary. This will be your personal journal.

The activities throughout all the units in this book will prompt you to develop your learning. You will participate in classroom activities and complete assignments set by your tutors and some of these activities will require you to use examples from your placements and other experience. Your learning from all these activities will contribute to your PPD.

Keeping a journal is an important way for you to keep track of your experiences – to record, for example, notes on:

- your responses to activities in this book
- practical details of work activities in which you participated
- descriptions of events and unforeseen incidents
- observations of routines and practices

- ideas and thoughts you have about your learning and development
- your feelings and emotions
- oral feedback received from peers, tutors, supervisors and others
- notes from discussions
- regular reflection on your overall development.

Remember!

It is important to make your journal entries *as soon as possible after the event*. You may think you will remember later but you almost certainly will not remember accurately or in enough detail.

All your entries should be dated so you can see how you are developing over time. You might find it useful to number the pages of the journal for easy referencing later.

You will use the notes you make in your journal entries as a resource to refer to later in the course. You may want to quote extracts from your journal to submit with assignments as advised by your tutors. Your journal notes are confidential to you and your tutor who will need to see your journal regularly.

Theory into practice

Make detailed notes in your journal about your feelings and concerns:

- on the first day of starting your course
- at the end of the induction period for the course
- before you start your first work placement
- after you have attended placement for a few days
- at the end of the placement.

Suggest reasons for your feelings and concerns and note how they change on each occasion.

You could make notes about each placement or new experience as you go along.

Remember!

Completing the 'Theory into practice' boxes throughout this unit will help you reflect on your learning. If you do this as you go along, you will collect evidence that will be useful for assessment.

Unit 6 and Unit 44

This unit explores your overall development as a learner, with some time spent in placements to gain an understanding of health and care work. The specialist unit, Unit 44: Vocational experience, integrates with Unit 6 and focuses much more on your professional development through extra time spent in placements. If it is included in your course, your journal and portfolio will contribute to the assessment of both units. Unit 44 in this book provides guidance relating to the additional evidence from your placements needed for assessment of the unit.

Theories of learning

Two theories of learning are introduced in this section and you will use the theories to help you plan your own development and to understand how you can learn from your experience while on the course.

The simplest way of looking at learning from experience is using the experience-reflection-action cycle, or the 'plan, do, reflect' cycle shown in Figure 6.2.

You may already know what sort of learner you are i.e. whether you are:

- a visual (seeing)
- auditory (hearing)
- kinaesthetic (movement) or
- tactile (touching/feeling) type of learner.

There are many theories of learning but two of the most well known are presented here to take your understanding of your own learning further. The two

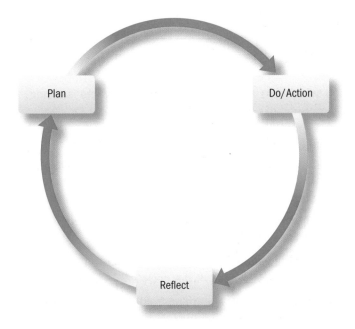

▲ **Figure 6.2 The plan, do, reflect cycle**

theories will prepare you particularly for professional training in health and social care. Kolb's experiential learning cycle (1984) and Honey and Mumford's learning styles theory (1985) are well known and widely used.

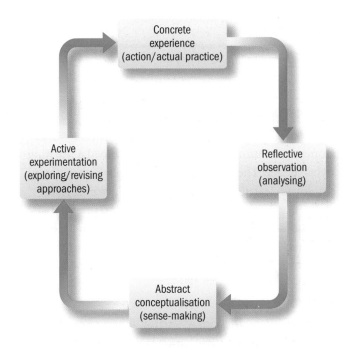

▲ **Figure 6.3 Kolb's experiential learning cycle**

Kolb helps us to understand how adults learn. The ways in which people learn are called their **cognitive abilities**. He suggested that during adolescence and early adulthood we begin to develop instinctive preferences for the way in which we process information and use it to make sense of our experiences. Kolb identified two pairs of opposing factors which, combined together, show learning as a cycle with four different stages of learning. It is possible to enter the cycle at any stage but for learning to be effective, each stage must be followed in the correct sequence. The four stages are shown in Figure 6.3.

Key term

Cognitive abilities The ways in which you think, using your knowledge and experience.

Kolb described each stage as follows:

- **Concrete experience**: the *doing* stage where you actually carry out or participate in an action or actions.
- **Reflective observation**: the reviewing or *reflecting* stage where you think about what you did and what happened during the concrete experience.
- **Abstract conceptualisation**: the *concluding* stage in relation to the concrete experience, sometimes called the *theorising* stage. It is the stage where you use all the information you have gained about the experience to organise your thoughts into some sort of order and make sense of the experience.
- **Active experimentation**: This is the *planning* or *trying out* stage of Kolb's cycle. The important point here is that you tackle an aspect of the activity *differently* from the first time, thus demonstrating that you have *learned* from the first concrete experience.

In context

Usma is on placement in a residential home and is trying to have a conversation with Mr Stevens who is 90 years old and deaf. She knows it is important to him that he still communicates with people. She starts by asking him about his family. She speaks loudly but notices that Mr Stevens does not respond to any of her questions about his family. Usma decides there is no point in continuing the conversation.

In the staff room, she talks about the situation with one of the care assistants who says that Mr Stevens is able to lip read. Usma thinks about the conversation and realises that she had not been sitting in a position where Mr Stevens could see her face. She goes back to Mr Stevens and pulls up a chair so that she is facing him. She asks the same questions about his family and, this time, Mr Stevens is very talkative, so much so that Usma has to interrupt him to give out tea. When she asks Mr Stevens if he would like a drink, she remembers to pause and face him when she asks the question.

1 **At what stage did Usma start Kolb's learning cycle?**

2 **What did she do in respect of each of the subsequent stages of the cycle?**

3 **What was Usma's learning from this experience?**

From the example above, you can see how Kolb's learning cycle theory can be applied to everyday practice.

Theory into practice

Now use the Kolb experiential learning cycle to review three different tasks you have carried out for the first time in the last 2–3 days.

For each, note down:

- the aspects you judged to be successful and why
- the aspects you judged to be less successful and why
- what you would do differently for the 'active experimentation' stage before doing each of the activities again.

Take it further

Kolb developed his theory further and described four learning styles. Find out about Kolb's learning styles theory and his definitions. How well do the descriptors for each style match how you prefer to learn?

Remember!

The Kolb learning cycle can be entered at any one of the four stages *but* for learning to be effective (i.e. the process results in a *change* in the individual's knowledge/skills/understanding), each stage must be followed in turn within the cycle.

Honey and Mumford's learning styles theory

Honey and Mumford (1985) also developed a learning styles theory. They reviewed the way in which different employees learned and identified four *learning style preferences*: reflector, theorist, activist and pragmatist. The characteristics of each learning style help to identify preferred situations for learning, and situations that are less favourable (see Table 6.1).

Learning style	Characteristics	Preferred learning situations	Less favourable learning situations
Activists	• Like to be involved • Like new ideas • Lose interest quickly • 'Jump first/think later' mentality • Like to dominate	• New experiences • Working with others • Taking the lead • Taking on difficult tasks	• Listening e.g. lectures or when passive • Doing things on their own • Working to the 'rules'
Reflectors	• Like to observe from the edge of a group • Consider things from a range of different perspectives • Collect information before drawing conclusions • Let others contribute before they do	• Observing from the edge of a group • Time to think before contributing • Analysing • Working without tight deadlines	• Taking a lead or performing in front of others • No time to prepare in advance • Facing the unexpected • Feeling rushed or pressurised by deadlines
Theorists	• Like to bring together different ideas to produce new ways of looking at things • Think logically • Like things to fit into an ordered scheme • Often detached and remote rather than emotional	• Like the opportunity to apply their knowledge and skills in complex situations • Work with abstract ideas • Opportunities to question and probe for information and ideas • Like a clear structure and purpose	• Cannot identify with different approaches taken by others • Lack of structure or purpose • Working with emotions and feelings of others
Pragmatists	• Like to experiment/try things out • Seek feedback from others • Practical, liking to get on with things rather than talk about them • Relate things to their own role	• Clear link between thinking and what has to be done • Opportunity to try things out • Like new ideas that have clear benefits • Happy to copy from role models	• Cannot identify the relevance of what has to be done • No guidance on how to do things • If benefits are unclear • Focus is only on theory and does not include practical aspects

Table 6.1 Honey and Mumford's learning styles and their impact on learning

In context

Four health and social care students are to make a wall display for a health promotion assignment. Katya is already planning out her ideas on paper, referring back to the assignment task to check she has understood what is required. Sally is full of enthusiasm, talks eagerly, has lots of ideas and is trying to persuade the others to follow them. Lee is attentive but quiet and not contributing to the discussion. Surinder is picking up on some of Katya's and Sally's ideas and is trying to form them into a sensible order. After a while, Katya starts chattering to her friend in the neighbouring group, Lee gets up to go to the library and Surinder expresses exasperation at not having made any progress with the task.

1 **What are the preferred learning styles of each of the members of the group?**

2 **Why do you think the group has ceased to function?**

3 **What could you suggest to the group to help them achieve their task?**

Honey and Mumford devised a questionnaire for individuals to identify their preferred learning style. Most individuals tend to use a range of learning styles, depending on the situation, but we use our preferred learning style most easily, especially if we are stressed. Being aware of your preferred learning style helps you to work in a way that enhances your learning and to avoid situations that are unhelpful.

Take it further

Compare Honey and Mumford's learning styles with those of Kolb. To what extent are they the same or different?

Theory into practice

1 Identify your preferred learning style, if possible using an appropriate questionnaire.

2 Identify a situation where your learning was particularly effective from your:

- course
- placement
- home life.

Use the table to explain why your learning was particularly effective.

3 Repeat the exercise choosing one example from each situation where your learning was less effective.

4 What steps could you have taken to enhance your learning from the situations you have identified?

Knowing which learning style you prefer will help your personal development, and being aware of the characteristics of other learning styles can be helpful when you are working with other people in college or the workplace.

Take it further

Donald Schön is another theorist who has been influential in the training of workers in health and social care and in education. He introduced the terms 'double loop learning', 'reflection-in-practice' and 'reflection-on-practice'.

Research these theories to gain additional insight into how adults learn and develop from their experience. Identify two examples from your own experience where you have used Schön's theories and make some notes to explain how the theory fits your examples.

Remember!

The terms used by each theorist are unique to the theory. The relevant theorist should be acknowledged when you use them in your work.

Influences on learning

Learning style is just one influence on how people learn. Understanding what influences your learning is important for your progress on the course but you need to understand that learning in other people may also be influenced by different factors.

Theory into practice

Observe one of your peers learning a new skill or routine. Note the factors that seem to help the individual's learning and those that hinder it.

How could the learning experience be altered to improve the individual's learning?

What would have affected your learning in the same situation as your peer?

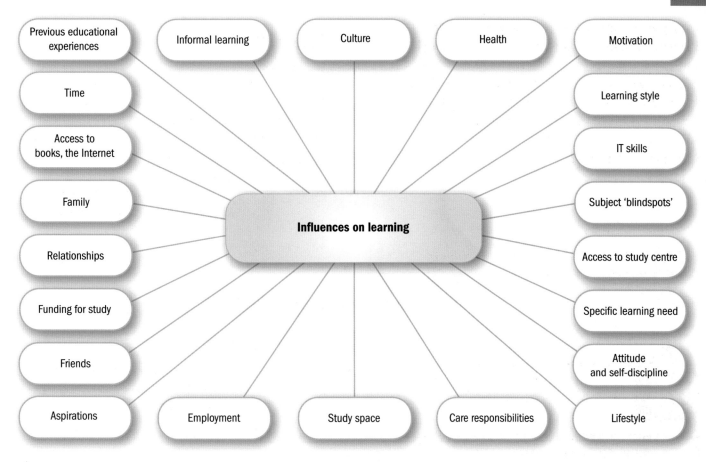

▲ **Figure 6.4 The range of influences on learning**

Kolb recognised that socialisation (the way in which you learn to fit into a group – see Unit 7) experiences affect your learning style. Personal habits and routines, beliefs, cultural customs, values, motivation and career aspirations are all influences because they can affect attitudes to study and its priority over other demands on an individual, such as home life or work.

Theory into practice

What factors influence your *own* learning?

How does each factor affect your learning?

What actions could you take to reduce the negative influences on your learning?

How might the other factors in Figure 6.4 affect how others learn?

The actions you have identified in this activity should help you to develop ways of overcoming barriers to your learning. You may wish to include them in your PPD action plan.

Skills for learning

In school you will have acquired the skills needed to achieve GCSEs. For this course, you will need additional skills to develop the capabilities needed for work in health and social care.

In your course induction, you may have completed diagnostic skills assessments. These are designed to identify factors that might hinder you from learning effectively, for example, specific weaknesses in your literacy, numeracy or language skills. Work in health and social care requires you to use and interpret complex information in both written and numerical formats and, in all workplaces, IT skills are essential.

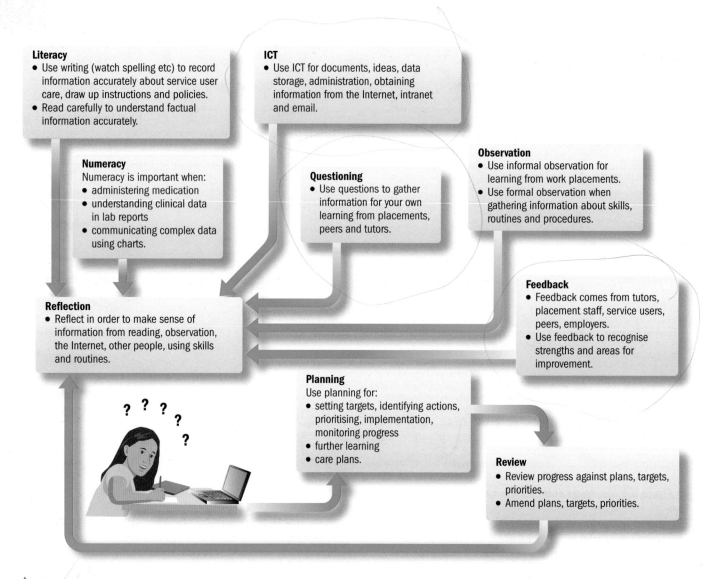

The following are the content boxes within Figure 6.5:

Literacy
- Use writing (watch spelling etc) to record information accurately about service user care, draw up instructions and policies.
- Read carefully to understand factual information accurately.

ICT
- Use ICT for documents, ideas, data storage, administration, obtaining information from the Internet, intranet and email.

Numeracy
Numeracy is important when:
- administering medication
- understanding clinical data in lab reports
- communicating complex data using charts.

Questioning
- Use questions to gather information for your own learning from placements, peers and tutors.

Observation
- Use informal observation for learning from work placements.
- Use formal observation when gathering information about skills, routines and procedures.

Feedback
- Feedback comes from tutors, placement staff, service users, peers, employers.
- Use feedback to recognise strengths and areas for improvement.

Reflection
- Reflect in order to make sense of information from reading, observation, the Internet, other people, using skills and routines.

Planning
Use planning for:
- setting targets, identifying actions, prioritising, implementation, monitoring progress
- further learning
- care plans.

Review
- Review progress against plans, targets, priorities.
- Amend plans, targets, priorities.

▲ Figure 6.5 All the skills that go into personal professional development for work in health and social care

Reflect

How do you think your preferred learning style might influence your skills for learning?

What could you do to help you develop your skills for learning?

You will need to use all these skills during the course and you might need dedicated teaching sessions to develop your literacy, numeracy and ICT skills. Additional study skills (those skills you need to complete a course of study successfully) to prepare you for higher education are explored in Book 2, Unit 47.

Support for learning

All learners require support to know how their learning is progressing. Learning may be measured by passing exams but, on this course, your knowledge and understanding of health and social care will be demonstrated through the course work you complete. You will receive written feedback on your assessed work to tell you what you have achieved and provide guidance on what still needs to be done or how you could improve future work.

Source of support	Type of support
Teaching	Sharing of new knowledge, facilitating development of new understanding
Tutorials	Support from specific subject tutors or for your whole programme from a personal tutor – a two-way exchange
Feedback	This tells you what you have achieved and gives specific and/or general guidance to help you improve your work next time
Coaching	Specific training for practical skills and improved performance
Supervision	When someone oversees your work in a practical situation
Mentoring	When an experienced person provides guidance and advice about your work
Meetings	Sharing, discussing ideas, making decisions
Help with specific learning needs	These might include language, literacy, numeracy, sensory impairment – access might be needed to specialist tutors, equipment etc
Seminars	Exploring topics and ideas in detail, sharing original research
Giving oral presentations	Talking about a topic, answering questions
Working with peers	Sharing ideas, sharing work, learning from each other
Self-awareness	Recognising when you need support from others
Accessing information and support	Knowing how and where to get the support you need

Table 6.2 Support for learning

Your responsibilities for supporting your learning are:

- to *acknowledge* the support you need for *your* learning
- to *accept* the support that is available to you.

You will probably use most of these different types of support at some stage during your course. Supervisors and mentors will be important sources of support for your learning about health and care practice in your placements.

Reflect

What support are you receiving?

How does the support you receive help you identify:

- what you have done well
- what you need to do better
- how you could make improvements?

What could you do to make better use of the support available to you?

Remember!

Always use your journal to record any informal feedback comments, however brief. Keeping your own notes of tutorials, discussions with placement mentors, peer feedback etc should become part of your routine work for this unit.

Learning opportunities

The opportunity for you to apply the Kolb experiential learning cycle to learn something new, or to increase your understanding, can happen at any time. This might be during formal learning in the classroom or in a placement (when you are being taught by a tutor or directed by a supervisor) or during an everyday experience. You might apply the Kolb theory soon after an active experience, for example, in a classroom discussion or when talking an issue through with your placement mentor, or you might apply it only later. Your formal learning in college may enable you to reflect differently on an experience in your past relating, for example, to what happened when you were ill. In this case, the reflection forms part of the reflective observation and active conceptualisation part of the cycle. Opportunities for learning can also come from experiences in paid employment or any voluntary work where you might gain experience of using and developing your communication skills working with customers in a shop or a restaurant.

Assessment activity 6.1

Discuss with your class peers the factors that influence learning in individuals. Use this section of the unit to structure your discussions.

Present a CV and write a concise descriptive personal profile of your experience to date that identifies the facts about your life, for example, home life, important events (moving to a new area, the death of a grandparent ...), employment. Once it has been seen by your assessor, file the profile in your PPD portfolio.

Explain key influences on personal learning processes of individuals

1   Write a report which explains the influences on how individuals learn.   **P1**

Grading tip for P1

Explain in some detail at least five influences that can affect learning and support your explanations by using the theories of Kolb and of Honey and Mumford. Not all the influences you explain need to have influenced your own learning.

Analyse the impact of key influences on personal learning processes on your own learning.

2   Analyse the factors that have influenced your own learning, using learning theories to explain how each influence has affected your learning to date.   **M1**

Grading tip for M1

Analyse all the main influences on your learning by identifying what the influences were (or are), how each influence helped you (or not) and why. Again, use learning theories to help you explain how the influences had the effect they did on your own learning and development.

Evaluate how personal learning and development may benefit others.

Evaluate how you could help others in your peer group and in your placements to learn. Use the understanding you have gained from reflection on your own learning experiences.   **D1**

Grading tip for D1

How well could you use your own learning to help others, for example, peers in class, staff in placements, service users or members of your family? What examples do you have from your own experience of your ability to help others and what skills and knowledge did you use to do this? How effective were you?

Introduction

This is the largest section of the unit and the focus is particularly on your development. Figure 6.1 on page 273 represents learning and development as a blend of your:

- knowledge and understanding
- skills and abilities
- experience.

You will assess your own learning up to the present time by reviewing:

- what you know and understand
- the skills and abilities you have acquired
- the experiences you have had.

Once you have assessed how much you have learnt, or have developed, *by the time you started your course*, you can:

- identify what knowledge, skills and experiences you need to develop while you are on the course to prepare you for working in health or social care, or another career
- draw up a plan to develop the aspects you have identified
- implement the plan and review your progress against it regularly
- reflect on your learning throughout the course.

In context

Sandy has come to college because there was no sixth form at her school. She has six GCSEs at grade C. She has a D in maths and finds it difficult to understand the numerical work within her BTEC course. After working in a local reception class during her Year 10 work experience placement and receiving much praise for her ability to communicate with the children, Sandy did have problems in planning a display because she miscalculated the spacing of the children's work. Sandy wants to be a social worker.

1 **What are Sandy's strengths?**

2 **What would be appropriate areas for development for Sandy?**

3 **What actions would address her areas for development and help her make a strong application for social work training at the end of her BTEC course?**

You are aware that you are good at some things but less good at others; you may have a clear career path or be uncertain. You may have made some new discoveries about yourself during the first few weeks of the course that have widened your career options. Through consciously thinking about what you need to do, checking your progress and reflecting on this regularly, you can make better use of opportunities available on the course to build on your existing abilities, develop new knowledge and skills and choose, and work towards, a fulfilling career.

These processes will help you to develop your abilities as a reflective practitioner, an ability that is required for all workers in health or care. It is your ability to *reflect* on your development and *learn* from this reflection, rather than how far you have developed, that is important in this unit. At this stage of your professional development, learning through reflection should help you to:

- maximise your achievement in each unit of the course
- better understand work in health and care
- understand yourself in preparation for future training or employment in health or care
- make an informed career choice for progression from the course.

Understanding yourself is important because care work involves you interacting with other people and your personal qualities and abilities will influence your interactions. Being aware of how your own attitudes and behaviour are influenced by your experiences – having **self-awareness** – is an important aspect of working professionally in care.

Key term

Self-awareness Knowing how you, personally, will respond to a fact or situation.

Placements

Work placements will give you experience of working with different service user groups such as adults receiving social care, young children in nurseries or schools, and patients in hospital. You may attend placement in a series of blocks or regularly for one day a week but your placements will be spaced over the length of the course. Placements in voluntary organisations are valid, provided you are involved in delivering care and are supervised by an appropriately experienced and qualified person. You will work alongside care workers, helping them with tasks and activities and watching how they interact with service users and each other. More information about working in placements is given later in this section.

Initial assessment of your own learning and development

Self-assessment

The first step in developing your self-awareness is for you to assess your abilities at the start of your course. This will act as a **benchmark** against which you can measure the progress of your development. This self-assessment will require you to make judgements about your:

- knowledge and understanding
- skills and abilities
- values and beliefs
- experience of caring

in the context of:

- your study on the course
- your work experience
- the career pathway you choose for progression at the end of the course.

Key term

Benchmark A measure against which an action/activity/performance can be measured.

The self-assessment should be carried out as soon as possible after starting your course, before you have been influenced by new learning on the course and before you start a work placement. You will make judgements about yourself to identify:

- your strengths
- areas for development.

You can then plan how to develop the areas identified, called here the SAP approach.

S	Strengths	In relation to the context: • What you do well or easily. For example, communicating orally, using IT and the Internet. • The qualities you have that are helpful for the context. For example, patience, recognising the need for support with numeracy.
A	Areas for development	In relation to the context: • Things you do less well, less easily or not at all. For example, using number in everyday activities. • What you cannot do at all but which you will need to develop for the context. For example, interacting with older people and those with learning disabilities.
P	Plan for development	• Setting goals of where you want to be. For example, getting a grade C in GCSE maths in order to be a social worker. • Drawing up an action plan to achieve the goals. For example, researching social work training, contacting old school to re-sit maths in November, joining a GCSE re-sit class in college, talking to tutor about additional support for numeracy and possible placements.

Table 6.3 The SAP approach

The judgements you make in your initial self-assessment should be based on as much independent information about yourself as possible. Exam results, references from your school or employer, or results of a functional skills diagnostic assessment would present an **objective assessment** of your knowledge and abilities. Peer feedback at the end of the course induction could also be used.

Key term

Objective assessment This is free from bias because judgements are based on evidence from independent sources, so are free from personal feelings and opinions.

Remember!

The SAP approach could be used to review an individual, specific activity as well as for your overall PPD.

Your initial self-assessment at the start of the course will look at the knowledge, skills and experience you already have.

Knowledge

Knowledge is the factual information you have acquired and understanding is your ability to use, or apply, your knowledge appropriately (for example, to retrieve the necessary information from your memory or use the appropriate practical skills). The range of your knowledge at the start of the course is likely to be based around subjects you have studied in school and possibly from a hobby or interest. If you are a mature learner, you may have acquired knowledge from being a parent or an employee. Your knowledge will develop through that gained in formal learning situations in the classroom and placements. You may have knowledge of responsibilities as an employee, for example, time management, working in a team or customer service in

Theory into practice

List all the subjects or topics you have studied or acquired specific knowledge of before you started the course.

Identify the subjects you find more difficult. Use learning theories from earlier in the unit to suggest why you have found them difficult.

What actions could you take to improve your learning in any of the subjects studied?

a part-time job. If you listen to major news bulletins and read a newspaper, you will be aware of developments in the NHS or services for older people in your local area. A news story about an illness or about stem cell research may spark a discussion with your peers in class or in the college canteen that introduces you to the views of other people.

Reflect

How do you think the subjects that you have studied, or other knowledge you have acquired before starting the course, might be useful to your studies or to your placement?

Identifying those aspects of your learning that you find more difficult is a useful way of identifying areas for development. Recognising your prior knowledge and identifying where and/or when it might be useful can help you learn more quickly or more effectively from experiences as they happen.

Skills

A skill is the ability to perform a practical activity appropriately, or with competence. If you are on the National course, you can probably read and write sufficiently well to achieve four GCSEs at grade C. You may well be able to ride a bicycle (a skill learnt during your childhood) or draw, use a PC, or have football skills. On this course you will have to think about your skills in communicating, working with others, using equipment (technical skills), researching information and organising yourself (personal skills).

■ Communicating

Being able to communicate effectively is an essential skill for care workers.

Reflect

Use feedback (formal and/or informal) to make judgements about how well you communicate:

- when using text (for example, your handwriting, expressing yourself in writing, reading, understanding what you read, using ITC-enabled text)
- orally (your use of language and what you say, how you say it and how you convey your intended meaning)
- non-verbally (how you listen, use gestures, facial expression and body language)
- when using the communication cycle (see Unit 1).

To what extent do you communicate your attitudes, beliefs, values and mood when you communicate?

Reflecting on the points above will help you assess your communication skills at the start of the course. Unit 1 explores communication in detail and you should use the communication cycle and the full range of other communication skills in your work placement. You can reflect on the feedback you receive in your end-of-placement reports and compare your development with your initial self-assessment. You can then identify further areas for development within your PPD plan.

Reflect

Reflect on the communication skills you have used so far on your course with:

- your class peers
- staff in your school/college.

Use your experiences so far of:

- induction
- group work in class
- tutorials.

Remember!

Communicating all *relevant* information clearly, *sufficiently* and *accurately* in health and care is essential so that the information is received and understood accurately by the recipient. Failure to do this could result in mistakes when providing care for an individual.

■ Working with others

Work in health or care requires the support of others who are contributing to providing care, whether they are professionals, specialist care workers, supervisors, managers, support staff or people who work in different agencies or organisations. Together, these individuals work as a team. You will work in teams in college and in placement and will be expected to:

- understand how your own skills, knowledge and experience contribute to the team task
- recognise how the skills, knowledge and experience of each of the other members of the team contribute to the team task
- support members of the team in contributing to the team task
- respect contributions from all members of the team
- evaluate the effectiveness of the team in carrying out its task
- evaluate your own contribution to the team effort.

In context

Tahira is a newly appointed health care assistant in and is only just beginning to understand the roles of the different professionals on the ward.

Mrs Ahmed, aged 79, is admitted to the ward from Accident and Emergency with a broken hip after a fall in the street. She is very distressed and confused and in a lot of pain. The staff nurse, Anna, asks Tahira to comfort Mrs Ahmed because she is aware that Tahira is bilingual and can speak with Mrs Ahmed in her own language. Mrs Ahmed appears calmed by Tahira. When the doctor arrives to prepare Mrs Ahmed for an operation, he asks if Tahira can interpret. She explains that she is not an interpreter and the doctor accepts this, but asks her to remain until Mrs Ahmed's husband arrives. An interpreter arrives and the doctor obtains the information he needs for Mrs Ahmed to have her operation.

Later, Anna thanks Tahira, saying she was right not to act as the formal interpreter but tells her about the hospital interpreter service. She makes suggestions as to how Tahira could develop her skills in comforting confused and distressed patients.

1 **Who were the members of the team?**

2 **What was the contribution each made to the care of Mrs Ahmed?**

3 **How did they work together as a team?**

Tahira faced a new situation but recognised the limitations of what she could contribute, communicated her concerns and yet was able to help Mrs Ahmed effectively alongside the professionals. Anna helped her gain new knowledge, a better understanding and gave her some tips to develop her skills.

You will work with service users with different care needs in your placements under the supervision of placement staff. You will probably talk to them on a one-to-one basis and will work with small groups of service users, helping them to meet their developmental, creative or recreational needs.

Theory into practice

Complete this activity when you are working on a group task in class.

1. Define the group task and draw up a plan to achieve it, identifying timescales and targets.

2. Agree the contribution to be made by each individual to the group task.

3. Plan for your contribution to the team task.

4. Implement the group and individual plans to complete the group task.

5. As a group, discuss how well the team did and the reasons for its strengths and weaknesses.

How successful was a) the team task, and b) your contribution to it?

How did the contributions of all members of the team affect the group task?

What could *you* have done differently to improve the outcomes for the team task?

Remember!

You should always be accompanied by a supervisor when in the presence of service users.

■ Technical skills

The most important technical skills you will use in health or care work are those associated with information and communication technology (ICT). You may already be confident using a computer (IT skills) to access information on the Internet or produce text documents. However, you will also be expected to use routine software:

- for your research
- when preparing assignment work
- when giving presentations

- when presenting numerical information
- when storing data.

You may have other skills too. Creative or musical skills could be an asset in some work placements or you may develop skills in using specialist equipment associated with your studies or work in care settings. When on work placement you might use equipment or you may only be able to observe others using it.

Theory into practice

Observe the technical skills used by your tutors and the workers in placements.

What does this tell you about:

- the training needed to use the equipment
- the purpose of the equipment in the context
- how it benefits learners, service users or workers
- health and safety considerations when using the equipment?

What should you take into account when you use technical equipment?

You should not use equipment that you have not been trained to use and it is unlikely that you will have authority to do so when on placements. You can observe how equipment is used and learn about its purpose, how it helps service users and gain an understanding of the health and safety considerations for yourself and the service user when using it.

■ Research skills

Research is planned investigation of a topic and you will need to carry out research for assignments in all units of the National course. Formal research is explored in Unit 22. However, for this unit, you need a basic understanding of research principles so that you can obtain information to complete assignments successfully. You will use both **qualitative information** (that based on description using words and images) and **quantitative information** (that which is described using numerical data, often as tables, charts or graphs). Primary research is research in which *you* will generate the data; you might do this through an interview, an observation, a survey using a questionnaire or through an experiment. The informal observations you make during your work placement will be valuable primary data to use as examples in your assignment work.

Theory into practice

Choose a topic of interest that is relevant to health or care and use three different secondary sources to retrieve quantitative and qualitative data on the topic.

Suggest how you might obtain primary data about the topic.

Key terms

Qualitative information is information based on description, using words and images.

Quantitative information is information that is described by using numerical data, for example, tables, charts or graphs.

Key terms

Validity A measure of the quality of information and how it is used.

Reliability A measure of the methods used to generate information.

Most of your study will involve secondary research, which is using information that has been produced by others. Useful secondary sources include:

- books
- the Internet
- specialist journals
- newspapers
- leaflets and brochures.

You should continually check that the secondary sources you use are **valid** for your purpose i.e. that the information or claim made is accurate in terms of it:

- measuring what it claims to measure
- being based on an accurate interpretation of the evidence presented
- being supported by sufficient evidence.

You should also check that your secondary sources are **reliable** – that you can trust the evidence retrieved (and therefore the claim made). The methods used to obtain the information should:

- reflect a realistic situation (rather than one that is unlikely to occur in normal circumstances)
- produce the same results if someone else repeated the research exactly.

You need to look for 'clues' that tell you about the validity and reliability of sources of information; doing this by *evaluating* each information source you use *and* what the source is *saying* is called making a **critique**.

Key term

Critique A process of detailed analysis.

The points in Figure 6.6 are useful to consider whenever you are researching a topic. Information that can be confirmed from more than one source is likely to be more reliable than that obtained from a source where you doubt its validity or reliability.

5 Does it present any evidence to support the claims/opinions/conclusions?
How robust were the methods used?
Is it based on a situation that would never happen in real life?

6 Is the claim valid?
Does it relate to the evidence presented?
Is it accurate given the evidence?
Is there enough evidence to support the claim?

4 When was this written?
Date?
Does it still apply now?

7 Does the author refer to the work of anyone else to back up their claims?
Do they present alternative arguments and justify the one they have chosen?
Is there a bibliography or reference list?

3 How neutral is the person/ organisation in relation to their claims?
Has a business sponsored the research on their brand/product?

8 Is the information relevant?
Does it come from the UK (or EU)?
To what extent does it relate to what I need here?

2 What do I know about the person who wrote this?
Organisation?
Qualifications/status (e.g. doctor/nurse/academic)?

9 What specific information is useful to me?
Statistics?
Images?
Opinions?
Conclusions?

1 Do I know who wrote this?
Names?
A well-known organisation?

1 Record the source details fully.
2 Make notes from the source.
3 Write up your work from your notes.

10 Can I find this source again?
RECORD the full reference details, including date accessed (for a website) and page numbers (for all direct quotes).

▲ Figure 6.6 Getting a handle on secondary sources

Theory into practice

Choose a topic from one of the units you are studying and research it using secondary sources. Obtain one source from each of those listed on page 289.

Identify three main points each source makes about the topic.

To what extent does each source say the same thing or make different points?

What do you know about the validity and reliability of each source and how do these factors affect your judgement?

Are the sources useful for the topic you are investigating? Justify your judgements.

'Data' is a plural word (the singular form is 'datum', though 'data' is nowadays often used in the singular) that describes several pieces of information (these will often be numerical). Being able to collect, organise (into tables, charts etc) and use numerical and statistical data to support the arguments you are making is an essential skill, sometimes called data handling. It is essential for study and in work environments.

Whenever you use secondary sources, you must acknowledge each source through a **bibliography** and a **reference** system. Good practice would be to include both at the end of your work and you will receive guidance on how to do this from your college.

Key terms

Bibliography A list of texts that have been used to provide general information and background knowledge.

Reference An acknowledgement of a source text used by someone else to contribute a specific idea, opinion, quotation, statistic, fact, diagram, chart etc. The reference will acknowledge the original author.

Failure to acknowledge the secondary sources you use is *plagiarism* and your college will have a policy on this. Plagiarism is a form of dishonesty and dishonesty undermines the trust expected of those who work in health or care.

Take it further

Use secondary sources to investigate research techniques such as:

- different types of observation
- different types of interview
- approaches to sampling for a survey
- different questioning formats for use in questionnaires.

For each, identify advantages and disadvantages

Remember!

Always acknowledge the secondary sources you have used in preparing your assignments by using referencing and a bibliography.

When accessing a source, *always record ALL* the details of each source needed to write the bibliography and reference lists later. You may not be able to find the source by the time you are writing up your research.

Developing good referencing habits is essential preparation for study in higher education.

■ Personal skills

Your personal skills and abilities relate to you as a person and your ability to organise yourself and take responsibility for your life; they often relate to your personality and temperament. Time-keeping and personal presentation is particularly important in care work. How you present yourself indicates your professional role to service users and other workers; some placements require you to wear specific clothing for this reason. Personal cleanliness is paramount for health and safety reasons so that you:

- do not *pass on* infection *to* others
- reduce the risk of *acquiring* infection *from* others.

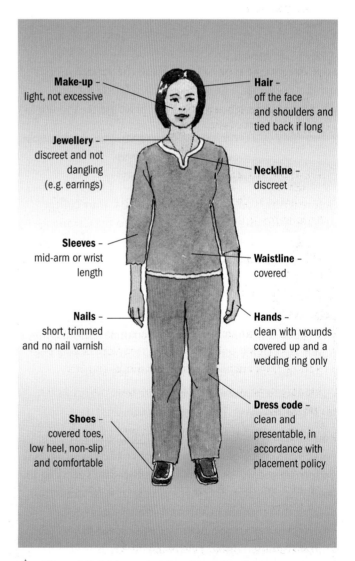

▲ Figure 6.7 Aspects of personal presentation

Care work sometimes requires you to work within an individual's personal space and lack of good personal hygiene would be particularly unpleasant for others.

Theory into practice

Find out how you should wash your hands when working in care.

Practice

Everything that you do in your placements is your 'practice' although the detail of your work will vary according to the type of setting and the service users using its services. The legal aspects relating to your placement experience apply to all placements and are explored below.

Legislation and codes of practice

Before letting you start your placements, your college will apply for an enhanced disclosure to the Criminal Records Bureau: this is a requirement under the Care Standards Act 2000 (CSA) for all those who work with children, young people and vulnerable adults. If you are under 18, then the CSA limits the practical care activities (for example, bathing, toileting and feeding) with which you can assist. You will also have personal responsibilities under the Health and Safety at Work Act 1974 (see Unit 3) and the Data Protection Act 1988 (see Unit 1).

■ Placement induction

You should receive guidance from your college before you go into your placement and, once there, you should be introduced to the policies and procedures relating to your work in each placement as part of your induction. This should include health and safety issues such as emergency evacuation procedures, first aid procedure, guidance about contact with body fluids as well as a briefing on your role in the placement. You will also be

allocated a work-based supervisor who will oversee what you do and be your regular contact in the placement.

■ Confidentiality

When on placement, you must be aware at all times that information relating to service users, workers, other people associated with the organisation (as well as that relating to the organisation itself) is confidential. Your induction should include confidentiality policies; some organisations use confidentiality agreements.

Remember!

When on placements, you will observe and listen as part of your role. Working within a care team and sharing information *within the team* is an essential part of your work, provided it is relevant to the work of the team and the safety and security of individuals. Information should only ever be shared with those who have a right to know it. Relatives do not have an automatic right to information about an individual using a service.

Information should be shared for a clear purpose and it should be accurate and sufficient. You may also encounter information that you have overheard or observed unintentionally. All information obtained in this way should be treated as confidential and not shared with others.

Most breaches of confidentiality occur through casual chatter amongst workers and between workers, family or friends. You must be continuously on your guard to ensure that you do not talk about your placement in a way that might identify a person or give details about an individual that might reveal their identity indirectly. Use pseudonyms for your portfolio and college work to maintain the anonymity of individuals.

■ Consent

You must obtain consent for specific activities which you undertake in any placement, especially those where you will work directly with service users. Placement policies should provide guidance but you should always seek clarification with your supervisor about when, and from whom, you should obtain consent. Activities for which specific consent should be obtained might include:

- non-participant or participant observations of service users, individual workers or work teams
- interviews with placement staff
- any activity you are carrying out to assist you with other aspects of your course.

Consent for informal general observations of job roles and responsibilities, daily routines and practice skills such as you might describe in your journal/diary are usually covered through the general consent associated with an organisation accepting a BTEC student for a placement.

Remember!

You should not take photographs of service users and especially not of children (even if the child is a relative). Written consent would be necessary from the placement organisation, as well as the individual service users. Provided you have obtained consent, you may photograph *artefacts* that service users have made or that you have prepared (for example, displays, raw materials for a craft activity) or equipment or the layout of a room. All such records should only be made if it is an essential part of the assessment and cannot be described in any other way.

You are unlikely to have had any experience of caring in a care setting at the start of the course but you may have some informal care experience such as looking after a relative, neighbour or friend. Whenever you help someone else to carry out their daily activities, you are providing informal care.

Your reflections on the following questions can assist your self-assessment. Your knowledge and understanding of care practices will develop as you

Reflect

Review your past experience of helping others, or, if you have not had any experience of this, review your first week or so on the course.

In what activities, however small, have you provided care or support to others (for example escorting a frail relative to the shops)? (You should note that supporting each other in a team is not care.)

In what ways did you give the support on each occasion?

What did you do well and what did you do less well? Did you get any feedback from others at the time? Explain why some of the support you gave was successful and why some was less successful.

What does this review of the different caring activities tell you about your potential as a worker in health or care? What skills and knowledge do you now have? What do you need to do to develop your caring abilities further? What are your feelings and emotions when you are helping others?

complete each work experience placement, working with different service user groups, in different care settings and with different work teams.

Values and beliefs

Values and beliefs are an important consideration in care work. Something which is valuable has value which is often measured in monetary worth but *values* are moral and ethical principles that are so important to you that they influence how you think and behave; they are an essential part of your personality. A belief is an understanding that is held with strong conviction; personal beliefs may be associated with a religious faith.

We all have personal values and beliefs and they influence how we lead our lives, for example how we see the world, other people or our priorities and the decisions we make. Another person may have similar values and beliefs to you or different ones. Your values and beliefs will have formed as a result of the influences of the people around you and your experiences from your childhood onwards and they may continue to develop as you go through your life. Unit 2 explores some of the factors that influence personal values, for example, experiences of family, friendships, diversity, education, religious faith or ethical beliefs.

You have probably identified several influences on your development that range from the people in your home life when you were a small child, to a wider circle of influence associated with school, friends, work etc that has influenced you during later childhood and adolescence as you have become more independent.

Reflect

To explore how your values and beliefs have developed so far in your life, identify how each of the following has influenced you from your early childhood onwards:

- how you see yourself
- close family and relatives
- friends, teachers, colleagues and other people in your life outside your family
- where you live, the local community, your neighbourhood etc
- wider influences from the media and wider society.

The rights of service users	Examples of how you could respect this right
Diversity and respect for differences	• Attending to the needs of each person as an individual • Encouraging service users to express their views, for example on a service they receive
Equality in care practice	• Showing just as much respect and care for a service user who may be of a different culture or have different values to yourself
Anti-discriminatory practice	• Learning how to challenge appropriately the behaviour of a worker or service user who subjects another person to discrimination or abuse • Reporting incidents to your supervisor or a manager
Confidentiality	• Never talking about any service users to others outside the care team • When discussing placement learning in class, never identifying a service user or member of staff
Control (autonomy) over own life, choice, independence	• Allowing service users to make choices about their day-to-day care and activities • Never presuming to carry out a task for a service user • Always asking whether a service user would like you to help
Dignity and privacy	• Not drawing attention to an individual in distress but helping them without fuss to a quiet area or to relieve their distress • Making sure a service user is dressed and covered, even if this is inconvenient for you
Effective communication	• Reporting events and observations accurately to staff • Explaining your actions to service users when providing care
Safety and security	• Being observant of potential hazards for service users and workers and reporting any hazards you see • Taking responsibility for your own safety • Being vigilant of your own safe practice • Reporting any abuse you witness
The right to take risks	• For example, allowing an individual to smoke (even though it may make their heart condition worse)

Table 6.4 Respecting a service user's rights

The values of care

In the UK, legislation and the regulatory framework for health and care provision is based on values that are shared across all health and care professions. Many of the values are those that are addressed within the European Convention on Human Rights (see Unit 2). These values are written into professional codes of conduct for all health and care practitioners registered in the UK and into the codes of practice and charters that apply to care provision. You will be expected to demonstrate respect for these values in your work placements.

Part of your development as a worker in health and social care is to show *through your behaviour* that you respect the rights of others. You must accept that this is part of your professional responsibility. Table 6.4 gives just a few examples of how you can demonstrate your responsibilities in care work. You will encounter a wide range of different circumstances in your placements in which you will need to think about care values.

Reflect

Thinking about the questions below will help you understand how your own values and beliefs affect your feelings and behaviour and the extent to which you may need to change your behaviour when working in care settings.

How do you feel when someone ignores or makes fun of your values or beliefs?

How do you react when you meet someone who has different values and beliefs to yourself?

How do your values and beliefs compare with those that underpin health and care work in the UK? What modifications to your attitude and behaviour might you need to make when on work placement to show respect for the values of care?

Taking it further

Service users also have responsibilities. Give some examples of the responsibilities expected of them.

What are your rights as a care worker?

Remember!

The ability to maintain an objective viewpoint (one that is free from bias) is an important attribute to develop in health and social care in order to avoid discrimination. Care practice should be based on evidence of need and not on stereotyping or prejudice.

Self-awareness is particularly important when reconciling your personal values and beliefs with the behaviour and attitude expected of you in work placements. Your ability to respect care values is likely to be a major influence on how placement professionals judge your practice.

Personal goals and career aspirations

You should complete your self-assessment within the first few weeks of your course to identify your strengths and the areas you wish to develop in the context of your career aspirations at the end of the course.

If you aim to pursue a career in health or care, then you will need to study for professional qualifications at the end of the course and there may be specific entry requirements or experience that would strengthen your application for a course. Before you can make decisions about your career pathway, you need to be aware of the options available to you.

Theory into practice

Research the career options available to you after completing your course.

Make a shortlist of at least three options and investigate in detail the qualifications and experience you will need to gain for each.

For each career option, what actions do you need to take:

- in the next few weeks
- within six months
- within eighteen months?

Using your self-assessment, analyse the extent to which your experience and learning could enable you to follow the three options you have chosen.

What actions would you need to take to pursue any of the three options?

Decisions about your career pathway do not need to be taken immediately but you do need to be aware of realistic options from which you can make choices later on in the course. Entry requirements for professional training may require achievement of specific grades or a UCAS (Universities and Colleges Application System) score and this is likely to influence your PPD plan for the course.

Remember!

You should make the most of the support systems available to you in your college to help you when you are making your career choices.

Assessment activity 6.2

Describe your own knowledge, skills, practice, values, beliefs and career aspirations at the start of the programme.

1   Review this section of the unit, including your responses to the activities.

2   Describe your knowledge, skills, practice, values, beliefs and career aspirations as they are at the start of your course.   **P2**

Grading tip for P2

Use each of the areas discussed in this section of the unit and your understanding of learning theory to help you.

Use examples from your experience and the understanding you have gained from the activities to support your description.

When describing your learning and development at the start of the course, ensure that you identify your strengths and the areas that you need to develop *during* the course (in class, work placements and other aspects of your life) and for your future career.

Your personal and professional development plan

Once your initial self-assessment is complete and you have identified your strengths, areas for development and some realistic career options, you can start to plan your PPD as part of the third stage in the SAP approach. To do this you will need to understand the principles of planning which include:

- setting goals or targets
- drawing up an action plan and implementing it
- monitoring your progress against the plan
- amending or adding to the plan in response to progress and/or changes to circumstances.

Goals and targets

The goals you set for yourself may be quite specific, for example, 'get a grade C for GCSE maths in my November re-sit' or more general such as 'participate more in group work'. Both will require specific actions to be achieved. Goals can also be short-term and long-term.

Short-term goals (up to 6 months ahead)	Long-term goals (18 months or more ahead)
<ul><li>Targets for each term of the course. For example, grades for specific units, researching university courses</li><li>Targets for next placement. For example, interactions for Unit 1, researching policies and procedures</li><li>Re-sitting GCSE English</li><li>Passing driving test</li><li>Achieving ITC Key Skill at Level 3</li></ul>	<ul><li>End of course. For example, higher education or employment</li><li>Making an UCAS/NMAS (Nursing and Midwifery Admissions Service) application</li><li>Improving listening skills</li><li>Gap-year plans</li></ul>

Table 6.5 Short- and long-term goals

In the case study below, Jamie will have to find out if he has the GCSEs needed for each of his options. He could include a target in his plan to observe and talk with an

In context

Jamie is unsure whether to become a midwife, an occupational therapist or a nurse. He has 8 GCSEs: 4 at grade C, maths at grade D, biology and English at grade B and an A in art. He visits his grandmother in a residential care home and has learnt a bit about care work through watching the staff in the home. He has started the BTEC course hoping that the work experience will help him make up his mind about which career to choose.

1. **How well qualified is Jamie for each of the career options he is interested in?**

2. **Explain what Jamie's priorities should be while he is on the course.**

3. **How could Jamie use his placement experience to strengthen his chances of being offered a place for professional training at the end of the course?**

occupational therapist when he is in placement. He may find he will have to study hard to ensure he gets good grades in each of his units of study.

Goals are a statement of what you *intend* to achieve *before* you start – they do not tell you *how* you will achieve them. They are sometimes called *objectives*.

Drawing up an action plan

An action plan identifies *how* you intend to achieve your goals or targets. The plan for your PPD should relate to your development as revealed by the:

- areas of weakness identified in your initial self-assessment
- aspects of development needed for your career options.

Each goal may require a more detailed breakdown into several small actions, for example to:

- make it more attainable through a step-by-step approach
- be able to take different actions at different times

- ensure you do not omit important steps
- allow you to plan in sufficient time for each activity involved
- allow some flexibility until a later stage.

The plan becomes a list of detailed actions that need to be taken but, in order to have a good chance of being achievable, each should be SMART.

S	Specific	Each action should be a short, clear statement of what is to be done.
M	Measurable	The outcome or result of each action can be specifically measured.
A	Actionable	Each action should be something which can be put into action; the action may need breaking down into smaller, more realistic steps so it becomes actionable.
R	Relevant	Each action should help you work towards one or more of the goals or targets you have set for yourself.
T	Timely	A deadline date is set for each action and the timing of each deadline is appropriate for other actions needed within the plan.

Table 6.6 SMART goals

For the purposes of this unit, you will be preparing a *personal* development plan and so the responsibility for all the actions will rest with you.

Theory into practice

Draw up at least six goals to work towards during your course.

A practical way to present an action plan is as a table. Design a table that could form the basis of the action plan you will need to prepare for your assessment. You will need several columns to identify each of the features to make it a SMART plan.

You could find it useful to see how other types of action plan can be presented, for example, the design of care planning forms used in your placements.

Opposite is an example of a PPD drawn up by a student on a BTEC National Diploma in Health and Social Care.

Reflect

When planning for a group activity, where several people have different responsibilities within the group task, it is good practice to name the person responsible for each action.

PPD goals	Goal target end date	Actions	Action target date	Review 1	Review 2	Review 3
Training as a children's nurse	Jan 2009	1 Get two work placements with children 2 Research universities for children's nursing 3 Apply for nurse training	Oct 07 –Jan 09 Jan 08 Nov 08	10/10/07 – First placement in reception class to start 26 Nov 15/10/07 – Careers talk Sept 07 – First draft of NMAS personal statement to tutor ACTION: revise statement	June 08 Decided to apply for adult branch April 08 First choice wants merit for BTEC ACTION: Make more use of learning in work; ask more questions	
Be more confident using Maths	1 Get Key Skill 1 Level 3 Numeracy 2 Use statistics in my work	June 09	June 09 From now	20 Nov 07 – Struggling so tutor arranged additional support	05 Feb 08 – First assignment back; error on one graph ACTION: resubmit in 2 weeks	
Get part-time job	Find job in a shop	Oct 07	Oct 07	Oct 07 – Fri, Sat and Suns in supermarket; tired	Mar 08 – Working in care home on Sats and one evening in week; helps college work	
Pass driving test	March 2009 – now revised to May 2009	1 Book lessons 2 Book theory test 3 Take theory test 4 Take driving test	Nov 08 Mar 09	Passed theory test Failed first test ACTION: More driving practice, reduce work hours at weekends		

Table 6.7 An example of a personal and professional development action plan for a BTEC National Diploma in Health and Social Care

In context

Kelly left school with low GCSE grades and got a job in a shop near her home. When she could, she helped care for her grandmother who was disabled with arthritis and she found she really enjoyed this. She became a care assistant in a residential care home and got an NVQ Level 2 in Health and Social Care. She is now 19 and working in a nursing home where the matron wants Kelly to get her NVQ Level 3 but Kelly wants to become a nurse as soon as possible.

1 Write three aims for Kelly's career plan.

2 Break down each aim into specific actions (you may need to carry out some research about nurse training for Kelly).

3 Identify suitable targets for Kelly to achieve within three months, one year and two years, and draw up a detailed and SMART action plan for Kelly.

In the case study on page 299, Kelly meets the age requirement for entry to nurse training but has no GCSE English Language or Level 3 qualification. Her experience of care work will be helpful when she applies but, first, she needs to find out about the quickest way for her to obtain the minimum qualifications needed to apply for nurse training. When she has achieved these, she will need to make choices about where she trains and then complete the application form.

Remember!

The principles of action planning apply to any activities that need preparation.

Use SMART principles whenever you are planning an assignment or placement activity.

Monitoring your action plan

Once you have developed your SMART action plan you can start to *implement* it by working through the actions as you have prioritised them. Implementation of your PPD plan will be spread over the length of the

National course at the very least and you will need to monitor your progress as you work through the plan very carefully. Even with careful and detailed planning, some actions may not happen as you intended, or your priorities might change. For example, you could change your career aspiration. Monitoring encourages you to check whether the plan is progressing as intended or whether it needs to be *amended*. The amendments could involve changing the:

- *aims* because you have changed your career goal, or the feedback from your tutors means that you decide to be more ambitious about your career plans
- *actions* because the original aims have changed or you have discovered that your preferred course requires you to have specific experience
- *priorities* (the order in which you do things) because your first choice placement only has a vacancy to take you early in year two of your course
- *timescales* because you have decided to take a year out to earn some money before you move on to further training.

If you check your progress regularly, you are more likely to identify early on any changes that you need to make. Therefore, any problems that arise can be resolved sooner and the plan is more likely to help you achieve your aims. Checking the progress of your plan and amending it while it is in progress is called *monitoring*.

In context

Kaleem has spent the first year of his course enjoying college, playing football and now cricket. He has been handing work in late and, although he has met the pass criteria, he has not been getting the merit grades of which he is capable. He has had two very positive placement reports from a day centre for adults with mental health problems and from a reception class and his tutors feel that Kaleem's college work does not reflect his abilities. It is the summer term of his first year and he is behind with assignments again: he has only just discovered that he needs to get merit grades to read psychology at his preferred university. Kaleem has admitted in a tutorial that he finds it difficult to

organise himself and his work. His tutor has suggested an appointment in supported learning to help him organise his portfolio and the outstanding work he needs to complete before the end of term.

1   **How has monitoring helped Kaleem to identify changes he needs to make?**

2   **What might have happened if neither Kaleem nor his tutor had monitored his progress?**

3   **What steps would you recommend Kaleem to take so that he can complete his first-year work and achieve the merit grades he needs?**

In context

Using the skills and understanding of action planning that she has gained from Unit 6, Ali has drawn up an action plan for the completion of her research project for Unit 22: Research methodology. The assignment brief was received in November and she must submit the final report before the May half-term. She has chosen to investigate college students' attitudes to healthy food options in the college canteen: she is planning to survey college students and interview the catering manager as well as carry out appropriate secondary research. She planned to compile a questionnaire and distribute it in three weeks in February. Unfortunately college was closed for three days because of snow and she was ill for a week in January. It is now the end of February and her secondary research is behind schedule so she is not really sure what questions she should be asking for the survey. Ali has not yet got copies of her questionnaire ready to distribute to students. She has underestimated the time it takes to construct the questionnaire and then get copies made. She forgot to organise the interview and has just discovered the catering manager is on leave for a week. Ali reviews her plan.

1 What are the factors that have contributed to Ali's plan for her project falling behind schedule?

2 How does she need to amend her plan to get back on track to complete her project?

3 What would you recommend that Ali does for the remaining time she has to reduce the risk of her plan not meeting its objectives (i.e. submitting the report by the deadline)?

The intervals between the checks on the progress of the plan will vary according to factors such as:
- the purpose of the plan
- the overall timescale of the plan
- the complexity of the actions involved
- other people who are involved in actions in the plan.

In the above case study, two factors are unforeseen and beyond Ali's control: being ill and the college closure. The catering manager's annual leave need not have been a problem if Ali had checked her plan earlier and made arrangements for the interview sooner.

It is good practice for the monitoring process to be included as an action in the plan itself. Whatever the time interval of the monitoring, you should record that monitoring has taken place, what progress has been made and what changes/amendments (if any) have been made to your plan.

Assessment activity 6.3

Produce and monitor an action plan for self-development and the achievement of your personal goals.

1 Within the first-half term of the course, draw up an action plan for your self-development and achievement of personal goals. Your plan should include short-term targets/goals (up to 6 months) and long-term goals (minimum of 18 months) – don't forget, the goals need to be SMART.

2 Monitor your progress against each part of the plan at least once a term/semester and at the end of each placement.

3 Amend your plan as necessary in order to meet your goals and ongoing learning needs on the course, personal development and career aspirations. **P3**

4 Record briefly on the plan your progress in achieving the action points and date the entries. Use feedback received to identify and plan for your further development.

Remember!

Ask your tutor to sign and date your plan each time you monitor it or make a change to it. Your action plan is a working document which you will refer to throughout this unit.

Grading tip for P3

Identify your personal goals in relation to the development of your knowledge, skills, practice, values, beliefs and career aspirations. The detailed action points should relate to these. Prioritise the action points and set time limits. Indicate how you will measure your progress in achieving them.

Monitor your progress against the action plan at the same time as you are describing your progress for P4.

Before amending your plan, copy the document containing it, add the amendments to the copy, insert a header or footer to show the date of the amendment, print it off for your portfolio and rename the electronic document with the review number and date.

Write a short justification of the amendments you have made to your plan (or why you have not amended it).

Review your plan *before* you start each placement, add specific goals and targets for the placement (for example, relating to a specific assignment) and extend the plan to help you implement them.

Work experience placements

Whichever placements you attend, you will need to plan carefully to maximise the learning opportunities placements provide. Several of the units require activities to be carried out in settings: you need to learn how to negotiate the arrangements for these with placement staff as part of your personal development. You may need to add to your PPD plan to allow for these requirements as you study each unit and monitor your progress and development through the plan. If possible, a placement in each of the following settings would provide you with the greatest breadth of experience:

- social care
- health care
- early years.

Placement activities

The activities in which you participate will depend on the setting – its regulatory framework, the service user group and its policies and procedures. They will also depend upon your age, amount of experience in placements, attitude, ability to demonstrate appropriate practices and possibly on your career aspirations.

Participation in placement work may include:

- making conversation with service users
- watching routines and activities carried out by health or care workers and identifying regular patterns and deviations from these
- supporting workers to carry out daily routines and activities
- supporting workers in providing care that you cannot deliver yourself
- distributing meals or refreshments to service users (not feeding unless explicit consent is given)
- seeking assistance/advice when you judge a situation to be beyond your experience or level of responsibility
- preparing/laying out materials and equipment
- assisting individual service users to participate in group activities
- clearing up after activities
- tidying up stores
- passing on messages within the team
- reporting events and observations you witness to your supervisor, especially if you think staff may not be aware of the full details of the situation
- using the specialist literature that is available in each placement in order to carry out research for your studies.

Once your placement supervisor and the team have confidence in your abilities, you may be permitted to carry out planned activities or to work one-to-one with a service user for specific activities. In placement, your role can only ever be that of an assistant, working under the direction of your supervisor.

■ Routines

A routine is a sequence of activities that is carried out regularly, in a similar way on each occasion. Routines operate at organisational and team levels and most individuals have set routines as part of their daily activities.

Routines may be an essential aspect of good care practice, particularly to ensure safety – routines for young children influence their learning and development. However, strict adherence to routines relating to other aspects of care may conflict with codes

Reflect

What routines do you practise on a day-to-day basis? For example, what are your routines for getting up and setting off for college or work, taking your lunch-break and working in the library?

How does it affect you when your usual routine is interrupted in some way?

What routines have you observed in placements? What are the advantages and disadvantages of routines in health or care for:

- service users
- workers?

of practice relating to respect, choice and diversity. Routines may become such a habit that insufficient attention is paid to individual needs which may then get overlooked.

■ Planning activities and routines

An activity here is any discrete task, or series of tasks, that you carry out for a specific purpose. Once you have become familiar with the routines of a setting, the needs of the service users and how the worker teams function, you could plan specific activities for service users. Each activity should be planned and have clear objectives and the context should be identified (accommodation, contribution to the care plan, recognition of developmental stage etc).

Remember!

A measure of the success of an activity or routine is not whether it is enjoyed by you or the service user. Instead, success should always be judged against the extent to which the activity or routine has *met its intended objectives*.

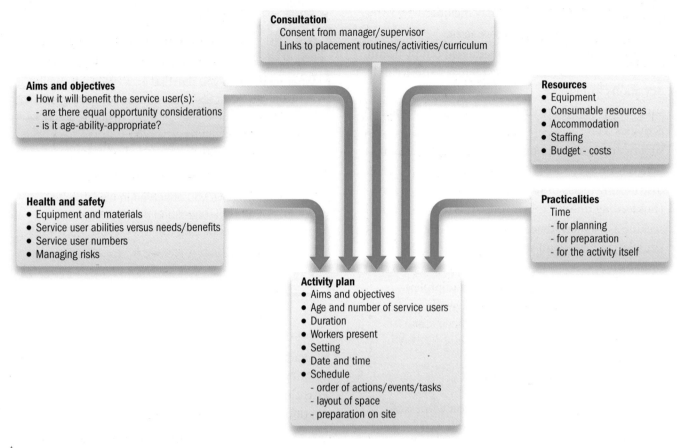

Consultation
Consent from manager/supervisor
Links to placement routines/activities/curriculum

Aims and objectives
- How it will benefit the service user(s):
  - are there equal opportunity considerations
  - is it age-ability-appropriate?

Resources
- Equipment
- Consumable resources
- Accommodation
- Staffing
- Budget - costs

Health and safety
- Equipment and materials
- Service user abilities versus needs/benefits
- Service user numbers
- Managing risks

Practicalities
Time
- for planning
- for preparation
- for the activity itself

Activity plan
- Aims and objectives
- Age and number of service users
- Duration
- Workers present
- Setting
- Date and time
- Schedule
  - order of actions/events/tasks
  - layout of space
  - preparation on site

▲ **Figure 6.8 Planning for specific activities in placement**

Planning activities in placement is good practice at all times. The materials you use as part of an activity can be collated and filed together within your PPD portfolio; artefacts (the cards, games and displays produced by you or by service users) should be kept by the service user or placement; you could take a digital photograph of the artefact (but NOT the service users).

Remember!

Always get a signed and dated observation record or witness testimony of your role in placement-specific activities.

All the activities you carry out in a placement should have a clear purpose which should relate to meeting the needs of service users or care workers.

Your PPD within placements

Three themes could be identified as particularly valuable for you to develop through placement experience:
- communicating effectively
- working safely in care settings
- demonstrating respect for care values.

These are key to all work in health and care, and developing your understanding by reflecting on your placement experience will help prepare you for professional training later.

BTEC National | Health & Social Care | Book 1

Theory into practice

You are to carry out an activity to develop your communication and interpersonal skills and must interact with a small group of service users (three to six people) for 20–30 minutes.

1 Use a spidergram to identify all the different aspects of organisation you will need to consider when making your plans for the activity.

2 Produce an action plan for *planning* the activity. Your action plan should identify:

- all that you need to do *in advance* of actually doing the activity, for example, negotiate a date, carry out research, make phone calls, discuss with your supervisor and prepare resources
- **prioritisation** of each action you have identified i.e. the order in which each action should be carried out
- how much time each action will require.

You might find it convenient to draw up your action plan as a table.

3 Produce a detailed action plan for *carrying out* the actual activity with the service users using the same process. This time your action plan will include what both you *and the service users* will be doing during the activity.

Discuss your plans with another student and identify its strengths and weaknesses.

How did this activity help you think about planning?

How will you use your learning from this activity?

What changes would you make in future and why?

Key term

Prioritisation Placing actions in the order in which they will be carried out. To prioritise, you need to assess the *order of importance* of the actions.

■ Communicating

You will use your communication skills from your first day in placement, beginning by introducing yourself to placement staff. You should plan to develop the full range of communication skills introduced in Unit 1. You will need to explore when and how to use the different techniques in your interactions with different service users, workers and managers.

You can also learn by observing other people's communication skills but you will also need to use communication skills to support your own learning in placement – particularly through the use of questioning.

Communication in care roles can be carried out through:

- listening
- observing
- reflecting
- reassuring
- empathising
- reporting
- using communication aids etc.

Communication in the learner role can be carried out through:

- negotiating
- consultation
- using open questioning
- confirming your understanding (after receiving and following instructions)
- listening to feedback
- clarifying ideas
- gaining a perspective on situations.

Your opportunity to practise some communication skills may be restricted (because of limitations on your authority to interact with service users) but you should be able to observe skills that are used routinely by care workers.

...municating	Examples in practice (there will be many others)
...uage	Avoid using language that could cause offence, that assumes too much familiarity or that is inappropriate for the recipient.
Different language	Use interpreters to communicate in a different spoken language, or by using non-verbal signs.
Cultural difference	Older people may have different perspectives from young people or in some cultures a woman may only talk with a man in the presence of another man they know.
Sensory impairment	Individuals with hearing loss may lip read, use a hearing aid (check it is switched on) or sign language. An individual with sight impairment will have glasses, may only see in part of the normal field of view (for example, have peripheral vision only) or use Braille.
Physical impairment	This might include absence of teeth, a stutter or loss of use of muscles needed for speech e.g. after a stroke.
Learning disability	Individuals may have difficulty concentrating or understanding as easily as you might expect for their age.
Dementia	An individual suffering with dementia might be Incoherent, their speech might not make sense and their responses may bear no relationship to questions.
Life stage of individuals	The vocabulary used with adults (and its complexity) is likely to be different from that you might use with children.
Individuals' emotions	Distress may limit communication, for example, if someone is grieving, disorientated, stressed, embarrassed or in despair.
What you say	Use appropriate vocabulary (for example, to describe an aspect of care). The language you may use with your friends could be inappropriate in care situations.
How you say it	The tone of the words you use and the accompanying gestures and body language may convey more, or a different message from, that conveyed by the words themselves.
Non-verbal skills e.g. eye contact, touch, body language	Use skills that are consistent with the message to be conveyed – a smile or touch can reassure or create a sense of belonging in a new situation.
Barriers to communication	These could include a lack of awareness of the factors influencing an interaction or not addressing specific communication needs.
Using the telephone	Always identify yourself by name and as a BTEC student when using the phone in connection with your course. Electronic interference can cause difficulties for individuals with hearing aids.
Written communication	This should be appropriate for the audience to which it is addressed, for example, a peer worker or a relative. It should also be appropriate for the purpose of the document, for example, a letter has a different purpose from a report or memo.
Recorded information about individuals	Ensure that written records about service users are accurate, confidential and can only be accessed by the service user and authorised others. It will not be appropriate for you to record information about service users. Your journal is confidential to you and your tutor or assessor.
Storing information	Confidential records must be kept securely so they cannot be accessed by unauthorised individuals.

Table 6.8 Different aspects of communication in health and care

6.2

Remember!

You can use your placement to obtain evidence of your use of communication skills as a carer (as required for assessment in Unit 1).

Reflect

Review your communication skills as a carer and as a learner.

To what extent are they the same or different from the skills you observe being used by care workers?

What communication skills do you need to develop to enhance:

- your abilities as a carer
- your ability to learn from your placement experience?

To develop your communication skills during the course, you could focus your practice on:

- building trust through communication
- providing information relating to care that is accurate, relevant and sufficient
- separating fact clearly from opinion or interpretation
- communicating appropriately for different purposes and audiences
- using open questions to elicit information for your understanding
- self-evaluating your performance orally and in writing
- providing support and feedback to others (mainly to peers in class at this stage of your development).

You may notice a detail that has not been observed by a care worker but you should report it, describing the situation as accurately and concisely as possible and without any attempt to interpret your observation. You do not have the authority to intervene in the situation and it is up to the member of staff to interpret the information you communicate and then respond appropriately to your report.

In context

Anita is in a placement and notices Mr Jackson weeping at the end of his son's visit. She is not sure why this is and reports her observation to her supervisor who seems surprised. Anita did notice that the son left in a hurry, striding to the door and then pushing it open rather violently. She mentions this and the supervisor realises that Mr Jackson and his son have had a disagreement. She goes over to Mr Jackson to distract his attention quietly.

1 **What communication skills did Anita demonstrate?**
2 **What caring skills did the supervisor demonstrate?**
3 **What good practices did Anita and the supervisor demonstrate?**

You will not have access to recorded information about service users but you can observe the procedures and practices used when records are made.

■ Health and safety

You will observe many examples of how health and safety considerations can influence practices in placements. The detail of health and safety considerations will vary with each setting, particularly with the service user group, the care being delivered and the location of the setting.

Because you are a learner on placement and not yet trained or qualified, you should never be left to work unsupervised. You should always be aware of health and safety policies and procedures and should observe how they are applied in different situations.

Evidence of your practice

You can obtain feedback evidence of your practice using a range of different records.

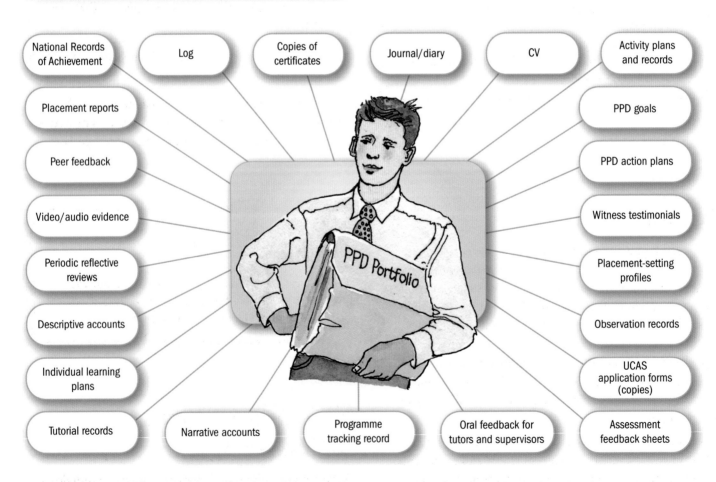

▲ Figure 6.9 Potential sources of evidence for personal development for health and care practice

Theory into practice

Identify a task or activity that you have carried out at least twice in your work experience placements, for example, conversing with service users, following instructions, working alongside a member of staff.

Describe the differences in the way in which you carried out the activity/task on the different occasions.

Identify the factors that influenced how you carried out the activity/task and explain *how they influenced* what you did.

How did you observe reflectively and actively conceptualise (Kolb, see page 275) to help your learning? What was your active experimentation?

From all the occasions on which you carried out the activity/task, what have you learned *overall* about:

- how you need to adapt what you do for different circumstances
- how you could develop or improve your contributions to the benefit of the service user(s) and other care workers?

Personal and professional development portfolio

A portfolio describes a *systematically presented* collection of documents that reflects your professional experience of health and social care. Evidence of your practice in your PPD portfolio should be as objective as possible, so ideally it should consist of records about activities carried out as a routine part of your work in placement. Evidence should be verified by a worker or tutor who is professionally *qualified* or sufficiently *experienced* to make judgements on the quality of your performance.

For this unit, you will use your portfolio *as a resource* that provides evidence of your personal and professional development throughout your programme. You will need to add to the portfolio *your own periodic reflections*

on your experience to demonstrate what you have *learnt* from your collected experience.

You should be able to collect evidence from a variety of sources including:

- work experience
- classroom-based learning activities
- assignments
- your personal journal
- objective feedback (this is particularly valuable).

Remember!

When you are preparing reflective accounts of your practice, always refer to evidence in your portfolio and journal when commenting on the quality of your practice performance, using referencing conventions (see Unit 22).

You should have dates in your journal but you might find it helpful to file your portfolio evidence using a code number system, as shown in the example on page 310.

Remember!

Whenever you are making a judgement about your abilities you should try to base it on objective evidence from an independent source.

Reflecting on your development

Reflection on your experience could focus on individual activities in the early stages of the course.

BTEC NATIONAL DIPLOMA IN HEALTH AND SOCIAL CARE

Unit 6

PERSONAL AND PROFESSIONAL DEVELOPMENT PORTFOLIO

CONTENTS

1 Curriculum vitae

2 Personal profile

3 Unit 6 Tracking record

(Unit 44 Tracking record)

4 Journal

5 Initial self-assessment

6 PPD Action Plan

7 Log of placement attendance Sept 2007 – June 2009

8 Placements attended with placement profiles

9 Reflective accounts

 – Placement 1 – Residential care home

 – Placement 2 – Reception class, primary school

 – Placement 3 – Day centre for older people

10 Practice evidence

 R – placement reports

 A – activity records

 O – observation records

 D – descriptive accounts

 W – witness testimony

▲ Figure 6.10 An example of a portfolio contents list

Theory into practice

After your first few days in your first placement, share your experiences of placement with your peers.

For each service user group, draw a spidergram to show the different activities, however small, that you and your peers have observed the care workers carrying out in different settings.

Explain the knowledge and skills you have used in your placement so far.

Analyse your own learning from your placement at this stage, and identify how you could improve your practice next time you are on work placement.

Your reflective observation and active conceptualisation will develop over time and, depending on your learning style, you may find this is more effective if it is done through conversation and some discussion with professionals. This will help you to develop a professional perspective. Reflection may be structured through:

- describing what happened (a descriptive account) – this can be useful to identify details
- analysing what happened – exploring influencing factors and teasing out reasons etc
- evaluating the activity – thinking about how successful it was.

As you gain more experience, you can start to reflect on your experience overall (drawing on several occasions) to review your learning.

You should reflect on:
- the ways that you are able to link theory to practice
- the progress you are making in achieving your personal goals
- the influence your personal values and beliefs have on your development
- the impact of others on your development.

In Figure 6.11, the learner has reflected, using Kolb's theory, on her own practice and the practice of others. She has referred to her learning in other units of the course and referenced a comment to a published source, thereby demonstrating links between theory and practice.

In context

In her first placement (a residential home for older people) Yasmin organised a quiz afternoon for the residents. She consulted with staff and used quiz books to select appropriate questions. Half of the residents participated and enjoyed the session. She received some positive feedback about the event from her supervisor but Yasmin was advised to assert herself a bit more, project her voice over the residents' conversation and to encourage *all* the participants to contribute (one resident did not speak at all).

In her next placement (a reception class), Yasmin was asked to plan an activity with a spring theme for the pupils. She decided to make Mothering Sunday cards to involve every child and the teacher approved her daffodil design. She planned that three children at a time would glue three shapes on to their own card. The first group of children had difficulty gluing the shapes and got covered in glue. For the next group, Yasmin decided she would put the glue on while the children held the shapes and then stuck them on the card. The activity ran out of time before break and some children still had difficulty sticking the paper pieces on to look like a daffodil. Afterwards, Yasmin discussed the activity with the teacher.

1 **How did Yasmin use Kolb's experiential learning cycle and what did she learn about leading activities for service users?**

2 **What could Yasmin have done in the school so the activity was more successful for the children?**

3 **What communication skills could Yasmin develop to enhance her effectiveness in future activities?**

Reflection 3 End of year 1

My placement in residential care (Sunnyside) has given me experience of working with older adults and I have collected evidence of my practice towards Units 6 and 44. In college I have completed all the assignments for Units 1, 2, 3, 4, 5, 7, 8 and 12.

The table shows how I have used my placement experience in a residential home to:

- complete two interactions for Unit 1
- develop my confidence in communicating with service users and staff
- better understand the needs of older adults
- understand the work of an OT and find out about OT training
- assist care assistants with daily routines
- escort SUs* to day room, toilets
- make SUs comfortable in chairs
- assist with exercise, creative and recreational activities
- prepare and give out drinks
- watch a physiotherapist work individually and with a group of SUs to maintain mobility
- watch a speech therapist work with a SU with stroke
- accompany OT on a home visit
- plan and implement quizzes on sport, famous people, healthy eating
- make conversation with SUs
- contribute to team meeting discussions
- observe a MDT care planning meeting
- help with an emergency evacuation practice
- find out about policies and procedures
- iron and sort out laundry.

* SU – service user

This placement has been really helpful for understanding the changes that happen in later life stages (Unit 4). One woman in Sunnyside was 95 years old and very frail. She wasn't able to feed herself very well because her co-ordination was not very good. The carers offered to help her but she refused and they gave her time to feed herself independently so she maintained her autonomy, which is good practice (Nolan 2003). Most of the residents were able to use the toilet on their own but needed help walking to the toilet because they were unsteady walking alone. I noticed how the carers always asked SUs if they wanted help with toileting. Once, I helped a new resident to the toilet door and although she asked for me to stay, I showed her how to use the support handles and closed the door so she could maintain her privacy.

My communication skills have improved during the first year of my BTEC. My last placement report (R4) has rated them as an A whereas my first placement I had a B/C rating (R2). In my first placement (Sunnyside), I was really nervous at first and when the tutor visited from college in my fourth week, the care supervisor told her I was aloof and didn't join in very well (R1). The tutor observed me helping to give out the teas and we talked afterwards (J6). She suggested that I work on my non-verbal communication skills by being more aware of my body language. Apparently I tend to stand rather stiffly when I am observing other people (R1) and the service users so I look unwilling to help. She suggested that I learnt from the staff how they interact with the residents. The next week in placement (J7), I noticed a resident (J) was very upset when his daughter left after visiting, so I went over to J and crouched down beside his chair, touching him gently on the arm; I didn't say anything but placed a box of tissues beside his chair and he helped himself to a tissue to blow his nose. After a few minutes he seemed calmer and I asked him if he would like a cup of tea. He nodded and when I came back with the cup, he helped me move a table to put it on and apologised for being a nuisance. We had a conversation about the weather and when another resident came and sat next to J, I was able to include her in the conversation so the two residents ended up talking with each other and J was distracted from thinking about his daughter. I tried to look more interested and to ask questions of the carers and they started to involve me in doing things. When we had coffee break in the staff room, they all talked about the residents and how each was that day. On one day, when a resident had been a bit aggressive, the carers helped me understand that the resident was frustrated at not being able to look after himself. It made me realise that the loss of autonomy can be really distressing for older people.

The conversation with my tutor helped my learning at the reflective observation stage of Kolb's cycle and made me more aware of how I am perceived by others. Using the knowledge about communication I had learnt in Unit 1, I was able to try out some different skills (the active experimentation stage of Kolb's cycle) and I was pleased that my skills had helped J feel more cheerful and that being more positive with the carer helped me learn more.

▲ **Figure 6.11 One student's reflections on work placement experience**

Assessment activity 6.4

Describe your progress against your action plan over the duration of the programme.

1   Describe your progress against your PPD plan each term/semester and at the end of each placement. Amend your plan as necessary for your learning on the course, personal development and career aspirations. Use feedback received to identify and plan for your further development.

2   Write an account of the progress you have made since your last review. Your final review should be at the end of your course. **P4**

Grading tip for P4

Your description of progress against your PPD plan would be best completed at the same time as you review and amend your PPD plan for P3.

Your first review will look at your development since your initial self-assessment.

Your assessment of your progress should be supported by objective evidence filed in your portfolio.

Over the length of the course, you should produce at least three written reviews of your overall PPD since the previous review.

Explain how the action plan has helped support your development over the duration of the programme.

3   At the end of the course, explain how your PPD plan has helped you develop during the course. Use several examples from your journal and portfolio evidence to illustrate the points you make. **M2**

Grading tip for M2

Your explanation could include an exploration of how well you planned. For example, how appropriate were your goals, your action points, your priorities and your timescales?

What difference did these make to the usefulness of your plan in supporting your own development?

Evaluate your development over the duration of the programme.

4   Evaluate how well you have developed over the whole duration of the programme.

5   Explain why you have developed more in some areas and less in others. **D2**

Grading tip for D2

Identify where you have made most progress and where you have made less progress, justifying your judgement using portfolio and journal evidence.

You could focus your evaluation on the development of some core aspects of practice, for example, your communication skills, ability to demonstrate care values and understanding of safe practices.

To what extent has your development differed according to the type of setting in which you worked, the different service user groups you have worked with or the different approaches to study needed in different units of the course?

You will review your plan regularly throughout the course but cannot complete this activity until you are at the end of the course. Similarly, you will need to *start* the following assessment activity after your first placement and then after each subsequent placement but you cannot *complete* it until the end of the course.

Assessment activity 6.5

Produce and reflect on your personal and professional development portfolio.

1   Organise your PPD portfolio systematically, adding new evidence as it is generated throughout the course.

2   Write at least three reflective accounts of your PPD at intervals during the course ensuring that you draw on your experience from each of your placements. **P5**

Reflect on your experiences and use three examples to explain links between theory and practice.

3   Selecting three examples from your experiences on the course, explore in depth how the links between theory and practice have enhanced your PPD. **M3**

Grading tip for P5

Use learning theories introduced in this unit to assist your reflection.

Make reference to knowledge and theory from other parts of the course.

Include consideration of your personal values and beliefs, the influence of others and the personal goals set for your PPD.

Grading tip for M3

Refer back to the different aspects of learning and development explored in your initial self-assessment, as well as knowledge and theories introduced in all units of the course, to help you obtain the depth required for M3.

6.3 Understanding service provision

This section of the unit explains how health and social care services are organised and provided. Your work in placements will help your understanding.

Provision of services

Most people identify readily with health and social care services that are available locally. Workers in health and care services need to understand how provision in their locality fits into provision at national level so that service users can have maximum benefit from the services available.

In the UK, health and social care services are provided predominantly by the public sector of the economy but some services are also provided by the private and voluntary sectors.

Public sector

Public sector organisations are funded by the state through taxes. Health services are paid for almost entirely through central taxation, with a small proportion funded from national insurance contributions. All *public health services* in the UK are funded through the Department of Health (DH) and provided directly or indirectly by the National Health Service (NHS).

Social care services are funded through local authorities (metropolitan boroughs, county councils and unitary authorities) from both central and local taxes (the council tax in England). Local authorities (LAs) receive central funding via the Department of Communities and Local Government (DCLG). State schools are also funded through central taxes (via the Department for Education and Skills (DfES)) and local taxes.

In England, dental, optician and social care services are only completely free to those in receipt of certain welfare benefits. Everyone else pays a contribution to, or the full cost of, the health or social care service by paying charges or fees, for example, prescription charges for medicines and spectacles or residential home fees.

Private sector

Services in the private sector are funded by fees paid to the service provider. Services provided by the private sector include:

- day care nurseries
- residential and nursing homes for older people
- private schools
- specialist treatment centres
- hospitals.

Professionals such as doctors and dentists work mainly in the public sector but may also provide private services to fee-paying patients. In the UK, service users who choose private health care usually subscribe to health insurance schemes so the insurance company pays the fees for care, subject to the conditions of the insurance policy.

Voluntary and community sector

Voluntary organisations are charities funded by donations from the public and businesses. The voluntary sector makes an important contribution to health and social care services in the UK. Sometimes local authorities commission (contract) national voluntary organisations (NVOs) to deliver services on their behalf. Patient support groups are examples of NVOs supporting health care, and examples of organisations providing social care services are Age Concern, Barnardo's, Help the Aged, Mencap, National Children's Home, Red Cross and many others. Community-based voluntary organisations such as hospices also provide health and social care services.

Theory into practice

Investigate the role of the voluntary sector in your area by visiting your local Council for Voluntary Organisations office and www.ncvo-vol.org.uk.

The boundary between the public, private and voluntary sectors has become less distinct as local partnerships have been formed. An example is the use of Public Finance Initiative (PFI) finance to build new hospitals and schools.

Service provision in the UK home countries

The DH negotiates an allocation of funds for the NHS from the Treasury and distributes these between the NHS in England, Wales, Northern Ireland and Scotland. Responsibility for the delivery of health and social care services differs in each of the four home countries of the UK with the Welsh Assembly, the Northern Ireland Office/Assembly and the Scottish Parliament deciding how the funds are to be spent in each country.

In England, health and community care services are provided through the DH and social care services through LAs. Government policies now require more co-operation between the NHS and local social services departments. In Northern Ireland, health and social care services have been organised together since 1972 by Health and Social Services Boards. Since devolution, health and social care services have been integrated in both Wales (through the Minister for Health and Social Services) and in Scotland.

Theory into practice

Use your local knowledge, the Internet and local sources of information to find out how health and social care services are organised in your home country and in the local community.

Change and health and social care

Change is always happening in health and social care services because of expectations for continuous improvement in services and advances in technology.

Reflect

Identify recent technological advances that affect health care, for example, MRI scanners that provide information about the working of the brain. In what way are these advances altering how health care is delivered? How are these advances affecting how services are organised?

Taking it further

Use www.statistics.gov.uk and local sources to investigate how the population profile is changing in your local authority and in your region.

The structures of services described here are current at the time of writing but may change during the lifetime of your course and you will certainly encounter change that will affect your future working life in health and social care.

Remember!

Always check the currency of data relating to the NHS and social care services to ensure your sources reflect the most up-to-date situation.

Levels of services

Care is provided at different levels: primary, secondary and tertiary.

Level of services	Referral	Examples
Primary	Self	General practitioners (GPs), dentists, pharmacists, social care
Secondary	GP	District general hospitals, outpatients, Accident and Emergency
Tertiary	Inter-specialist	Spinal injuries units, burns units

Table 6.9 The three levels of care

The differences between the three levels of services are sometimes unclear. For example, some GPs carry out minor surgical procedures in community-based facilities.

The National Health Service (NHS)

The NHS was formed in 1948, to provide a service of health care that was free at the point of care. During the decades since it began, the NHS has seen many changes and is now the largest organisation in Europe. Current policy is for the NHS to ensure ongoing improvements in the *quality of care* for service users, especially those with the greatest needs, and to develop its *workforce* so it has the skills and flexibility required to provide this service. The DH has developed National Service Frameworks (NSFs) which set long-term goals for a range of health care priorities, for example, for cancer, diabetes and coronary heart disease.

■ Local health services

- *Primary care trusts* (PCTs) are responsible for the majority of the NHS budget. Each local PCT commissions doctors (GPs), health centres and other community-based services to provide primary care.
- Community hospitals are run by PCTs but they pay *acute trusts*, responsible for one or two local hospitals, to provide secondary care for patients in their geographical area.
- *Foundation trusts* are hospitals that have opted to be self-governing rather than governed by the DH.

- *Mental health trusts* provide hospital- and community-based care for those with mental illness.
- *Ambulance trusts* are responsible for transporting patients to hospital for emergency care and for planned treatment.
- The NHS is involved in *children's trusts* as they become established across the country.
- *Strategic health authorities* (SHAs) were established in 2002 but in 2006 the number was reduced to 10. SHAs operate locally to develop plans for health services in the area they serve, monitor the quality of the services, ensure that local plans incorporate national priorities for health and report to the DH.

■ Special health authorities

The special health authorities operate nationally. Examples of special authorities:

- *NHS Direct* provides a 24-hour health care information and advice service remotely by telephone, online and by digital television.

In context

The Valley Health Centre is located in the retail park on the outskirts of a small town. It accommodates a general practice of four GPs who work together in a partnership. They have recently moved from cramped, older premises in the middle of the town where parking and a steep ramp presented difficulties for service users. The new premises include a small crèche facility, rooms for each of the doctors and the practice nurse, a waiting room, reception and patient records areas. There is a separate room for health promotion activities, ante-natal classes etc and a minor surgery unit with the necessary anaesthetic and recovery areas. Accommodation for talking therapies and visiting professionals such as social workers, speech therapists etc is also available on the premises. Next door, there is a pharmacy and there is ample car parking on the same level as the entrance. There is a lift to the top floor services.

Since it moved, the practice has taken on some new patients, mainly workers from the retail park, but some

of its older patients have transferred to another GP practice nearer to where they live.

Two of the GP partners have the training needed to carry out minor operations and the surgical unit was part-funded by the PCT. The practice now carries out minor elective surgical procedures. The younger patients find this convenient but the older patients choose the district general hospital in the city 10 miles away. The PCT would like to see greater use of the surgical and health promotion facilities.

1 **Describe how this service provision fits into national frameworks.**

2 **Analyse the advantages and disadvantages of this type of service facility for the local population.**

3 **Evaluate how this model of health care might affect the local acute trust.**

- The *National Institute of Health and Clinical Excellence* (NICE) develops public health guidance, produces guidelines for clinical practice and evaluates new medications and technological techniques. Clinical guidelines also influence the curriculum of professional training for health care workers and help inform patients. NICE incorporates the former Health Development Agency.
- The *Health Protection Agency* monitors communicable diseases and environmental, chemical and radiological hazards and contributes to national emergency planning. Most HPA workers are scientists.
- The *NHS Blood and Transplant* authority was established in October 2005 and manages the National Blood Service, supplying blood products, organs and tissues for transplantation.

Remember!

PCTs can commission any acute trust to provide elective (planned) surgery for patients living in its area. This means that secondary care can be carried out by a hospital outside of the PCT's geographical area. This choice can be attractive to a patient if it means that treatment is received more quickly.

■ Service user involvement in the NHS

The Commission of Patient and Public Involvement in Health (CPPIH) gathers the views of people across the country about health services; it is independent but is sponsored by the DH. It receives the views of Patient and Public Involvement forums (PPI), one for each

Remember!

Anyone can apply to be a member of their local PPI forum. The membership of each PPI is made up of a wide range of representatives from local communities.

NHS Trust, and so involves patients and the public in decisions about health care provision.

Local authority services

The majority of expenditure of English LAs is spent on schools and social care services.

Remember!

Local authorities have responsibilities to provide a range of local government services, several of which relate to health, for example, environmental health and housing.

■ Social care services

The Children Act 2004 required LAs to bring social care, health and education services for children together by April 2006. Most LAs have social care services organised into services for older people, disabilities and mental health.

Theory into practice

Access your local authority website and find out how it organises its social care services. Research the local priorities for each aspect of its care services.

■ Children's services

You will probably have a placement with the early years age group (up to 8 years) in a daycare or education setting. Children's services departments were recommended by the Laming Report into the death of Victoria Climbié (who suffered neglect and abuse). Children's services are responsible for all services for children and young people (up to the age of 19) and their families. This inquiry has resulted in many policy changes relating to children.

Some recent policy initiatives relating to children and young people include:

- the appointment of a cabinet-level Minister for Children, Young People and Families
- Every Child Matters (ECM) Green Paper in 2003
- Every Child Matters: Change for Children in 2004
- Children Act 2004
- Children's services integrating education, health, playwork, youth justice and social care
- Every Child Matters website providing information for parents and professionals
- Children's trusts
- in England, the appointment of a Children's Commissioner for Children
- the inspection of children's services by Ofsted
- 10-year Childcare Strategy published in 2004
- Childcare Act 2006 including integrated education and children's social care inspections (to start in 2008)
- Safeguarding Children Boards in place by April 2006
- Directors of Children's Services in post by 2008.

Taking it further

Research the Laming Report into the death of Victoria Climbié that gave rise to Every Child Matters, the 2004 Children Act and the 2006 Childcare Act.

Find out how your local authority has responded to these national policies.

For the 0–3 age group, the Birth to Three Matters framework within ECM is organised jointly by the Department for Education and Skills (DfES) and the DH through the Sure Start and Extended Schools Childcare Group. It is the responsibility of the Minister for Children, Young People and Families.

Partnership working

ECM and other government policies require public sector agencies (for example, PCTs and LAs) to work co-operatively with each other and other organisations

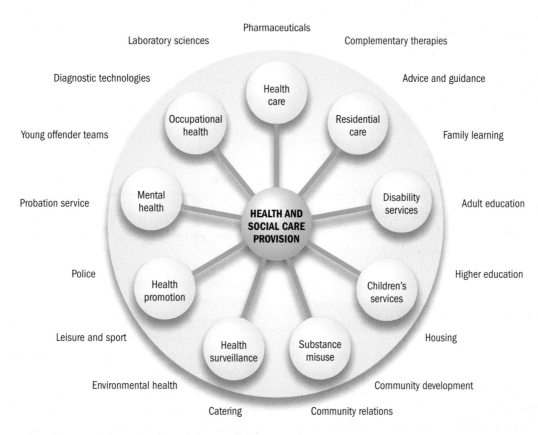

▲ Figure 6.12 Partners in health and social care and the wider context

in the private and voluntary sectors. These relationships are formalised in local partnership agreements (LPAs) to improve the services available for different service user groups. LPAs set partnership goals and identify how the partners will achieve these. Local Area Agreements (LAAs) are agreements drawn up between local and central government to ensure that LAs meet their local needs in the context of central government policies and priorities.

In context

Hilda is 69 years old and has always looked after her 38-year-old son, Alan, who has moderate learning difficulties. She has done this alone since she was widowed three years ago. Alan attends a day centre each day but Hilda is finding it increasingly difficult to look after Alan, particularly as he has hit her on occasions when he has been angry. Alan is very dependent on Hilda for his meals and general care, including bathing.

Hilda does not like to make a fuss but is experiencing giddy spells and goes to see her GP where she breaks down in tears in the surgery.

1 **What are the major health and care problems faced by the household?**

2 **Which agencies would be useful to provide the support needed by the household?**

3 **What could the challenges be in ensuring that all the support agencies work together to help Hilda and Alan?**

Regulation of health and social care services

All health and social care service providers in the UK are regulated by government through legislation and regulatory bodies. The NHS National Service Frameworks (NSF) and the Care **Minimum Standards** set out the standards expected for the provision of health and care services and regulators judge the quality

of care against these. Reports from all the regulators are available to the public on line.

■ Healthcare Commission

The Healthcare Commission is the regulator for the NHS in England and Wales, though its role is less extensive in Wales. It is sponsored by the NHS but is an independent organisation that aims to safeguard patients, promote continuous improvement and rights of access to health care. It inspects NHS provision and maintains a register of independent health care providers (private hospitals, hospices and cosmetic surgery units). The Commission produces an annual rating of NHS Trusts in England and an annual report to the DH. The Healthcare Commission investigates complaints and failures in services.

From 2006, the Commission introduced annual checks on quality of service and use of resources to report on the performance of NHS trusts, special authorities, independent providers and school health services in delivering effective services.

Theory into practice

Access www.healthcarecommisssion.org.uk to find out how NHS trusts in your area performed in their last annual review.

■ Commission for Social Care Inspection (CSCI)

The CSCI was established in 2004 and it registers, inspects and reports on all social care provision in England, including:

- LA social care services
- private care homes
- care delivered in people's homes
- nursing agencies
- fostering and adoption agencies
- residential family centres
- children's homes
- residential schools and colleges.

The CSCI sets the Care Minimum Standards and the Minimum Standards for Social Care Employers.

CSCI inspection reports currently use a star rating system. The CSCI can close down provision if the standard of care is unsatisfactory.

■ Ofsted

Ofsted is the regulator responsible for the inspection of schools, colleges, children's services, youth work and teacher training. It is directly answerable to Parliament. From April 2007 it took on the responsibilities for inspection of LA children's services and became the Office for Standards in Education, Children Services and Skills. It continued to be known as Ofsted.

Theory into practice

Read the most recent inspection report on one of your placement settings. What are the implications of the inspector's findings, as presented in the report, from the perspective of:

- a service user (or a parent)
- workers in the setting?

Note the actions and/or recommendations made by the inspector and find out from your placement mentor what actions were taken in response to the report.

■ Social Care Institute for Excellence (SCIE)

SCIE was established in 2001 as an independent charity operating in England, Wales and Northern Ireland. It supports social care services for both adults and children and families, promoting good practice and sharing information with service users to enhance the quality of care they receive. SCIE works with the CSCI, social work educators, and policy makers and commissions research. It will merge with the Healthcare Commission in 2008.

Local health or social care providers

A person who carries out activities specifically to support the well-being of another person is providing care. Caring for a family member, friend or neighbour is **informal care**. **Formal care** is different because it is subject to external regulation even if the care is being provided by a voluntary organisation. This unit is preparing you to work professionally, delivering formal care in a provider organisation such as the settings for your work placements.

Key terms

Informal care is care provided for others on a good-neighbourly basis.

Formal care is care provided by workers who are part of a health or care service organisation.

This section of the unit requires you to investigate one health or social care provider. You could choose a placement setting but this is not a requirement.

Health and social care service provider organisations

Health care and social care provider organisations differ widely, depending on a range of factors such as:

- service user group
- social or health care needs
- residential or day care

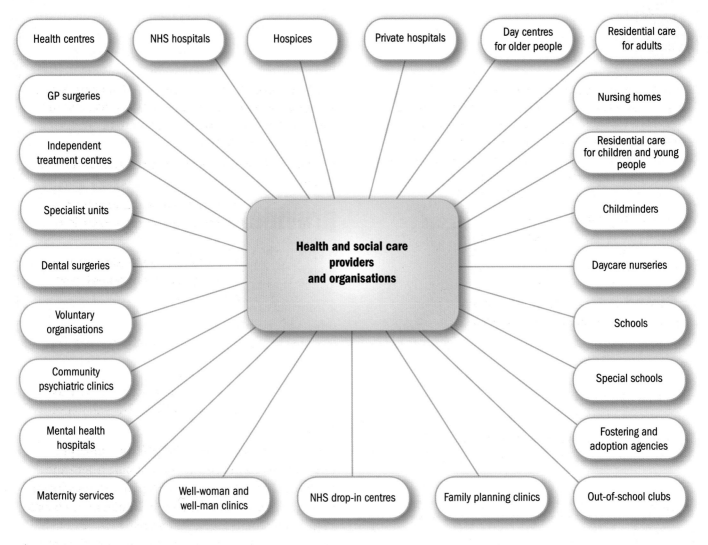

Figure 6.13 Examples of health and social care service providers

- short-term or long-term care
- the number of service users being provided for.

Health and social care providers are the organisations that deliver services directly to service users. Increasingly, the provider organisations are in the voluntary sector but the funding for the services comes from the public sector, mostly through the PCTs, with some services paid for by local authorities and others by private fees.

Provider organisations vary in size, location and the type of premises used, regulation, their internal structure, the number of employees and their qualifications These differences are explored in more detail in Unit 44.

Access to services

A health or care service must be accessible to the people who use the service. Access may involve consideration of transport or physical access to the provider premises. The Disability Act 1995 requires premises to be accessible to those with disabilities. Other barriers to individuals actually using a service could be financial (for example, the cost of dental treatment), emotional (for example, embarrassment about talking about health) or the way the provider offers the service (for example, being made to feel unwelcome or if the service is only available at an inconvenient time or location).

In context

Mrs Smith has lived in a small village all her life. She was widowed several years ago and has maintained an active life. She uses the bus to get to the nearest town (which is 10 miles away) for her shopping, the post office and her doctor. Her son lives with his family near London and only gets to visit his mother every few weeks due to work commitments abroad.

A month ago she had a fall and was taken in an ambulance to the district general hospital in a town 30 miles away because her local town only has a hospital with a minor injuries unit. She was admitted for observation for a couple of days but only has a few bruises and a graze. Mrs Smith is eager to get home and the hospital discharge assessment concludes that she is well enough to look after herself at home. When she gets home, Mrs Smith discovers she has lost her confidence and is not able to cope with the weekly bus journey to do her shopping.

1 **Explain the barriers to access to services for Mrs Smith.**

2 **What sort of services could be provided for Mrs Smith to support her to live independently in her own home?**

3 **What difficulties might Mrs Smith experience in adjusting to her changed circumstances? How might these be addressed?**

Policies and procedures

Legislation and national policies and frameworks directly influence practices in care settings. Each setting is required to develop its own policies to ensure its practices are in accordance with the law and national policies.

A *policy* is a statement of principles that underpin different aspects of practice, for example health and safety, discrimination or abuse. A policy states when it should be applied and the responsibilities of key people in implementing the policy. A *procedure* is a detailed description of the steps to be taken to apply the policy.

All employees should be aware of the policies and procedures in their setting. Some procedures will be embedded in routine (for example, washing hands for infection control); others parts of a policy may only become active when there is a critical incident (for example, when several patients on a ward get the same infection).

Theory into practice

Your induction to each placement should introduce you to its policies and procedures which are specific to the setting and its service users.

1 Identify all of the policies in each placement setting and summarise the purpose of each.

2 Study the policies in your first placement and make notes summarising the procedures and responsibilities within each policy.

3 Compare the similarities and differences between the policies and procedures in different settings.

Note: If you are on a placement (and, therefore, not an employee), you cannot expect to retain a copy of each setting's policies. Use quiet periods in the settings to carry out this research.

Theory into practice

Observe and make notes on how policies are put into practice on a day-to-day basis in your placements.

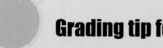
Health and social care workers

Work in health and social care settings

A sizeable proportion of the total workforce in the UK is involved directly or indirectly in health or care service provision. The government has made development of the health and care workforce a priority, to enable services to adapt effectively to demographic and technological changes. In this way, workers will have the skills to deliver care in new ways and raise standards.

Health and care work differs according to the provider organisation. Acute trusts employ large numbers of workers including health professionals, support staff such as scientists and others, for example, administrators who may not have direct contact with patients. Care workers usually work shifts. Workers in community care may work daytime hours only and some workers may work independently in a service user's home or an outreach centre, only meeting colleagues occasionally. In the smallest social care settings, there may be only two or three staff on duty at any one time, with all of them working directly with service users.

■ Care teams

Whatever the provider setting, health and care workers work *together* as a *team* to deliver care that meets each service user's needs. You will work as part of a professional team in placements with each member of the team bringing different professional expertise. Some team members may work for a partner organisation.

■ Job roles

There are a very large number of different job roles available in health and care work. Those with professional qualifications and experience have more senior job roles and more responsibility for making decisions about others (both service users and staff). Job role titles give some indication of the level of training and responsibilities expected but conventions can vary in different professions.

Examples of job titles and qualification level	Outline of possible responsibilities
Assistant Level 2	Work directly with service users in relation to activities of daily living
Senior assistant Level 3	Make routine decisions about care, care planning, supervise a team of assistants
Technical/professional Cert HE equivalent	Make more complex decisions about care, responsibilities for managing and training others
Senior technical/ practitioner Dip HE equivalent	Staff nurse, manager of small care unit, laboratory technician
Professional Honours degree	Nursing sister, health care professions, early years teacher
Senior professional Postgraduate/Masters	Junior doctors, nurse managers
Expert/specialist Doctorate, advanced professional qualifications	Senior doctors, leaders of other professionals

Table 6.10 Job titles and responsibilities

Theory into practice

Use your local paper to investigate the range of employment opportunities available in your locality in the NHS, GP surgeries, social care and childcare settings.

Education and training for work in health and social care

If you aim to work as a professional in health or care, you will need to achieve an initial professional qualification, usually after training for three or four years. This will include an assessment of practice in care settings. Specific qualifications are required for each health or care profession and the curriculum for training is influenced by NSF, regulators and the organisations representing each profession.

Sub-professional level qualifications for support workers in health and social care are influenced by National Occupational Standards (NOS) set by the relevant Sector Skills Councils (SSCs), particularly:

- Skills for Health
- Skills for Care
- Childcare Workforce Development Council.

The qualifications required are competence-based NVQs. Each BTEC National unit is mapped to NOS units and provides underpinning knowledge.

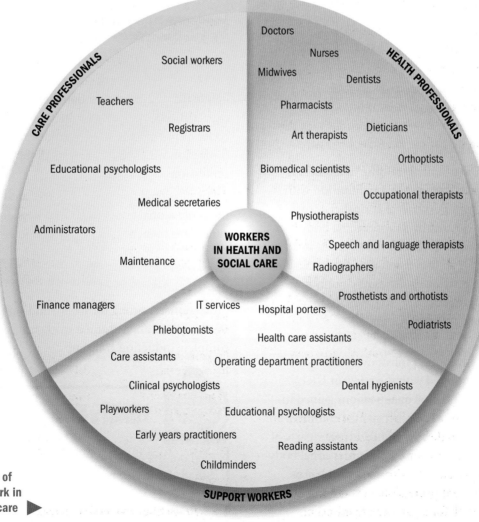

Figure 6.14 Some of the people who work in health and social care ▶

The SSCs have identified specific skills used in health and care work and these are part of the NHS Knowledge and Skills Framework (KSF). Workers will be expected to acquire competence in the skills needed for their job role.

In context

Pete is a care assistant with an NVQ Level 2 in Care and has left his job caring for older people. His new job is working with young adults with learning disability. He finds he has to achieve competence units relevant to his work with learning disability.

1 **What does an NVQ Level 2 involve?**

2 **How might the needs of each service user group be the same or different?**

3 **What additional skills would Pete need in his new job?**

Professional training and registration

■ Professional bodies

Successful completion of initial training in the health and care professions leads to a legal qualification with a licence to practise as a nurse, teacher or social worker. Each profession is regulated by a professional body that maintains a register of its licensed professionals. It is now a requirement for all professionals in health, social care and teaching to provide evidence of Continuing Professional Development (CPD) to maintain their registration with their professional body.

All health, care and education professionals who work in the UK must be registered with the relevant UK professional body. Professional qualifications gained in the European Union and a few other named countries are accepted automatically but those gained in other parts of the world are subject to scrutiny by the professional body before registration is granted. All workers whose first language is not English are required to pass an English language proficiency test before gaining registration.

Profession	Professional body
Nurse, midwife, specialist community public health nurses	Nursing and Midwifery Council (NMC)
Social worker Social care employers	General Social Care Council (GSCC)
Professions allied to medicine (PAMs)	Health Professions Council (HPC) Currently 13 professions, for example, physiotherapists, occupational therapists, paramedics, biomedical scientists, dieticians
Teachers	General Teaching Council for England
Doctors	General Medical Council (GMC)
Dentists	General Dental Council (part of Royal College of Surgeons of England)

Table 6.11 Professions and their associated bodies

Professional codes of conduct

Professional bodies regulate their profession by establishing codes of conduct for all registrants which define the minimum standards of behaviour that are expected. The codes of conduct (sometimes known as codes of practice) reflect the ethics and values of the profession which are similar in all the health and care professions.

All professional bodies can remove an individual from the professional register if the professional code of conduct is breached.

Others workers in health and social care services

Professional training for health and care work is statutory and an untrained worker in social care must complete induction training.

Theory into practice

Find out the requirements of the GSCC Induction Standards 2006 for those commencing work in social care.

Care assistants do not have to be registered with a professional body but this situation may change in the future. Care employers must ensure that at least 50 per cent of their workers are qualified at least to NVQ Level 2 and managers must be registered with the GSCC and have an approved management qualification. Care assistants with an NVQ Level 3 may be able to reduce their time in nurse training by having their skills accredited as prior learning.

Theory into practice

Investigate the qualifications and experience of three different types of worker in your setting.

What training has been completed and how was it obtained (for example, through day release or full-time study)?

How does experience brought from training or previous employment help in the current job role?

What opportunities are there in the placement setting for PPD/CPD?

Remember!

Once you are qualified, you will gain experience, attend study days, complete training for specific skills, equipment or job roles. Certificates of attendance or qualification certificates are essential evidence to maintain registration. You should always keep the original version of any certificates and qualifications (from GCSEs onwards) safe because you will have to provide them for every job you do throughout your working life.

Multi-disciplinary teams

The service user is the most important person in any care setting and all work activity in a health or care organisation is either directly or indirectly associated with meeting the needs of its service users. It is probable that for any one service user, the expertise of several different types of health and care worker will be required to meet their needs. Each worker will have a different job role but, by working together, they can meet the needs of the individual service user. This group of workers, each with different and specific roles, is known as a multi-disciplinary team (MDT).

In context

Tom is 5 years old and has been in the reception class for one term. He is heavy and tall for his age and speaks with a marked lisp which makes his speech difficult to follow. He also has great difficulty in sitting still or concentrating and his behaviour is disrupting other pupils. The head teacher has called a case conference for everyone involved in Tom's care.

1 **Which health, care or early years professionals could provide support for Tom's needs?**

2 **What contribution does each of these professionals make towards meeting Tom's needs?**

3 **How would the case conference help the head teacher meet the needs of the pupil?**

Career pathways

In health and care work, the pathways to reach a particular job role become more diverse as you proceed beyond your initial practitioner or professional qualification. With an increasing amount of partnership working, health and care professionals find themselves working routinely in non-traditional settings within multi-disciplinary teams.

Interaction with different professionals in different settings, and working with different service users and at different levels of responsibility, provide diverse experiences that may be relevant for a wide range of job roles, sometimes only later in a career. Experience

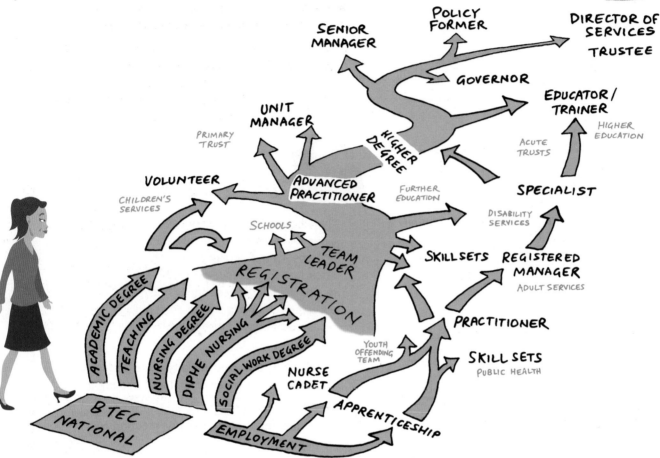

SENIOR MANAGER

POLICY FORMER

DIRECTOR OF SERVICES

TRUSTEE

GOVERNOR

UNIT MANAGER

PRIMARY TRUST

HIGHER DEGREE

EDUCATOR / TRAINER

HIGHER EDUCATION

ACUTE TRUSTS

VOLUNTEER

CHILDREN'S SERVICES

ADVANCED PRACTITIONER

FURTHER EDUCATION

SPECIALIST

DISABILITY SERVICES

SCHOOLS

TEAM LEADER

REGISTRATION

SKILLSETS

REGISTERED MANAGER

ADULT SERVICES

ACADEMIC DEGREE

TEACHING

NURSING DEGREE

DIPHE NURSING

SOCIAL WORK DEGREE

YOUTH OFFENDING TEAM

PRACTITIONER

SKILL SETS

PUBLIC HEALTH

NURSE CADET

BTEC NATIONAL

EMPLOYMENT

APPRENTICESHIP

▲ Figure 6.15 **Where next? Career pathways in health and social care**

of health or care work is valued in a wide range of workplaces, not just those in health and social care – the career pathways may take you into industry, work abroad, and the voluntary sector.

Broad pathway options after gaining practice qualifications may be in management, education and training, research or as an advanced practitioner in a specialist area.

A higher level qualification develops your abilities to use knowledge and understanding and to work with, and lead, others. With a licence to practise, you can work as a professional in an appropriate setting. Whatever career choices you make in the future, ongoing reflection on your experience of working with service users, other workers and different providers and agencies will continue to add to your knowledge and understanding.

Theory into practice

Review the evidence filed in your PPD portfolio and the information you have obtained about career options at the end of your course.

What practical experiences have you had that will support your application for your next career choice?

What relevant knowledge and understanding have you gained from the course to support your career choice?

What personal skills have you developed from completing the course?

This activity would be helpful for preparing your personal statement for progression.

Gaining objective evidence of this CPD through formal qualifications and skill-set competencies will enhance your opportunity to progress your career in the direction you choose.

Figure 6.16 **Continuing professional development**

Assessment activity 6.7

Describe the roles, responsibilities and career pathways of three health or social care workers.

1 Describe the roles and responsibilities and career pathways of three health or social care workers. Think about the role of professional bodies, codes of conduct and the training and development of staff in the work of the health or social care provider.

 P7

Grading tip for P7

The workers could work in the provider organisation described for P6.

Think about how health and social care, technical and other support professionals work together to contribute to the work of the provider.

Knowledge check

1 What are the main features of Kolb's experiential learning cycle?

2 Which is your preferred Honey and Mumford learning style and why?

3 Given your preferred learning style, which skills for study are the most appropriate for you to use to help you learn?

4 List all the different ways in which you have received support for your learning on the course.

5 To what extent have your strengths and areas for improvement changed and/or developed since you started the course?

6 Assess your initial plan and how well you monitored it: what were its strengths (how did it help your development) and what were its weaknesses (how did it not help)?

7 Summarise how well your knowledge and understanding, and your skills and abilities, have developed over the course.

8 How have your values and beliefs developed and changed over the course, enabling you to better demonstrate the value base underpinning care work?

9 How did your different placements compare in relation to:

  a how they fitted into national frameworks
  b their funding
  c the people who worked in them?

10 In what ways were the policies and procedures in each placement similar or different? Explain the reasons for these similarities or differences.

Preparation for assessment

1 Discuss with friends and other people the factors that have influenced their learning. Try and include people of different age groups in your discussions to get a wider perspective. Explain how at least five influences can affect the different ways people learn and use your understanding of learning theories to support your explanations. You should also explain how people can be supported to learn by teachers and other people, access to resources for learning (for example, books, a computer) and both formal and informal opportunities for learning. **P1**

2 Analyse the factors that have influenced your own learning by explaining the influences and the positive and negative effects they have had on your learning. Your analysis should include discussion of influences from your home, the demands of other aspects of your life such as work, volunteering or family commitments, the skills you have to help you study (literacy, numeracy, ICT, research skills) as well as factors that have influenced your formal education, for example, school experiences. You should also consider in your analysis how your personal characteristics affect your ability to learn, for example, preferred learning style, attitude, aspirations, time-keeping etc. **M1**

3 Evaluate how your learning could help other people, for example, in your class, college, family or community, or service users and staff in your placements. To evaluate, you should explore and explain the different ways your own learning has helped others and make a reasoned judgement about the value of your help to them. **D1**

4 Prepare an initial personal profile of yourself by describing what you have learnt up to starting the National course. You should provide a summary of your knowledge and skills including:

- communicating (verbal and non-verbal)
- working with others (for example, peers, professionals)
- technical (for example, ICT, research)
- personal skills (for example, organisational skills, personal presentation).

You should include a description of your values and beliefs and how they compare with the value base of care and your career aspirations (options possible or choices made). Show awareness of the things you do well, those you do less well and those things that you need to develop but have no experience of to date. **P2**

5 Taking those aspects of your profile that you do less well and/or need to develop, set yourself five or six main goals to achieve while you are on your course. You should include both short-term (to be achieved within 6 months) and long-term (achievable in 18 months) goals and make sure they are expressed in accordance with SMART principles. Draw up a personal development action plan to achieve each goal, breaking each one down into two or three actions that you need to take. **P3**

6 You should check your progress against the action points in your personal development plan regularly. Suitable times for this might be at the end of each term and each placement. Record your progress on the plan, dating each entry. Change or add to your action points in accordance with your progress against them or to take account of changed priorities (for example, changing your career choice). Put a date header or footer in your plan and print it off for your portfolio each time you amend it. Your final review should be at the end of the course. **P4**

7 During the final part of your course, write a short report to explain how your action plan has helped you develop your knowledge, understanding and skills in preparation for work in health and/or social care. **M2**

8 Include in your report an evaluation of how well you have developed personally and professionally over the duration of the programme. Make justified judgements about your abilities. You could evaluate your abilities in relation to your intended career progression at the end of the programme. **D2**

9 Throughout the course, collect evidence of your learning and placement practice, filing it systematically in your PPD portfolio in accordance with your Contents page. Make sure placement reports, observation and witness testimony records are validated by signatures from qualified professionals and that all items of evidence are dated. You might find it helpful to use a coding system to file the evidence. You should have practice evidence from every placement.

Compare your evidence records from the first part of the course with those you collect later on to show how far you have developed. You should produce a minimum (more if your course is two years long) of three reflective accounts spaced over the programme that show you can reflect on your experiences to gain knowledge and understanding. Select examples from your evidence to illustrate the points you make in your reflection about your knowledge, skills and practice, including working in accordance with the value base of care. Use references to theory acquired in other units of the course in your reflection as well as learning theories and show within your reflections where theory has helped your understanding of practice. **P5**

10 Use three examples taken from your observations of practice seen in placements and study of theory on the course, to explore in some detail how theoretical knowledge informs care practices and how awareness of practice helps make sense of theory. **M3**

11 Use one of your placements to describe the role of a local health or social care service provider. Your description should include how the service fits into the national framework of provision at primary, secondary and tertiary levels and should include information about how the local service is funded, how service users access its services and should describe how the organisation's policies and procedures take account of the needs of its service users. **P6**

12 Choose three contrasting workers in health or social care services you have met through work placements or elsewhere. Describe the role and responsibilities of each worker and the career pathway each has taken to reach their current role. **P6**

Resources and further reading

Honey, P., Mumford, A. (1985) *The Manual of Learning Styles* Maidenhead: Peter Honey

Kolb, D.A. (1984) *Experiential Learning* Englewood Cliffs: Prentice Hall

Useful websites

Care Council for Wales
www.ccwales.org.uk

Chartered Institute of Personnel and Development
www.cipd.org.uk

Children's Workforce Development Council
www.cwdcouncil.org.uk

Communities and Local Government
www.communities.gov.uk

Commission for Patient and Public Involvement in Health
www.cppih.org.uk

Commission for Social Care Inspection:
www.csci.org.uk

General Social Care Council
www.gscc.org.uk

Healthcare Commission
www.healthcarecommission.org.uk

Health Professions Council
www.hpc-uk.org.uk

Learning and Skills Council
www.lsc.org.uk

National Council for Voluntary Organisations
www.ncvo-vol.org.uk

National Institute for Health and Clinical Excellence
www.nice.org.uk

National Statistics Online
www.statistics.gov.uk

NHS Careers
www.nhscareers.nhs.uk

NHS
www.nhs.uk

Northern Ireland Social Care Council
www.niscc.org.uk

Nursing and Midwifery Admissions Service
www.nmas.ac.uk

Nursing and Midwifery Council
www.nmc-uk.org.uk

Sector Skills Council: Skills for Care and Development
www.skillsforcare.org.uk

Sector Skills Council for Health: Skills for Health
www.skillsforhealth.org.uk

Social Care Institute for Excellence
www.scie.org.uk

Grading criteria

To achieve a pass grade the evidence must show that the learner is able to:	To achieve a merit grade the evidence must show that, in addition to the pass criteria, the learner is able to:	To achieve a distinction grade the evidence must show that, in addition to the pass and merit criteria, the learner is able to:
P1 explain key influences on personal learning processes of individuals **Assessment activity 6.1 page 282**	**M1** analyse the impact of key influences on personal learning processes on own learning **Assessment activity 6.1 page 282**	**D1** evaluate how personal learning and development may benefit others **Assessment activity 6.1 page 282**
P2 describe own knowledge, skills, practice, values, beliefs and career aspirations at start of programme **Assessment activity 6.2 page 296**		
P3 produce and monitor an action plan for self-development and the achievement of own personal goals **Assessment activity 6.3 page 302**		
P4 describe own progress against action plan over the duration of the programme **Assessment activity 6.4 page 313**	**M2** explain how the action plan has helped support own development over the duration of the programme **Assessment activity 6.4 page 313**	**D2** evaluate own development over the duration of the programme **Assessment activity 6.4 page 313**
P5 produce and reflect on own personal and professional development portfolio **Assessment activity 6.5 page 314**	**M3** reflect on own experiences and use three examples to explain links between theory and practice **Assessment activity 6.5 page 314**	
P6 describe one local health or social care service provider and identify its place in national provision **Assessment activity 6.6 page 324**		
P7 describe the roles, responsibilities and career pathways of three health or social care workers **Assessment activity 6.7 page 329**		

Sociological perspectives

Introduction

This unit provides an introduction to sociology and explains how the approaches that sociologists use can help us to understand our society. You will, specifically, study the different approaches that sociologists have used to explain and understand health and social care issues.

The unit will open with an introduction to key sociological terms, and the key sociological perspectives or approaches, followed by a discussion of how they illuminate the study of health and social care issues. You will consider different definitions of health and illness and consider the impact that the family, occupation and social class and other aspects of our environment can have on our health and well-being. There will be particular consideration of the differences in levels of health and illness among different social groups, particularly different groups identified by employment, social class, ethnicity and gender.

This unit will provide a very helpful foundation for those who, later in the course, will go on to study Unit 19: Applied sociological perspectives.

How you will be assessed

This unit is internally assessed by your tutor. A variety of exercises and activities are included to help you understand the language and approach of sociologists and to apply this understanding to health and social care practice.

After completing this unit you should be able to achieve the following outcomes:

- Understand sociological approaches to study
- Be able to apply sociological approaches to health and social care.

Thinking points

Imagine two families in very different social circumstances.

How might these differences affect their health and well-being?

Think about how these differences influence other aspects of the children's lives – the opportunity to make friends, to take part in other social activities and their achievements at school.

In this unit you will be exploring the very wide range of social factors that can affect health and well-being.

Key sociological terms

Sociology is a word drawn from the Latin *socios* meaning 'companion' and the Greek *ology* meaning 'study of'. Sociologists are concerned with the study of human societies, but most specifically the groups within those societies and how they relate to each other and how they influence individual behaviour.

Social structures

Society can be viewed as the sum of its **social institutions**, or major building blocks, including the family, the education system, work and the economic system, the political system, religious groups and the mass media. Sociologists are concerned with the way these institutions relate to each other and influence our behaviour.

Key terms

Social institution A major building block of society which functions according to widely accepted customs, rules or regulations, for example, the family, the education system or the legal system.

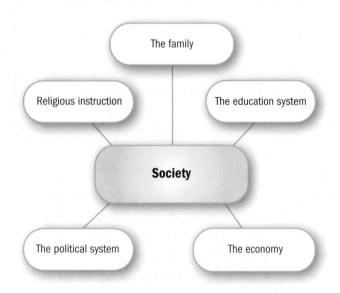

Figure 7.1 Key institutions in our society

Sociologists are concerned with describing the different forms of the family in our society, the changes that are taking place within the family, how it influences our behaviour and how it relates to other institutions: how, for example, our family background may influence our attitudes, religious beliefs, achievements within the education system, employment prospects and indeed our health and well-being. Within these institutions there are smaller groups which influence our behaviour, for example, our family group, friendship or peer groups and groups formed at school, college or work.

Reflect

List the social groups to which you belong and try to identify how one of these may have influenced your behaviour.

Socialisation

Sociology is based on the idea and belief that very little of our behaviour is instinctive and most of our behaviour is learnt through the process of **socialisation**. Socialisation is the process by which individuals learn the **culture** of their society, that is, the language, values and beliefs, customs and ways of behaving that are seen as acceptable. It may be argued that the most critical period of socialisation is in the early years of life. This is called the period of **primary socialisation** which takes place for most of us within a family – either our birth family, a family of adoption or a foster family. Very few children in the West are brought up in large children's homes these days. **Secondary socialisation** is the process that carries on as our social life develops through playgroups, nursery, school, friendship or peer groups, religious groups, the mass media and employment.

Key terms

Socialisation The process of learning the usual ways of behaving in a society.

Culture The values, beliefs, language, rituals, customs and rules that are associated with a particular society or social group.

Primary socialisation The first socialisation of children that normally takes place within the family.

Secondary socialisation The socialisation that takes place as we move into social settings beyond the family or place of our primary socialisation, for example, nursery, school and friendship groups.

The **norms**, or expected way of behaving, of the society or group to which you belong are learnt, it is argued, by copying, absorbing, reflecting and acting on the behaviour of others and by obeying the instructions of those in authority. Those who do not absorb and conform to expectations, i.e. who disregard the norms of the society or group, are said to be **deviant.**

Key terms

Norms The guidelines or rules that govern how we behave in society or in groups within that society.

Deviant People who do not conform to the norms of the society or group are said to be deviant.

Remember!

The socialisation process will vary from one society to another and at different times in history. Health and care workers will need to be mindful of the different and contrasting socialisation of people living in a multicultural society.

There are a small number of enlightening reports of children who have been found 'wild' – sometimes called feral children (see page 339). The behaviour of these children has not been socialised to the norms of any human group.

■ Social roles and expectations

You may have identified a number of social groups of which you are a member. Membership brings a range of expectations and obligations. These expectations in sociology are called **social roles**. For example, there are expectations linked with the social position of being a parent, a son or daughter or a student. It may be said that the social expectations or the social roles of parents in our society are that they will protect their children, ensure that they are kept safe and warm, provide a home, teach them the acceptable ways of behaving and ensure that they attend school ready to learn.

Key terms

Social role The social expectations associated with holding a particular position in a society or group.

Theory into practice

Try to identify the expectations of your role as a learner. Compare your list with that of others in your group.

Of course the groups to which we belong will change throughout our lives and our position in those groups will change. For example, within our family we may at various times be the teenager, the married son or daughter, a parent or a grandparent.

Most of us at any one time occupy multiple roles, sometimes referred to as our 'role set'. You may be a son or daughter, a brother or sister, a sibling, a student, an employee, a carer and a member of a youth group. Sometimes the associated role expectations will have competing and conflicting demands. **Role conflict** is the term used to describe a situation where the demands of our various social roles are in disagreement or cause strain.

Key terms

Role conflict Role conflict exists where the demands of the social roles that you are expected to perform are not consistent with each other, making it difficult and sometimes impossible to meet all demands.

Reflect

Can you identify role conflict within your own role set i.e. the range of social roles that you are expected to perform?

In context Multiple roles

Philippa is married and has three children aged 2, 5 and 7. Her elderly mother lives nearby. She has asked Philippa to help with the shopping and some of the heavier household jobs. Philippa's husband has very bad arthritis and is unable to take paid work or provide significant practical support within the family. Philippa works part time as a health care assistant. She also helps at the local Brownies group.

1 **Identify the groups to which Philippa belongs and her social position within those groups.**

2 **Describe the social expectations or social roles associated with those positions.**

3 **Discuss where the various role expectations may cause role conflict.**

■ Nature versus nurture

The **nature-nurture** debate focuses on the relative importance of our environment and the socialisation process (nurture) in human development as compared to the impact of heredity (nature). This debate has been particularly important in the sociology of:

- **education** – where social scientists have debated whether our educational achievements are more influenced by inherited intelligence or by our upbringing
- **crime** – whether criminal tendencies are inherited or are a product of environment
- **gender** – whether observed differences between the behaviour and achievements of men and women are genetically determined or a result of different opportunities.

Sociologists tend towards explanations that favour environment and socialisation as explanations of individual differences. You will also discuss the nature-nurture debate in Unit 4 of your course.

Key terms

Nature Those human characteristics that are genetically determined.

Nurture Those human characteristics that are learnt through the process of socialisation.

■ Social control

Social control refers to the methods used by societies to ensure that members conform to the expectations associated with their social roles. It is impossible to

Key terms

Social control The strategies used to ensure that people conform to the norms of their society or group.

In context Feral children

There is a famous example of two children who were found 'in the wild' by missionaries in India (Singh and Zingg, 1942). The girls had been living with and had been 'brought up' (or we could say 'socialised') by wolves. The children seemed to be separated by about one year in age and were approximately 7 and 8.

When 'captured' neither of them stood upright – they ran on all fours in a crouched position, rather like animals. They kept humans at a distance. They did not speak, laugh or sing. They did not point at things or use any of our other familiar non-verbal means of communication. They ate with the dogs, lapping from a bowl and licking from the plate rather than using their fingers.

In another case, a girl of 10 was discovered living in a chicken coop in Portugal. Similarly, she was not toilet-trained and she could not stand. Her gestures and sounds resembled that of the chickens and she scratched food up with her hands.

1 Describe the ways in which the development of the 'feral' children differs from the expectations of children that you know of a similar age.

2 Consider skills that they may have gained that children in our society may not have acquired.

3 Defend the view that nurture plays a significant part in human development.

conceive of a society that does not have norms and rules which guide behaviour and which does not have ways of dealing with those who are deviant. Formal methods of social control in our society include the police and judicial system, disciplinary systems in schools, colleges and in employment. Informal systems of social control can include exclusion from group activities, embarrassment, ridicule and subjecting people to gossip. Methods of social control can be positive or negative. Positive methods include giving praise and other rewards for conformity; negative methods include punishment and other reactions to deviance.

Theory into practice

In groups, identify and briefly explain two formal and two informal methods of social control used in your school or college. Present your ideas to the rest of the group. Be prepared to take questions at the end of your presentation.

Social diversity

■ Social stratification

Social stratification is a term that is used by sociologists and borrowed from geology. In geology, 'strata' refers to different layers of rock laid on top of each other. In sociology, the term is used to describe hierarchies and inequalities in societies – it highlights that some groups of people are seen as having more status and prestige than other groups. People who are identified as being of higher status are often more wealthy and have easier access to the possessions and way of life most valued in that society. Almost all known societies have some form of stratification and a sense of some groups being of higher status than others.

Key terms

Social stratification A term borrowed from geology which describes the hierarchies in society – how some groups have more status and prestige than other groups.

In African countries following colonization, and in America prior to the civil war, groupings were based on race; black communities had far less social status than white communities. Some people would argue that, despite legislation, such hierarchies still exist.

In India, the Hindu caste system identifies five clearly defined social strata ascribed at birth:

- Brahmins – the highest caste, the priestly caste
- Kshatriya – the military, rulers and administrators
- Vaisya – merchants and farmers
- Sudras – manual workers
- The Dalits, or social outcasts – the people who have almost no status (they have no caste at all).

There is no inter-marriage and very little social contact between the castes. There is no possibility of **social mobility** i.e. of improving or indeed changing your position in society at all. It is a closed system of stratification. Indian governments in recent years have attempted to remove the inequalities of the caste system but with limited success.

Key terms

Social mobility The process of moving from one social stratum to another. Social mobility can be either upward or downward.

In feudal England the different strata were called 'estates' and were based on the ownership of land. The monarchy and the knights, barons and earls formed the highest estate, the church and clergy were in the second estate and the merchants, peasants and serfs were in the lowest estate.

■ Social class

Social class is the form of stratification that describes the social hierarchies in most modern industrialised societies. Social class is based largely on economic factors linked with income, the ownership of property and other forms of wealth. Sociologists have been particularly interested in the link between our social class position and other aspects of our lives – the link between social class and educational achievement,

lifestyle choices and indeed our health and well-being.

The official classification of social class used by British governments to measure and analyse changes in the population began in 1851. The broad classification of occupations into social 'grades' (later called social classes) was used for the analysis of death rates.

The five social classes identified by the Registrar General of 1921, based largely on perceived occupational skill, remained in place until 2001. It was these categories that were used by government statisticians and others to analyse population trends until very recently.

The Registrar General's Scale of Social Class included:

- Class 1: Professional class
- Class 2: Managerial and technical occupations
- Class 3: Skilled occupations
  Non-manual (3N)
  Manual (3M)
- Class 4: Semi-skilled occupations
- Class 5: Unskilled occupations.

Since 2001, the National Statistics Socio-economic Classification (NS-SEC) has been used for official government statistics and surveys. It is still based on occupation but has been altered in line with employment changes and has categories to include the vast majority of the adult population:

- Class 1: Higher managerial and professional occupations
- Class 2: Lower managerial and professional occupations
- Class 3: Intermediate occupations
- Class 4: Small employers and own-account workers
- Class 5: Lower supervisory and technical occupations
- Class 6: Semi-routine occupations
- Class 7: Routine occupations
- Class 8: Never worked and long-term unemployed.

Social class differs from the more closed systems of the caste or feudal systems, or those based on race or gender, in that:

- the class differences are more difficult to define
- the class differences are not backed by law or regulation
- social class barriers are arguably far less rigid
- there is the possibility of social mobility
- people can rise, or indeed fall, in the class system.

Reflect

In groups try to agree a definition of the term 'social class' that could apply to our society.

In context

There have been experiments to create more **egalitarian** (or more equal) **societies**. Probably the most well developed is the Israeli kibbutz system developed early in the twentieth century in an attempt to re-establish a Jewish community in Palestine. All property and land was owned by the community (the kibbutz) and all goods distributed according to individual need. Members were paid with housing, food, clothing and other necessities rather than by monetary wages. Children were brought up and educated by the community. From a very early age they were looked after by 'metapelets' (children's carers) rather than by their birth parents.

1   **Explain the difference between an egalitarian society and a hierarchical society.**

2   **Describe three differences between the experience of children in an Israeli kibbutz and the experience of children in our society.**

3   **Discuss two advantages and two disadvantages of a hierarchical society based on social class in supporting the healthy development of young people.**

Key terms

Egalitarian society A society without hierarchies, where all members are regarded as equal.

Communes (small and relatively self-contained communities) were established during the 1960s in

the USA, Britain and other parts of western Europe by groups of people (mainly young) who wanted to establish alternative and less materialistic lifestyles. Many of these were short-lived but more longstanding religious communities and therapeutic communities still exist that support people with identified health and care needs.

Reflect

Would you like to live in an egalitarian society where all members are regarded as equal?

Remember!

Official classifications of social class are linked to occupation. We will be studying the link between health and sickness and level of social class.

Principal sociological perspectives

You are now going to look at the key sociological perspectives, or approaches, that have been used to describe and understand societies and the behaviour of individuals within societies. You will then consider how these approaches can help explain the impact of social life on health and well-being. You will notice that the key terms introduced earlier will be the main vocabulary for this discussion.

The first two perspectives, or approaches, that we will consider are structuralist theories. Structuralists are interested in describing and understanding the main institutions of societies. In modern industrialised societies this would include: the family, the education system, the health services, the economy, the political institutions, religious groups and the media. They are concerned with how the institutions relate to each other and how they influence and mould individual behaviour. The two structuralist approaches that we will describe and discuss are known as **functionalism** (or the consensus model) and Marxism, the **conflict model**. Feminism, considered separately on page 346, is normally regarded as an example of a conflict model with the focus on the continuing oppression of women in our society.

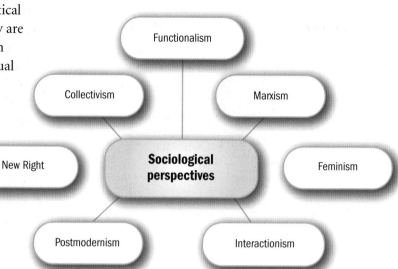

▲ Figure 7.2 Key sociological perspectives

Key terms

Functionalism A sociological approach which sees the social institutions of the society as working in harmony with each other, making specific and clear contributions towards the smooth running of the society.

Conflict model A sociological approach first associated with Karl Marx which sees the institutions of society as organised to meet the interests of the ruling classes.

The functionalist or consensus model

The functionalist approach to sociology, which can be traced back to Auguste Comte (1798–1857), may be best understood by using a biological analogy. Just as the body can be understood and studied by considering its constituent parts, for example, the lungs, heart, liver and kidneys, so society can be studied in terms of its institutions. Just as the body functions through the efficient interrelationship of major organs and there are mechanisms to deal with disease, so the different institutions in society have particular contributions to make; they work together and have methods of social control to deal with 'deviant' members or groups.

Talcott Parsons (1902–79) was key in the development of functionalism as a sociological approach. He saw society as a system made up of interrelated institutions which contributed to its smooth running and continuity.

He thought that the main role of an institution was to socialise individuals and ensure that they understood the underlying values of the society and behaved in acceptable ways. In this way there was order in society.

We can go on to consider the functions of the family and how it contributes to the order and stability of society, or the social system (a term that functionalists would often use). George Murdock (1949) in his classic study of the family examined over 250 societies ranging from small hunter-gatherer communities to large industrialised societies and found some form of the family in all societies.

George Murdock claimed that the family had four universal functions:

- The sexual function allowed for the expression of sexuality in an approved context.
- The reproductive function provided stability for the rearing of children.
- Socialisation included the responsibility for teaching children the acceptable ways of behaving in society.
- The economic function meant that food, shelter and financial security had to be provided for family members.

Talcott Parsons (1951), writing about American society, argued that the family had two 'basic and irreducible functions':

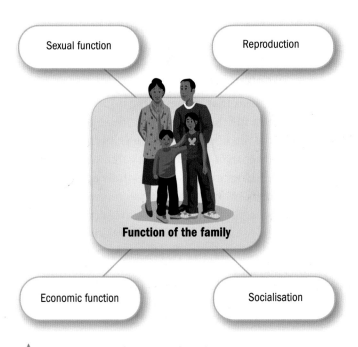

Figure 7.3 The functions of the family

- The primary socialisation of children identified by Murdock.
- The stabilisation of adult personalities – in a complex, stressful and demanding world the family provides warmth and emotional security, especially, as Parsons saw it, for the male breadwinner.

Theory into practice

In your group answer the following question:

What are the functions of the family today?

Compare and discuss the range of answers. Are you able to agree on the principal functions of the family in our society?

■ Criticisms of the functionalist model

Probably the most fundamental criticism of the functionalist approach is that it does not address areas of conflict which certainly characterise modern societies and in principle could be found in all societies.

Functionalists emphasise areas of consensus and agreement and paint a rather rosy picture of institutions having clear, positive functions and co-operating effectively for the good of all. That does not on the face of it reflect many people's experience of the modern world where in many societies there are clear winners and losers and many non-conformists.

Functionalism is based on the idea that members in all societies share some basic values and beliefs – that there is **value consensus** and that this underpins the socialisation process and the working of the main institutions. Researchers have not been able to find that common values are clearly shared in modern societies.

Key terms

Value consensus A general agreement as to the values and beliefs of a society.

Reflect

Do you think that there is a common value system in our society to which most people would subscribe?

Functionalists are also very clear that how we behave is a direct result of the socialisation process and that very little of our behaviour is the result of our personal choices. We are very largely programmed to behave in particular ways. There is very little freedom of choice. The interactionist model that we will consider later in this chapter provides an alternative to this view.

Reflect

Do you think that we are programmed by our socialisation or do we have some freedom of choice?

Finally, functionalists tend to present a picture of a socialisation process that does not fail. There is no clear explanation of the prevalence of deviant behaviour and especially the extreme forms of deviance found in crime, delinquency and abuse which are destabilising for society as a whole.

Marxism

Marxism, as well as being a conflict model, is also a structuralist model. It was first developed by Karl Marx (1818–83). He also thought that individual behaviour was shaped by society but he believed that it was the economic system that defined society and people's place within it. Marx held the view that in the industrial society of his time there were two social classes:

- **the bourgeoisie**, or **capitalists** – the small powerful group who owned the factories and other places of employment
- **the proletariat** – a much larger, poorer group of 'workers' (the people or 'hands' that the bourgeoisie employed).

His view was that these two social class groups would always be in conflict: the owners of the factories, land and offices would want high profits and the employees would want higher wages that would eat into the profits. This is why Marxism is often called the conflict model. He thought that this conflict would lead to revolution. There was an unequal relationship between the bourgeoisie and the proletariat and conflict was inherent in the economic system.

Key terms

The bourgeoisie In Marxist theory, the bourgeoisie, or the capitalists, are the powerful class in society who own the factories, land and other capital and are able to organise the economy and other important institutions in society to their own advantage.

The proletariat In Marxist theory the proletariat are the 'working class', who have only their labour to sell. They work for and are exploited by the bourgeoisie.

Marxists argue that the ruling class (the bourgeoisie) also hold power in the other institutions of society and that they shape the society and its major institutions. They control the mass media and the legal system and it is their ideas that influence the organisation and curriculum in schools. Through the socialisation process it is the ideology of the ruling class that is passed on, rather than the common value system of the functionalists; this is so successfully achieved that the majority of the proletariat do not realise that they are being exploited or that they are serving the interests of the bourgeoisie rather than their own class. This lack of awareness by the proletariat is called **false consciousness** – it is the explanation as to why the conflicting interests do not often erupt into actual conflict or revolution.

Key terms

False consciousness In Marxist theory, false consciousness is the taking on, by the proletariat, of the views and beliefs of their class enemy – the bourgeoisie. They do not realise that, by working hard, they are serving the interests of the capitalists much more than their own.

Like functionalists, Marxists have a structuralist perspective – they see the family as contributing to a stable social system but would regard the family as the servant of the capitalist system. They believe that it provides the context for the socialisation of children, preparing them for the disciplines and routines of work. Just as children have limited power in the family, so they are prepared to be obedient to their bosses at work as adults. In addition, Marxists see the family as providing a secure emotional base, a home, from which people will return to work rested and refreshed. As a servant of the capitalists, the ordered family is necessary for passing on inheritance. Children born within the nuclear family are the rightful inheritors of the family's wealth.

Reflect

Do you think that the education system works in favour of the higher social classes or are there equal opportunities for all?

■ Criticisms of the Marxist model

Like functionalists, Marxists believe that individual behaviour is the direct result of the socialisation process, with very little accommodation for individual choice. In the case of Marxist conflict theorists, however, it is a socialisation that meets the values and interests of the ruling classes.

Closely linked with this point is the view that Marxists put too much emphasis on different class interests and potential conflicts of interest. Although clear inequalities remain, the standard of living in industrialised societies has improved immensely and arguably employers and employees share some common interests. All will potentially benefit from a successful company.

Some writers hold the view that the Marxist model, which sees the economy as the institution that drives all others, does not give sufficient emphasis to the separate power of other institutions –religion, race and family life – in moulding our behaviour.

In context Nineteenth-century poverty

Friedrich Engels, a friend and collaborator of Karl Marx, wrote about the conditions of the poor in the mid-nineteenth century:

'The manner in which the great multitude of the poor is treated by society today is revolting. They are drawn into large cities where they breathe a poorer atmosphere than in the country; they are relegated to districts which, by reason of the method of construction, are worse ventilated than any others; they are deprived of all means of cleanliness, of water itself, since pipes are laid only when paid for, and the rivers so polluted that they are useless for such purposes; they are obliged to throw all offal and garbage, all dirty water, often all disgusting drainage and excrement into the streets being without other means of disposing of them; they are thus compelled to infect the region of their own dwellings …

… How is it possible, under such circumstances, for the lower classes to be healthy and live long lives? What else can be expected than excessive mortality, an unbroken series of epidemics, and a progressive deterioration of the physique of the working population?'

The Conditions of the Working Class in England (1845)

1 **Which of the two social classes identified in the Marxist model does Engels describe in this passage?**

2 **Explain why Marx expected that these conditions would lead to conflict and revolution.**

3 **Consider the measures that needed to be taken to improve the health and well-being of the people described.**

▲ In the nineteenth century, large numbers of the poor lived in dreadful conditions in UK cities

Remember!

Functionalist sociologists believe that societies are united by common values that are shared across society and which lead to the smooth running of that society. This is contrasted with the Marxist perspective, which holds that societies are organised and controlled by powerful groups to meet the needs of these groups.

Feminism in sociology

Feminism is normally seen as an example of a conflict model within which three main approaches can be identified:

- Marxist feminism
- radical feminism
- liberal feminism.

Feminists have argued that sociology, as an academic discipline, was developed and dominated by men. Hence the term 'malestream' sociology was introduced. Pamela Abbot and Claire Wallace (1997) clearly summarised the concerns and criticisms of mainstream, or malestream, sociology from a feminist point of view. They argue that this male dominance has produced biased descriptions and analysis and that not enough attention has been paid to the issues of women and their unequal place in society.

■ Marxist feminism

Marxist feminists see women, especially working class women, as oppressed both by capitalism and by men or the patriarchal society. Women produce the next generation of workers. They meet the physical, social and emotional needs of their children so that they are ready to work in the offices and factories of the future. They support their husbands and partners, cook meals, care for their children and clean their houses – for no pay! Thus they are dominated by their husbands and they are also subsidising industry. The family would not be ready for work if somebody did not take

responsibility for domestic life and this, it is argued, remains the primary responsibility of women.

■ Radical feminism

For radical feminists, it is not capitalism that dominates women, but men. The family is seen as a patriarchal institution. They see the socialisation of women as housewives and mothers as a form of oppression and this oppression as a characteristic of nuclear family life.

Reflect

Are these views dated? Who in your family would normally cook the meals, do the washing up, vacuum, clean and tidy the house and/or mend electrical equipment? Are the traditional gender roles still in place?

■ Liberal feminism

Liberal feminists would argue that changes have taken place. They believe that, through changing attitudes and recent legislation (for example, the Equal Pay Act (1970) and the Equal Opportunities Act (1975)), there is more equality. Liberal feminists believe that improvements will continue through legislation and policy.

Theory into practice

Referring to the legislation section at: www.harcourt.co.uk/btechsc/, and other sources, identify the key changes in the law relating to sexual equality.

Discuss in groups how far changes in the law can influence the position of women, especially their role in the family.

Key terms

Interactionism A sociological approach which focuses on the influence of small groups on our behaviour rather than the power of large institutions. These theorists believe that our behaviour is driven by how, in smaller groups, we interpret situations – how we see ourselves in relation to other people in the group, how we see other members and how they see us.

is on *small* groups and how they influence individual behaviour and shape society. Interactionists may study groups as diverse as teenage gangs, staff, patients and visitors on hospital wards or social interaction in school classrooms. They will study the dynamics within those groups. For example:

- How do different people see themselves?
- Do some have more power than others?
- Who are the formal leaders?
- Are there some informal leaders who actually have power in the group?

Social action or interactionist theorists do not hold the view that we are programmed by the socialisation process. They see individuals as *influenced* by the socialisation process but having the power to choose how they will actually behave. We create our own roles. These theorists focus on the aspects of sociology that are concerned with behaviour in small groups and how those groups influence our behaviour. They have very little interest in social structure as a whole. They see our behaviour as driven by how we interpret situations, how we see ourselves and other people and how they see us.

In the family, a mother may understand what is expected of a 'good' mother but social action theorists think that social roles are not clearly defined. They believe that the mother will interpret what that means for her in the context of her family, her relationship with her children and her links with the wider society. There is no blueprint. For the social action theorist, the main aim of the sociologist is to understand how people interpret situations and behave in small-group face-to-face situations.

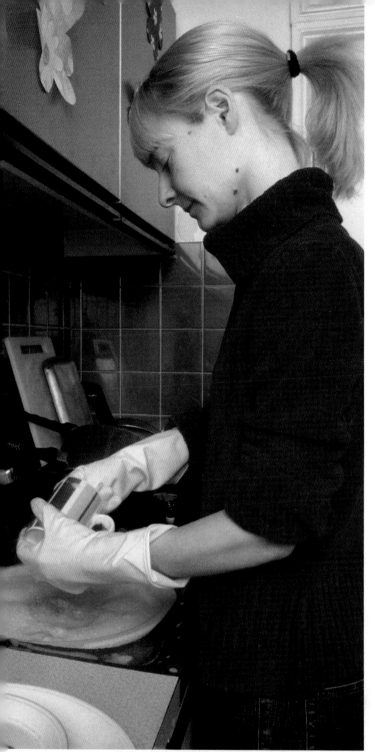

▲ **Many women remain in traditional domestic roles**

Interactionist model

The **interactionist**, or social action, approach contrasts with the structuralist perspectives in that the focus is not on the large institutions and how they are structured and function and link with each other. Instead, the focus

■ Criticisms of the social action approach

Social action theorists, although they emphasise individual choice, accept that there are social roles even if they are not clearly defined. They do not, however, study where they come from. They are criticised for paying insufficient attention to issues of power in society. Although they would say that social roles are only vaguely defined, they do not explain where these roles come from and they do not explain why people largely behave in very predictable ways.

In addition, they are sometimes criticised for describing social behaviour 'in a vacuum'. They describe behaviour in delinquent gangs or the relationship between staff and patients in a hospital ward but they do not describe the wider social factors that have influenced this or the historical factors that might have defined or caused the situation. Social action theorists tend to focus on the interactions within the group rather than these wider issues.

Postmodernism

Postmodernism is an approach to sociology, or understanding society, that focuses on the rapid change and uncertainty in our society – some would even say chaos. Postmodernists would suggest that we can no longer talk about established institutions like the family, religion or the economy because nothing is staying the same. Domestic arrangements are so various these days that social institutions like 'the family' are in a state of constant change. It is no longer possible to talk of the 'typical' family. Postmodernists hold the view that, because of the constant change, structuralist perspectives like functionalism and Marxism no longer help us to understand society. The institutions have become fragmented. Individuals and groups of people make their own individual lifestyle decisions, choosing from the many leisure activities and consumer goods that are now available.

Collectivism

Collectivism is an approach to providing health and care services, underpinned by a government commitment to provide care and support for the vulnerable. This is funded through taxation and national insurance. This is contrasted with the New Right (see page 349), who consider welfare to be the responsibility of the individual and their family and that the state should play a minimal role.

Collectivism and the New Right are examples of political responses to the role of government in our society and, for our purposes, their response to meeting identified areas of welfare need. In all societies there are groups of people who are potentially vulnerable. These may include children, older people, people with physical impairments and those with mental health needs. In some societies the care of these people will be seen as the responsibility of the individual or their family; in other societies it will be seen as the responsibility of religious groups, the commune or the local community.

The state has played a role in the care of the vulnerable in Britain since the passing of the Poor Law in 1601. However, it was not until the nineteenth century that governments took a significant role in the support of the vulnerable (many would say this did not happen until after World War 2 with the 'birth of the Welfare State'). The Beveridge Report in 1942 provided the political foundation to provide a comprehensive range of welfare services. Lord Beveridge in his *Report on Social Insurance and Allied Services* identified five giant evils that needed urgently to be challenged.

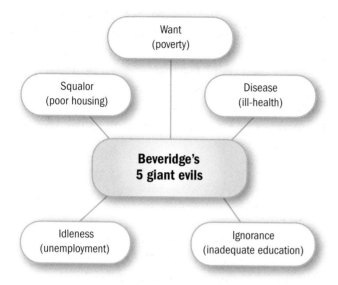

Figure 7.4 Beveridge's five giant evils

There was cross-party agreement that the state should take a collective responsibility to:

- address poverty through a wide range of welfare benefits including Family Allowance, unemployment and sickness benefit and retirement pensions
- fight disease through the National Health Service
- combat ignorance through the expansion of secondary education for all
- eradicate squalor through the building of council houses
- remove idleness by supporting policies of full employment and the development of labour exchanges.

This placed the provision of key services in the hands of the state, working co-operatively with families and voluntary organisations, and was to be financed through taxes and national insurance.

Reflect

Can you think of services that were introduced in the 1940s, following the Beveridge Report, that still remain – even if their name has changed?

Compare your list with those of others in your group.

The New Right

The post-war collectivist approach to welfare remained largely in place for over a generation and was not seriously challenged or questioned until the election of Margaret Thatcher's government in 1979. The view of this government was that the state should play as small a role as possible in the provision of welfare. They believed that welfare should be largely seen as the responsibility of the individual and their family. The New Right regarded state support as intrusive and supporting a dependency culture. Mrs Thatcher and her government were of the view that the welfare state generated a society in which people relied on state benefits rather than planning for the future and taking responsibility for the needs of themselves and their families.

Remember!

The collectivist approach to welfare believes that care needs are the responsibility of the state. This is contrasted with the New Right, who regard the meeting of care needs to be largely the responsibility of the individual and their family.

Theory into practice

Divide into five groups and using your knowledge of local services, the Internet and library resources, list the range of state provision in each of the following areas:

- education
- health services
- care services
- housing
- welfare benefits.

Would you say that we still live in a collectivist welfare state?

7.2 Sociological approaches to health and social care

Functionalist approaches

The functionalist approach to considering health and illness derives from the work of Talcott Parsons. Using the traditional functionalist approach, he described how, for society to function efficiently, its members need to be healthy. He described illness as a form of deviance and ill members as performing a form of social role – the sick role. This became a very powerful concept in the sociology of illness. In his view, if people declared themselves ill, specific rights and responsibilities came with their new role.

The rights associated with the sick role were the right of the individual:

- to be exempt from normal social obligations, for example, to go to school, college or work, and from meeting normal family obligations
- to be cared for.

Parsons would see it as one of the key functions of the family to care for the sick and other dependent members of the family group.

The responsibilities of the sick role included the individual:

- taking all reasonable steps to get better and seeking to resume their normal place in society as soon as possible
- co-operating with medical professionals, particularly doctors and their staff.

The functionalist view (and it might be said that this is the view of governments) is that illness has a social consequence and must be swiftly dealt with, where possible, for the smooth running of society.

Marxist approaches

Marxist approaches believe that the definitions of health and illness, and the health and care services provided, serve the interests of the more powerful dominant social classes. Doctors are seen as agents who ensure that people go back to work as soon as possible, working in the interests of the employers rather than those of the patient. Their job is to provide the company owner with a healthy workforce. In addition, the government allows companies to make profits from products that cause ill health, for example, tobacco and junk food. Firms and factories continue to produce toxic waste and large cars pollute the atmosphere.

Unlike the functionalists, who regard ill health as something that occurs almost randomly, conflict theorists see levels of illness as related to differences in social class. For example, there is a higher level of illness and lower life expectancy in areas of poverty, high unemployment and environmental pollution. The government does not do enough to tackle the issues that lead to illness as this will cost money which would have to be found by the most advantaged in society.

Reflect

In what ways could it be said that the health services in modern Britain are organised to serve the interests of employers and other powerful groups rather than those of the patient?

Interactionist or social action approaches

Interactionism is probably the theoretical approach that has devoted the most attention to issues of health and illness. It is concerned with:

- the processes that lead a person to define themselves as ill – people with the same 'complaint' vary as to whether they will call themselves ill and certainly vary as to whether they will seek professional help. Some people with very serious illnesses do not regard themselves as ill.

- the interaction between the professional and the patient in agreeing how ill they are – interactionists, although they understand that there are sometimes quite clear diagnoses, are interested in the negotiation that takes place with the professional in trying to agree on the impact of the illness. Should the patient

be signed off work or not? How far should their bad back limit daily activities?

- the impact on people's self-image and on their relationships if they are labelled as 'ill'.

Interactionists, in studying the sociology of health and illness, do not look at structures and institutions but study the complex relationships between people, their family and friends and their links with the professional services. They think that these relationships have as much influence as any medical diagnosis on whether people declare themselves to be ill.

Critics of the interactionist approach say that, in concentrating on these relationships and the negotiations that take place, it ignores the 'real' causes of ill health. These include medical explanations and environmental factors arising from pollution, stress and poverty.

Reflect

Do your friends and family differ in how willing they are to declare themselves ill? Do some 'soldier on' and others take to their beds easily? What do you think might explain the differences?

Feminist approaches

Feminist writers have been concerned with male domination in the medical professions and its impact on women. They have been particularly concerned with the way in which pregnancy and childbirth have been regarded as medical issues rather than as natural processes, even sometimes as illnesses. Feminist writers also comment on the way in which the medical profession and the related pharmaceutical industries have given a relatively low priority to the development and promotion of the male contraceptive pill (which arguably has fewer harmful side-effects than the contraceptive methods used by women). In considering issues of mental health, anxiety and depression and the fact that relatively higher levels of women suffer from these conditions, feminists would see this partly as a result of their exploited position in society and especially in the family. These issues are, however, defined as a medical problem for which medicines are a solution. This shifts attention away from the fact that a woman's day-to-day life circumstances may be the cause of stress.

Marxist and other socialist feminists have been more concerned with the impact of social inequalities on women's health. In *What Makes Women Sick?* Lesley Doyal (1995) particularly highlights the increasingly dual role of women, or the 'double day' as she calls it: women often have full-time jobs outside the home and then take most of the responsibility for domestic life as well.

Understanding different concepts of health and ill health

Concepts of health

It will come as no surprise that sociologists have great difficulty in agreeing on a definition of what it means to be healthy. Health can be defined in terms of the 'absence of disease', sometimes described as a negative approach to health. This is contrasted with a positive definition such as that provided by the World Health Organisation (WHO) (1974): 'not merely an absence of disease, but a state of complete physical, mental, spiritual and social well-being'.

In the health and care sectors, care professionals would adopt a holistic approach to care and support. They see their role as addressing the needs of the 'whole' person rather than specific issues or identified problems.

A person with complex needs, for example a young mother with multiple sclerosis, may be supported by a range of professionals. These would include a GP, a community nurse, an occupational therapist, a social worker and a health visitor, often referred to as a multi-disciplinary team. They will each have their particular roles and responsibilities for her care and support but they will want to carry out a **holistic assessment**; they will recognise the importance of the young woman's wider needs when providing their specialist care.

Mildred Blaxter (1990) interviewed almost 10,000 people in her large-scale study, *Health and Lifestyles*. She

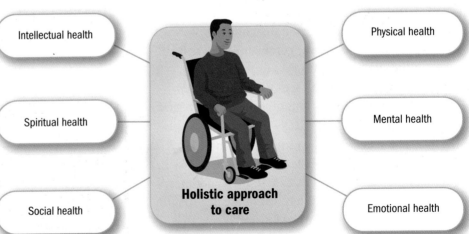

Figure 7.5 A holistic approach to care

identified three strands to people's understanding of health and well-being:

- a positive definition – regarding health as feeling fit and well
- a negative definition – defining health as being free from pain or discomfort
- functional health – defining health in terms of being able to perform certain, often day-to-day, tasks.

Defining health, then, is not easy and there is certainly no clear agreement amongst scholars.

Ironically, most sociological research concerned with studying levels of health within and between societies actually focuses on issues of ill health. There is, for example, a great deal of information used by sociologists about death rates, visits to GPs' surgeries, the incidence of notifiable diseases, admissions to mental health units and indeed suicide statistics, and

this is analysed by social class, occupation, ethnicity, gender, age and geographical location. This type of information can be measured statistically and is generally clearly defined. It is much more difficult to measure the more positive indicators of health and well-being as in the WHO definition on page 352.

Remember!

A negative concept of health regards health as the absence of disease. A positive concept of health is concerned with people's physical, intellectual, social and emotional well-being.

Assessment activity 7.2

Describe different concepts of health.

1 Describe in your own words the different concepts of health introduced in this unit:

- negative
- positive
- holistic
- World Health Organisation definition of health.

Grading tip for P2

The differences between the concepts of health will be clarified if examples are used to illustrate the definition. In your answer you may wish to point to the close links between the positive model, the holistic model and the World Health Organisation's definition.

Use two sociological perspectives to explain different concepts of health.

2 Explain in your own words, using two sociological perspectives, different concepts of health. The perspective could be drawn from:

- functionalism
- Marxism
- feminism
- interactionism
- collectivism
- postmodernism
- the New Right.

Grading tip for M1

You may choose two from any of the sociological perspectives introduced earlier in this chapter. To achieve the merit grade you will need to illustrate how the two sociological perspectives explain the different concepts of health.

Biomedical model

The model of health that has dominated Western industrialised societies, certainly since the industrial revolution of the mid-nineteenth century, has been the **biomedical model.** This view underpins the policies and practice of the National Health Service (NHS). The proponents of the model regard health as being largely the absence of disease and see the intervention of health professionals as necessary in times of illness. The main purpose of the health services is to cure disease and health professionals will use scientifically tested methods to address diagnosed illnesses. Sociologists believe that the focus on the individual patient for whom a cure should be found is a limitation of this model; there is little regard paid to environmental and social factors that may lead to ill health. The causes of illness may be many and varied and the focus of the biomedical approach leads to a focus on the individual. Environmental factors that might cause disease are largely ignored.

Key terms

Biomedical model An approach to health and illness which identifies health as the absence of disease.

The biomedical model fits well with the functionalist perspective discussed earlier in the chapter where illness is regarded as in itself dysfunctional for society. If people are ill they cannot make their normal contribution to the smooth running of society. For the functionalist, if people adopt the sick role and are exempt from their usual social responsibilities, they do have a responsibility to co-operate with the health professionals and to take all reasonable steps to get better.

Socio-medical model

The **socio-medical model** of health focuses on the social factors that contribute to health and well-being in our society. Research indicates that life expectancy rose and death rates began to fall, especially infant mortality rates, with the improvements in sanitation and the provision of clean water, the building of new council houses and generally improved standards of living in the late-nineteenth/early-twentieth centuries. This was long before 1946 and the introduction of universal free personal health care through the NHS. It is evidence of this sort that supports a view that a significant source of disease and ill health lies in the environmental and social conditions of society, and it is not solely located in the individual.

The socio-medical model sits more easily with the conflict theorists than the functionalists. The conflict theorist would explain the shorter life expectancy and the relatively higher rates of ill health among the poor as a consequence of the inequalities in society and the life circumstances of the disadvantaged. The poor, they would say, are more likely to have inadequate diets, live in damp houses, often in inner city areas where the impact of unemployment and environmental pollution is arguably highest. The ruling groups in society, the politicians and the owners of industries, are not willing, they would say, to make the changes that would be necessary to protect the poor from ill health and disease.

Key terms

Socio-medical model An approach to health and illness with a focus on the social and environmental factors that influence our health and well-being, including the impact of poverty, poor housing, diet and pollution.

Take it further

In groups make a poster illustrating the range of social and environmental factors that may lead to ill health.

In context Life expectancy in Africa

Rank	Country/Region	Infant mortality rate (deaths per 1000 live births)
1	Angola	187.49
2	Afghanistan	163.07
3	Sierra Leone	162.55
4	Liberia	161.99
5	Mozambique	130.79
198	United Kingdom	5.15
223	Japan	3.26
224	Hong Kong	2.96
225	Sweden	2.77
226	Singapore	2.29

Table 7.1 Countries with the highest and lowest infant mortality rates

In Zimbabwe the life expectancy for women is 34. Zimbabwe has found itself at the centre of an AIDS pandemic, a food crisis and economic disaster. In Zambia the life expectancy is 40; in Mozambique 46; in Botswana 40; in South Africa 49.

Adapted from The Independent *17 November 2006*

These are levels of life expectancy similar to those in mid-nineteenth-century Britain.

1 **Identify five reasons why levels of life expectancy are so low and infant mortality rates so high in developing countries.**

2 **Explain why the levels of life expectancy may be similar to those of mid-nineteenth-century Britain.**

3 **Discuss the view that this evidence supports the arguments for the socio-medical model of health.**

Remember!

The biomedical model of health has a clear focus on individual diagnosed illness and the socio-medical model is concerned with the environmental causes of illness. They can be seen as two complementary approaches to the study of health and illness.

Assessment activity 7.3

Describe the biomedical and socio-medical models of health.

Aziz and Tamsela have four young children. Tamsela's elderly parents live with them. Their 3-bedroom house is in a deprived and rather depressing area of London. Their house is in a poor state of repair; it is damp and very expensive to keep warm in the winter. Neither Aziz nor Tamsela is currently in paid work.

The family is in poor health. In the winter the children seem to have permanent colds. Tamsela suffers from asthma and her father has bronchitis. Tamsela's mother is depressed and has been prescribed drugs for this condition.

1 In your own words, describe the biomedical and socio-medical models of health.

Grading tip for P3

The descriptions of the different models can be quite brief but they should clearly point to the different focus of the approaches – the biomedical, which focuses on the individual and the absence of disease, and the socio-medical, which foregrounds the environmental factors that are linked with health and illness.

Explain the biomedical and socio-medical models of health.

2 Explain how the biomedical and socio-medical models of health might be applied when considering the health and well-being of Aziz and Tamsela's family. **M2**

Grading tip for M2

To achieve the merit grade you are required to explain the models of health. Explanations require more detail than a definition or a description. In this case, this can be achieved by using appropriate examples to illustrate the concepts introduced

Evaluate the biomedical and socio-medical models of health.

3 Discuss the strengths and weaknesses of the biomedical and socio-medical models of health and come to your own conclusion about their usefulness in health and social care. **D1**

Grading tip for D1

To achieve a distinction grade an evaluation is required, which involves considering the strengths and weaknesses of the two models in discussions of health and well-being. You also need to come to a balanced conclusion as to which is the most helpful approach. You may use illustrative examples to support your arguments.

Take it further

Discuss the view that the biomedical and socio-medical models could be seen as complementary – that both perspectives give valuable insights.

■ Disability and impairment

The related ideas of disability and impairment are very closely linked with the medical and social models of health. As with many of the other sociological terms that have been introduced in this unit, the terms 'disability' and 'impairment' may be used in different ways by different writers and the term 'disability' is not easy to define. It is important that you are absolutely clear how you are using the terms when considering the issues. Tom Shakespeare (1998) formalised a helpful distinction between disability and impairment.

Impairment has a focus on the individual and refers to the day-to-day restrictions that may arise because of a long-term physical or mental condition, for example, the loss of a limb, a sensory impairment or depression. This can be seen as a similar point of view to that of the biomedical model of health and illness. The patient from this point of view would need to co-operate with the health and care professionals to limit the restrictions caused by the impairment. They will have similar social obligations to a person in the sick role discussed earlier.

Disability, in contrast, is seen by Shakespeare as a problem which arises when a society does not take into account the needs of people with impairments. There may be no ramps into buildings, and doorways may be too narrow for people who use wheelchairs. A person with a hearing impairment may only be disabled if

they do not have access to a hearing aid or have not been taught to lip read. Disability, from this point of view, is seen as the restricted opportunity to take part in the normal life of the community due to physical, social or attitudinal barriers. In this context writers will sometimes refer to the **disabling environment** – an environment where adaptions and other facilities are not in place to ensure that people with impairments can take full part in a social life; this is a social model of disability.

Key terms

Disabling environment A social context where adaptions and other facilities are not in place to ensure that people with impairments can take a full part in social life.

In context

David is a regular attender and committee member of the local youth centre. He is a wheelchair user. The youth centre is based in a large community centre that was once a warehouse. Some adaptions have been made to improve access for people with disabilities but the only way to the first floor of the building is by using the old tradesmen's lift. David cannot reach the controls so can only go upstairs if someone is available to help. Few of the buses have wheelchair access so David is dependent on the family and willing volunteers for transport to the centre.

1 **Explain what is meant by the terms 'impairment' and 'disability' in this context.**

2 **Briefly discuss the view that the youth centre is a disabling environment.**

3 **Evaluate the usefulness of the distinction between impairment and disability in this context.**

Key terms

Impairment The restrictions on day-to-day activity caused by a physical or mental dysfunction or abnormality, for example, the loss of a limb, a sensory impairment or a learning difficulty such as Down's syndrome.

Disability Sociologists will often refer to disability as the restrictions that arise for a person with an impairment because of the attitudes and the lack of appropriate services and facilities to meet their needs.

Theory into practice

Write a short report describing either:

- how accessible your college is for people who are wheelchair users, or
- how easy it is for wheelchair users to do their shopping in your local high street.

■ Iatrogenesis or 'doctor-generated' illness

Iatrogenesis refers to illness generated by medical activity and practice. It was a term introduced by Ivan Illich (1976) and was part of his more general attack on, and criticism of, industrialised society and its large bureaucratic institutions. However, it is still very much part of current debate. Particular areas of concern include the side-effects of drugs, the risks attached to medical drugs trials and concerns about infections spread within hospitals. Illich identified three major types of iatrogenesis:

- clinical iatrogenesis – the unwanted side-effects of medical intervention
- social iatrogenesis – medicine has gained so much power and status that people too quickly and easily place themselves in the hands of the professional and become mass consumers of medical products
- cultural iatrogenesis – society becomes over-concerned with perfect health, so making it difficult to develop positive attitudes towards impairment and to cope appropriately with death.

■ The clinical iceberg

Official statistics on levels of illness are sometimes called 'the clinical iceberg' because it is thought that the 'true' levels of illness are largely concealed; this is because people who are ill do not necessarily visit their doctor. This may be for a wide range of reasons.

Assessment activity 7.4

Describe different concepts of ill health.

1 Drawing on examples from your placement and from other life experiences, describe the different concepts of ill health introduced in this unit:

- disability
- iatrogenesis
- the sick role
- the clinical iceberg.

Grading tip for P4

You can provide evidence of linking theory to practice by using well-chosen examples to illustrate concepts.

Take it further

Consider how concepts of ill health may help care workers in evaluating their own care practice.

Understanding patterns and trends in health and illness

Statistical trends in the levels of health and illness are generated from three main sources.

1 **Government statistics** – the government department that provides ongoing data on the wide range of health, social and economic issues that affect policy and planning is the Office of National Statistics (ONS). Publications include *Social Trends*, *Population Trends* and, for more detailed information on health issues, *Health Statistical Quarterly*. They are available in hard copy and electronically. These publications will provide a very wide range of clearly presented information on birth rates and death rates, infant mortality and suicide rates,

statistical information on health events such as the level of appointments at GPs' surgeries and hospital admissions and these are often analysed by social class, gender, geographical location and age. *Health Statistical Quarterly* in 2007 included articles on childhood mortality, cancer survival, and abortions and statistical information on alcohol-related mortality, infant mortality rates and the prevalence of treated asthma. But as discussed earlier in this unit, the focus of these statistics is on areas of ill health and death, and on the incidence and prevalence of disease rather than on levels of health and well-being, which are arguably more difficult to define and track.

2 **Charitable organisations and pressure groups** – many charitable groups and special interest groups also collect and publish statistical and other information which informs the discussion and debate on issues of health and illness. For example MIND (www.mind.org.uk) and YOUNG MINDS (www.youngminds.org.uk) are charities which support people and young people with mental health needs, and www.youreable.com (formerly www.disabilitynet.co.uk) is a website which provides an Internet-based disability and news service. All provide ongoing and up-to-date information relating to their areas of concern.

3 **Academic researchers and other authors** – largely based in universities, they also contribute to the evidence and debate on a wide range of health and care issues.

Throughout this book you will find references to evidence drawn from all these sources.

Government statistics include reports of the **mortality rates** or death rates in the population and also the **morbidity rates**, the number of people who have particular diseases during a specified period, usually a year. The trends will be compared over periods of time. Have rates increased or decreased? They may be analysed by sex, age, geographical location or social class. Are mortality and morbidity rates higher in some parts of the country than in others? Is there a difference in mortality and morbidity between social classes? Specific morbidity rates may be measured in terms of the prevalence of a disease. **Disease prevalence** is the total number of cases of a specific disease in a population during a specified period of time. **Disease incidence** is the number of new cases of a specific disease occurring in a population during a specified period of time. Mortality rates, especially **infant mortality rates**, are often used as an indicator of the general health and well-being of the population as a whole. If they are higher or rising in a particular location, or among a particular social group compared to others, this is seen as a possible indicator that levels of general health and well-being may be declining within those groups and that the causes of this lie in their social and economic environment. A high mortality rate will often point to inadequacies in a range of social and economic services and to higher levels of poverty and economic hardship.

Key terms

Morbidity rate This refers to the number of people who have a particular illness during a given period, normally a year.

Disease prevalence The total number of cases of a specific disease in a population during a specified period of time.

Disease incidence The number of new cases of a specific disease occurring in a population during a specified period of time.

Infant mortality rate The number of deaths occurring to infants under one year old per thousand live births.

Key terms

Mortality rate The number of people who have died in the population in a given year. The crude death rate is expressed as the number of deaths in a year per thousand of the population.

Mortality rates are collected from the official and required registration of deaths, and the cause of death from the legally required death certificates. Morbidity rates are drawn from official data including GP and hospital appointments, hospital admissions and the registration of notifiable diseases. There have also been more general studies that measure levels of ill health i.e. they are not related to a specific condition; they use self-reported measures of health which ask people to describe or rank on a scale of 1 to10 how healthy they feel.

Can we rely on the statistics?

When referring to statistics and using them in your work, it is always important to quote the source of the data. Were they collected by a particular group in order to persuade and gather support? Should you consult data from an organisation with an opposing view? Was the information published in a newspaper to satisfy the views and prejudices of their readers? Does the newspaper support a particular political party? Statistics must be used with care!

Reflect

Can you think of an organisation which might present statistical information in a way that will support its cause rather than presenting the information objectively? What statistical picture would it want to portray?

Further, statistics gathered from official sources may not accurately reflect the 'true' situation; they may not provide an accurate picture of patterns of health and illness. For example, some people who are ill may not go to the doctor and conversely some people who visit the doctor may not really be ill.

Doctors presented with similar symptoms may suggest a different diagnosis. For example, a patient describing persistent fatigue and no interest in life or no energy may be described by one doctor as depressed while another doctor may diagnose ME or post-viral fatigue syndrome – another doctor might decide that they are

a malingerer who simply does not want to go to work. This would certainly distort the official figures of the number of people with a specific illness.

Ken Browne (2006) provided a useful framework to explain this:

'For people to be labelled "sick" – and to be recorded as a health statistic – there are at least four stages involved:

Stage 1: Individuals must first realise that they have a problem.

Stage 2: They must then define their problem as serious enough to go to the doctor.

Stage 3: They must then actually go to the doctor.

Stage 4: The doctor must then be persuaded that they have a medical or mental condition capable of being labelled as an illness requiring treatment.'

Reflect

Consider the factors that may affect the decisions members of your family take about whether to go to the doctor. Are there differences to be seen? What are they?

Similarly the reasons for death (as recorded on death certificates) may not always be accurate or reflect the 'real' causes of death. The cause of death of a street person dying in freezing conditions may be stated as 'hypothermia' but it could be argued that the 'real' cause of death was years of malnutrition, substance abuse and inadequate or no housing. A person with AIDS may die of liver failure but it is likely that it is AIDS that has given rise to this condition. The cause of death recorded on the death certificate will depend on the doctor's interpretation of the symptoms. On occasion the doctor may record a condition that is one of a number of contributory reasons, but they choose the one that will cause least distress to the relatives of the deceased. Statistics drawn from death certificates need to be used with care and an understanding of their limitations.

Social class and patterns of health and illness

Despite the caution with which official statistics must be treated, there is overwhelming evidence that standards of health, the incidence of ill health or morbidity and life expectancy vary according to social group in our society and especially to social class. Members of the higher social classes are living longer and enjoying better health than members of the lower social groups. The most influential modern studies that consider the reasons for this difference are *The Black Report* (Townsend et al, 1980) followed by *The Acheson Report* (1998). They provide detailed and comprehensive explanations of the relationships between social and environmental factors and health, illness and life expectancy.

The findings of *The Black Report* were so significant and serious in exposing the vast differences in the levels of health and illness between different social classes that the government of the time suppressed its publication. A small number of duplicated copies were circulated and made available just before an August bank holiday weekend when they would expect to get very little press coverage. However, this study has been extremely influential and the categories of explanations offered are still used by sociologists today when examining and considering these issues.

The Black Report considered four types of explanation that might account for the differences in levels of illness and life expectancy experienced by different social classes. The researchers were persuaded that the differences in health and well-being were an effect of the level of people's income, the quality of their housing and the environment in which they lived and worked.

The four possible sociological explanations were:

1 the statistical artefact explanation
2 natural or social selection
3 cultural or behavioural explanations
4 material or structural explanations.

■ The statistical artefact explanation

Here the researchers working on *The Black Report* suggested that the differences could be explained by the fact that the statistics themselves produced a biased picture – that of all those people in the lowest social classes, there was a higher proportion of older people and people working in traditional and more dangerous industries and so it would be expected that they had higher levels of illness than the more prosperous, younger people working in offices, call centres and other service industries. This explanation would suggest that it is not really social class but the age structure and patterns of employment of people in the lowest social classes that really explain the differences. More recent studies have shown that even when the researchers account for this bias in employment and age, they still find a link between low social class and high levels of illness, and lower life expectancy.

People's lifestyle choices, such as the amount of exercise they take, can have a dramatic impact on their health

Natural or social selection

This explanation suggests that it is not low social class and the associated low wages, poverty and poorer housing that *cause* illness, higher levels of infant mortality rates and lower life expectancy for adults – it is in fact the other way round. People are in the lower classes *because* of their poor health, absenteeism and lack of energy needed for success and promotion. This explanation has been rejected by sociologists because there is evidence to show that ill health is caused *by* the deprived circumstances rather than causing it.

Cultural or behavioural explanations

This explanation focuses on the behaviour and lifestyle choices of people in the lower social classes. There was evidence that people in the lower social classes smoked more, drank more heavily, were more likely to eat junk food and take insufficient exercise. The poor lifestyle choices were linked to a range of chronic illnesses including heart disease, some forms of cancer, bronchitis and diabetes. However, for many in economically deprived circumstances, smoking and alcohol, sadly, help them to cope with their difficult circumstances. It is their difficult circumstances that lead to their lifestyle choices – not the other way round.

Material or structural explanations

Material explanations claim that those social groups for whom life expectancy is shorter, and for whom infant mortality rates are higher, suffer poorer health than other groups because of inequalities in wealth and income. Poverty and persistently low incomes are associated with poorer diets, poor housing in poor environments, and more dangerous and insecure employment. It is these inequalities and the associated deprivation that lead to the differences in health and well-being – an explanation that can be traced back to the work of Marx and Engels in the nineteenth century. The writers of *The Black Report* (Townsend et al) presented very persuasive evidence to support the materialist explanation. Shaw et al (1999) completed a major review of all the research in this area and concluded that the major factors that contributed to these differences in health and illness were social factors. Put simply, a consequence of poverty in a community is poor health and lower life expectancy.

Although the life expectancy for women is higher than that of men, with women in our society typically living some five years longer than men and with the infant mortality rates for boys being persistently higher than those for baby girls, studies consistently report higher levels of illness for women than for men. The social factors that contribute to these differences can be identified as:

- the risk factors
- economic inequalities
- the impact of the female role, especially in the family.

Risk factors

The higher death rate of men can be linked with the higher levels of cigarette smoking and drinking by men, and their participation in more risky and dangerous sports and other activities. The relatively high death rate

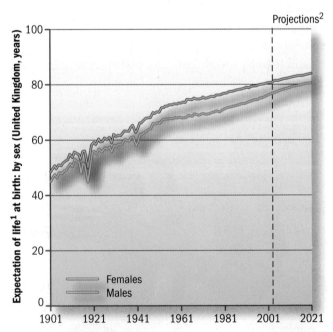

1 Expectation of life. The average number of years a new-born baby would survive if he or she experienced age-specific mortality rates for that time period throughout his or her life.
2 2004-based projections for 2005 to 2021.

Source: *Government Actuary's Department*

 Figure 7.6 Expectation of life at birth by sex, *Social Trends* **(2006)**

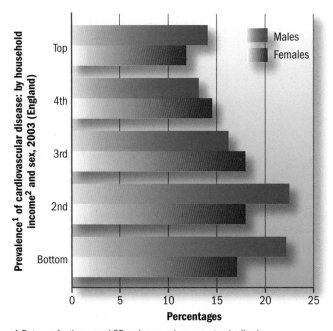

1 Data are for those aged 35 and over and are age-standardised.
2 Equivalised household income is a measure of household income that takes account of the number of persons in the household. Equivalised gross income has been used for ranking the household.

Source: *Health Survey for England, Department of Health*

 Figure 7.7 Prevalence of cardiovascular disease by household income and sex, *Social Trends* (2006)

of young men between 17 and 24 is specifically linked with this risk-taking and the associated deaths from road accidents.

■ Economic inequalities

Despite changes in the law, women still earn less than men. According to the Equal Opportunities Commission (2005) 'Almost 30 years after the Equal Pay Act made it illegal to pay women less for doing the same job, a pay gap of 18 per cent still exists between women and men working full-time.' A higher proportion of women than men are in low-paid part-time work, they are far more likely to be the main carer in a lone-parent family and are more likely to be on state means-tested benefits. In older age they are more likely to be in poverty because they are less likely to have employer's pensions and may not, because of family responsibilities, have a full state pension either. As we have discussed earlier in the unit there are clear and direct links between poverty and poor health.

■ The female role

Women still take the responsibility for the housework in most homes. The higher incidence of depression may be linked with the dull repetitive nature of the work. Popay and Bartley (1998), studying the hours spent on domestic labour in 1700 households in London, found that women spent up to 87 hours per week on housework and that women with children spent 64 hours per week even if they had a full-time job. Often women will be managing on a limited budget, working long hours and have little time to themselves. However, it may be that the higher rates of diagnosed stress-related illness for women are due to the willingness of women to discuss mental health issues with their doctor rather than there actually being a higher rate of stress-related illnesses.

Ethnicity and patterns of health and illness

Evidence for a link between race or ethnicity and illness is difficult to systematically study because there are difficulties of definition. In addition, a high proportion of people from minority ethnic groups live in areas of deprivation in inner city areas with associated poor housing, pollution and relatively high unemployment – it is therefore difficult to know whether the poorer health is due to poverty or ethnicity. Nevertheless, compared to the white majority ethnic group, there is evidence that:

- there is a higher incidence of rickets in children from the Asian sub-continent because of a deficiency of vitamin D in their diet
- most minority ethnic groups have a shorter life expectancy
- most minority ethnic groups have higher infant mortality rates.

In addition to the health implications of higher levels of poverty, there are issues of access to the health services. Language and other cultural barriers may limit full use of the health services. Asian women are often reluctant to see a male doctor, many of them speak little English and, despite improvements, translators are in short supply and much important information is not translated into minority languages. In addition, racism, or the fear of racism, is stressful. Unless health and care

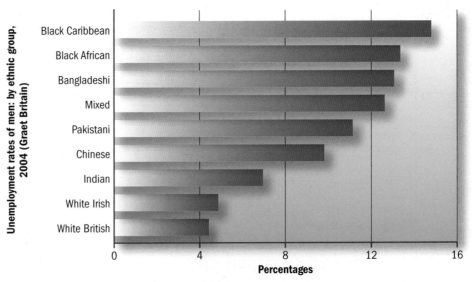

Source: *Annual Population Survey, Office for National Statistics*

workers understand the religious and cultural beliefs and practices of minority ethnic groups, their care needs are unlikely to be fully met, leaving them vulnerable to higher levels of ill health.

Age and patterns of health and illness

Many people over retirement age are fit, healthy and making valued contributions to our society through paid work, voluntary activities and playing important roles in the care and support of their families. In fact, the 2001 census revealed that 342,032 people aged 65 and over provided 50 hours or more unpaid care per week. However, it is also true that there are higher levels of illness amongst the older population and particularly those people over the age of 75. In 2003, 60 per cent of people aged 65–74 and 64 per cent of people aged 75 and over reported a long-standing illness (General Household Survey 2003). The Alzheimer's Society in 2007 estimates that there are currently over 750,000 people in the UK with dementia, of which only 18,000 are aged under 65, and that one in 20 people over 65 and one in five people over the age of 80 suffer from dementia. In addition, during a three-month period in 2003, 24 per cent of people over the age of 75 had attended the casualty or out-patient department of a

hospital, compared with 14 per cent of people of all ages (General Household Survey 2003).

Local patterns in health and illness

There are regional variations in patterns of health and illness. Mortality and morbidity rates vary in different parts of the country and also within towns and cities in the UK. It is probably no surprise to learn that it is in the poorer regions and the poorer parts of cities that higher levels of illness are recorded.

For example, research has shown that there are regional trends in the incidence of lung cancer across the UK. Within England the rates for lung cancer are higher than average in the north-west, northern and Yorkshire regions and below average in the south-western, southern and eastern regions.

Reflect

Can you think of reasons why these regional differences in health and well-being might exist?

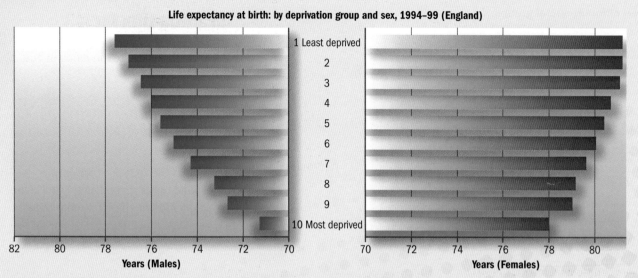

Life expectancy at birth: by deprivation group and sex, 1994–99 (England)

1 Least deprived
2
3
4
5
6
7
8
9
10 Most deprived

Years (Males)
Years (Females)

Source: *Health Survey for England, Department of Health; Census 1991, Office for National Statistics; Small Area Health Statistics Unit, Imperial College*

▲ Figure 7.9 Life expectancy at birth by deprivation group and sex, *Social Trends* (2006)

1 Describe the rates of life expectancy in the table above.

2 Explain, using sociological explanations, the possible reasons for the patterns of life expectancy illustrated.

3 Evaluate the usefulness of the four sociological explanations of *The Black Report* in explaining the pattern in life expectancy in the table.

Assessment activity 7.5

Compare the patterns and trends of health and illness in three different social groups.

1   Using statistical data from a range of sources, compare the patterns and trends of health and illness in three different social groups.

Grading tip for P5

You can look at different groups according to:

- social class
- gender
- ethnicity
- age
- geographical location.

Use sociological explanations for health inequalities to explain the patterns and trends of health and illness in three different social groups.

2   Use sociological explanations for health inequalities to explain the patterns for the groups that you have chosen. **M3**

Grading tips for M3

This should include the four explanations in *The Black Report*:

- statistical artefact
- natural or social selection
- cultural or behavioural
- material or structural.

The consideration of the four sociological explanations should be described clearly but quite briefly. Each explanation need be no more than 100 words.

Evaluate the four sociological explanations for health inequalities in terms of explaining the patterns and trends of health and illness in three different social groups.

3   Evaluate the four sociological explanations for health inequalities in terms of explaining the patterns in the three groups that you have chosen. **D2**

Grading tip for D2

The evaluation involves reviewing the evidence for the different explanations and forming a conclusion based on the strengths and weaknesses of their cases.

Knowledge check

Ruth and Mohammed live in London with their baby son Joshua. Ruth was brought up in the north of England and met Mohammed at school. He was from a strict Muslim family. His parents were originally from Pakistan. Ruth and Mohammed work full-time for a local IT firm and Joshua attends a local nursery. They say that they are in good health, although Ruth recently had flu but she hasn't been to the doctor.

Ruth's parents, Eve and Chris, are not well. Eve has bad arthritis and now uses a wheelchair when shopping. Chris has been diagnosed with lung cancer. They are on a low income and need help at home.

1 Define the terms:

- socialisation
- culture
- norms
- values
- roles
- deviance.

2 In a short paragraph, explain how these terms may be used to describe how Ruth and Mohammed's life experiences may have differed when they were children.

3 Briefly describe (in no more than 100 words) the sociological perspectives of functionalism and Marxism. How would a Marxist sociologist describe Ruth and Mohammed's position in the IT company?

4 Briefly describe the sociological perspectives of the New Right and collectivism and explain how Ruth's parents' health and care needs would be met by each approach.

5 Describe and explain the following concepts of health:

- negative concept
- positive concept
- holistic concept
- World Health Organisation definition of health.

6 Explain how a description of the health of Ruth and her family would differ using:

- a negative concept of health, and
- a positive concept of health.

7 Define the biomedical model of health and the socio-medical model of health.

8 Use the biomedical model of health to describe the health and well-being of Ruth and her family.

9 Identify the advantages and disadvantages of using the biomedical model.

10 Explain the sick role as it is used in the sociology of health and illness. How might this concept have been applied to Ruth's circumstances when she had flu?

11 Explain the term 'disability'. What is meant by the idea of the 'disabling environment'? Describe how, with the deterioration in their health, Eve and Chris may discover aspects of a disabling environment.

12 Identify and give examples of three main sources of statistical information about trends in health and illness.

13 What is meant by the clinical iceberg? Why could Ruth be said to be evidence for the existence of a clinical iceberg?

14 Discuss two other reasons why statistical evidence for trends in health and illness may be unreliable.

15 There is overwhelming evidence that standards of health and well-being vary by social group. Identify five social groups that have higher levels of illness than the population as a whole. Do Ruth and her family belong to any of these groups?

16 Discuss the evidence for the higher levels of illness for three of the groups that you have identified.

Preparation for assessment

1 Knowledge of the sociological terms introduced at the beginning of the unit (for example, socialisation, culture, social class, gender and ethnicity) is not assessed in isolation but in the context of sociological perspectives and the application of sociology to health and social care provision and practice. **P1**

2 When you are describing the different concepts of health, use examples to illustrate the definitions. The illustrations will bring the concepts to life and show that you are able to relate them to health and social care practice. Use examples from your own experience or from your work placement. **P2**

3 When approaching these tasks, summarise clearly in your own words the sociological approaches that you have selected and then for each one make the link with the concepts of health. **M1**

4 To achieve P3 and M2 you are required to describe and explain the biomedical and socio-medical models of health. Explanations require more detail than a definition or a description. In this case, the grades can be achieved by using appropriate examples to illustrate the concepts introduced. You could also consider how the approaches may be linked with the sociological perspectives introduced earlier in the unit. **P3** and **M2**

5 To achieve a distinction grade for D1 an evaluation is required, which involves considering the strengths and weaknesses of the two models in discussions of health and well-being. You may in your conclusion consider whether they *are* competing and opposite approaches. Consider the importance of both the quality of individual care and medical research in improving health and well-being and also the evidence that links environmental and social conditions to levels of health and well-being. It may be that both are

essential if we are to effectively address the health and care needs of our society. **D1**

6 When describing the concepts of ill health for P4, this unit provides one or two simple examples as illustrations. For example, to illustrate the idea of iatrogenesis, MRSA could be used as an example of illness developed in the context of medical intervention. **P4**

7 For P5, draw on up-to-date research on the three groups that you chose. You may find government statistics helpful, for example, *Social Trends* or www.statistics.gov.uk. Websites from relevant interest groups can be very informative. Age Concern, for example, have a very good and detailed website (www.ace.org.uk). Shelter have information on homelessness and poverty and its impact on health and well-being on www.shelter.org.uk. The Kings Fund (www.kingsfund.org.uk) is an independent organisation which researches health and social care issues. Newspapers, such as *The Guardian* through Guardian Unlimited, have a wealth of information on trends in health and illness by social group. **P5**

8 For M3, the sociological explanations outlined in *The Black Report* should be described clearly but quite briefly. You should give clear explanations of how the four approaches in the report apply to your chosen social groups. **M3**

9 For D2, you may present the evaluation in separate paragraphs, one for each of the four sociological explanations, reviewing the evidence as it applies to the groups you have chosen. A final paragraph should present your conclusion. For example, are the explanations helpful in explaining the differences? Is one explanation stronger than the others? You will need to give reasons to support your conclusions. **D2**

Resources and further reading

Abbot, P., Wallace, C. (1997) *An Introduction to Sociology: Feminist Perspectives,* second ed. London: Routledge

Acheson, D. (1998) *Independent Inquiry into Inequalities in Health* London: HMSO

Blaxter, M. (1990) *Health and Lifestyles* London: Routledge

Browne, B. (2006) *Introducing Sociology for AS Level* Cambridge: Polity Press

Doyal, L. (1995) *What Makes Women Sick?* London: Macmillan

Engels, F. (1845) *The Conditions of the Working Class in England* London: Panther Books

Illich, I. (1976) *Limits to Medicine* Marion Boyars: London

Murdock, G.P. (1949) *Social Structure* New York: Macmillan

Oliver, M. (1990) *The Politics of Disablement* London: Macmillan

Parsons, T. (1951) *The Social System* New York: The Free Press

Popay, J., Bartley, M. (1998) 'Conditions of labour and women's health', in C. Martin and D. McQueen *Readings for a New Public Health* Edinburgh: Edinburgh University Press

Shakespeare, T. (1998) *The Disability Reader: Social Science Perspectives* London: Casssell

Shaw, M., Dorling, G., Davey, G. (1999) *The Widening Gap* Bristol: Policy Press

Singh, J.A., Zingg R.N, (1942) *Wolf-children and the Feral Man* New York: Harper

Social Trends, Vol. 36 (2006) London: HMSO

Townrow, C., Yates, G. (1990) *Sociology for GCSE* Harlow: Longman

Townsend, P., Davidson, N., Whitehead, M. (1980) *Inequalities in Health: The Black Report* Harmondsworth: Penguin

World Health Organisation (1974) *Alma-Ata Declaration*

Useful websites

Age Concern:
www.ace.org.uk

disabilitynet:
www.disabilitynet.co.uk

Equal Opportunities Commission
www.eoc.org.uk

King's Fund:
www.kingsfund.org.uk

MIND:
www.mind.org.uk

National Statistics:
www.statistics.gov.uk

Shelter:
www.shelter.org.uk

YOUNG MINDS:
www.youngminds.org.uk

Grading criteria

To achieve a pass grade the evidence must show that the learner is able to:	To achieve a merit grade the evidence must show that, in addition to the pass criteria, the learner is able to:	To achieve a distinction grade the evidence must show that, in addition to the pass and merit criteria, the learner is able to:
P1 use sociological terminology to describe the principal sociological perspectives **Assessment activity 7.1 page 350**		
P2 describe different concepts of health **Assessment activity 7.2 page 353**	**M1** use two sociological perspectives to explain different concepts of health **Assessment activity 7.2 page 353**	
P3 describe the biomedical and socio-medical models of health **Assessment activity 7.3 page 356**	**M2** explain the biomedical and socio-medical models of health **Assessment activity 7.3 page 356**	**D1** evaluate the biomedical and socio-medical models of health **Assessment activity 7.3 page 356**
P4 describe different concepts of ill health **Assessment activity 7.4 page 358**		
P5 compare patterns and trends of health and illness in three different social groups. **Assessment activity 7.5 page 366**	**M3** use sociological explanations for health inequalities to explain the patterns and trends of health and illness in three different social groups. **Assessment activity 7.5 page 366**	**D2** evaluate the four sociological explanations for health inequalities in terms of explaining the patterns and trends of health and illness in three different social groups. **Assessment activity 7.5 page 366**

Psychological perspectives

Introduction

Psychological perspectives are ways of investigating and understanding human behaviour. Each perspective, or approach, has a different understanding of why we behave the way we do, what the influences are on our behaviour and how we can understand human growth and development. The different approaches apply understanding to human behaviour according to their underlying beliefs. For example, a biological psychologist might see challenging behaviour as resulting from an imbalance in brain chemicals, which needs to be addressed by identifying the imbalance and treating it with chemical methods (for example, using Ritalin to treat Attention Deficit Hyperactivity Disorder). By contrast, a psychologist working within the social learning theory approach would see this behaviour as resulting from past learning experiences, perhaps connected to having seen others being rewarded from an early age for challenging behaviour. They would try to change this behaviour by identifying triggers and encouraging those dealing with the individual to avoid responding to negative behaviour but giving plenty of praise and encouragement for more positive behaviour. All approaches have their strengths and weaknesses and, in practice, most practitioners use a mixture of two or more (this is called an eclectic approach).

How you will be assessed

This unit is internally assessed by your tutor. It includes a variety of exercises, case studies and other materials to help you prepare for this assessment.

After completing this unit you should be able to achieve the following outcomes:

- Understand psychological approaches to study
- Be able to apply psychological approaches to health and social care.

Thinking points

Have you ever woken up feeling a bit down? Your mum asks you to tidy your room and you snap at her, 'Why are you always nagging me?' You then find your bike has a puncture so you will have to catch the bus. When you ask your mum for the bus fare she snaps at you and you have a blazing row. You arrive at college feeling hot, stressed and anxious. When you get there your tutor is annoyed with you for being late. You respond angrily and get told off again! This is an example of the self-fulfilling prophecy, a psychological theory which states that how we feel about ourselves affects how we behave towards others which in turn affects how they behave towards us.

This unit will take you through some key psychological theories about human behaviour which will give you a deeper insight into both your own behaviour and the behaviour of others you will encounter (clients, patients, colleagues, team leaders, supervisors etc). This knowledge will help you to become an effective practitioner.

The behaviourist approach

This approach seeks to understand human behaviour in terms of what has been learnt. So if, for example, an individual persistently behaves in a very dependent and clingy way, it would be assumed that they have at some point learnt to behave in this way. If, on the other hand, they are easily aroused to aggression, tend to be hostile and fly off the handle at the slightest thing, this would also be believed by the behaviourist approach to represent learnt behaviour.

The behaviourist approach seeks to understand all behaviour as being the result of either classical conditioning or operant conditioning. Although these two theories of learning believe that different processes are involved, they both explain all types of behaviour as being the result of learning – everything from shyness to aggression, from happiness to depression. This is quite different from, say, the psychodynamic or biological approaches which are explored later in this unit.

Classical conditioning

The first theory of learning we shall investigate is called classical conditioning. This theory was developed by a Russian physiologist called Ivan Pavlov. He was working with dogs to investigate their digestive systems. The dogs were attached to a harness, as shown below, and Pavlov attached monitors to their stomachs and mouths so he could measure the rate of salivation (production of saliva).

He noticed one day that a dog began to salivate when the laboratory assistant entered the room with a bowl of food, but before it had actually tasted the food. Since salivation is a reflexive response which until then was thought to be produced only as a result of food touching the tongue, this seemed an unusual phenomenon. Pavlov speculated that the dog was salivating because it had learnt to associate the entrance of the laboratory assistant with food. He then developed his theory in the following way.

Food automatically led to the response of salivation. Since salivation is an automatic, not learnt, response he called this an **unconditioned response** (UR). Unconditioned means unlearnt. Since food automatically leads to this response he called this an

Key terms

Unconditioned response An instinctive response that is evoked by the presentation of a stimulus (for example, the startle reflex in response to a door banging).

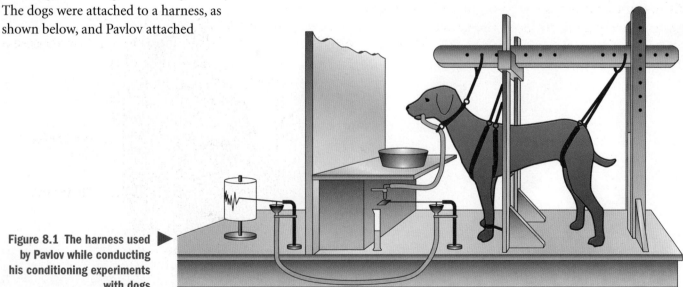

Figure 8.1 The harness used by Pavlov while conducting his conditioning experiments with dogs

unconditioned stimulus. Pavlov then presented food at the same time as ringing a bell, to see if the dog would associate the bell with food – the bell acted as a **conditioned stimulus** (CR). Over several trials the dog learnt that the bell was associated with food and eventually it began to salivate when only the bell was rung and no food was presented. It had thus learnt the **conditioned response** (CR) of salivation to the conditioned stimulus of the bell.

Key terms

Unconditioned stimulus A naturally occurring event in the environment which provokes a response (for example, a door banging).

Conditioned stimulus A new, neutral stimulus that has been paired with the unconditioned stimulus and can be substituted for this.

Conditioned response A learnt response to the new, conditioned stimulus.

Operant conditioning

This type of learning is associated with the theories of Burrhus Frederic Skinner. (For a fuller description of the work of Skinner and other behaviourists, see *Learning and Behaviour* by L. Barker – see page 405 for details.) Skinner was an American psychologist working, mostly with rats and pigeons, to discover some of the key principles of learning new behaviours. He used a very famous device called a Skinner box.

The box contains a lever which, when pressed, allows a food pellet to be released into the box. When the rat is first placed in the box it will run around, sniff the various items and at some point it will accidentally press the lever, at which point a food pellet will be released. After a period of time, when the rat has repeatedly performed this action, it will learn that pressing the lever is followed by the release of a food pellet. Because the pellet is experienced as *reinforcing* (something the rat would like to have more of), this consequence increases the probability of the behaviour (lever-pressing) being repeated. There are two types of reinforcement: positive and negative.

- *Positive reinforcement* happens when the consequence following a particular behaviour is experienced as desirable.
- *Negative reinforcement* happens when behaviour results in a consequence that removes something unpleasant.

Skinner investigated this by putting a very small electrical current onto the floor of the Skinner box. The current could be de-activated if the rat pressed the lever. The behaviour of lever pressing was thus negatively reinforcing. For people, this can be demonstrated in the example of using pain relief. For example, if you have a headache and you take a painkiller, which results in the headache going away, you are negatively reinforced for taking a painkiller.

Punishment occurs when behaviour is followed by a consequence that is experienced as aversive. Skinner

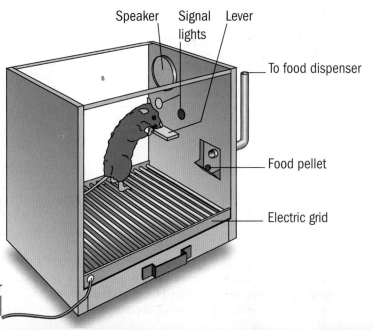

Figure 8.2 A rat in a typical ▶ Skinner box

investigated this by giving a small electric shock to the rat when it pressed the lever. The consequence of lever pressing (the electric shock) was experienced as unpleasant, so the rat learnt to stop pressing the lever.

Application of behaviourist principles to health and social care practice

We can apply the principles of classical conditioning to everyday life in a very practical way. This is a very good theory for explaining fears and phobias. A stimulus that is not in any way threatening (for example, smelling a particular type of perfume or listening to an advertisement jingle) is paired with an event that leads to an extremely unpleasant fear or aversion response. Let's say the event is choking on a sweet so severely that you nearly die at the time you are smelling the perfume. The next time you smell that particular perfume, the original fear response will be re-activated. You will then have learnt to be afraid of a particular type of perfume!

A method of treating acquired fears is known as systematic desensitisation. This involves first creating a hierarchy of 'fear'. Supposing the feared object is hospitals. The individual would create a list of aspects associated with going to hospital. It might look something like this:

Systematic desensitisation: creating a hierarchy of fear	
Most feared:	The procedure itself
	Smells associated with hospital
	People in green gowns
	Hospital equipment and machinery
	Hospital wards
	Taking a lift to a ward
	Walking into the building
	Driving to the building
Least feared:	Receiving an appointment card

Table 8.1 The patient enters a state of deep relaxation and confronts each of these items, moving from the bottom of the list to the top, until none of them causes any anxiety

The basic principle of this procedure is to help the patient achieve a state of very deep relaxation on the basis that relaxation and anxiety are incompatible. The aim is to replace the anxiety and fear with a state of calm and relaxation. An image of the least feared object or situation is then shown to them and they are encouraged to relax until they are able to view this without fear or anxiety. This may take more than one session. When this level of fear has been satisfactorily overcome, the patient moves to the object or situation at the next level, again working on relaxing until they are able to contemplate the object or situation without a trace of anxiety. Over a period of time the procedure is repeated until the final, most fear-invoking, object or situation can be faced without worry. With some treatments, the patient is encouraged to practise some of the lower level fear-invoking situations (for example, opening an envelope containing an appointment card or driving as close to the hospital as is tolerable without arousing too much anxiety).

Just as we can learn inappropriate or unhelpful behaviours, so we can use the principles of operant conditioning to create new, more helpful, behaviours and eliminate the unhelpful ones. Using the principles of reinforcement and punishment is a very powerful way to change someone's behaviour: this is sometimes called behaviour modification. With autistic children, for example, the use of reinforcement can encourage the use of eye contact. Parenting courses cover these principles extensively, as shown in the case study opposite.

Remember!

Classical conditioning involves associating two events at an automatic, physiological level. Operant conditioning is concerned with an awareness that a particular behaviour leads to a consequence that is perceived as either reinforcing or punishing.

In context

Alexis is 5 years old and has one older and 2 younger siblings. His mum, Rosanna, is a single parent who is stressed and busy and he gets hardly any attention. When he hits his younger brother, his mother tells him off but it doesn't seem to affect his behaviour: if anything it makes it worse. He is beginning to show this behaviour at school and with his playmates. Rosanna has received a phone call from the school stating that Alexis is likely to be excluded if his behaviour doesn't improve.

Rosanna speaks to her health visitor who gives her the following advice.

- Put a star chart up on the fridge door so that every time Alexis does something positive he gets a star. Praise all the positive behaviour that Alexis shows (however small). This is positive reinforcement and Alexis will begin to repeat these positive behaviours until they become more frequent.
- If Alexis shows irritating, attention-seeking behaviours, ignore them (as long as they are not dangerous). Praise his little brother for appropriate behaviour, and Alexis will soon start to imitate

this, because he wants a star for his own 'good' behaviour.

- Explain to Alexis which behaviours are inappropriate (specifically, hitting his younger brother). Tell him that he will have to spend 1 to 2 minutes on the 'naughty step' (for example, the bottom stair) if he does this.
- Before long, Alexis will be eager to perform the appropriate behaviour that you want to see more of, and less likely to perform the inappropriate behaviour of hitting his younger brother. Over time, you can solve the problem of Alexis's behaviour.

1 **Explain how a star chart can act as positive reinforcement for Alexis.**

2 **Getting Alexis to sit on the 'naughty step' if he hits his brother is an example of punishment. Suggest why it is important to explain to a child of this age just why punishment is necessary.**

3 **Write a short leaflet of guidance to parents or carers on how to use these principles to encourage a child to sit at the table at meal times.**

Assessment activity 8.1

Describe the application of behaviourist perspectives in health and social care.

1 Describe how the principles of operant conditioning could explain why a child has persistent tantrums.

2 Describe how the principles of classical conditioning can explain why a patient is petrified of having injections.

P1

Grading tip for P1

To meet this criterion, you need to *describe* how the theories of classical conditioning or operant conditioning can be applied in health and social care practice. An effective way to do this is by applying the concepts associated with classical conditioning and/or operant conditioning to explaining behaviour. This is what the assessment activity described requires you to do.

The social learning approach

Albert Bandura was an American psychologist who developed social learning theory which recognises that we can learn by observing others: we do not have to be directly reinforced or punished to learn new behaviour. Bandura explained that behaviour can be learnt according to the following principles. He called this kind of learning **observational learning**. The person being observed is called a **model**, and imitating the behaviour of a model is known as **modelling**. For learning to take place the factors outlined below need to exist.

- **Availability** – the behaviour to be learnt must be *available* (i.e. performed somewhere for the individual to see). This may be on television or a computer game or observing a peer or family member performing it.
- **Attention** – we must notice the behaviour or we will not be able to learn it. (You may sometimes find that if you are tired or unwell you don't pay full attention to a procedure you see being performed. This lack of attention will affect the next step in the learning process – you probably won't remember the procedure!). The amount of attention we pay is influenced by the characteristics of the model. If the model is attractive, prestigious (has high status or appeal, such as a model or famous footballer) or powerful (such as a prime minister) we are more likely to pay attention than if the model is unattractive, of low status and with little power (for example, our younger brother!).
- **Retention** – the behaviour must be *retained* (i.e. the individual must be old enough or interested enough to be capable of keeping information about this behaviour in their memory).
- **Reproduction** – the individual must be capable of actually performing the behaviour (so we may watch someone else perform a particular dance step, retain a memory of this but not actually be able to reproduce the step because we lack the skills).
- **Motivation** – the new behaviour may now have been learnt and the individual be perfectly capable of performing it, but whether or not they do so depends on whether they are motivated to copy the behaviour.

Key terms

Observational learning A type of learning that involves watching someone else perform a behaviour. This new behaviour (such as smoking, drinking, wearing a cycle helmet) can be learnt but does not have to be reproduced unless the individual is motivated to actually perform the behaviour.

Model An individual who has characteristics which inspire us (for example, because they are prestigious, attractive, of high status etc) to copy the behaviour.

Modelling The process of basing behaviour, attitude, style of speech or dress on someone we admire or want to be like.

▼ Children may imitate the behaviour of a role model such as a parent

BTEC National | Health & Social Care | Book 1

Latent learning

The learning described up to this point is called **latent learning**. This means that learning has taken place and is stored in the memory, but the learnt behaviour may not be performed until the time is right. The individual has learnt a new behaviour or set of behaviours simply through observing someone else. Bandura's ideas about latent learning are very important as they can explain behaviour that may seem to come from nowhere. The case study on page 380 illustrates how behaviour that a young child learns during childhood can be brought to life later on in adulthood.

Latent learning A type of learning of a new behaviour which may lie dormant until the individual is motivated to perform the behaviour (for example, performing breast examination).

Reflect

Think about your own experience of copying someone else's behaviour. In your early adolescence you may have been influenced to dress in a particular way or adopt a particular manner of speech because you saw someone you admired doing this and being reinforced for it (perhaps by being popular).

Now think about someone you have worked with and admired during a work experience placement. Did they have ways of doing things, ways of talking or moving or presenting themselves that you admired? We often learn skills of professionalism by observing how other, skilled practitioners do things. Use the concepts of observational learning to reflect on what you have learnt from observing other people.

The effects of observing others

So far we have seen how social learning theory can explain ways in which we can learn and perform behaviour from observing others. You will find that others also learn from observing you! You are a role model to others; especially people who look up to you because they are younger than you or less powerful than you or who admire you for qualities you possess. It is important to remember that the way we behave influences the way other people respond to us. If you are calm, patient and dignified when dealing with a difficult client you will find that the situation is much more likely to be resolved effectively than if you get cross and angry and flustered.

The self-fulfilling prophecy

This two-way interaction between how we behave and how others perceive us and behave towards us has consequences for future behaviour and expectations. This is called the self-fulfilling prophecy. Imagine a family where all the children go to the same school. The eldest and second child, Ben and Lewis, are badly behaved and develop a reputation as 'troublemakers'. As a new Y7 intake is being planned, a form tutor notices that a third member of the family, Frank, is joining the school. Such is the reputation of his older brothers that Frank is met on his first day with sarcasm. He is immediately placed at the front of the class and told not to put a foot wrong 'or else'. Frank responds to this with hostility, thus confirming his form tutor's expectations that he will be difficult. In the staffroom his form tutor comments that, just as she had expected, Frank is as bad as the others, if not worse. As he goes from lesson to lesson, his 'reputation' preceding him, Frank is treated as if he is a time bomb waiting to go off. Not surprisingly, Frank begins to play up and the self-fulfilling prophecy is well and truly confirmed!

Role theory

There is a similarity between role theory and the self-fulfilling prophecy in that this theory suggests that, because we live within a particular culture, society and social groups, we are influenced by other people. Part of this influence leads to us adopting certain roles and trying to live up to the expectations that go with this role. For example, a nurse is expected to be level-headed, warm and competent but whereas we might expect a surgeon to be similarly level-headed and competent, we would not necessarily expect warmth as a central part of this role. Since we all take on many different roles our behaviour will change according to the role we are currently in. A woman visiting the zoo with her children will take on the role of a mother; when she goes to work she may be a colleague, a supervisor or a subordinate and she will adopt the expectations of her job role. Later,

if she goes out to a party she may adopt the role of a friend.

Application of social learning principles to health and social care practice

The principles of observational learning can explain how people may acquire undesirable behaviours.

The importance of modelling has been well-utilised within health and social care. For example, Melamed et al (1983) found that children in hospital suffer reduced stress and recover better from surgery if the procedures they are about to undergo are modelled, for example using films or video tapes (cited in Sarafino, 1990, page 149). It may be that by watching such procedures they learn more about what they will experience than by simply listening to information. In public health advertising, the use of celebrities to model desirable behaviour has been effective. The images on page 381 shows how the power of celebrities can be harnessed to send an anti-smoking message to teenagers.

Reflect

Consider the roles you take on during the course of a week. What are the expectations others have of you when you take on a particular role, and are there informal rules that go with this (for example, how to behave, what to wear)?

In context

Shabhaz lives in a household where his father frequently gets drunk and abusive and hits his mother. Shabhaz sees this behaviour around him (availability), pays attention to this because the role model is particularly important (attention), retains it in his memory (retention) and has the capacity to reproduce the behaviour (motor reproduction). Whether or not he is motivated to do so is, however, a different story. Some of the factors that influence motivation include whether the model is reinforced or punished for the behaviour. If Shabhaz's father is seen to get his own way by behaving in this fashion, Shabhaz may store this information in his memory and later, when he is married, treat his wife in the same way (an example of latent learning). This is more likely to happen if

Shabhaz does not have an alternative model available to learn from: someone who is kind, gentle and respectful to his wife. If, on the other hand, his father gets arrested and imprisoned for beating his wife, Shabhaz will see that the model is punished and this may reduce the likelihood of him beating and abusing his wife when he himself gets married.

1 **Summarise the stages involved in observational learning.**

2 **Do you think that learning can explain why Shabhaz's father is himself violent and abusive?**

3 **Discuss the importance of teaching children who have witnessed this type of abuse alternative ways of dealing with anger or conflict.**

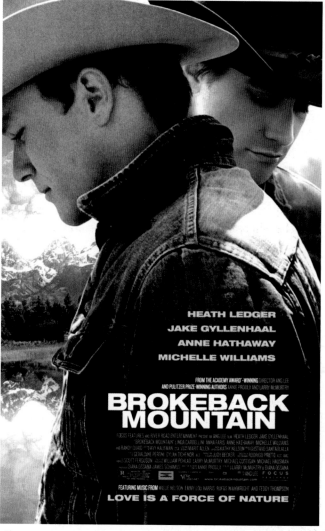

▲ Figure 8.3 The power of celebrities can send a message to teens on public health issues such as smoking

▲ Figure 8.4 The film *Brokeback Mountain* features young actors highlighting issues of prejudice and discrimination

Promotion of anti-discriminatory behaviours and practices

Since we tend to be influenced by the behaviour of others, the principles of social learning theory can be used to promote desirable behaviours. If we observe behaviour or attitudes being promoted by role models we perceive to be of high status we are more likely to pay attention to the message. In order to promote anti-discriminatory behaviours and practices, therefore, it is important that messages are put forward in a way that maximises attention. The film *Brokeback Mountain*, highlights the prejudice and discrimination which face gay men. The anti-discriminatory message conveyed by this moving and skilled film is much more powerful than a dozen government information leaflets could ever be! Such is the power of using models to promote messages.

The psychodynamic approach

This approach is associated with the Austrian psychologist Sigmund Freud, who developed the theory of psychodynamic psychology and the treatment known as psychoanalysis.

Sigmund Freud

Freud was one of the earliest thinkers to bring to public attention the idea that we are not always aware of all aspects of ourselves. He suggested that what we are aware of is represented in our conscious mind but that many of our memories, feelings and past experiences are locked up in a part of our mind he called the 'unconscious'. We cannot get access to the contents of our unconscious, but they do often 'leak out' in dreams and slips of the tongue. Freud believed that the conscious mind was like the tip of an iceberg, only a small part being available to awareness. The rest, well under the surface, consisted of the unconscious.

Freud suggested that the mind (which he called the **psyche**) is divided into three dynamic parts. The **id** is a part of the mind which is totally unconscious and which exists at birth. If you look at a tiny baby crying you will see that its entire body and as yet unformed personality is consumed by its rage/hurt/sadness/disappointment etc. The id is like that tiny baby even as we grow up. It is focused on getting what it wants and consists of aggressive, sexual and loving instincts. It is the part of us that says 'I want it now!' The **superego** is formed as a result of socialisation. It consists of all the instructions, morals and values that are repeatedly enforced as we are

Key terms

Psyche A structure of the mind consisting of three dynamic parts.

Id Part of the psyche which we are born with. It consists of all the raw emotions we are capable of feeling. The id operates on what is called the 'pleasure principle': it wants what it wants, when it wants it!

growing up. It takes on the form of a conscience and also represents our view of our ideal self. The main role of the superego is to try to subdue the activity of the id. The **ego** tries to balance the demands of the id and the superego. It is the rational part of the mind, always seeking to do what is most helpful for the individual. Different behaviours can be understood by trying to infer which part of the psyche is dominant at any time.

- A person who is very submissive, guilty and always wanting to please may have a very strong superego.
- A person who is impulsive, careless of other people's feelings, doesn't think through the consequences of their actions and is perhaps inclined to aggression, either verbal or physical, probably has a dominant id.
- A person who can be submissive and assertive when necessary, who is able to think about other people's feelings but also consider and value their own needs, has probably got a strong enough ego to balance the demands of the id and the superego. They are likely to have quite a rational and realistic outlook on life.

Key terms

Superego This aspect of the mind is roughly equivalent to a conscience. It consists of an internalisation of all the values and aspects of right and wrong we have been socialised to believe in. It also contains an image of our ideal self.

Ego This part of the mind develops at around the age of 3. Its function is to moderate the demands of the id, and prevent the superego being too harsh.

Freud believed that early childhood experiences linger on into adulthood. This is shown in the behaviours caused by the psyche, as described above. It is also shown in what he calls **ego defence mechanisms**. These form at any time in life when we experience something that is so traumatic or so difficult for us to deal with that we would be overwhelmed by anxiety if we were fully aware of the experience. The use of a defence mechanism allows us to block out these painful feelings. An example might be a child who witnesses the death of a parent in

Key terms

Ego defence mechanisms These are unconscious protective devices which prevent us from being overwhelmed by anxiety. If a traumatic event occurs before we are ready psychologically to deal with it we may use the ego defence mechanism of repression to push the event into our unconscious. The type of ego defence mechanism which is used tends to reflect the source of anxiety we are trying to avoid.

a car crash repressing knowledge of this event. Another example would be when we are aware of something we feel that is against all our principles, for example, an adult who has always been restrained and devoutly Christian feeling overwhelmingly attracted to his sister-in-law). These ego defences protect us from actually being aware of our feelings or the events that cause such pain. Examples of these are given below.

- **Repression** is a defence mechanism which causes the person to forget an event. A child whose parent was killed in a car crash may grow up with no memory of this event because they have simply pushed this into the unconscious and aren't aware of it at all.
- **Regression** is a defence mechanism involving the individual going back to ways of behaving that are associated with a safer, more carefree or happier time of life.
- **Denial** involves being apparently unaware of an event or emotion. The person is not pretending to others (lying) but is genuinely unaware of the event or feeling they are denying. It is too painful to acknowledge so they push all knowledge into their unconscious mind. Denial is quite commonly associated with traumatic loss.
- **Displacement** is when someone redirects repressed desires and impulses onto a relatively safe target. For example, someone comes home from work having wanted to strangle his boss, enters the house and yells at his young son for having left toys on the floor.
- **Sublimation** involves the process of transforming aggressive and sexual desires into some socially acceptable expression. For example, a young boy brought up to believe that any expression of anger or

hostility is unhealthy will avoid expressing hate and jealousy of his younger sister. He may channel this anger into the socially acceptable release of playing sport.

Freud developed a theory of personality development known as a psycho-sexual theory. This term refers to the explanation that, at different stages of development, the individual's libido (energy) is focused on a particular part of the body that is particularly relevant at that stage. If the needs of the developing child are met at each stage, it moves on to the next developmental stage. If, however, there is struggle or conflict or some unsatisfactory experience, the individual becomes 'fixated' (stuck) at this stage. This results in certain ways of being, or personality characteristics, which are carried through into adulthood and which can explain behaviour later in life.

The earliest stage is the oral stage. The focus here is on the mouth and activities such as sucking, biting, licking etc. (You will probably have seen that young babies seem to put everything to their mouth!) Freud believed that there could be two reasons for fixation. If the infant was weaned too early, it would feel forever under-gratified and unsatisfied and would develop into a pessimistic, sarcastic person. If, on the other hand, it was over-gratified (weaned too late) the individual would develop a gullible personality, naively trusting in others and with a tendency to 'swallow anything'. (The modern term, 'sucker' illustrates how Freud's views have entered our everyday understanding!) This stage lasts from birth to approximately eighteen months.

If the infant successfully passes through the oral stage without becoming fixated, the next stage is the anal stage which lasts from approximately 1½ to 3 years. Here the libido is focused on aspects to do with potty training. If there is a battle with parents about potty training, with the child feeling forced to use the potty before they are ready, or feeling over-controlled in a variety of areas, they may rebel by retaining their faeces: the child refuses to 'go' thus holding onto control and withholding satisfaction from the parent. This type of fixation is called anally-retentive and is associated with later personality characteristics of obstinacy, miserliness and obsessive traits. The alternative scenario is that the child is not given enough boundaries over potty training so they take excessive pleasure in excretion and become a messy, creative, disorganised sort of person.

▲ Figure 8.5 According to Freud, fixation at the anal stage results in one of two distinct personality types

During the ages 4–5 the child passes through the phallic stage. Fixation at this stage is associated with anxiety and guilty feelings about sex and fear of castration for males. If this stage is not resolved, the boy may become homosexual and the girl may become a lesbian. Freud thought these were abnormal fixations, although now we may consider them to be life choices.

Erik Erikson

Erik Erikson was a psychologist who agreed with much of Freud's theories in so far as he thought that we developed through a series of conflicts. However, he thought that these continued throughout our lifetimes and were essentially social in nature. He also believed that Freud put too much emphasis on our desire for individual gratification of needs and not enough on our need to be an accepted part of society and lead a meaningful life. Erikson suggested that we move through a series of psychosocial crises with a different social focus at each stage. For example between the ages of 0 and 1 the life crisis concerns developing trust or mistrust in self and others. The social focus at this stage is the mother.

■ Stage 1: Trust versus basic mistrust (ages 0–1)

At this stage the infant is totally helpless and relies entirely on others to meet its needs and provide good quality emotional and physical care. If the main parenting figure is able to meet the infant's needs in a satisfactory, responsive and caring way, the infant learns a sense of trust. Self-confidence grows and the world is believed to be a dependable and predictable place. It learnt that it has some influence over others and this will transfer to later stages. If, by contrast, the carer is unresponsive, lacks warmth and affection and doesn't meet the infant's needs or is inconsistent (maybe leaving the baby to cry alone for long periods of time coupled with being over-indulgent) the infant will develop a basic mistrust of others. It will feel a fundamental sense of not being able to influence others. In terms of later personality development this child will be filled with fear and suspicion. It may be withdrawn or apathetic.

■ Stage 2: Autonomy versus shame and doubt (ages 1–3)

The child is now more mobile. They are beginning to think more and are also developing a sense of being separate from their parents. They want to be independent and to do things for themselves. Toilet training is an important crisis to work through. If this is begun too early, or is very harsh, the child may feel a sense of shame at lack of control over their bowels.

- **Autonomy** – the child is allowed to experience things without being controlled. They are supported, not criticised, through failure/accidents etc. They feel competent and have a sense of self-belief.

▲ A toddler enjoying playing by herself

- **Shame and doubt** – the child is controlled and this induces doubt about their own abilities. The child fails frequently (perhaps they are being expected to do too much too soon) and/or is criticised (which induces shame). The child feels powerless and may revert to thumb sucking and is likely to become attention-seeking. The child rejects others and becomes closed off.

■ Stage 3: Initiative versus guilt (ages 3–6)

There is rapid social, emotional, physical and intellectual growth and development at this stage. The child is acquiring new skills through interaction with the world and others. If development is impeded at this stage, the child may lose their sense of initiative and become passive and unwilling to try new things.

Initiative can be fostered when the child's curiosity about life is welcomed and met with interest and encouragement to explore new ideas and learn new skills. When play of all varieties is encouraged, this enhances the development of initiative, as does physical activity which helps the child to develop skills. The negative potential outcome of the crisis at this stage is *guilt*. This may occur if parents dampen their child's curiosity about the world – perhaps by ignoring their questions or telling them not to be silly. Similarly if fantasy play is discouraged and physical activities are banned as 'too dangerous' the child's sense of growing competence and ability to take initiative will dwindle and they will be left with a sense of guilt and a belief in their own lack of competence.

■ Stage 4: Industry versus inferiority (ages 6–12)

The child is concerned at this stage with understanding how things are made and how they work (including making things themselves).

Significant others now begin to include teachers and other adults as well as parents.

The peer group begins to be important – children compare themselves in order to assess their own achievements. This is influential in the child's development of the self. A sense of *industry* is developed when the individual is encouraged to take on realistic tasks where there is a high degree of success along with being supported and encouraged to try things out. This results in high self-esteem and a sense of competence. *Inferiority* results if the child is pushed to do things they are not ready for without enough guidance and encouragement, and then criticised for failure.

If unfavourable comparisons are made with others (either by the child or by others), a sense of inferiority will develop, leading to a negative self-concept and low self-esteem.

■ Stage 5: Identity versus role confusion (ages 12–18)

Erikson saw adolescence as a time of *storm and stress* – a period of psychological turmoil which has a far-reaching effect on the self-concept. The self-concept is affected by the following factors.

- Physical changes bring about an altered body image which affects one's sense of self.

- Intellectual development allows the adolescent to become aware of what is potentially possible as well as what currently exists.
- Emotional development involves increasing emotional independence.
- The individual is also involved in making decisions about careers, values and sexual behaviour.

The main goal of the individual at this stage is to achieve a lasting and secure sense of self, or *ego identity*. This has three parts:

1 a sense of consistency in the ways they see themselves

2 a sense of continuity of the self over time

3 a sense of mutuality (i.e. agreement between one's own perceptions of self and the perceptions of others).

The peer group is very important in this process and the developmental task of the adolescent is to establish a vocational and social identity so that they see themselves as a consistent and integrated person. If this does not happen, they will not develop a sense of their role in life and will be unable to be faithful to people, work or a set of values. In extreme cases, they may develop a negative identity, particularly if they feel they cannot live up to the demands being made of them.

Application of psychodynamic principles to health and social care practice

Freud developed a treatment for disorders caused by defence mechanisms and psychic conflict called psychoanalysis. This is a very long-term treatment, usually involving spending an hour up to four times a week in therapy over a number of years with a trained psychoanalyst! In everyday health and social care practice, however, simply knowing and understanding the basic principles will help you to understand some of the causes of behaviour.

In context

Khalia asked the health visitor to come and see her daughter Sonia, aged 4. Sonia had been making good progress at nursery school and had been happy and outgoing until the birth of her younger brother six months previously. Since this time Sonia had been having fierce tantrums, was frequently wetting the bed and insisted on being fed and dressed, whereas previously she had taken pride in doing these tasks herself. When she is asked how she feels about having a new baby brother she always says, 'Oh I love having a new brother. Now I shall have someone to play with.'

Khalia's health visitor suggests that maybe Sonia is repressing or denying anxiety about being 'replaced' in her mother's affections by the younger brother. She advises Khalia to consider the possibility that Sonia feels rejected and unimportant because of the attention given to the new baby and is experiencing the ego defence mechanism known as regression. Sonia is unconscious of this: she is not doing it deliberately to be annoying but she is yearning for the undivided love and attention she had when she was a baby. Her statement that she loves having a younger brother contains an element of truth but also suggests that the ego defence mechanism of denial is being used. She knows, consciously, that it is 'wrong' to hate or resent her younger brother, so she tries to think she loves the idea of having a younger sibling.

The health visitor suggests that Khalia and Sonia spend time together when the brother is asleep or being looked after. She advises that Sonia's need to be 'babied' should be acknowledged and suggests that the mother broaches the subject of how it might feel to suddenly not be the only person getting her attention. Khalia is also advised to involve Sonia, where possible, as her 'helper' in caring for the brother. In this way the alliance between mother and daughter will be recognised by Sonia and her resentment may fade.

Khalia does this and, over the course of time, Sonia is reassured about her place in her mother's affections. She takes pride in helping her mum look after her little brother and is proud of her new, special place within the family. Little by little her tantrums are reduced and she stops wetting the bed and goes back to feeding and dressing herself. She still has moments when she needs to play the baby, and her mother is sensitive to this and allows her to do so when she needs it.

1 **Explain what is meant by the ego defences denial and regression.**

2 **Explain why Sonia is using the ego defences of denial and regression.**

3 **Why is Sonia using ego defences and not just outwardly showing resentment towards her brother?**

Assessment activity 8.3

Describe the application of psychodynamic perspectives in health and social care.

Explain how an understanding of the psychodynamic perspective can be applied to the following two situations:

1 an individual who has been given a diagnosis of cancer but is refusing to accept that they have the disease

2 an adolescent in a children's home who is continually rebelling against all the rules and appears to be developing signs of delinquent behaviour.

Grading tip for P3

In order to describe how the psychodynamic perspective can be applied to these two scenarios you need to use key concepts from Freud and/or Erikson's theory. For example, you could use ego defences to explain why the first individual is refusing to accept the diagnosis of cancer. For the second situation involving the adolescent, ideas from Erikson's stages of development will be helpful.

Reflect

Do you ever find yourself thinking someone really dislikes you? Maybe you think they are constantly judging you and criticising you. This could be an example of the defence mechanism called projection. If you secretly dislike them, and are judging and criticising them, but believe yourself to be a kind and gentle person, it is too anxiety-provoking to acknowledge that this is what you are feeling. Instead, it is safer to project these feelings onto the other person.

The humanistic approach

Humanistic psychology describes an approach to understanding human experience from the position of the individual. It focuses on the ideas of free will and the belief that we are all capable of making choices. Two psychologists associated with this approach are Abraham Maslow and Carl Rogers.

Abraham Maslow

Maslow was an American psychologist who believed that we are all seeking to become the best that we can possibly be – spiritually, physically, emotionally, intellectually and so on. He called this self-actualisation. He constructed a theory known as the hierarchy of needs in which he explained that every human being requires certain basic

Self-actualisation needs
(achieving full potential)

Self-esteem need
(respect, including self-respect)

Love and emotional need
(affection from others, being with others)

Safety and security needs
(freedom from anxiety and chaos, stability, predictability)

Basic physical needs
(oxygen, food, drink, warmth, sleep)

Figure 8.6 Maslow's hierarchy of needs – according to Maslow, we need to progress through each level before we can reach self-actualisation

needs to be met before they can approach the next level. This hierarchy of needs is shown in Figure 8.6.

As the diagram shows, Maslow believed that until our basic physiological needs are met, we will focus all our energies on getting them met and not be able to progress further. When we are well-housed, well-fed and comfortable physically we begin to focus on our emotional needs, such as the need to belong and be loved and to feel high self-esteem. When our lives are such that these needs are also met, we strive to self-actualise. As Maslow said, 'A musician must make music, an artist must paint, a poet must write, if he is to be ultimately at peace with himself. What a man can be, he must be. This need we may call self-actualisation.'

Carl Rogers

Rogers was particularly interested in the concept of self. There are many aspects of the self but two are especially important here. **Self-concept** refers to how

Key terms

Self-concept The way in which we see ourselves. In early life this comes from what we are told about ourselves ('you're so pretty', 'you're a good footballer', 'what a kind girl you are' etc). As we grow older, our ability to think about ourselves develops and we begin to incorporate our own judgments ('I did well at that test – I'm good at maths', 'I wasn't invited to that party – I must be unpopular').

we view ourselves. This includes physical and biological attributes such as being male or female, blonde or brunette, tall or short as well as personality traits such as kind, humble, assertive, hard-working. The self-concept is formed from an early age and young children **internalise** the judgements made of them by others, which then become part of their self-concept. If a child is told they are silly, naughty and will come to no good, part of their self-concept will contain these aspects. If on the other hand a child is praised, encouraged to succeed and told they are valued, they will have a positive self-concept and see themselves as someone who is worthwhile and competent.

Self-esteem is slightly different and it refers to how much we feel we are valuable – literally, the amount of esteem we give to ourselves. Someone with high self-esteem will believe they are loved and lovable and that they are important and valued. By contrast, an individual with low self-esteem may feel themselves to be worthless, of no value to anyone else, unloved and unlovable.

Rogers believed that we also hold a concept of self called the ideal self. This represents a view of ourselves as we feel we should be and as we would like to be. When there is incongruence (a mismatch) between our actual self and our ideal self we become troubled and unhappy. The poem below by Dorothy Law Nolte illustrates many of the aspects of Rogers's theory.

Key terms

Internalise This is to do with the way we take in information from the outside world and build it into our sense of self. If we are consistently valued, loved, praised, given positive attention etc we will believe ourselves to be valuable, lovable, worthwhile etc.

Self-esteem The way in which we value ourselves, believe ourselves to be worthy, lovable, etc. This is learnt from the way we are valued and loved by others. Self-esteem is not stable. It can go up and down according to our personality and the way we typically view the world and our past experiences. People can, however, be taught how to increase their self-esteem.

Children Learn What They Live

If children live with criticism, they learn to
    condemn.
If children live with hostility, they learn to fight.
If children live with fear, they learn to be
    apprehensive.
If children live with pity, they learn to feel sorry for
    themselves.
If children live with ridicule, they learn to feel
    shy.
If children live with jealousy, they learn to feel
    envy.
If children live with shame, they learn to feel guilty.
If children live with encouragement, they learn
    confidence.
If children live with tolerance, they learn patience.
If children live with praise, they learn appreciation.
If children live with acceptance, they learn to love.
If children live with approval, they learn to like
    themselves.
If children live with recognition, they learn it is good
    to have a goal.
If children live with sharing, they learn generosity.
If children live with honesty, they learn truthfulness.
If children live with fairness, they learn justice.
If children live with kindness and consideration, they
    learn respect.
If children live with security, they learn to have faith
    in themselves and in those about them.
If children live with friendliness, they learn the world
    is a nice place in which to live.

Dorothy Law Nolte

Reflect

- Write down 20 statements about yourself. How many of these are positive and how many negative?
- Do you ever think: I must do this perfectly or I am not worthwhile? This is an example of an unrealistic ideal self. Can you think of any other examples?
- Think about influences on your self-esteem. How much praise/criticism did you receive from others when you were growing up?
- Are you able to feel good about your achievements and accept praise from others or do you tend to brush it off? Why do you think you feel or do this?

Application of humanistic psychology to health and social care

Rogers is famous for developing a particular type of counselling based on **unconditional positive regard** from the counsellor to help the client develop a more positive sense of self. Unconditional positive regard refers to the idea that the therapist supports and validates the client's experiences, feelings, beliefs, emotions unconditionally (i.e. without making a judgement about whether they are good or bad). In this way, over time, the client comes to accept themselves as they really are and to see themselves as worthy. The incongruence between the actual self and the ideal self dissolves as the two become closer or unrealistic expectations associated with the ideal self are let go of.

One crucial feature of this approach to helping others is to develop empathy. Unlike sympathy, where we feel sorry for someone, empathy requires us to really listen to the other person, be in tune with their emotions and respect them for who they are. This is not always easy as we do not always understand why someone feels so badly about an issue we could easily dismiss. However, if we try to respect the individual we are working with and understand that the issue is of crucial importance to them, we can come closer to empathy. True empathy requires us to put aside judgements about another and do all we can to put ourselves 'in their shoes'.

Tips for achieving empathy

Suppose you are working with a client or patient who is terrified that eating more than three grains of rice will make them obese and ruin their lives. You are probably aware that this is factually incorrect. You may find it difficult to understand let alone feel empathy for such an extreme view.

Now try really listening to them. Observe their body language. They may be so frozen with fear that they appear calm and indifferent. Or they may be so anxious that they are pale and sweaty with huge fearful eyes almost bulging out of their head.

Next, think of something that brings you out in a cold sweat of paralysing fear. This may be something 'real' such as having been buried under an avalanche of snow and being in fear for your life, or something imaginary. Recollect this fear. Did it help for people to tell you, 'Well, you were alright, weren't you? You didn't die! Here you are as well as anything!'? Now put aside all judgement about the individual's fear or terror. Recognise that what they are feeling makes sense to them. It is painful, agonising, terrifying. Tune in to those feelings and you will be many steps closer to true empathy.

Key terms

Unconditional positive regard This refers to a totally non-judgemental way of being with and viewing a client. The therapist does not like or approve of the client at times and disapprove of them at others: they value the client in a positive way with no conditions attached.

Remember!

The fundamentals of applying the humanistic approach to health and social care include:

- unconditional positive regard
- empathy
- understanding
- respecting other individuals
- active listening
- adopting a non-judgemental approach.

In context

Paula is a single mother of three who is a partner in a firm of solicitors. She is very concerned to put the children first and has arranged to leave work early every day so she can pick the children up, feed them and take them to their various activities before putting them to bed. She then works well into the night to complete her work. Although her friends and colleagues admire Paula for her calm and unflappable manner, her devotion to her children and her considerable skills as both a parent and a solicitor, Paula is constantly critical of herself. She thinks she is a poor parent who lets her children down and a poor colleague because she isn't at the office all day. She believes no one will ever want to be with her, and fears growing old alone.

1 **There may well be an incongruence between Paula's self-concept and her ideal self. Explain what this means, giving examples from Paula's story.**

2 **Suggest ways in which Paula has learnt her views of her ideal self from others she has encountered in life.**

3 **Compare this approach to developing an ideal self with the notion of the superego suggested by Freud. What similarities and differences can you find?**

Assessment activity 8.4

Describe the value of the humanistic approach to health and social care service provision.

1 Explain how the humanistic approach to health and social care provision can be of value in the following two situations:

- training staff in understanding the importance of unconditional positive regard in working with patients and clients
- providing counselling services in health and social care settings.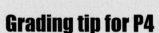

Grading tip for P4

To achieve P4 you could describe how the humanistic approach can be used by many staff in a variety of different settings. For example, people in hospital may be ashamed that they are not being 'brave enough' in dealing with illness – this could be explained by an incongruence between actual self and ideal self.

The cognitive/information processing approach

This psychological perspective has gained enormous ground since the 1960s, when the influence of behaviourism began to wane. With the development of computers came the idea that brain activity is like the operation of a computer. A huge body of research has gone into understanding cognitive processes such as attention, memory, perception, information processing, problem solving, thought, language and other aspects of cognition. For the purposes of understanding this perspective as it relates to health and social care, however, we shall concentrate on just two theorists: Jean Piaget and George Kelly.

Jean Piaget (1896–1980) was a Swiss psychologist who showed advanced academic ability from an early age. In his early adulthood he worked on research into measuring intelligence and became interested in the types of mistakes that children made at the same age, however bright they were. He came to the conclusion that cognition develops through a series of stages, each new stage building on the previous one. The stages and key associated features are described below.

■ Stage 1: The sensori-motor stage (birth to about 2 years)

The child is only able to experience the world through immediate perceptions (sensory, for example, smell, touch, sight etc) and through motor activity. The child lacks a concept of object permanence: they believe that if an object they have previously been playing with, such as a soft toy, is removed it ceases to exist. The end of this stage is reached when the child begins to use memory and language.

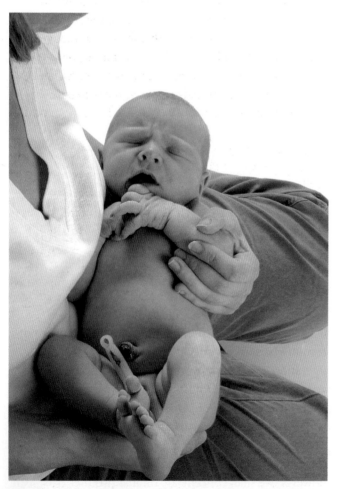

▲ A baby is only able to experience the world through sense perceptions and motor activity – the sensori-motor stage

■ Stage 2: The pre-operational stage (about 2–7 years)

This stage involves the development of thinking and the ability to use language, thought and memory to represent objects mentally. At this stage the child is *egocentric* (they only see the world from their own point of view) and is unable to *conserve*. This means that they cannot understand the concept that an object (such as plasticine) remains the same whether it is rolled out into a long sausage shape or squashed tight into a ball. Similarly, if water is poured from a short squat glass into a tall thin glass, the child will claim that there is more water in the tall thin glass even though they have actually seen that no water has been added or removed.

■ Stage 3: The concrete operational stage (about 7–11 years)

The child develops the ability to conserve. They will now recognise that plasticine is the same however it is shaped, and are able to realise that the amount of water remains the same regardless of how it looks (tall and thin or short and squat). The child still needs to deal with concrete objects and cannot represent problems in abstract form. Thus, for example, 'the child at this stage will have difficulty dealing with the verbal problem "Joan is taller than Susan; Joan is smaller than Mary; who is the smallest?" in his head, but would have no difficulty if given three dolls to represent Joan, Susan and Mary' (Birch and Malim (1988)).

■ Stage 4: The formal operational stage (about 11 years onwards)

The child can now think in the abstract: they do not need concrete objects to manipulate in order to reason and solve problems.

George Kelly

George Kelly (1905–66) developed a unique psychological theory known as the Psychology of Personal Constructs. He sees the individual as a scientist, making predictions about the future, testing them and, if necessary, revising them according to new evidence. A construct is a way of construing (interpreting and making sense of) reality and the environment. For example, if an individual develops deafness in middle age they may construe this as a disaster, withdraw from the world and become socially isolated. Alternatively, if they construe this as a challenge, they may seek out new, exciting opportunities, work around their deafness and continue to live a rich, fulfilling life. Kelly (1970) states 'the events we face today are subject to as great a variety of constructions as our wits will enable us to contrive … Even the most obvious occurrences of everyday life might appear utterly transformed if we were inventive enough to construe them differently.'

Kelly believes that we are free to choose alternative explanations and meanings for events. We do not have to be constrained by our past history but can seek out new, alternative, more positive meanings. Suppose, for example, we have been brought up in such a way that the world is presented as harsh and dangerous. If we go for a walk on a dark evening and hear someone walking quickly behind us, we can construe this as a mugger about to attack us or, alternatively, reject this and choose an alternative construal of a person hurrying to get home to his children after a late meeting at the office.

Applying cognitive psychological perspectives to health and social care

Piaget's ideas about cognitive development in children have been highly influential in education. The view has changed from a pupil as a passive recipient of knowledge to a child as an active and creative being who is capable of adapting to, and learning from, the environment. Teaching methods have been adapted to meet the developmental stages of children by including a high focus on learning by doing and making new information available in small steps.

A second use of cognitive theory is in the field of abnormal behaviour with the use of cognitive therapy or cognitive behavioural therapy. This approach focuses on understanding how an individual's thoughts influence their emotions which in turn influence behaviour. The psychologist Aaron Beck has formulated a helpful approach to understanding both eating disorders and depression.

This perspective begins by understanding how distorted and irrational negative thoughts influence feelings, which then lead to changes in behaviour. An example of this process is given on page 394.

This pattern of behaviour is described by Beck as a cognitive triad. To begin with, the individual feels themselves to be worthless and inadequate. This self-appraisal then leads to the belief that this lack of worth means that the future will be just as bad as the present. This then generalises to a conviction that the world contains problems and difficulties that the individual is powerless to overcome. The goal of cognitive therapy is to challenge these negative thoughts and encourage the patient to develop alternative, more positive, ways of seeing the world.

Identifying negative, irrational or distorted thinking

This can be done by keeping a diary and recording every instance of negative thoughts and feelings. Initially this can be difficult as these are so automatic it can be difficult to notice them. However, this will improve over time. For each example, try to challenge the thinking. Ask yourself:

- What is the evidence for such negative thinking?
- Are there alternative explanations? It can be helpful to think how other people would respond, or even ask them.
- How does it affect me to think so negatively? (This helps you develop self-awareness.)
- What type of thinking errors am I making (for example, magnifying, catastrophising)?

For more information on this type of therapy, visit the following website: www.rcpsych.ac.uk.

In context

Jamala tends to interpret negative events as being her own fault; they are due to some character flaw she has. This affects her feelings about such events and then leads to her behaviour changing as a result of her thoughts and feelings. One day, Jamala goes to college as usual. In the corridor she meets Rob and smiles brightly at him. Rob ignores her. Jamala's thoughts are racing, 'Rob thinks I'm pathetic and ridiculous. He doesn't want anything to do with me.' When she enters the classroom for the first lecture of the day, Rob is in a corner of the classroom surrounded by five students. They are all laughing. One of the students looks up at Jamala and gestures for her to sit with them. Jamala, however, is thinking, 'They're all laughing at me. He's told them about me in the corridor and they think I'm coming on to him. He's said he thinks I'm ugly and geeky. If I sit with them they'll just snigger about me. I'll sit by myself.' At the end of the double lecture it is the coffee break. Jamala stays behind in the classroom because she believes the other group will continue

laughing at her and winding her up if she joins them. Because of this hurt to her self-esteem and self-concept, Jamala goes to the library instead. The minute she is free to leave college, she escapes, alone, to catch the bus home. At home she broods on the events of the day, convincing herself that she is pathetic and unpopular. The next day she misses college. Over the course of the next six weeks she misses more than 80 per cent of college. Eventually she drops out, believing she won't be missed. By now, Jamala is convinced that she is unpopular, ridiculed and disliked by the group of people she had believed were becoming her friends.

1   **Identify the negative thoughts Jamala has in this scenario.**

2   **Identify Jamala's negative thoughts and explain how they lead to negative emotions.**

3   **Predict how Jamala's thoughts, feelings and behaviour may influence her future behaviour in other situations.**

Theory into practice

Working in pairs, role play a meeting with a cognitive therapist. The person playing the part of the therapist should help the client to identify negative thoughts and help them think through alternatives. Your job is not to give advice, but to help the individual recognise their negative thoughts and become aware that there are alternative explanations, even if these do not seem real or valid to them at the moment.

Supporting individuals with learning difficulties

Individuals with learning difficulties can experience enormous frustration in their daily lives as they seek to make sense of what can be bewildering experiences. The cognitive approach can be used to help individuals who misread situations. By identifying irrational thoughts, an individual can be guided to change them, with the consequent benefits to emotions and behaviour. Cognitive work of this type can improve self-esteem and reduce outbursts which are triggered by lack of understanding of the requirements of a given situation (for example, having to wait in turn for a meal).

A cognitive approach can be used to help people with learning difficulties

In context

The following is an excerpt from an interview with a 45-year-old man who could be helped by cognitive therapy.

'I teach ICT core and optional throughout the school and at GCSE and A level. Most of the time I'm OK but there are times when a year group comes into my classroom and I just start sweating. I give out the instructions for the class in (what I hope is) a calm voice and put a copy of this on Powerpoint for those who don't (or won't!) listen, so I have backup evidence of what I've said. In the classroom I am tentative but feel fairly OK being in charge. However, once I enter the staffroom or a Head of Department meeting I turn to jelly. My confidence completely leaves me and I am afraid of being "found out" as incompetent. Even though my exam results are good and the reports I write are usually praised by the Deputy Head as being thorough, I still have this underlying belief that I am worthless and I can't shake it. The staff are generally a friendly bunch but I am convinced they won't want my company so if I am asked out I always make an excuse. It's got to the point now where I just hide behind my computer and stay away from other teachers as much as possible. My doctor has diagnosed me with depression and I really don't know where to turn.'

1 **Identify the negative thoughts shown by the teacher.**

2 **Explain how these thoughts lead to negative feelings and self-defeating behaviour.**

3 **Suggest ways in which the teacher could begin to challenge these negative thoughts and introduce alternative explanations. Explain how this could lead to more positive behaviour that would help him to become more comfortable at school.**

The biological approach

Maturational theory

The process of maturation was described by Shaffer (1993) as: 'a biological unfolding of the individual according to a plan contained in the genes – the hereditary material passed from parents to their offspring at conception'.

■ Gesell's theory of maturation

Arnold Gesell (1880–1961) was a highly influential figure in the field of child development whose views were influential on Dr Spock, possibly the most famous 'baby doctor' of his time. Gesell developed a theory of maturation which explained the developmental processes and stages involved from conception onwards. The theory proposes that development occurs according to a sequence of maturational processes. For example, development in utero (in the womb) follows a fixed set of stages. For example, the heart begins to form first along with a rudimentary nervous system. The development of the lungs, liver and kidneys also begins early on in pregnancy. Bones and muscles develop

next and over time the organism develops into a fully functioning human being, ready to be born. As the child develops from birth onwards, its genes allow it to flower gradually into the person they are meant to be. The environment should provide support for this unfolding of talents, skills, personality, interests etc but the main thing driving this development is the maturational drive.

To find out more about prenatal development, with accompanying images, visit the following website: www.babycenter.com.

Genetic influences on behaviour

Genes can affect behaviour in a multitude of ways. Some disorders, such as Huntington's disease, are caused by a single dominant gene which either parent can pass on to their child. Others, such as cystic fibrosis and sickle cell anaemia, are caused when both parents pass on the gene for the disorder.

Disorders which occur regardless of environmental influences, such as those listed above, are genetically determined disorders. This means that the individual who inherits the gene or genes is certain to develop the disorder, regardless of environmental factors.

Huntington's disease is an example of how a gene can cause dramatic changes in behaviour and impair an individual's ability to function independently. This disorder usually begins to show when the individual is aged between 30 and 50. Symptoms of dementia appear and the individual is likely to die about 15 years after the onset. Some of the changes in behaviour are listed below, though this list is not comprehensive:

- hallucinations and delusions
- severe confusion
- progressive memory loss
- inappropriate speech; use of jargon or wrong words
- personality changes including anxiety and depression, withdrawal from social interaction, decreased ability to care for oneself and inability to maintain employment.

Disorders which are not genetically determined, but which may leave the individual with a vulnerability for developing the disorder, are far more common. A classic way of measuring the contribution of genes to any type of behaviour is through twin studies. There are two types of twins. Monozygotic (or identical) twins share 100 per cent of genetic material since they are formed from only one egg which has divided into two. Dizygotic (or fraternal) twins share only 50 per cent of genetic material since they occur when two eggs are fertilised at the same time. If, the reasoning goes, one of a pair of monozygotic twins has a disorder, it would be expected that, if genes are the only influence, the second twin *must* also have the disorder.

This is rarely the case so instead researchers look at what is known as the concordance rate between twins. This refers to the probability of a second twin sharing the disorder. In research carried out into autism by Ritvo, Freeman et al (1985) it was found that 22 of 23 pairs of monozygotic twins were concordant compared with a concordance rate of 4 out of 17 dizygotic twin pairs. This clearly shows that a genetic component is at work in this disorder.

▲ Identical (or monozygotic) twins share exactly the same genetic material

The influence of the nervous and endocrine systems on behaviour

There are two parts to the nervous system:

- **the central nervous system** (CNS), which consists of the brain and spinal cord. This system rapidly responds to stimuli and governs
- **the autonomic nervous system** (ANS), which regulates organs of the body, such as the heart, stomach, intestines, and processes such as heart rate and blood pressure, digestion and breathing. It is described as autonomic because it operates without any conscious effort on our part. There are two parts to this system, known as branches: the sympathetic branch and the parasympathetic branch. Only one branch can be dominant at any given time. The sympathetic branch is associated with arousal, whereas the parasympathetic branch is associated with rest and relaxation. Most of the functioning of the ANS is not under conscious control.

The *sympathetic branch* of the ANS is associated with a heightened state of physiological arousal. When this branch is dominant, digestive processes slow down, heart and breathing rate, increase, blood clotting is enhanced, sugars are released into the bloodstream and the muscles are primed for fast activity. This is known as the fight or flight response and is believed to be an adaptive response dating from prehistoric times when our ancestors needed to preserve life by running away from danger (the flight response) or running after and killing a wild animal for food (the fight response). This response is activated by a flood of adrenaline and noradrenaline released by part of the adrenal glands known as the adrenal medulla. These act as both neurotransmitters and hormones. When someone appears very agitated, with a fast pulse and heavy, rapid breathing it is likely that the fight or flight response has been activated.

The *parasympathetic* branch is concerned with repair and rest. When this branch is dominant, heart and breathing rate will be slowed down and digestion is at its optimal level. Domination by this branch is associated with rest and relaxation.

The ANS produces its effects through activation of nerve fibres throughout the nervous system, brain and body or by stimulating the release of hormones from endocrine glands (such as the adrenal and pineal glands). Hormones are biochemical substances which are released into the bloodstream and have a profound effect on target organs and on behaviour. They are present in very small quantities and individual molecules have a very short life, so their effects quickly disappear if they are not secreted continuously.

There are a large number of other hormones including:

- melatonin, which is released by the pineal gland and acts on the brainstem sleep mechanisms to help synchronise the phases of sleep and activity
- testosterone, which is released in the testicles and may influence aggressiveness
- oxytocin, which is released by the pituitary gland and stimulates milk production and female orgasms.

Some hormones are released as a response to external stimuli, such as the pineal gland which responds to reduced daylight by increasing production of melatonin. Other hormones follow a circadian rhythm, with one peak and one trough every 24 hours. (Circadian means 'about a day' and refers to a 24-hour rhythm.) For example, levels of cortisol rise about an hour before you wake up and contribute to your feelings of wakefulness or arousal.

Sex hormones are especially important in determining whether a developing foetus will emerge as a male or female. A biologically male embryo (one which has inherited an XY pattern of sex chromosomes which determine biological sex) should be born with male genitalia. During its development in the womb, hormones called androgens are released which contribute to the development of male sex organs. If, however, there is a problem in development and the foetus is insensitive to the hormones, the infant may have ambiguous genitalia and it may be unclear which sex the newborn baby should be assigned to.

Applying the biological perspective to health and social care practice

Developmental norms

Gesell developed an assessment scale to enable judgements to be made about whether a child's behaviour and understanding matches that of their chronological age (how old the child is). This scale enables the child's scores to be compared against their scores at an earlier age to determine whether development is proceeding satisfactorily. It also enables a skilled and trained assessor to identify developmental problems that may emerge for an individual, thus allowing for early and appropriate intervention. There are three overlapping points at which development can be measured:

- between 2½ years up to age 6
- between 4 and 6 years old
- between 6 and 9 years old.

At each age there is a variety of tests which assess different aspects of development. One test administered at around the age of 4 consists of comprehension questions.

> 'A child's performance in this area measures the ability to invent sensible coping solutions to social problem situations. The level of self care skills, and perceptual accuracy in a solution, will lead to comfort in social settings as children move to 5 years of age.'

The Cubes test, which is used primarily with children aged 2–6, provides:.

> 'information about visual perception, fine motor co-ordination, attention span and perception of form – as well as ability to follow directions and to function in a structured task. The visual motor integration skills exhibited relate to hand writing, colouring and cutting. The short-term visual memory skills relate to reading comprehension, spelling and math.'
>
> *www.freudianslip.co.uk*

This test can be used by people involved in assessing developmental norms.

Understanding genetic predisposition to certain illnesses

While it is far from easy to determine the extent to which genetic inheritance influences behaviour, there is a considerable body of evidence to suggest that genes have a role in behaviour. One example is infantile autism, a rare (but seemingly increasing) disorder which affects about one child in 2000. While there are psychological explanations for autism (for example, see Bruno Bettleheim, 1967) these have not been satisfactorily investigated and research on the contribution of genetic influences in this disorder is more convincing.

The disorder of schizophrenia similarly shows a genetic link, though not as strong as in autism. For monozygotic twins there has been found to be a 50 per cent concordance rate, while this is only 15 per cent for dizygotic twins.

In 1995 Sarafino and Goldfedder investigated the concordance rate for asthma. They found 59 per cent of monozygotic twins (23 out of 39 pairs) were concordant for the disease compared with 24 per cent of dizygotic twins (13 out of 55 pairs).

If these disorders were genetically determined, as with cystic fibrosis, it should be found that twins who share 100 per cent of their genes both develop a given disorder. There is clearly a genetic component in both disorders,

Theory into practice

Draw up a short questionnaire to give to parents at a local infant or nursery school. Ask if the child attending the school has asthma and, if so, do any other members of the family have asthma? Make sure you explain the purpose of the questionnaire before giving it out. When you have collected your data you can create a table of results indicating how many of the children who have asthma also have a relative with asthma and how many do not. In this way you can gain an idea of how many children develop asthma with no apparent genetic predisposition to the disease.

since monozygotic twins show a higher concordance rate than dizygotic twins, in line with the proportion of genetic material shared. However, environmental influences have to account for the proportion not accounted for. In schizophrenia, for example, it seems that an individual can inherit a vulnerability to this disorder but if life goes smoothly and is relatively free of stress, this person may live a life free of illness. Similarly with asthma, environmental factors such as stress, pollutants and pollen can be responsible for the onset of the disorder.

Understanding the effects of shift work on individuals

When we work shifts, particularly night shifts, we tend to find that there are certain times when we feel an overwhelming urge to sleep while we should be working. Alternatively, when we go home after our shift and try to sleep and get refreshed for a new day at work we may find ourselves pacing the floor, unable to sleep. These unpleasant physical effects occur because of disruption to circadian rhythms.

Circadian rhythms (or biological rhythms) govern a cycle of physiological bodily processes which last for between 24 and 25 hours. One example is our core body temperature which follows approximately a 24-hour cycle and influences levels of alertness. For most people the lowest core temperature is 97°F and the highest is 99°F. Core body temperature shows peaks and troughs over the course of the day. When it is at its highest we are at our most alert. As our temperature is reducing we begin to feel sleepy. The graph below shows typical fluctuations in body temperature.

Shift workers on an evening shift have to be awake and functioning at a high level when their body temperature is at its lowest and dropping, a time when our body is telling us to go to sleep. They therefore have to fight against an overwhelming urge to sleep. Upon return home, when their temperature levels are rising, they then need to try to sleep at a time when their body clock is telling them they should be awake and encouraging alertness.

The brain is also involved in governing our desire to sleep. A part of the brain called the pineal gland is responsible for production of the hormone melatonin.

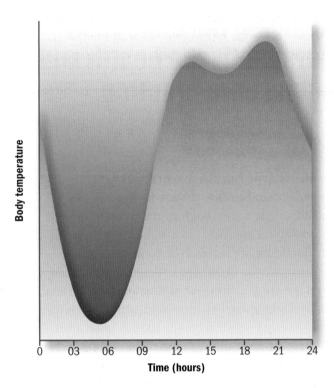

Figure 8.7 Typical fluctuations in core body temperature over a 24-hour period; as it rises we become increasingly alert

When levels of this hormone are high, we feel sleepy. As they begin to drop we become increasingly alert. The rhythm of this hormone production is linked to the sleep-wake cycle. As it gets dark, the pineal gland recognises this and triggers an increase in melatonin

Reflect

Are you the type of person who wakes easily in the early morning and is quite alert and able to work well, but needs to go to bed quite early at night? Or are you the sort of person who takes a long time to become alert in the morning and feels most awake as the day wears on, often going to bed late at night? These patterns of alertness are governed by circadian rhythms and can quite seriously affect your ability to do shift work.

production, while when light levels increase, production of melatonin is reduced. Levels of melatonin fluctuate throughout the day. Between about 8 p.m. and 10 p.m. these levels increase with the resulting feeling of sleepiness occurring about two hours after this increase. These levels then begin to fall from about 2 a.m. to 7 a.m. The onset of daylight is recognised by the pineal gland which then reduces the secretion of melatonin,

leading to increased alertness. For those who are trying to sleep during the day, their levels of melatonin are working against them as low levels encourage alertness. Similarly, those trying to work at night when the pineal gland is secreting large amounts of this hormone will have to fight against the sleep-inducing effects of melatonin.

Assessment activity 8.6

Describe the application of biological perspectives in health and social care.

Write a leaflet explaining what is meant by circadian rhythms. Explain why shift work may be a problem for some people, making reference to the influence of core body temperature and the role of the pineal gland. **P6**

Grading tip for P6

In order to show evidence that you are 'applying' the biological perspective to health and social care, it may be useful to give advice about how knowledge of biological rhythms can be used to guide managers in drawing up patterns of shift work.

Take it further

Biological approach

1 Research into the effects of shift work on levels of alertness and create a chart or table which shows when people are most alert and when they are least alert.

2 Carry out research into the effects of Huntington's disease on the brain. Find an image of a brain scan which shows the brain of a patient with

Huntington's disease compared with that of a 'normal' control.

3 Research case studies of testicular feminising syndrome and look at research by Imperato-McGinley et al. These give examples of cases where babies are assigned the 'wrong' sex at birth on the basis of their external genitalia rather than their chromosomal inheritance.

Assessment activity 8.7

Analyse the contribution of different psychological perspectives to the understanding and management of challenging behaviour.

Joe is 79 years old and has recently entered a private nursing home. His behaviour is proving a problem to all around him. He shouts at the nursing staff, is very demanding and constantly argues with other residents. He frequently hides the television remote control and insists that other people in the leisure room should be 'discussing important world events not watching trashy programmes'. The nursing staff and other clients initially indulged him but his behaviour seems to be getting worse. He is showing signs of depression and lethargy which alternates with his difficult behaviour. It has reached the point where the person in charge of the nursing home is so concerned about the negative effect on other clients that she is considering asking him to leave.

1   Explain how aggressive and unpredictable behaviour can be understood in terms of three or more psychological perspectives.

2   Use ideas from these perspectives about how to manage and change behaviour to explain how this would be achieved.

3   Make a judgement about the strengths and weaknesses of each perspective in terms of both understanding and managing challenging behaviour.   **M1**

Grading tip for M1

To analyse a perspective it is helpful to consider how much and how well it explains behaviour and what its methods are for managing challenging behaviour. If there are aspects that it does not adequately account for, it may be that another perspective can explain them better.

Analyse the contribution of different psychological perspectives to health and social care provision.

4   You have been appointed as director of a large health centre including GPs, counsellors, health visitor and social workers. You are working on setting up a training programme to teach staff about different psychological perspectives. Write a report outlining the training programme and explaining why you have chosen each particular perspective. Explain the strengths and weaknesses associated with each perspective.   **M2**

Grading tip for M2

To achieve M2 you need to think hard about why psychological perspectives are useful in health and social care provision. It may be that you consider some more useful than others, in which case you can say so as long as you can justify yourself. Alternatively, you could consider whether some perspectives are more useful in some areas than others and discuss the reasons for this.

Evaluate the roles of different psychological perspectives in health and social care.

5   Carry out the exercise above (for M2) but finish it with a recommendation to adopt training for only two or three perspectives. Explain why you have chosen these in terms of:

   •   how well they explain the behaviour of the majority of clients and patients who will be visiting the centre, and
   •   how useful they are in treating or helping patients and clients.   **D1**

Grading tip for D1

To evaluate means to weigh up strengths and weaknesses and arrive at an overall judgement. In this situation you need to be very clear about what the strengths and weaknesses are of the perspectives you have chosen. You can use examples to help explain why you are recommending the perspectives you have chosen and exactly how they are useful in treating/helping patients and clients.

Knowledge check

1 Which theory of learning is associated with Pavlov?

2 What is meant by positive reinforcement?

3 What is meant by latent learning?

4 What is the self-fulfilling prophecy?

5 Name the three parts of the psyche.

6 Explain what is meant by the ego defence mechanism denial.

7 Name the stages in Maslow's pyramid known as the hierarchy of needs.

8 What is the difference between self-concept and self-esteem?

9 Which theorist is associated with showing positive unconditional regard to clients in therapy?

10 Name the stages of development outlined by Piaget.

11 What are the three components of the cognitive triad?

12 What is the purpose of Gesell's assessment scale?

13 Explain what is meant by concordance rate in terms of genetic heritability and give at least one example of this.

14 Describe the effects on behaviour of the hormone melatonin.

Grading criteria

To achieve a pass grade the evidence must show that the learner is able to:	To achieve a merit grade the evidence must show that, in addition to the pass criteria, the learner is able to:	To achieve a distinction grade the evidence must show that, in addition to the pass and merit criteria, the learner is able to:
P1 describe the application of behaviourist perspectives in health and social care **Assessment activity 8.1 page 377**		
P2 explain the value of the social learning approach to health and social care service provision **Assessment activity 8.2 page 382**		
P3 describe the application of psychodynamic perspectives in health and social care **Assessment activity 8.3 page 387**	**M1** analyse the contribution of different psychological perspectives to the understanding and management of challenging behaviour **Assessment activity 8.7 page 402**	
P4 describe the value of the humanistic approach to health and social care service provision **Assessment activity 8.4 page 391**	**M2** analyse the contribution of different psychological perspectives to health and social care service provision. **Assessment activity 8.7 page 402**	**D1** evaluate the roles of different psychological perspectives in health and social care. **Assessment activity 8.7 page 402**
P5 explain the value of the cognitive perspective in supporting individuals **Assessment activity 8.5 page 396**		
P6 describe the application of biological perspectives in health and social care. **Assessment activity 8.6 page 401**		

Preparation for assessment

Prepare for your assessment by considering the following scenario, and the questions that follow. Remember that for pass criteria, you need to **describe** and **explain** the psychological perspectives and the way they can be applied to health and social care provision. For merit criteria, you need to **analyse** the contribution of the different perspectives – that is, look for reasons why they might be effective or ineffective in certain cases, and produce evidence to back up your theories. For a distinction, you need to complete an **evaluation**. To evaluate means to weigh up the evidence you have gathered and to draw conclusions from what the evidence shows.

Gerald is a 20-year-old man living in residential care. He was taken into care at the age of 12 because he showed severe behavioural problems and his mother (a single parent) could no longer manage to look after him. One of the reasons for his challenging behaviour was explained when he was diagnosed at the age of 13 with ADHD. He has recently been found to have insulin-dependent diabetes but has a phobia about injections and screams uncontrollably whenever he needs one. Gerald finds waiting intolerable. If a bus is late or if he has to queue for a meal, he becomes aggressive and screams and hits those near him. It has been noted that he finds it difficult to take responsibility for his own actions. At a recent case conference it was noted that he had blamed another resident for 'stirring up trouble' when in fact it was Gerald himself who caused an incident by his aggressive behaviour: the other resident was an innocent bystander! Gerald finds it difficult when he is not the centre of attention and quite often retreats to the laundry room to sulk if he believes he has been left out. He complains that other residents don't like him and are picking on him, even if they have invited him to join in an activity. Despite his often aggressive behaviour and his antagonism towards other residents and members of staff, Gerald appears to be suffering

from depression. When he is in a subdued mood he often says he thinks he is worthless and nobody will ever want him. He is angry with his mother for what he sees as her abandonment of him.

1 How can classical conditioning explain Gerald's fear of injections? **P1**

2 How could the principles of operant conditioning be used to modify Gerald's behaviour? **P1**

3 According to social learning theory we can learn behaviour by observing others. How could Gerald have learnt a fear of injections? **P2**

4 What ego defence mechanism is Gerald using when he blames others for his own behaviour? **P3**

5 Gerald is showing signs of low self-esteem. How can knowledge of the humanistic approach help his care workers to work with him to improve his self-esteem? **P4**

6 Explain how cognitive behavioural therapy could be used to help Gerald develop a clearer and more accurate view of the way other residents interact with him. **P5**

7 Gerald has been diagnosed as suffering from ADHD. How can the biological perspective shed light on the behaviour he is showing as a result of this disorder? **P6**

8 Compare the contributions made by the biological perspective and one other psychological perspective in understanding and managing Gerald's challenging behaviour. **M1**

9 Analyse the contribution of two or more psychological perspectives to health and social care provision in a residential setting and one other setting (for example, a hospital or day centre). **M2**

10 Write a report on the contribution of different psychological perspectives in health and social care. Explain how well each perspective can give an insight

into the behaviour of individuals and its strengths and weaknesses in managing challenging behaviour. Discuss the role of the perspectives you have chosen in helping to provide a valuable service in health and social care. **D1**

Resources and further reading

Barker, L.M. (1997) *Learning and Behaviour: Biological, Psychological and Sociocultural Perspectives*, second ed. New Jersey: Prentice Hall

Bettleheim, B. (1967) *The Empty Fortress: Infantile Autism and the Birth of the Self* New York: Macmillan Publishing

Birch, A., Malim, T. (1988) *Developmental Psychology: From Infancy to Adulthood* Bristol: Intertext Limited

Ewen, R.B. (1993) *An Introduction to Theories of Personality,* fourth ed. Hove: Lawrence Erlbaum Associates

Eysenck, M.W. (1994) *Perspectives on Psychology* Hove: Psychology Press

Kalat, J.W. (1995) *Biological Psychology*, fifth ed. Pacific Grove: Brooks/Cole Publishing Company

Kelly, G.A. (1970), cited in Ewen, R.B. (1993) *An Introduction to Theories of Personality*, fourth ed. Hove: Lawrence Erlbaum Associates Ltd

Melamed, B.G., Dearborn, M. and Hermecz, D.A. (1983), cited in Sarafino et al (1990)

Ritvo, E.R., Freeman, B.J. et al (1985), cited in Kalat, J.W. (1995) *Biological Psychology*, fifth ed. Pacific Grove, California: Brooks/Cole Publishing Company

Rogers, C.R. (1961) *On Becoming a Person* London: Constable & Robinson Ltd

Sarafino, E.P. (1998) *Health Psychology: Biopsychosocial Interactions*, third ed. New York: John Wiley & Sons

Sarafino, E.P. and Goldfedder, J. (1995), cited in *Asthma and Genetics* http://acc6.its.brooklyn.cuny.edu/~scintech/asthma/Genetics2.htm

Shaffer, D.R. (1993) *Developmental Psychology: Childhood and Adolescence*, third ed. Pacific Grove: Brooks/Cole Publishing Company

Useful websites

Cognitive behavioural therapy
www.rcpsych.ac.uk

Gesell's assessment scale
www.freudianslip.co.uk

Infantile autism
www.narsad.org

MIND
www.mind.org.uk

Stages of prenatal development
www.babycenter.com

Research methodology

Introduction

Research involves finding out about a particular topic for a specific purpose, such as gaining a greater understanding of human behaviour, improving facilities or understanding the causes of disease. Research enables us to gain understanding which can be applied in a variety of settings and situations. It allows a body of knowledge to be built up and used to benefit society.

As part of your studies you need to understand the research process and be able to carry out a research project of your own. By understanding how and why research is carried out in health and social care, and the methods used to conduct it, you will be able to bring a critical eye to any claims made about service needs, new 'wonder drugs' and a whole range of issues you will encounter both as a student and as a practitioner.

In this unit you will learn about different methods that can be used and the advantages and limitations of such methods. You will also learn about the importance of the ethical issues involved in the research process. You will be introduced to the guidelines you need to work within to ensure that research is carried out ethically, and given advice on how to gain permission to carry out your own research project.

You will also learn how to collect data and present it in a manner that can be easily understood by a reader. Undertaking a research project yourself will allow you to put theory into practice and give you the skills necessary to carry out a research project of your own as a practitioner in this field. As you work your way through this unit you will be given practice assessment tasks which will help you to complete your assessment for the unit.

How you will be assessed

This unit is internally assessed. You will produce a written piece of work which will cover the learning outcomes opposite.

Thinking points

Imagine you move to a rural area where the nearest doctor's surgery is five miles away but you have no transport and the local bus service only runs once a day. You would be concerned at the lack of provision. It would be difficult to take your children to the surgery to get them immunised and you might be more likely to put off going to see your GP because of the difficulties involved. This means that you would suffer compared to someone living in an urban area where it is easy to access facilities. Research into access to high quality health care would draw attention to your situation and be the first step towards improving it. You will be learning about the purpose and role of research in more detail as you work through this unit.

Research is a crucial aspect of health and social care. However, the research process is a fairly lengthy one and needs to be thought through carefully. A major area of concern is about conducting sensitive, but important, research in an ethical way. For example, it is important to know about the experiences of people with HIV and AIDS, but how would you go about getting a sample (a group of people to investigate) for such a research project? Would people be anxious about having their health status revealed to employers? How would you reassure them that this wouldn't happen? Another area of concern is child protection.

You will be looking carefully at these issues in this unit and will be able to carry out some research in an area of interest to you (within limits).

Can you think of any areas that might interest you?

What might some of the ethical and practical issues be?

- Understand the purpose and role of research within health and social care
- Understand the research methodologies relevant to health and social care
- Be able to identify a suitable topic and produce a plan for a research proposal
- Be able to conduct the research and present the findings
- Be able to evaluate the research project

The purpose of research

As stated in the introduction, research involves finding out about a topic for a particular purpose. Some of these specific purposes are described below.

Research to identify need

All service providers need information about the needs of a community, or group of people, before they can decide what resources and services are required to meet this need. For example, if a new housing estate is being developed and there is an anticipated influx of people from outside the area, does a new health centre need to be built? How many health care professionals (GPs, nurses, chiropodists etc) will be needed? This involves the collection of **demographic data**, in this case information about population trends. An example of how research has identified the need for health care interventions is given below.

This example is just one of a number of current topics which have an intensive research focus. The research is aimed at finding out more about important public

Key terms

Demographic data Any data that locate, identify or describe populations and their properties or characteristics. For example, demographic data will describe the age groups of people living in certain geographical areas, or perhaps in certain income categories. Other dimensions or characteristics of demographic data include race, religion, political preferences, spending preferences, family size etc.

health issues, with a view to implementing initiatives to improve the situation.

Reflect

How often do you eat food from fast food outlets such as McDonalds? When you do, do you regard this as a treat? Would you be willing to feed your own children with this food? If not, why not?

In context Promoting better sexual health

Good sexual health is becoming an increasingly important public health issue. In 2003, more than 3000 people in London were diagnosed as having HIV – the highest ever level. Between 1996 and 2002, the number of cases of gonorrhoea diagnosed rose by 83 per cent, while identified cases of chlamydia increased by 132 per cent.

The incidence of sexually transmitted infections is particularly high in London's black and minority ethnic communities. There is a strong belief that access to sexual health services and effective preventative services does not adequately meet their needs.*

1 **Summarise the trends in the three sexually transmitted diseases mentioned in the extract.**

2 **Why do you think black and ethnic minority communities in London suffer particularly high rates of sexually transmitted diseases?**

3 **The issue of sexually transmitted diseases is described as a 'public health issue'. Do you agree that this is a public, not a private, issue? Do you think there should be special powers to deal with this? If so, what?**

*Source: www.kingsfund.org.uk

From your own experience, how much good quality information did you receive, at an appropriate time, about how to protect yourself against sexually transmitted diseases? What was effective and what wasn't? What might *you* do differently if you were in charge of a campaign?

Within medicine and social care there is a constant need to update knowledge about illness and disease as well as best practice in providing social care provision (for

In context

'Scottish scientists have developed a test that can predict whether a wound will become infected, making it possible to stop superbug infections before they begin … The technique measures the levels of biological molecules associated with an immune response by the body to bacteria in a wound. By measuring the presence of these molecules, doctors can tell if the wound is likely to become infected.

Breda Cullen, the researcher who invented this test, claims that it would also reduce the requirement to use antibiotics to fight superbugs such as MRSA by stopping them before they cause an infection. She said: 'If clinicians could respond to wound infection as early as possible the infection could be treated topically (i.e. by applying an ointment or cream directly to the skin) as opposed to having to use antibiotics. The use of the invention is envisaged as being most useful in predicting or diagnosing clinical infection of a chronic wound such as ulcers and sores.'

Source: www.talentscotland.com

A finding from another research project investigating MRSA has identified a promising means of promoting the healing of infected wounds, which may both prevent and potentially cure MRSA. A

company called ZooBiotic has found promising results from research into the use of maggots to treat patients with infected wounds such as leg ulcers and bed sores. 'The tiny grubs clean up nasty injuries by devouring dead and dying tissue. Enzymes in their saliva sterilise the infected area by killing bacteria, including the MRSA bug.'
Source: www.business.timesonline.co.uk

1   **Summarise the method suggested of predicting whether a wound will become infected and one advantage of this technique.**

2   **Summarise the advantages and disadvantages of using maggots to treat infected wounds.**

3   **Do you think that patients with infected wounds that would respond to treatment using maggots should be offered only this treatment, and refused antibiotics except in very unusual circumstances?**

Figure 22.1 Unpleasant as it may seem, the use of maggots is a highly effective way of treating infections!

example, ways of organising residential care). Although there have been sudden, famous breakthroughs in research (such as the discovery of penicillin) most research is carried out in a slow and painstaking manner, building on prior knowledge. To use the example of **MRSA** (a worrying infection that is resistant to most antibiotics) a considerable amount of research funding and time have been devoted to finding ways of identifying patients at risk as the example below demonstrates.

Key terms

MRSA This is short for methicillin-resistant Staphylococcus aureus. In some media, it has been dubbed the 'killer bug' or 'hospital super bug' because it has developed resistance to many antibiotics. Even the antibiotics that are effective against MRSA have to be given in much higher doses over much longer periods to be successful.

We have referred earlier to the purpose of research in identifying needs. It is also carried out to identify if there are gaps in provision, or groups of people in the community who are, for whatever reason, missing out on health and social care provision. Despite the availability of a wide number of health centres, hospitals and community initiatives designed to make health care available to all, there are always members of society who fail to take up such provision, for one reason or another. One such group is asylum seekers, as illustrated below.

Theory into practice

Conduct a short interview with a representative of your local health centre and ask them about other groups within society who miss out on care provision, for whatever reason.

In context

An interview survey was carried out by the British Medical Association (BMA) among asylum seekers and refugees, to investigate the reasons for low uptake of health care provision. It was found that many suffered from communicable diseases such as tuberculosis, hepatitis A, B and C and HIV/AIDS. Psychological and social health problems such as depression, anxiety and stress were also common. In order to attempt to meet the health care needs of asylum seekers, the report recommended the setting up of dedicated medical clinics in areas where there are large numbers of asylum seekers. Additional funding has been provided by the Home Office and dedicated asylum teams have been established in areas where there is a high concentration of asylum seekers.

Source: www.bma.org.uk/ap.nsf/Content/Asylumseekers

1 **List three communicable diseases and two psychological problems identified as being common among asylum seekers.**

2 **Choose one communicable disease and one psychological illness and identify why asylum seekers may suffer from these.**

3 **To what extent do you think the health of the nation could be improved by adopting the recommendation that the government should set up dedicated medical clinics in areas where there are a lot of asylum seekers?**

Research to plan provision

Having identified needs and gaps in provision, this type of research is carried out to find out what services are available for those who need them. Research lacks value if its findings are not put into practice and it is important that, having identified any kind of need or gap in provision, attempts are made to fill the gaps so that all those resident in this country can receive the best quality health and social care to which they are entitled. However, some groups may be overlooked in society. An example of research to plan provision for such a group is a programme of work set up by the Kings Fund – its aim is to find out more about the needs of black and ethnic minority individuals in terms of accessing health care. One specific goal of this research is to 'suggest new … initiatives that could be used to encourage NHS organisations to improve access to care for such groups'.

The role of research

Having carried out a piece of research, the research body will then publish its findings, usually in a **peer-reviewed** journal such as *The Lancet* or another specialist journal. Research findings alone, however, are of no benefit unless they are put to use. This means that policy makers and administrators must keep abreast of newly published findings and take steps to implement the key findings in the course of daily practice.

Key terms

Peer-reviewed This means that before an article is printed in a specialist journal (such as *The Lancet* which is for doctors and other medical professionals) it must first be scrutinised by other doctors and specialists in the field. They will examine the method and sample used and scrutinise the findings to make sure that any claims made about the findings are accurate and truthful. This method ensures that only high-quality research is published and made available to the general public.

Research to inform policy or practice

In the example given on page 410, about asylum seekers who were not receiving adequate health care, decisions were made about how changes could be implemented in order to fill these gaps and ensure that the needs of this particular group were adequately met. In a similar way, findings about transmission of disease, effectiveness of vaccinations or best practice in looking after the elderly must be followed up and adopted by policy makers. The guidelines on page 412 were issued by Addenbrooke's Hospital to its staff. They are based on knowledge about the means by which MRSA can be spread. To read the full document from which the guidelines were extracted, visit the following website: http://www.addenbrookes. org.uk/standards/index.html.

Similar detailed instructions are given in the document for the other four standards.

Research to extend knowledge and understanding

This refers to research where there is already some existing knowledge but which needs to be built on in order to widen and deepen understanding of some social or medical phenomenon. An example of this is shown in the experiment described on page 413. In this case, there was a general awareness among psychologists and social care practitioners that having a sense of control was beneficial to health. High control enables an individual to maintain a healthy lifestyle by believing 'I can do something to prevent illness'. Following an illness, a high sense of control enables an individual to change their behaviour. Even though they are not well, if they believe there is something they can do to make themselves better, they will. The case study illustrates a piece of research carried out in order to extend these findings to the elderly in nursing homes.

Search

Contact us | Home

Cambridge University Hospitals **NHS**
NHS Foundation Trust

About us   Patients   Visitors   Press   Services   Research   Teaching   Careers   A to Z

About the Trust | Infection control

Standards – Take 5 campaign

On 28 February 2005, we launched for our staff our **standards for a clean and safe hospital**.

We ask our staff to follow the five steps for each of our five standards to help keep Addenbrooke's clean and safe for patients, visitors and staff:

1. Hand hygiene

2. Dress code and uniform

3. Personal protective equipment

4. Intravascular Cannula Care

5. Urinary Catheter Care

They are mainly for staff who have direct contact with patients but all staff need to be aware of them and follow them as appropriate. They are backed up by full policies, which are available to our staff on our Intranet.

You can help our staff meet these standards by reporting any problems and helping to keep your bed area clutter-free.

If staff have any queries about the standards, they are asked to speak to their manager or one of the senior clinical nurses (our 'modern matrons').

Take 5

Together we can fight infection

1. Hand hygiene

1. Use alcohol gel every time you enter or leave a ward or clinic

2. Clean your hands before and after every hands-on patient contact

3. Clean your hands when you enter a patient curtain area

4. Wash your hands with liquid soap and water whenever your hands are visibly soiled

5. Wash your hands with liquid soap and water after five alcohol gel applications

Figure 22.2 An extract from Addenbrooke's Hospital Take 5 Campaign, which tackles MRSA

In context

Langer and Rodin (1976) carried out an **experiment** using a **sample** of elderly residents in a nursing home. The home had two floors, each containing residents of similar physical and psychological health and who had a similar **socio-economic status**. On one floor, the residents were allowed to have more responsibilities than those on the other floor. These included looking after house plants, making decisions about what activities to take part in and rearranging furniture. The residents on the other floor, however, were given no plants, no choice over what activities they would take part in and no permission to move the furniture around. The researchers found that for as much as a year and a half later, the residents with control were happier, more active and more alert than the others.

Note: The ethical implications of this experiment merit serious discussion within your group, in the light of the section on ethics on pages 429–31.

1 Describe *three* differences in the amount of control given to one group of elderly residents over the other. Briefly explain the psychological and physical consequences of this level of control.

2 Explain why this type of research is useful in extending knowledge and understanding. Make reference to details from the research cited above and give one additional example of your own.

3 Write a short report to an individual who is making an application to open a nursing home for the elderly. Include details of what is known about existing research about the role of control in promoting health and well-being. Make at least five suggestions of things this individual could do to ensure that their clients have the best possible psychological and physical health while in the nursing home.

Key terms

Experiment A research method involving a high level of control (see page 422 for a fuller description).

Sample A group of participants chosen from the target population. To avoid bias, samples must be representative of the target population. (In this case, the target population is all residents of nursing homes and the sample is those actually involved in the experiment.)

Socio-economic status A measure of an individual's or family's social and economic status and ranking compared with other groups in society (for example, a doctor is seen as having a higher social status and economic means than a hospital porter).

Research to improve practice

Once findings from research have been published and made available to health and social care practitioners and administrators, it is then important to use these findings in order to improve the way in which such individuals carry out their duties. An example has been given earlier of research into the spread of MRSA which has led to initiatives to change practice in line with up-to-date research.

Research to aid reflection and allow progress to be monitored

At some point you have probably been asked to complete an evaluation form where you are asked to comment on what you felt was helpful and less helpful about an event (for example, the way a particular course was taught). You may have been asked to make suggestions for improvements. Information from all these forms would then have been collated by the organiser who would then examine trends to see what was going well and what not so well. This information allows the provider to *reflect* upon the service being provided and to identify any gaps or flaws in the provision. Reflection (or evaluation) is an essential part of the research process. It may, for example, highlight

In context

Janis (1958) interviewed patients before an operation to find out the level of fear they were experiencing and the effects different types of information could have in aiding recovery and reducing distress. On the basis of these findings, practice was changed so patients were given different types of information according to the type of operation they were about to undergo. Sensory information is an example. This involves telling patients about information which will enter the senses, such as the taste of the anaesthetic, any feelings of discomfort that may be experienced, difficulty focusing when coming round after an operation etc. For example, patients about to undergo an endoscopy were given sensory information and suffered less distress afterwards. Procedural information, designed to help

the patient learn how the procedures would be carried out, also resulted in lower post-operative distress and decreased recovery times. Such practices are now commonplace but they would not have happened if it had not been for the role of research in providing relevant findings.

1 **Explain what is meant by sensory information and give one example of this type of information.**

2 **Summarise the role of procedural pre-operative information in aiding recovery from surgery.**

3 **Write a paragraph giving guidance to nursing staff on how and why pre-operative information can aid recovery.**

---

a need for further research or a change in a particular public health implementation.

Suppose, for example, you were in charge of an initiative designed to raise awareness among young teenagers of the types of sexually transmitted diseases that exist and methods of protection. You might organise a programme which can be delivered by a nurse or other health care professional to groups of individuals in that age group. It could be, however, that the programme is ineffective in a number of ways – the information might be presented in such a way that it goes over the heads of the youngsters. If they don't understand the content, then clearly they cannot act on it. On the other hand, it may be that a large proportion of these young teenagers are already sexually active and are worried that they may have already acquired a sexually transmitted disease: as the programme is aimed at prevention, and not cure, no information may be given as to what to do next if you are in this situation. By encouraging the teenagers to communicate on these issues when they evaluate the programme, the organisers can then reflect upon (consider in depth) how effective it was and consider how they could improve the initiative in future.

■ Monitoring progress

Monitoring progress is also a crucial part of the research role. Imagine a local health centre identifies a gap in the uptake of ante-natal care among a particular group of women: it may decide to set up particular initiatives to increase participation amongst this particular group. Without monitoring, however, there is no way of knowing whether such initiatives are useful or not. A likely way of monitoring this might be to take a baseline figure of total numbers attending over a set period and then compare this with the total attending over an identical time period following the implementation of the new system.

Theory into practice

Arrange to speak to a health visitor, social worker or equal opportunities expert and ask what groups of women they think might be reluctant to attend ante-natal sessions, and for what reasons? Ask for suggestions as to the kind of initiatives that could be implemented to encourage them to attend.

Remember!

If a researcher only obtains data about people attending after the introduction of the new initiative, they have not gained any information about who is not attending.

Research to examine topics of contemporary importance

All the examples given above relate to topics that have immediate, everyday importance in the field of health care. It is also important to conduct research in areas of social care in order to identify needs, provide further knowledge and highlight gaps in provision. A relevant current topic in this field concerns the best way to look after children who, for whatever reason, cannot be looked after at home. In 2004 it was reported in a national newspaper that, due to a shortage of people willing to take on the role of foster parents, many children are being placed in families not suited to taking on this role. Research carried out by a charity, The Fostering Network, has identified a 6000 shortfall in suitable foster carers which represents a 35 per cent rise since the last survey was carried out in 2002.

Other contemporary topics of importance include genetic research, cloning, the use of stem cell research and the emergence (or re-emergence) and/or increase of life-threatening diseases, viruses and illnesses such as HIV/AIDS, tuberculosis and Legionnaires' disease.

Assessment activity 22.1

Explain the purpose and role of research for the health and social care sectors.

The Joseph Rowntree Foundation is a charity involved in researching the causes of a variety of social difficulties and ways to overcome them (for example, child poverty, the need for public housing etc). One project it is currently involved in researching is called 'What will it take to end child poverty in the UK?' and its purpose is to 'estimate how much it will cost to end child poverty by 2020'. It will include a review of associated issues, such as employment, education and mental health'. For more information, go to: www.jrf.org.uk/research-and-policy/poverty-and-disadvantage/summary.asp.

1 Explain the purpose and role of this piece of research for the health and social care sector.

Grading tip for P1

To achieve P1 you need to decide whether this is research to identify need, to provide further knowledge or for other purposes, and the role of the research (for example, to inform policy or practice).

Take it further

Log on to the Joseph Rowntree Foundation website and find other examples of work they are carrying out. See if there is a topic there that you might investigate for your own research project.

Types of research

Quantitative

This refers to research where the type of data collected consists of numbers. This allows for the use of descriptive statistics such as averages and percentages and it can be easily represented using graphs and charts. It is **objective data** and is useful when you want to compare large numbers of people on one particular dimension. The following are examples of quantitative data:

- the number of children aged 2–4 who attend a particular nursery
- the number of people answering 'yes' to the question 'Do you think abortion is immoral?'
- the number of times a child chooses a toy lorry, car or tractor during the course of a 30-minute observational study
- the length of time taken to measure a patient's blood pressure
- the percentage of people agreeing with the statement 'It is not possible for a heterosexual male to contract the HIV virus.'
- the average age of adults over the age of 65 attending a clinic for a flu vaccination.

Key terms

Objective data This refers to data which is collected without any need for interpretation by the researcher (for example, the number of students on a health and social care course; total immunisations given to children aged 18–36 months in a local health centre).

Research methods that generate quantitative data include the following:

- experiments
- observations
- closed questions (see page 420) in interviews or questionnaires.

Qualitative

This type of research is used to obtain data in a non-numerical form – usually in the form of words. An individual can express themselves in their own words. This method is usually used when the researcher wants to find out about the feelings and thoughts a person has. The data obtained is **subjective** and gives great insight into how an individual experiences an event. Examples of research methods that obtain qualitative data are:

- questionnaires consisting of open questions
- unstructured (or semi-structured) interviews.

Both quantitative and qualitative data have a variety of advantages and disadvantages which you need to consider when selecting and evaluating your research methodology. Some examples are given in the table below.

Quantitative data	
Advantages	**Disadvantages**
Easy and quick to analyse	Gives information about facts and behaviour but not reasons for behaviour
Data tends to be very precise and easy to measure	The data are limited in scope and only focus on certain predetermined aspects of the participants' experiences and behaviour
Enables comparisons to be made across participants	
Qualitative data	
Advantages	**Disadvantages**
Lets you find out about an individual's subjective experience	Very time-consuming to analyse
Gives rich insights into people's experiences which cannot be obtained using quantitative methods	Can be difficult to **replicate**
	May be subject to **researcher bias**

Table 22.1 The pros and cons of quantitative and qualitative data

Key terms

Subjective data This refers to data that expresses a personal point of view (for example, the reasons for choosing to study health and social care; beliefs about the causes of mental disorder).

Replication This refers to a situation where a research investigation is carried out based on a previous one, using a similar sample and the same methodology. If replication occurs, the second research will come out with the same findings.

Researcher bias This refers to the possibility that the researcher may interpret data in a way that suits their **hypothesis**. If an answer is given that is ambiguous (i.e. it could be interpreted in different ways), they may interpret it in a way that supports what they wanted to find out in the first place. Alternatively, they may give some sort of prompt, or cue, to the participant in a face-to-face study which influences the participant to behave in a particular way (sometimes called 'investigator effects' or 'demand characteristics').

Hypothesis A precise, testable statement which makes a prediction about the findings the researcher expects to make. For example, 'the more control elderly residents are given in a nursing home, the better their health outcomes'.

■ Methods that produce quantitative and qualitative data

Some researchers use a combination of different research methods to obtain both types of data. For example, in an experimental study, participants may be asked afterwards what they thought or felt as they were taking part in the experiment. Questionnaires can contain a mixture of both closed and open questions (see pages 420 and 421). A question such as 'Do you think primary school children should be given sex education lessons?' could be answered with 'yes' or 'no' (closed question generating quantitative data) and then followed up by an open question such as 'Could you explain your reasons for this answer?' A similar mixture of items can be used in an interview method.

Primary research

This refers to data that is collected by a researcher or group of researchers. It can be either quantitative or qualitative data and can be obtained by using any of the research methods listed and discussed below under 'Primary sources'.

Secondary research

This involves using material that has been published by someone else. A common use of secondary sources is to gain background information on a topic you want to investigate. Usually for a project of this kind, you would find four or five articles on the topic you are interested in and use these as a background to your particular research. So if, for example, you were interested in finding out about asthma in pre-school children, you might use statistics to find out the prevalence of asthma and whether it varies across regions or over time. This gives a good factual basis to your project. You may also look for articles which discuss theories about why asthma affects some children and not others. You could also look at people's stories about living with asthma. All this material would enable you to write what is called a literature review at the start of your project.

Primary sources

These refer to sources of data you obtain yourself. The data can be collected using any of the research methods detailed below, such as experimental methods and questionnaires. Probably the most commonly used primary sources of data in health and social care are questionnaires and interviews.

Questionnaires

A questionnaire survey involves asking participants about some aspect of their attitudes, behaviours or intentions. The use of a questionnaire allows the researcher to gain information from large numbers of participants relatively quickly and efficiently. The researcher obtains information from a specified population of interest, by administering a questionnaire to a *sample* of the relevant population.

Questionnaires can consist of open or closed questions, or a mixture of the two. They can also be administered in different ways, either indirectly or directly.

Indirect (sometimes called self-completion)	Direct (completed by interviewer)
• By post • By telephone • Via the Internet • Left for the participants to collect from a central point	Asking people directly to take part in the research, reading out the questions to them and then writing down their answers

Table 22.2 Direct and indirect methods of administering questionnaire surveys

Advantages of self-completion questionnaires

- They are inexpensive to administer.
- A large sample can be obtained.
- There is no interviewer bias.
- People may respond more honestly without the presence of a researcher.

Disadvantages of self-completion questionnaires

- There is a lower response rate than for questionnaires administered by a researcher.
- Participants may misunderstand the questions and give a 'best guess' answer.

Advantages of interviewer-completed (face-to-face) questionnaires

- There is a high response rate.
- Fuller, more accurate, information is available.
- There may be higher validity since the researcher is there to answer questions and give a full explanation of any questions which may be imprecise or ambiguous. For example, if a question is worded as 'Do you ever take aerobic exercise?' the respondent (the person completing the interview) may not understand the word 'aerobic' and so would not be able to answer correctly.

Disadvantages of interviewer-completed (face-to-face) questionnaires

- This is a costly and time-consuming method of obtaining data.
- There is a danger of interviewer bias.

Theory into practice

You want to carry out a project to collect primary data about the use of breast and testicular self-examination among students at your local college. Which type of method would you use – interview or questionnaire? Justify your choice of method and make notes on the advantages and disadvantages of the method you have chosen.

Interviews

Interviews are a method of gathering primary data which involve face-to-face communication between the researcher and one or more participants. They range from casual chats to formal, standardised set questions which have to be asked in a particular way. There are three types of interview:

- structured
- semi-structured
- unstructured.

Structured interviews

These involve asking a set of questions which have been decided on previously by the researcher. The questions are asked in a set sequence, using the same wording for each participant. The purpose of this is to be able to compare answers to the same question from a large number of people.

Advantages of the structured interview method include:

- It is easier to generalise findings providing a large enough sample is used.

- It is quick to administer.
- Responses are relatively easy to analyse because the researcher simply compares answers from different participants to the same question.

Disadvantages of the structured interview method include:

- Answers are restricted to the questions that have been pre-set. Not so many insights can be gained as with an unstructured or clinical interview.
- There may be less validity and a loss of realism due to the fixed nature of the questions.
- Information may be unclear if the wording is ambiguous or complex.

■ Semi-structured interviews

These consist of a set of questions that are asked of all participants, as with structured interviews. However, the researcher is also free to follow up certain questions with additional, open-ended questions such as 'How did you feel about that?' or 'Could you tell me a bit more about how you felt when that happened?'

Advantages of the semi-structured interview method include:

- It generates data that can be compared across participants. In addition, though, it enables researchers to gain subjective meanings i.e. what the experience actually means to the individual (for example, what it feels like to have chemotherapy).
- It enables complex issues to be explored. These may be difficult to investigate through quantitative techniques. Questions can be tailored to the responses of the interviewees so that issues can be explored which may not initially have been thought of as important. Thus this method allows considerably more flexibility and the possibility of uncovering new perspectives that had previously not been considered.
- Researchers are enabled to identify personal aspects of behaviour. If carried out sensitively, information about aspects of behaviour which are private or personal to the individuals concerned can be obtained.

Disadvantages of the semi-structured interview method include:

- Conducting interviews is complex, highly labour-intensive and requires specialist training on the part of the interviewer. If an interviewer is insensitive, the interviewee may stop talking and refuse to answer further questions, or answer them untruthfully. It takes a long time to build up trust.
- In order to avoid bias, the interviewer must be detached, which can be difficult to achieve in a face-to-face situation. There is a possibility of the interviewer misrepresenting or only partially interpreting the data obtained.
- Aspects of the interviewer can have an effect on the interviewee (for example, age, gender, ethnic group, physical attractiveness, style of dress etc). These may affect the responses of the interviewee and result in the data being invalid.
- The respondent may be influenced in their answers by a desire to appear socially acceptable. For example, it is now considered desirable for us all 'to do our bit' to reduce global warming. A question which asks about situations when you use a car could prompt the respondent to claim untruthfully that they use public transport or walk/cycle when they can, and only use a car when absolutely necessary. This would result in inaccurate data being obtained by the researcher.
- Qualitative data obtained from unstructured interviews may not be easy to analyse (see section on qualitative analysis see page 416).

■ Unstructured interviews

Unstructured interviews have no defined structure – no pre-determined questions or format for delivery: they are sometimes compared with a conversation that is recorded. The interviewer asks questions that arise naturally out of the course of the interview and follows up answers with new questions which guide the interviewee into explaining or revealing more about their views and beliefs. This type of interview may be used when the researcher is more interested in the experiences of a particular individual than in making comparisons across a group of people.

Advantages of the unstructured interview method include:

- It is useful for obtaining an in-depth account of the experiences of a single individual.
- It can help a researcher to gain ideas for further research, perhaps generating ideas for specific topics that can be pursued or questions to be answered.

Disadvantages of the unstructured interview method include:

- It requires considerable confidence and skill on the part of the interviewer. They need to know how to put the interviewee at ease and how to guide the interview if there are any difficult pauses or breaks.
- Particular skill and experience are required if sensitive or emotional topics are being discussed or emerge during the course of the interview.

■ How to construct items for a questionnaire or interview

You need to decide whether to use closed or open questions, or a mixture of both.

Closed questions

Closed questions do not allow the respondent to answer in their own words. The researcher pre-determines the format of the question so that there is a 'forced-choice' answer (for example, yes/no). This type of question generates quantitative data.

Closed questions are useful when you want to compare data across a set of participants on the same dimension (for example, gender, number of children, number of times admitted to hospital as an in-patient). You can summarise responses quickly and easily and produce the results as descriptive statistics (averages or percentages) and present them clearly using graphs or charts.

Types of closed questions include:

- **Checklists**

  Here, respondents tick any items that apply. For example:

Please tick all the statements below which you believe to be true about Auto-Immune Deficiency Syndrome (AIDS).	
☐	A person can 'carry' and pass on whatever causes AIDS without necessarily getting AIDS or looking sick.
☐	All people who have the HIV virus have AIDS.
☐	Homosexual men are at particular risk of AIDS.
☐	You can catch the AIDS virus if you have oral sex and the man ejaculates.
☐	The AIDS virus can be caught from a blood transfusion in the UK.
☐	You cannot get AIDS if you are heterosexual.
☐	Drug abusers catch AIDS because they share needles and syringes.

- **Placing items in rank order**

  An example would be:

Please place a number against each of the following aspects of a healthy lifestyle you believe to be most important, placing them in rank order from 1 (most important) to 5 (least important).	
☐	Getting enough sleep
☐	Avoiding smoking tobacco
☐	Taking at least 30 minutes' exercise three times a week
☐	Avoiding alcohol altogether
☐	Eating a low-fat, high-fibre diet

- **Attitude scales**

An example of an attitude scale would be:

☐	Strongly disagree
☐	Neither agree nor disagree
☐	Agree
☐	Strongly agree

Please tick the response that best reflects your attitude to the statement 'An individual who develops lung cancer having spent some years smoking should pay for their treatment from the NHS'.

Reflect

If you were asked 'Are you a heavy smoker?' you only have to answer 'yes' or 'no'. How do you decide what is meant by 'heavy'? Do you think you might be tempted to say 'no' because you don't want to be seen in a bad light?

- **Likert scales**

These are based on a numerical rating. For example:

How important are the following factors in assessing the quality of care you receive as a patient in this hospital? (Please circle the appropriate number.)	Very important		Neither important nor unimportant		Very unimportant
Professionalism of staff	1	2	3	4	5
Interest and sympathy in me personally	1	2	3	4	5
Being given the opportunity to ask questions	1	2	3	4	5

Examples of closed questions include:

Question	Range of answers available
1 Are you male or female?	Male/Female
2 Please circle your age: [15–19] [20–24] [25–29] [30–34] [35–39] [40–44] [45–49] [50–54] [55–59] [60–64]	Only one age range can be chosen
3 Do you smoke?	Yes/No
4 Are you a heavy smoker?	Yes/No
5 Do you smoke cannabis?	Yes/No
6 Do you smoke cannabis often?	Yes/No

Open questions

Open questions are worded in such a way that the respondent is able to answer using their own words. This type of question generates qualitative data and is usually asked when the researcher wants to find out about the subjective experience, beliefs and attitudes of the respondent. Typically, this type of question is used in unstructured or semi-structured interviews, although open questions can also be included in questionnaires.

Examples of open questions include:

- What are your views about day care for children under the age of 3?
- What sort of information do you think primary school children receive about safe sex?
- Why do you think some people choose to have an abortion?
- Do you have any ideas about the reasons why people choose not to have their children immunised with the MMR vaccine?

Open questions can also be used to avoid 'leading' the participant (i.e. wording a question in such a way as to encourage them to answer in a particular way). For example, if the question about day care above was worded as 'Do you agree that children under the age of three should not be placed in day care?' it seems clear that the researcher wants people to agree with this statement: there is a danger that agreement may not represent the person's real views but just be an example of them trying to please the researcher.

Theory into practice

Consider which of the closed questions below could be converted to open questions. Explain your reasoning.

1. Do you think parents are to blame if their child is obese?
2. Do you think peer pressure is responsible for binge drinking?
3. Do you think children are more likely to smoke if one of their parents does?
4. Do you think smoking cannabis inevitably leads to taking harder drugs such as heroin or cocaine?
5. Do you think day care under the age of 5 is harmful to children's social and emotional well-being?

Scientific experiment

This method is widely used in both the natural sciences (biology, chemistry, physics etc) and in some social sciences subjects (for example, psychology). Its chief purpose is to keep all aspects of a situation constant except the one the researcher is looking at.

Imagine the researcher is interested in the effects of caffeine on levels of alertness. They might set up an experiment where one group of participants is given no caffeine and another is given two cups of strong coffee. Both groups are then asked to perform a fairly simple task (for example, pressing a button whenever a dot appears on a screen) to see if the group which has been given caffeine is more vigilant (alert and quick) than the other. The aspect of the situation that is changed by the researcher is called the **independent variable** (or IV), while the response by the participant is called the **dependent variable** (DV). In this example, caffeine is the IV and measured response time is the DV. The response time is a dependent variable because it depends on whether the participant has had caffeine or not. The researcher tries to keep all other variables constant (the same) so that they can be sure that the dependent variable isn't a result of some other, unknown, cause (for example, being very good at the task in the first place).

Remember!

- *Qualitative data* produces data in the form of words. It can be obtained from interviews and questionnaires that use open questions.
- *Quantitative data* takes the form of numbers. It can be obtained from observations and closed questions in interviews or questionnaires.
- *Open questions* are useful when you want to know what people think or feel.
- *Closed questions* are useful when you want to compare a number of people on just one dimension (for example, their age, gender, whether they vote or not etc).
- *Leading questions* should be avoided as people may respond with what you want them to say and not what they really think.

The other variables to be considered include:

- situational variables, for example, the time of day, lighting conditions, noise and temperature
- people variables, for example, the amount of caffeine normally drunk, state of alertness/tiredness, ability at this type of task, gender, age, physical health etc.

If variables that are not the IV or DV are not controlled, they are called **confounding variables** and will, effectively, spoil the experiment since it won't be possible to say with any degree of confidence that caffeine affects performance on a vigilance task.

Key terms

Independent variable The aspect of an experimental set-up that is controlled by the researcher.

Dependent variable The performance of participants as a result of manipulation of the independent variable.

Confounding variables Variables that are not intended to be measured but which, if left uncontrolled, may spoil the experiment. They are a potential source of error.

■ Advantages of the experimental method

- It is possible to achieve a high level of control.
- By controlling extraneous variables it can be said with some certainty that the IV causes the DV.
- The researcher can decide which participants take part in which condition.

■ Disadvantages of the experimental method

- A very high degree of control may make the whole situation artificial.
- Some participants may respond differently because they are in an experimental setting.
- Because the experimental set-up is artificial, care must be taken in assuming that behaviour in the outside world will be the same.

The main purpose of an observational method is to gain information on behaviour rather than thoughts, attitudes or feelings. Observation is often used to provide information which can then be used as a basis for further study, or for generating a hypothesis about some aspect of behaviour. Both formal and informal observational methods involve collecting data by observing an individual or a group of individuals. The difference lies in how the observational research is set up by the researcher.

■ Formal observation

In a formal observation, individuals may be asked to come to a particular place and take part in a particular task. A lot of research into children's development uses this method. Investigations into **attachment theory** often use a formal observational method known as the 'strange situation'. This involves bringing infants with their main caregiver into a specially equipped room which is pleasant and bright and contains toys. The room contains a two-way mirror behind which one or more observers are seated ready to take notes. There follows a sequence of events and, during one of them, the main caregiver leaves the room and observers make careful note of how the infant reacts to their absence and how easily they are soothed by the caregiver's return. According to this behaviour (among others), the infant can then be categorised as securely or insecurely attached.

Key terms

Attachment theory A theory formulated by child psychologist John Bowlby (1907–90) who believed that children need to form a secure and long-lasting attachment to an individual (usually the primary care-giver) in order to have positive psychological development in later life.

■ Gathering data from an observational study

Records of an observation can be made using any of the following methods:

- film or video recording
- audio tape

- digital camera
- handwritten notes created at the time of the observation.

To carry out an observational study where you use handwritten notes, it is necessary to decide beforehand what types of behaviours you intend to examine and create a checklist of behaviours you intend to record. There are a number of ways of constructing the checklists and you need to decide which is most suited to the purpose of your observation and the data you want to collect.

They include:

- **Recording events**

Here you make a record each time an event occurs within the period of the observation. You are then able to total up the events. An example is given below of an observational checklist used to gain data on social interactions shown by a child in a nursery setting.

Behaviour to observe	0–9 minutes	10–19 minutes	20–29 minutes	Totals
Asks for help from adult	III		III	
Asks for help from child		II		
Offers help to child		II	III	
Touches another child		I		
Smiles	IIII	III	II	

- **Recording sequences**

This type of observational checklist tends to focus on one individual performing a behaviour of interest to the researcher. This is valuable when examining interactions between people. An example is given below of a checklist designed to gain data on interactions within a staff meeting.

	Asks for information	Offers information	Asks for clarification	Disagrees	Agrees	Sums up
Person 1						
Person 2						
Person 3						

Theory into practice

Devise an observational checklist to gain information on one of the following examples (or use an example of your own):

1 nurses' behaviour towards their patients

2 adherence to MRSA guidelines

3 independent behaviour shown by children in a post-operative ward.

■ Advantages of formal observations

- Target behaviours which are of interest to the researcher can be identified beforehand and focused on.
- The researcher can set up a situation which restricts the participants' choice to only those aspects which are relevant to the research hypothesis (for example, bringing children into a play room with a limited selection of toys to observe what they choose to play with).

■ Disadvantages of formal observations

- Certain behaviours may only occur in a natural, everyday situation and, consequently, would not be observed in formal observations.
- There may be behaviours of interest which have not been previously identified as important for observation.

■ Informal observation

This type of research method is aimed at obtaining data from people's behaviour in their natural environment.

Probably the most famous use of this type of method is when people study the behaviour of animals in the wild (when hidden cameras are used in order not to disturb the natural environment). In a similar way, with people, a researcher will try to observe behaviour without making it known that this is what they are doing. A psychologist, D.L. Rosenhan, used this technique in a famous study when he and a number of colleagues managed to have themselves admitted to a psychiatric hospital by feigning the symptoms of schizophrenia. While they were in the hospital, they took detailed notes of the behaviour of the nurses, doctors and other patients. Rosenhan and his colleagues found that, although they showed no symptoms of the disorder once they had been admitted, they were treated by the medical staff as if they were still behaving in an abnormal way. The patients, by contrast, were not fooled by them! Rosenhan noted that, 'During the first three hospitalisations, when accurate counts were kept, 35 of a total of 118 patients on the admissions ward voiced their suspicions, some vigorously. "You're not crazy. You're a journalist, or a professor [referring to the continual note-taking]. You're checking up on the hospital."' (To read the whole study, visit this website: http://courses.ucsd.edu/fall2003/ps163f/Rosenhan.htm#_ftn1.)

■ Advantages of informal observations

- The full range of behaviours can be observed as they occur – this increases validity.
- We can see exactly what it is people do, which may not be the same as what they say they would do!

■ Disadvantages of informal observations

- It is not easy to record all behaviour – there may be actions or movements that we miss while we are watching something else.
- This method requires very careful planning and considerable practice to be carried out effectively.
- The researcher may interpret behaviour according to their own set of beliefs. For example, a child moving suddenly towards another might be noted as 'child 1 moves aggressively forward', when in fact the child may just be excited and not aggressive at all.
- It is a very time-consuming method of collecting data.

Secondary sources/ literature research

Secondary data refers to data that has already been collected by someone else and, usually, published in some source. Examples include magazine or journal articles, official statistics, other people's research reports etc. Secondary data is a rich source of material for an individual embarking on their own personal research project. The collection of secondary data is known as a literature review. Researchers often begin investigating a topic by looking up official statistics relevant to their focus. Statistics can be found both in the reference section of your library and on the Internet. They are a useful source of information for researchers and provide a wide range of data on relevant topics, relating to the whole population. For example, an individual investigating the types of illnesses associated with alcohol abuse would often begin their literature review by finding out some facts and figures (statistics) about illnesses and mortality associated with alcohol abuse. If they are interested in gender differences or variations by region, this information would be available from a source of official statistics. For each type of secondary source you obtain, you need to keep details of where you found it so another researcher, or a reader, can access your source to obtain further information. The details you need to keep are given in the relevant sections below.

Sources of secondary data

■ Internet

If used properly, the Internet can be an excellent source of up-to-date information which is very quickly available through the use of powerful search engines such as Google. You can access official statistics, newspaper articles and information published by specialist organisations devoted to a particular topic such as mental health. Information you need to keep during your literature search includes:

- the full address or URL of the website you accessed (http://www ...)
- the date when you found this article and details of the author and/or organisation.

Since it is not uncommon for web pages to move, it is usual to add to these details the date when you accessed the site.

Some useful search engines are outlined below:

- Alltheweb – www.alltheweb.com
- Altavista® – www.altavista.com
- Excite® – www.excite.com
- Google™ – www.google.com
- Lycos™ – www.lycos.com.

The Internet hosts a number of specialist sites devoted to particular areas of interest. Details of some sites that are useful for obtaining secondary data on health and social care are given below.

- www.kingsfund.org.uk – a site devoted to research into health and social care issues
- www.bbc.co.uk – the BBC website contains a wealth of information on science, health and social issues
- www.york.ac.uk/inst/crd/ehcb.htm – the Centre for Reviews and Dissemination publishes online articles on various health topics; it also publishes a monthly bulletin 'Effective Health Care' which is available for the public to download
- www.mmrthefacts.nhs.uk – a site devoted entirely to articles about the MMR vaccine
- www.nationalobesityforum.org.uk – the National Obesity Forum
- www.alcoholconcern.org.uk – the official site of Alcohol Concern.

Official statistics can be found at:

- www.health-promis.hea.org.uk – Health Education Authority statistics
- www.statistics.gov.uk – Office for National Statistics

Newspaper websites are also useful sources, such as:

- www.guardian.co.uk
- www.telegraph.co.uk
- www.timesonline.co.uk.

■ Journals

These are an excellent source of information for a literature review or even when deciding on a research project. They are expensive to buy but you will probably find that your college library stocks them. If not, ask them if they would be prepared to take out a subscription. Journals that could be helpful include:

- www.nursingtimes.net (Nursing Times online magazine)
- Community Care
- Nursery World
- Nursing Standard
- Journal of Paediatric Nursing.

■ Media

Television and radio programmes are an excellent source of inspiration when embarking on a research project. Programmes on television that might be relevant include:

- Horizon
- Omnibus
- Cutting Edge.

BBC Radio 4 is a rich source of information for relevant topics in this field. If you have access to the Internet you can use the Listen Again service which enables you to select a programme you may have missed, or wish to review, and listen again. Some allow you to download the programme as an MP3 file. Suggestions for some useful Radio 4 programmes include:

All in the Mind A programme devoted to all matters psychological, from memory to mental disorders.	Building a Healthier Britain This looks at research findings on a wide variety of health issues, from diabetes to the use of fluoride in drinking water.	Case Notes A topical programme on all aspects of health.
Check-up A health phone-in programme.	Emotional Rollercoaster A programme investigating what emotions are and what they do.	Gut Reaction An exploration of all things interesting about the intestines, including the relationship between the gut and the brain and immune system.
Herbs, Pills and Potions This programme explores Indian health systems.	Life as a Teenager A series of programmes examining all aspects of adolescence.	Life in Middle Age This programme focuses on the years 40–60 for both men and women.

Life in Old Age A programme dealing with life for people in their 60s and 70s. It deals with issues such as chronic illness (for example, osteoporosis) and the importance of social networks.	**Life after 80** A focus on health and well-being among people over 80 years of age.	**Living with Pain** Topics include the nature of pain, pain experienced by athletes and living with chronic pain.

Ask your local library if they have any taped copies of programmes that may be relevant to your project.

■ Books

In addition to books within the health and social care section of your library, you may also want to look in the sections devoted to psychology and sociology. Within the psychology section you will find books related to health psychology, physiological psychology and child development, while the sociology section contains books devoted to social care and the sociology of health. Other useful sources include the 'Issues' publications. These consist of a selection of extracts from newspapers and other media on a large range of topics. A few examples that would be helpful to you in your studies are: *the drugs debate; homelessness; AIDS – It's not over yet; living with disabilities; surrogacy and IVF; body image; the abortion debate; poverty; stress; mental illness; the ethics of genetic engineering.* Your librarian will be happy to help you with your literature search, so do make use of this additional resource.

Remember!

If you are using Internet articles, you must keep the details of the website where you obtained the information. Check the source of the article as well, to ensure it is reputable. (For example, articles from government and university websites are more likely to contain high quality research than an article written by a group of people who have extreme beliefs.)

Assessment activity 22.2

Describe the key elements of research methodologies.

1   Create a table of the different research methods described in Section 22.2 above. Include a column for a description of the method, an example of its usage in health and social care and a brief summary of advantages and disadvantages of this method.

Grading tip for P2

To achieve P2 you need to be sure that you have included the key elements of each type of methodology. This means you need to include the most important features. For example, the most important feature of an experiment is the high level of control that can be obtained, whereas the most important feature of an observational method is that people are seen behaving naturally.

Take it further

Find two methods that have been used to investigate a relevant topic in health and social care, such as the use of sunscreen, the reasons for changing to a low-fat diet, taking exercise etc. Consider what advantages and disadvantages each method has in terms of how useful the findings are in shedding light on such important issues.

Topic and hypothesis

All research begins by selecting a manageable topic of interest and identifying an aspect of this topic to investigate. The researcher makes a prediction about what they may find from their research. This is known as a hypothesis and you will be given guidance later on how to formulate this.

Theory into practice

Decide whether or not the following students' projects are suitable in terms of their relevance to health and social care. If you decide they are not suitable, discuss and make notes on any problems you can foresee.

1 Winston is interested in finding out whether social class affects educational prospects. From his own experience of talking to classmates and what he has heard on television and read about, he believes that the children of parents with a university education tend to fare better in the education system than those whose parents left school at 16.

2 Josanne wants to find out what factors are involved in girls' choice of post-16 education. She has noticed on her health and social care course that there were only two boys who began the course and they have both left, whereas in the engineering department of the same college there are 185 boys but no girls!

3 Sadia is interested in finding out about the relationship between beliefs about schizophrenia and the portrayal in the media of people who suffer from this disorder. She feels sure that the media portrayal is so negative, and so few people actually encounter someone with schizophrenia, that the misleading coverage given by the media is bound to influence the beliefs of those who have no other information by which to judge this situation.

Suitable health and social care topic

Your goal here is to identify a topic that is not only related to health and social care but is also suitable to investigate. You need to consider aspects such as the scale of the project (for example, time frame, number of participants required, funding issues) as well as the ethical issues involved. When choosing a topic it is a good idea to select something you will be genuinely interested in. You will be required to do a considerable amount of 'reading around' the project and may change your research aim and/or hypothesis more than once before arriving at a final decision about exactly what it is you want to investigate.

Remember: while you are considering your topic and hypothesis you need to check with your tutor whether you would be able to gain consent to carry out research, and whether it is a topic you can safely conduct ethically.

Literature search

Having identified a topic, you need to begin your literature search. Ideally you want to find four to five pieces of secondary research which are relevant to your research aim. (Remember, you may refine or change your aim or hypothesis during the early stages of your project. This is fine, but it is important not to begin devising a methodology until you decide for sure what your aim and hypothesis consist of.) For full details of how to conduct a literature search, see pages 425–427, 'Secondary sources/literature research'.

Theory into practice

Think of a topic that interests you and find four to five pieces of material relevant to it, using any of the sources mentioned in the section 'secondary sources/literature research'. You may also want to speak to a lecturer or teacher about your choice of topic, as they may have further ideas on where you could get secondary material suitable for your topic.

Figure 22.3 Conducting a literature research can be a lengthy business but, the more you find out about the topic, the easier it will be to conduct your own research ▶

Suitability of topic with reference to ethical issues

Research carried out in health and social care often involves private, sensitive and personal issues which could potentially cause some discomfort, embarrassment or psychological harm to participants. For example, in order to find out about an individual's experience of the mental health system, a researcher will need to ask questions about this which may well bring up distressing memories for the participant. The following key principles apply to all aspects of research:

- *Do no harm.* This is a fundamental ethical principle which requires researchers to take all steps possible to ensure that there is no distress caused to their participants. Ethical guidelines designed to guide researchers to abide by this principle include **informed consent** and **protection from harm**.

- *All participants should have voluntary status.* This means that nobody should be forced or misled into taking part when, if they had known all the facts or been given a genuine choice, they would have chosen not to take part. Guidelines to ensure this ethical principle is adhered to include informed consent, avoidance of any kind of **deception** and, if deception

Key terms

Informed consent This means that participants are given full details of the aim of the research, the methodology to be used and the likely outcomes in terms of how it will affect them. They must be told this *before* the research is carried out. With this information they are able to make an informed choice about whether or not they wish to take part.

Protection from harm This refers to the obligation on the part of the researcher to ensure that no physical or psychological harm will occur to the participant. It is the responsibility of the researcher to do all they can to foresee any potential harm and, in this event, either change the design of the study or, if this is not possible, make the participant aware of this before they take part.

Deception This refers to a situation where some details of the investigation are withheld from the participant in order to ensure that their behaviour remains as true-to-life as possible. Participants are therefore unable to give informed consent.

is absolutely necessary, **debriefing** following the investigation. Participants should also be made aware at the beginning of the investigation of their **right to withdraw** from the research study and again, at the end of the study, of their right to withdraw their data.

- *Confidentiality.* This refers to the right (both morally and legally) of any participant in a research investigation not to be identified in any way. The ethical guideline of **confidentiality** covers this ethical principle. The Data Protection Act 1998 provides legal rights to participants involved in research and sets out obligations that must be kept to by the researchers. For more information on this act (as it relates to research) visit the following website: www.city.ac.uk/dataprotection/Data_Protection/Data_Protection_Rese.html.

Key terms

Debriefing The purpose of debriefing, which occurs at the end of the investigation, is to restore participants to the physical or psychological state they were in at the beginning of the investigation. This usually involves telling them the true aim and hypothesis of the research, reassuring them that their response is 'normal' and answering any questions they may have.

Right to withdraw To ensure that participants in a research project are true volunteers, they must be given every opportunity to withdraw from the process if, at any point, they wish to do so. At the end of the project, usually after the debriefing, it is advisable to remind participants that they have the right to withdraw their data *for any reason*. They should not be forced to justify their reasons for wishing to withdraw.

Confidentiality This is usually achieved by specifying that no participant will be identified to anyone other than the researcher, and that no details of their results will be published or otherwise made available to anyone outside the research project. Confidentiality can be achieved by giving each participant a number instead of a name.

Go through the ethics planning list opposite to decide whether your planned research meets ethical guidelines. Make notes now on any instructions you may need to give

Remember!

You need to ensure that your choice of topic is suitable with reference to ethical issues.

to participants either at the beginning or end of the project. If you have any doubts or concerns about the ethics of your proposed method of data collection, ask your tutor for guidance. If, on the basis of this exercise, you decide you cannot use the methodology you originally planned, make notes in your research diary now. This will help you to gain the merit criterion M2: Review the research methods chosen in relation to the results obtained, any sources of bias or error and ethical considerations.

Ethics planning list

In the light of the guidelines on page 431, answer 'yes' or 'no' to the questions below. If you answer 'yes' at any point you need to take note of the *What you should do* instructions.

Reflect

Are the following projects ethical? If not, why not? Discuss this with your group and with your tutor.

- A face-to-face questionnaire asking students in your college if they, or a close relative, have had an episode of mental illness.
- A survey into provision for the disabled in your local college (or town centre).
- An investigation asking under-16 smokers what influenced their decision to begin smoking.
- An investigation (using college students) into experience of sexual abuse in childhood.
- A questionnaire survey asking individuals if they have had an abortion.
- A project to find out what, if any, long-term effects arise from being in foster care for the majority of one's life.
- An investigation into whether 14–16-year-olds practise safe sex.

Deception

Will you be using any type of deception? | YES/NO | If *yes*, you cannot obtain informed consent.

What you should do

1. Justify the acceptability of the deception and suggest one way of obtaining an alternative form of consent (for example, **presumptive consent** or **prior general consent**).
2. Carry out a thorough debriefing, explaining in full the purpose of the investigation and the reason why deception was included. Offer participants the right to withdraw their data if they want to and answer all questions fully about the purpose of the investigation and the uses to which their data will be put.

Protection of participants

Could it be foreseen that your participants might experience any kind of harm? (This could include embarrassment, feeling foolish in front of others, discussion topics that bring up painful memories?) | YES/NO |

What you should do

Conduct a pilot study, maybe using members of your class. Ask if they feel that your proposed method might cause psychological harm of any sort. If they say 'yes', consider using an alternative method. (Suppose, for example, you are interested in the way mothers feel towards their other children if a youngest child dies from cot death. Instead of asking individuals about their personal experience of cot death, you could ask health visitors what changes they have observed in mothers to whom this has happened.)

Informed consent

Will you be conducting an observation? | YES/NO | If yes, you cannot gain informed consent.

What you should do

Look up the BPS Ethical Guidelines and note what they state about observational research. Visit www.bps.org.uk/the-society/ethics-rules-charter-code-of-conduct/code-of-conduct/ethical-principles-for-conducting-research-with-human-participants.cfm.

Right to withdraw

Are you going to offer your participants the right to withdraw? | YES/NO | Despite the most careful planning, you can never anticipate whether a participant may feel under any pressure to remain involved in the research investigation when they might prefer to withdraw. Not everyone is confident about speaking up about this so you, as researcher, need to be very clear that they are volunteers.

What you should do

Inform your participants at the beginning of the investigation that they can withdraw at any time and do not have to give reasons for this. At the end, re-state this right to withdraw and let them know they can withdraw their data for any reason should they wish to do so.

Confidentiality

Is there any danger that participants could be identified? | YES/NO | If yes, then you need to take steps to ensure that this doesn't happen.

What you should do

Tell all your participants that they will not be identified at any stage in the investigation. Ask them not to put their names or any other identifying details on a questionnaire. If the method is an experiment you need to tell participants that any data collected from them will only be identified by the researcher as a number.

Key terms

Presumptive consent This is when a group of people similar to the sample that will be used in a research investigation are told the full details of that investigation and asked if they think it is acceptable. If they agree that it is, the researcher can be said to have gained presumptive consent.

Prior general consent This method involves the researcher asking actual participants beforehand if they would object in principle to being deceived about some or all aspects of the investigation. If they say 'no', then prior general consent has been obtained.

A hypothesis is a testable statement of what you expect to find. Your hypothesis must be written in such a way that a clear prediction is made of the outcome you expect. This will depend on what you have found in your literature review. There are two types of hypotheses. A **one-tailed hypothesis** predicts that a certain effect will happen in a particular direction, based on previous findings that would make this likely. For example, 'People who exercise vigorously for 30 minutes three times a week will report a *greater* sense of well-being than those who take no exercise'. When you analyse your data, you can look at the findings to see if it supports your hypothesis and your findings are as predicted. If your literature review suggests that there will be a difference between two groups but does not suggest that the difference lies in a particular direction, you need to formulate a **two-tailed hypothesis**. An example of this might be: 'there will be a *difference* in the sense of well-being experienced by males and females who exercise vigorously for 30 minutes three times a week'. Here you are suggesting that males and females will feel the benefits differently, but not which group will feel better.

Key terms

One-tailed hypothesis This predicts the nature of the finding. For example, you may predict that *more* girls than boys take up smoking in order to fit in with their peer group.

Two-tailed hypothesis This predicts that there are different reasons for girls and boys taking up smoking, but that you don't yet know what they are. Your hypothesis will be tested against the data collected to find out if, in fact, there are different reasons.

A **research question** is broader than a hypothesis. It does not make a specific prediction: rather it outlines the area you wish to investigate. For example, a research question might be something like 'What are the experiences of young people looking after sick parents?'

Key terms

Research question An investigation into a broad area of research which does not have a specific prediction. For example, you may just want to find out what the factors are that distinguish those girls (or boys, or both) who do take up smoking from those who do not.

Achievable aims

Be wary of trying to cover too much. Your aim is to conduct a research project that is manageable in terms of your level of skill, the sample you are likely to have access to, the time you have to complete the project … all within the ethical constraints that apply. However tempting, don't try to conduct a piece of research that would require government funding and a team of researchers working full-time for five years! You need to consider some of the following aspects when considering whether the aims of your research project are achievable:

- How much time do you have to plan your method and create materials (for example, design a questionnaire, select questions for an interview, create an observational checklist, set up an experiment)?
- What are the costs involved (for example, stamps, self-addressed envelopes, travel to places to interview or observe people or drop off and collect questionnaires)?
- How long will the data collection take? (Interviews and observations tend to take up more time than questionnaires and experiments, although all involve considerable time spent planning.)
- Do you have access to an appropriate sample?

Produce an outline of the planned research

Methodology

Here, you need to decide what method you will use to collect your data. You can choose from the following:

- **Questionnaire** – decide whether you will use open or closed questions. Will you administer this face-to-face or indirectly?
- **Interview** – will this be structured or semi-structured?
- **Experiment** – what are your independent and dependent variables? What potential confounding variables will you need to control?
- **Formal or informal observation** – will you focus on events or sequences? What method of recording will you use? Where will you carry out the observation? How will you gain permission and be sure you stick to the ethical guidelines?

Target group and sample

Sampling refers to the collection of data from a small number, or 'sample' of the population of interest. Imagine you were interested in finding out whether 14–16-year-olds practised safe sex. You could in theory find all 14–16-year-olds in the country (your population of interest) and contact them to ask them this question. In practice, however, researchers tend to obtain a 'sample' of the population of interest (in this case *some* of the 14–16-year-olds in the UK). Your job is to try to find a sample that is as representative as possible of the population you are researching. An unrepresentative sample might be Catholic or Muslim girls, who might have religious reasons for not having under-age sex at all. The findings from this group would not represent the population at large. Your task, therefore, is to find a group that is representative of the population at large so that your findings can be generalised to that whole population (and not just to all practising Catholics or Muslims).

Some of the most commonly used sampling methods are given below, together with the strengths and weaknesses of each method and special considerations.

■ Random sampling

This is a method in which all members of the population have a statistically equal probability of being chosen.

Random sampling techniques include the following:

1 **Manual selection** (for example, numbers drawn out of a hat). In this method, each member of a sampling frame is given a number and the required number is picked from a hat.

2 **Random numbers tables** The way in which this table works is that to select your sample you generate a list of potential participants (for example, a printout of all the students in your college). You then look at the first number on the top left row of the tables (in this case number 30) and select the thirtieth person in your list to be the first member of your sample.

30 89 34 43 98	38 51 15 30 26	02 57 93 32 67	19 91 72 23 06	59 24 11 06 50
79 50 49 98 07	05 88 29 05 29	73 15 65 17 92	26 05 21 60 73	55 48 97 54 50
53 64 54 20 36	05 26 90 12 98	73 98 56 47 60	44 54 45 97 21	25 70 96 58 72
87 23 75 21 50	54 47 46 35 72	11 66 30 44 63	69 50 82 74 58	98 25 68 47 79
91 54 58 41 48	70 11 94 79 12	36 63 12 52 72	43 41 11 52 98	91 77 91 85 00
92 41 24 08 42	64 96 82 07 01	40 00 95 09 30	23 40 08 19 78	55 50 92 84 96
65 63 25 34 62	93 01 96 23 23	81 31 94 09 02	75 98 27 85 59	53 09 94 37 37
93 64 13 39 70	98 38 71 77 89	47 98 47 22 09	98 85 91 86 42	30 60 34 07 23
92 44 97 54 10	53 06 50 66 76	13 89 09 41 28	93 04 75 68 09	78 22 82 88 10
69 37 57 14 85	43 72 12 89 80	07 01 17 91 30	17 00 49 53 99	46 51 26 74 28
88 13 45 79 30	32 44 38 84 94	26 65 83 04 43	88 70 99 09 89	31 59 08 29 11
30 86 16 00 13	89 22 16 01 29	98 65 92 13 36	26 88 58 18 89	67 19 71 92 28
19 39 94 95 22	70 99 77 50 29	30 16 69 87 18	48 56 34 92 85	42 54 25 72 84
04 01 90 59 21	33 16 80 53 51	90 02 92 76 72	03 82 77 75 72	33 44 87 58 29
17 45 23 69 94	53 68 59 13 13	68 39 80 62 31	70 44 32 01 47	54 43 70 97 08
13 35 10 58 52	66 73 38 05 80	45 71 76 21 80	10 58 72 17 06	50 72 97 41 48
07 48 12 02 82	51 55 21 61 13	44 27 63 97 04	56 13 88 48 02	34 15 84 30 87
08 16 12 72 05	72 10 63 76 44	92 84 98 81 43	71 66 24 27 16	06 32 39 21 89
51 94 42 32 70	21 82 38 94 46	59 34 75 61 97	72 76 50 50 30	70 27 08 16 72
06 78 72 46 93	36 77 57 19 49	99 18 26 11 63	74 29 96 14 57	76 72 92 86 28
39 14 12 52 96	24 33 70 06 77	56 59 42 11 80	33 05 63 40 14	22 70 62 17 05
71 31 34 36 97	98 57 79 44 68	06 62 74 23 69	77 41 05 17 26	41 68 37 19 53
57 64 15 98 66	13 41 98 06 19	64 53 36 19 16	19 90 71 70 74	04 03 30 05 34
64 26 20 69 40	12 85 65 75 73	92 57 43 97 70	71 28 02 89 91	86 98 64 56 73
91 38 37 54 09	99 35 01 78 03	09 53 57 79 53	50 23 00 90 49	45 28 45 00 94
89 29 45 54 07	22 17 50 32 64	07 30 41 19 36	32 18 08 94 48	20 84 02 47 95
81 31 03 44 27	43 93 91 10 38	72 95 27 58 65	02 23 61 23 17	17 70 26 19 79
05 45 30 21 51	05 14 61 37 61	47 39 50 22 73	28 06 14 72 89	53 64 75 09 70
03 61 43 09 65	35 22 77 22 50	50 37 79 34 14	65 03 56 93 62	34 03 93 18 14
82 75 76 86 14	93 52 73 37 68	83 46 04 11 96	24 14 84 07 19	88 54 05 04 29
62 91 08 18 91	52 65 53 89 39	95 43 21 88 25	36 97 60 89 07	12 03 57 31 39
99 61 53 27 31	18 30 38 21 32	91 03 04 61 53	19 81 45 69 05	35 63 25 00 53
44 29 75 03 84	52 19 73 07 26	92 21 25 48 18	98 14 24 72 12	26 24 89 86 53
51 17 94 61 54	16 39 17 30 32	41 23 37 62 20	51 62 33 09 66	51 95 89 43 55
87 51 27 95 72	31 82 22 31 18	20 31 03 93 60	50 93 18 75 26	62 64 57 46 85
58 12 50 48 30	85 34 65 89 19	63 58 41 42 56	03 67 41 69 48	81 13 44 42 70
78 25 85 91 28	01 85 26 47 58	66 11 84 77 18	30 47 19 42 74	80 13 53 72 66
97 09 87 30 35	04 26 88 10 58	18 44 75 06 52	92 49 73 70 79	49 42 20 09 96
69 08 45 81 37	89 68 51 99 15	33 07 14 39 61	78 05 50 34 14	72 32 78 30 59
82 74 69 78 50	51 47 00 57 40	51 84 26 51 23	14 08 30 96 92	56 71 54 59 96
71 08 26 53 23	43 60 71 41 63	95 26 14 78 09	73 74 63 73 21	06 79 69 81 90
17 60 07 10 21	77 42 60 77 01	20 14 04 09 89	55 79 97 62 57	13 59 38 42 41
90 07 13 82 73	77 37 58 21 35	29 81 98 80 85	51 58 49 82 66	46 94 59 42 25
14 04 16 79 09	72 01 15 51 47	01 12 32 87 84	65 27 89 34 07	40 57 95 06 77
42 44 93 98 30	13 10 61 85 30	46 82 99 79 93	48 62 46 26 71	19 98 34 48 28

▲ **Figure 22.4 A random numbers table helps you to obtain a truly random sample**

You continue along the row, so person 89 is the next person, person 34 the next and so on. If you do not have a large enough sample, simply miss out the numbers which go above your cut-off point (for example, all numbers above 50) and move on to the next number which will fit into your sample size. This is a truly random sample since you have not introduced any element of bias into it at all.

3 **Computer-generated samples** This is similar to the above, but the computer produces random numbers.

■ Systematic sampling

This is a technique which targets particular groups. Some members thus have a greater likelihood of being chosen than others.

Systematic sampling techniques include the following:

1 **Quota sampling** For example, 10 men, 10 women, 10 girls, 10 boys.

2 **Stratified sampling** The population is divided into layers (or strata) and a selection is chosen from each strata (for example, elderly, unemployed and single parent families to investigate poverty).

3 **Snowball sampling** This is used when the research population is not easily accessible. Existing subjects are asked to contact others known to them to invite them to take part (for example, people with HIV, members of religious cults etc).

4 **Convenience sampling** This involves a sample taken from those to whom the researcher has easy access (for example, students studying on your course at college and/or family and friends).

■ Self-selecting sampling

This method uses volunteers, for example, members of a course in health and social care. The researcher may post a notice on a communal notice board, stating the aim of the research and asking for volunteers.

Rationale

Explain *why* you plan to carry out this research project. A useful way to do this is to explain why it is relevant

and important to the field of health and social care and you may find it helpful to find some statistics (from your literature search) to back up your rationale. In the case study on page 436, Sanjay was able to demonstrate that alcohol-related deaths in England and Wales had risen over a period of 10 years. This is clearly relevant to the topic of health. As the problem is likely to be ongoing it is important to investigate this (research to provide further knowledge) so that, by finding out the causes, it may be possible to produce interventions that minimise or stem this rising tide of illness (research to inform practice).

Time scales

You need to begin by finding out exactly how much time you have available to:

- conduct the research
- analyse the data
- write up the project.

This will give you a structure of the time scale involved so you can create an action plan.

Action plan, monitoring and modification

Next make a list of everything you have to do. You can do this initially as a brainstorm and then re-write it as a sequence of events.

Having broken down the project into manageable chunks, make a note of how you will go about achieving each item and how long you think it will take. Now put dates alongside each item. These are dates by which you should have completed each section of the research. Include a section for monitoring and modification.

It is also a good idea to start a research diary, which you monitor regularly so you can update it and make any changes.

An example is given below of an action plan (Table 22.3). It is for a project which uses a questionnaire to collect data from a sample of parents with children at pre-school to ask them whether they have had (or plan to have) their children immunised with the MMR vaccine.

Action	By when?	Done?	Modifications
Write a draft list of questions	1 November	Yes	None
Show draft to my tutor for checking	4 November	Yes	Change questions 3, 6 and 8 and add speech at beginning
Begin to write up the literature review	22 December		
Make list of five local pre-schools	4 November	Partly	Need to get two more addresses
Telephone pre-school leaders to ask for permission to put up a letter asking for volunteers	10 November	Yes	None
Create permission letter and put up in pre-schools I have chosen	15 November	Yes	None
Proofread questionnaire and arrange for 50 copies to be printed off	20 November	Yes	None
Begin to write method section for checking by my tutor on 15 December	10 December		
Ask my tutor to arrange for 50 return-addressed envelopes to be printed	20 November	Yes	None
Go into pre-school to hand out questionnaires	27 November	Partly	Need to go back to two more – not enough people at this session took the questionnaire
Begin to enter data onto Excel spreadsheet	11 December	Partly	Need some help from IT tutor to do this as columns don't fit
Create summary table of averages, percentages. Use Excel to create an appropriate chart or graph	18 December	Yes	None
Write conclusions about the data based on whether it supports my hypothesis	22 December	No	I need help from my tutor in interpreting the data. I think it supports my hypothesis but I've got so much data I'm not sure where to include it
Write up the results section			
Complete the whole document, proofread it and get it bound for submission	15 January		

Table 22.3 An example of an action plan for a student project

Remember!

Plan your project carefully to make sure it is manageable in the time allowed. Check with your tutor that you have covered ethical issues before you go ahead with it.

Resources

Primary and secondary resources

You need to use primary resources to collect data and secondary sources to find out about the background to the topic. The use of a range of resources will improve the quality of your project. The case study below illustrates how this can be done.

To begin with, Sanjay wants to get some data about the scale of the problem of misuse of alcohol in general. As he is keen on using the Internet, he decides to search here first for information. He first visits the website of the Office for National Statistics to get an overview of the scale of the problem and finds the following information.

'The number of alcohol-related deaths in England and Wales, which rose throughout the 1980s and 1990s, has continued to rise in more recent years. Numbers increased from 5970 in 2001 to 6580 in 2003. Death rates per 100,000 population also increased from 10.7 in 2001 to 11.6 in 2003.'

> source: www.statistics.gov.uk/cci/nugget.asp?id=1091; accessed 23.9.2007

Since he wants to use a questionnaire method to find out about people's drinking habits, he decides he needs to find some advice about what constitutes safe drinking and what would be classed as alcohol misuse so he can include this in the questionnaire. He then visits the website of the King's Fund and uses a keyword search for alcohol misuse. He soon finds a report by the Department of Health called 'Sensible Drinking'. This is a long report which opens as an Adobe file, so he right clicks on the download button and saves it to his user area so he can refer to it at a later date. Scanning through the contents page, Sanjay soon finds what he needs: a chapter called 'The current sensible drinking message'. This outlines guidance on safe limits on drinking. He finds the following guidelines: 'The Department of Health advises that men should not drink more than 3–4 units of alcohol per day, and women should drink no more than 2–3 units of alcohol per day. These daily benchmarks apply whether you drink every day, once or twice a week, or occasionally.'

His next step is to find some facts and figures. He accesses the Office for National Statistics (ONS) on the Internet, selects the theme Health and types in a search item of alcohol. The results are shown in Figure 22.5. He clicks on the link 'alcohol-related deaths' and finds, from an easy-to-read line graph, that deaths have been rising steadily from 6 per 100,000 population for males and 4 per 100,000 population for females in 1979 to 16 per 100,000 population for males and 5 per 100,000 population for females in 2003.

Although the data on deaths shows clearly that males consistently outnumber females in mortality rates due to alcohol, Sanjay observes that the rate is still increasing for women. He also seems to remember hearing something recently about women catching up with men in the binge-drinking stakes. He thinks it might be interesting to investigate gender differences in binge-drinking, so he decides to investigate this further. He clicks on the next link on the ONS page and copies the following information:

'Since the late 1980s there has been an increase in the proportion ... of men and women exceeding levels of safe drinking ... almost entirely due to an increase

---

Alcohol - Facts, Statistics, Resources, and Impairment Charts
Facts, **statistics**, and resources related to the abuse of **alcohol**.
www.gdcada.org/statistics/alcohol.htm - 29k - Cached - Similar pages

Alcohol Use Statistics
Information on the use and abuse of **alcohol** in the United States. Provided by the National Center for Health **Statistics**.
www.cdc.gov/nchs/fastats/alcohol.htm - 39k - Cached - Similar pages

Statistics on alcohol: England, 2004 : The Department of Health ...
This statistical bulletin presents the most up-to-date information on **alcohol** use and misuse available at the time of publication in September 2004.
www.dh.gov.uk/.../StatisticalPublicHealthArticle/ fs/en?CONTENT_ID=4095318&chk=vg4R24 - 20k - Cached - Similar pages

MADD Online: General Statistics
About 40 percent of all crimes (violent and non-violent) are committed under the influence of **alcohol**. (Bureau of Justice **Statistics**, 1998) ...
www.madd.org/stats/0,1056,1789,00.html - 18k - Cached - Similar pages

alcohol statistics & alcohol abuse treatment by drug statistics.com
alcohol statistics & alcohol abuse treatment presented by drug **statistics**.com.
www.drug-statistics.com/alcohol.htm - 36k - 20 Mar 2007 - Cached - Similar pages

National Statistics Online
Male **alcohol**-related death rates by age group, United Kingdom, 1991-2005 ... Health **Statistics** Quarterly · Data: **Alcohol**-related deaths in England & Wales ...
www.statistics.gov.uk/cci/nugget.asp?id=1091 - 22k - 20 Mar 2007 - Cached - Similar pages

Teenage Alcohol Statistics
Statistics on alcohol use by teenagers and youth. Data from studies show that **alcohol** is, by far, the most abused drug by teenagers which leads to death, ...
www.marininstitute.org/Youth/alcohol_youth.htm - 22k - Cached - Similar pages

Statistics on Alcohol: England, 2006 [NS] — Portal
This statistical bulletin presents a range of information on **alcohol** use and misuse; drawn together from a variety of sources. The topics covered include ...
www.ic.nhs.uk/pubs/alcoholeng2006 - 43k - Cached - Similar pages

Statistical work areas - Public Health
Statistics and surveys produced by the Department of Health for England.
... Official UK **statistics** and information about **statistics**.
www.publications.doh.gov.uk/ public/work_public_health.htm - 23k - Cached - Similar pages

▲ **Figure 22.5 The screen results for a search for alcohol statistics**

among women. The proportion of women exceeding the weekly benchmark increased from 10 per cent in 1988/89 to 17 per cent in 2002/03 compared with an increase from 26 per cent to 27 per cent for men over the same period … Drinking above the weekly benchmark increased across all age groups among women, but most markedly among young women aged 16 to 24. Their rate more than doubled from 15 per cent in 1988/89 to 33 per cent in 2002/03. This compared with an increase from 31 per cent to 37 per cent over the same period for young men of the same age.'

Source: *www.statistics.gov.uk/cci/nugget_print.asp?ID=922*; accessed 1.1.2007

Since he has taken a direct quote from the document, Sanjay is careful to copy down the URL and makes a note of the date he accessed this information. His interest in this younger age group being heightened,

Sanjay decides to go further afield to find more information about binge-drinking in the younger age groups. He finds an article by using a keyword search (binge-drinking) in the archive search of a newspaper website. The article reports that recent research into drinking among school children has found that girls outnumber boys in their binge-drinking. He summarises all this material in a literature review and sets about constructing a hypothesis and choosing the most appropriate methodology.

1 **List all the secondary sources Sanjay has used. Do you think he has missed anything out?**

2 **Visit the Department for Health website and find out how many units are contained in a range of popular drinks (for example, red wine, Bacardi Breezer).**

3 **If you were doing this project, what would you do to monitor it and evaluate the methodology used?**

Remember!

To find the information contained in a search, click on the text in blue. If the URL includes the word 'gov' (government) you can be fairly sure that it is a reputable source.

Assessment activity 22.3

Identify a research topic and carry out a literature search.

1 You have now read about a variety of different research projects and research methods and may already have an idea about what you would like to investigate. This will be your research topic. Write down the name of your topic and use the library and other sources to begin to find background information on the topic.

Grading tip for P3

Your goal here is to identify a topic that is not only related to health and social care but is also suitable to investigate in terms of ethical considerations – you may want to check this with your tutor. You need to consider aspects such as the scale of the project (for example, time frame, number of participants required, funding issues) as well as the ethical issues involved. When choosing a topic it is a good idea to select something you will be interested in. You will need to do a considerable amount of 'reading around' the project and may change your research aim and/or hypothesis more than once before arriving at a final decision about exactly what it is you want to investigate. Try also to choose a topic where you are likely to find enough background information to conduct a literature search.

Justify the choice of topic and hypothesis.

2 Explain why the topic you have chosen is important and relevant to health and social care. Write a hypothesis for your topic clearly stating what you expect to find. Add a sentence explaining why your background reading leads you to expect this finding.

Grading tip for M1

To justify the choice of topic you need to explain clearly why it is an important area of research. For example, if you want to investigate reasons why youngsters choose not to take up (or to stop) smoking, you may want to explain why these findings would be useful. To justify your hypothesis you need to use some theory or research to explain why you are making a particular prediction. In the example above, Sanjay would be justified in writing a hypothesis 'girls are more likely than boys to binge-drink' as he has found evidence to support this.

Take it further

Conduct a short literature research for the following topics of relevance in health and social care:

- the prevalence of elder abuse
- the quality of care in homes for the elderly
- a review of child protection cases following the Victoria Climbié case.

Undertaking research

The following gives an outline of the research process. You will be guided throughout this section on just what you need to do as you go along.

Primary research

You need to choose a suitable method to carry out your primary research and justify your choice of methodology.

Secondary research

You need to choose a range of secondary sources to find background information on the topic of interest.

Statistics

Having collected your data you need to summarise it using descriptive statistics and present it visually using charts and graphs. If you have chosen a hypothesis, you will also need to explain whether your findings support this or not. If you have selected a research question only, you need to explain how your findings throw light on the original question. This will go in the results section.

Monitor and review

As you work through the project you need to monitor your methodology and review your action plan regularly. Keeping a research diary where you have space to write a fairly lengthy commentary will help you record information which will later be useful when you evaluate your project.

To present your report you should use the following sections, in order:

- Title page
- Introduction
- Literature Search
- Method
- Results
- Discussion
- Conclusion
- Recommendations.

Any other documents you have used (for example, a questionnaire or instructions to participants) should be included at the end of the report.

Introduction

This will consist of a short paragraph describing your topic of research. You need to explain here why it is a relevant topic to investigate.

Summary of current research in the field

Often called a 'literature search' or 'literature review' this refers to the information you have gained from between three and five secondary sources. This should explain clearly the rationale of the research, including why it is relevant to health and social care. You then need to outline the findings made in the area you are investigating (see Section 22.2: 'Secondary sources/ literature research', for more detailed guidance, on page 425).

Method

An explanation of the methodology used is needed here. The aim of this section is to provide enough information for this study to be replicated (repeated) by another researcher. It must be clear and detailed.

Hypothesis

Begin by stating the hypothesis you are testing, or the research aim you are investigating.

Describe how many participants took part, the sampling frame and the sampling method. Give details of age and gender and any other details that are relevant.

Primary research methods

- Describe the method you used to collect data (for example, questionnaire, interview, observation etc).
- If you used a questionnaire taken from a secondary source (for example, the Internet or a journal or book) make a note of the author, the website or the publication so you can reference this. If you created it yourself, describe how many questions you used, whether they were open or closed, what they were designed to find out etc.
- If you used an observational method, explain what coding scheme you used and how you set up the situation in order to conduct the observation.
- If you used an experiment, describe the independent variable and dependent variable and explain how you set about controlling potential confounding variables.
- Procedure: explain how you distributed the questionnaires; how you approached participants etc. Include any standardised instructions that you gave.
- Reference to ethical considerations should be included here. Explain what you did in order to be ethically correct in carrying out the research.

Secondary research

You will write up all the details of this in the section called 'Literature Search'.

Recording of data

Explain what method you used to record data. If you used a questionnaire, explain how you scored it. If you used an interview method, explain whether you asked the questions and then wrote the responses down straightaway or used a tape recorder and transcribed the tape later.

For an observational method you need to explain the type of coding you used and whether you used time, event or sequence sampling.

If you used an experiment, what method did you use to record data? Did people write down answers to questions on a sheet which you then checked for accuracy? Did you use a stopwatch to measure performance on a particular task?

Triangulation

This is a method often used within social sciences whereby a researcher uses more than one method or investigator to test the same topic of interest. For example, two interviewers could interview the same person about their views on abortion. In this way a richer variety of data is obtained which in turn increases validity.

Results

This is the section where you present your findings. The aim is to summarise your findings clearly so that a reader can understand the main aspects of the data. Record it in such a way that the reader can see at a glance whether it supports your hypothesis or not. Use the advice given in the sections on statistical presentation of findings and methods of presentation to present your results clearly.

Compiling and presenting data

Use the information from the section 'Methods of presentation' on page 443 for guidance on how to compile data effectively – you need to present it clearly in your report write-up.

Do not include **raw data** (i.e. scores or tally charts for every single participant) in this section, but instead use summary tables. Raw data should be presented at the end of the report. Depending on your hypothesis you can choose percentages or averages. Choose whichever form makes it clearest to see at a glance whether your hypothesis is supported or not.

Key terms

Raw data This refers to data as it is collected. For example, this may include all completed questionnaires, all participants' test papers, an observation schedule with tally marks etc. It is the data which you then summarise to present as findings.

You need to present your data so it gives a clear, at-a-glance visual summary of what you have found. See 'Methods of presentation' on page 443 for a discussion on graphical methods of presenting your results.

It is advisable to use a program such as Excel to create graphs and charts. This is explained in more detail below. Unless you are expert at using this software, you may prefer to use the table menu in Microsoft Word as this is easier to format than importing an Excel file. This is described in greater detail below.

Statistical presentation of findings

It is usual, when presenting your findings, to give visual displays of your data in the form of **descriptive statistics** such as graphs and charts. This helps the reader to see at a glance what you have found. For example, if you are comparing males and females on the number of hours they spend each week on exercise, the use of a bar chart makes it easy to see whether one gender spends

longer than another. In addition, tables giving averages or percentages enable the reader to identify differences between the two groups.

Percentages

Percentages give information on the proportion of your sample that fits into any given category. The example below shows how raw data has been converted into percentages so the reader can see at a glance the key information needed to investigate the hypothesis.

In context

One hundred people took part in a survey. 65 per cent of them were males aged between 21 and 45, and 35 per cent were females aged between 21 and 48. The table below represents descriptive data by gender on smoking habits and attempts made to give up smoking.

	% smokers	% who failed to give up smoking	% who succeeded in giving up smoking
Females	35%	21%	14%
Males	54%	14%	40%

N = 100

Table 22.4 The percentage of males and females who succeeded and failed in giving up smoking

1   The summary table above gives four categories of information, all expressed as a percentage. One of these categories is for males who failed to give up smoking. Name the other three categories.

2   Which gender was more successful at giving up smoking?

3   Suppose the sample size consisted of only 10 smokers. Would this cause a problem? What does this tell you about the use of percentages in summarising data?

Key terms

Descriptive statistics This refers to data which is summarised in numerical form, such as mean, median or mode. This forms the first stage of data analysis for calculating **inferential statistics**. The data is normally shown in a table and graph.

Inferential statistics A mathematical calculation looking into the probability that an outcome happens by chance. For example, if a group of participants who have taken vigorous exercise do better in an arithmetic test than a similar group who took no exercise, it may just be chance, in which case we cannot draw strong conclusions from these findings. However, if an inferential statistical test shows us that there is a 95 per cent probability that this didn't happen by chance, we would be safe to say that exercise improves performance on this task.

Mean

We often talk about averages when we want to describe how most people in a set of data have performed. This usually refers to the mean but there are other ways of summarising how most people perform. The mean, median and mode are also known as *measures of central tendency* and they are used to show the mid-point of a set of frequency data. You use these in a summary table when you need to illustrate an average score in a set of data. The mean is calculated by adding up all the numbers in your set of data and dividing by the total number of scores.

Let's conduct another experiment with caffeine! Imagine you want to find out if two groups of maths students perform differently on a maths test depending on whether they have drunk coffee beforehand or not. You could construct a set of test items (for example, 10 questions) and ask both groups of participants to complete the same test having given all those in one group a set amount of coffee beforehand and those in the other group no coffee. You might arrive at a set of scores like the ones in Table 22.5.

Although there is some similarity between individual scores for both groups (for example, some participants in each group have scored 5) in general it looks as though the participants in group 2 are getting higher scores than those in group 1. To compare the two groups in a meaningful way, therefore, and to decide whether coffee does seem to improve performance in a maths test, it is usual to calculate the mean to be able to say how the average person in each group performs. It can be seen from the table that the average mean performance is 7 for the group which was given coffee, which is higher than the average mean performance of 5 for the group which had no coffee.

	Group 1 (no coffee)	Group 2 (coffee)
	4	7
	5	6
	3	3
	8	9
	7	8
	6	10
	4	6
	3	5
	6	8
	8	3
	5	9
	2	10
	5	5
	4	6
	6	4
	6	8
	1	7
	4	9
	5	9
	3	6
Average	5	7

Table 22.5 The results of performing with and without coffee

Median

This is the halfway point that separates the lower 50 per cent of the data from the higher 50 per cent. The median is a useful **measure of central tendency** to use

Theory into practice

What conclusion could you draw about the effects of coffee on performance in a maths test?

Key terms

Measures of central tendency This is a method used to summarise the mid-point of a set of data. It includes the mean, median and mode.

where there are some very high or very low scores, which can create a misleading average if using the mean. For example, a student carries out an experiment to find out if people complete a task more quickly when they have taken vigorous exercise. The data she obtains is in the form of total seconds taken to complete the task and is shown below:

| 70 | 74 | 75 | 77 | 78 | 100 |

Calculating the mean gives an average score of 79. This is, however, misleading as only one individual actually scored above 78, and yet this is supposed to represent an average. The median is 76 and this represents the data in a more realistic and accurate way.

Mode

This is the score that occurs most frequently in a set of data. The set of data below represents scores on a test.

| 30 | 30 | 30 | 50 | 96 | 100 |

If we calculate the mean, this gives an average of 56, which is misleading since no score is near this. The median would be 40, which again is misleading. The mode is 30 and is the most accurate measure of central tendency for this data since it represents the most frequently obtained score.

Methods of presentation

Bar charts

Bar charts show data for the categories that the researcher wants to compare. An example is given below of a student project asking people about the number of hours they spend exercising each week.

Write a set of four statements summarising what you consider to be the interesting and important information shown in Figure 22.6.

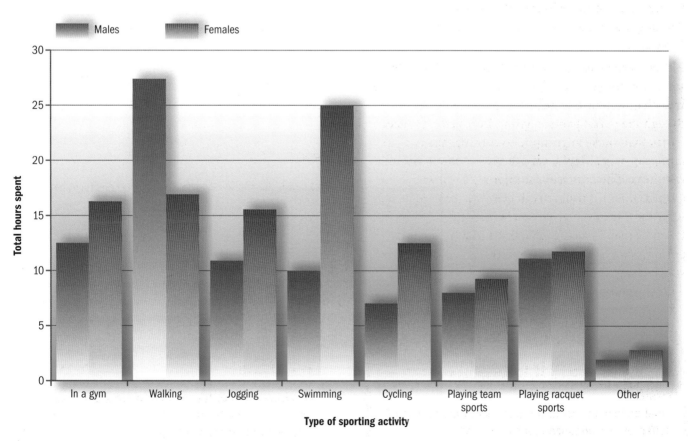

▲ Figure 22.6 Total time spent on sport each week, by gender

Theory into practice

From the bar chart in Figure 22.6, a number of findings can be seen very easily. There are clear differences between the types of exercise taken by all individuals and there are differences between the total amount taken by individuals. Summarise the gender differences both in the total amount of exercise taken and in the type of exercise.

Theory into practice

Draw two conclusions from the graph in Figure 22.7 about the scores achieved by students on this test. Write one recommendation for the teacher.

Scattergrams

These are used when the researcher wants to show how two variables relate. A student who travels over an hour a day to get to college notices that people seem to be showing more signs of stress as the journey becomes longer (for example, fidgeting, tapping fingers impatiently etc). She decides to construct a questionnaire about the experience of stress which she asks fellow passengers to complete at the end of their journey. Each question is answerable on a scale of 1 to 5 with 1 representing a low-stress score and 5 a high-stress score. At the bottom of the questionnaire she asks them to state the length of time they travel to work each day. As she is interested in the way these two variables (subjective feeling of stress and time spent travelling) are related, she uses a scattergram to represent the data.

Histograms

The purpose of a histogram is to show the frequency (number of times) a particular score occurs. Unlike bar charts, where the purpose is to show differences in categories, these graphs tend to be used when the researcher wants to show a range of scores from 0 upwards. Examples of their use would be if time or scores on a test were being measured and displayed. The graph below represents test scores obtained by students in a mock exam which tests their knowledge of the functions of the heart and lungs. The maximum possible score was 69 and the minimum was 0 (i.e. if no questions were correctly answered!).

Figure 22.7 A histogram to show the frequency of scores on a test ▶

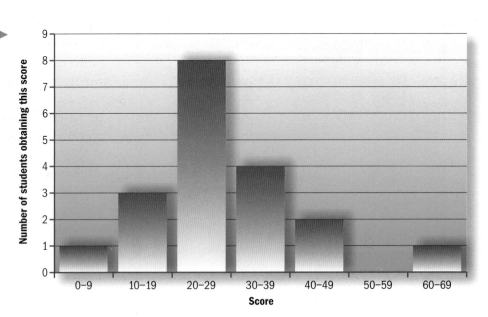

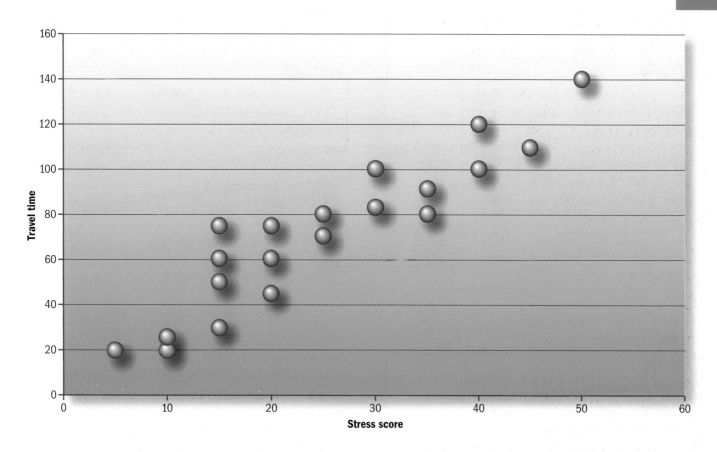

Figure 22.8 This scattergraph plots two variables for each participant: stress score and length of time travelled

Theory into practice

Draw one conclusion from Figure 22.8 about the relationship between stress and travel time.

Line graphs or frequency polygons

These are used to show two sets of data on the same graph. For example, a student's research project involves an observational study of two children in a nursery. Both children have been noted to be particularly disruptive and a young trainee is allocated to one of the children (Jo) for a period of two weeks to give her special attention. The number of disruptive acts carried out by both children is recorded and transferred to a line graph, as shown below in Figure 22.9.

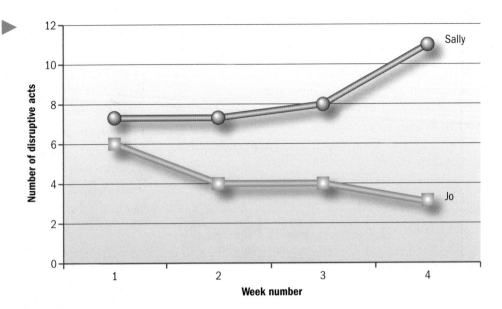

Figure 22.9 This line graph shows two sets of data for two individuals

Theory into practice

Looking at the graph above, draw two conclusions about the change in behaviour shown by Sally and Jo.

Pie charts

These are useful when you want to show the relative contribution of parts which make up a whole. It is even more useful if the percentage is put into each section of the pie. An example is given in Figure 22.10 of data collected by a student who was observing children over a one-hour period. The type of play they exhibited was totalled using a tally chart and an observational schedule. Entering the data onto a spreadsheet, the student calculated percentages for each type of play and then used the insert chart function to create a pie chart. To obtain percentages, choose data labels (once the pie chart is displayed) and click on percentages.

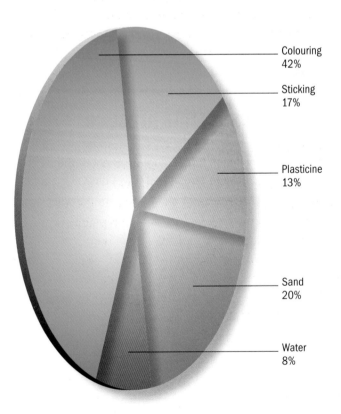

Colouring
42%

Sticking
17%

Plasticine
13%

Sand
20%

Water
8%

Figure 22.10 This pie chart shows activities engaged in as a proportion of the observation period

Theory into practice

Draw two conclusions from the pie chart in Figure 22.10 about this child's play preferences as illustrated over the course of this observation.

Reflect

If it is believed that special attention from a trainee will improve a child's behaviour, is it fair to pay attention to only one child?

Tables

Tables are a quick way of presenting information to allow for comparisons to be made between different categories or conditions.

Electronic presentation

To be really professional you could use a spreadsheet package such as Excel to enter your raw data and obtain calculations such as totals, averages and percentages. This package also enables you to insert charts and graphs. You can easily cut and paste the finished product and insert it into a Word document to present under the 'Results' section of your report write-up. More detailed information on how to use spreadsheet functions is given below.

Drawn presentation

It is not always a requirement for you to present your findings electronically, although this is a skill that is needed more and more. Check with your tutor about guidance on presentation of your results in the form of summary tables and charts. If it is acceptable to use hand-drawn graphs, you need to ensure that these are neatly drawn with the horizontal and vertical axes properly labelled. Give the chart a meaningful title and make it clear whether you are representing the data as totals, averages or percentages.

Methods of analysis

Use of IT software for processing statistical information

Probably the most useful IT software you can use to analyse and present your data is a spreadsheet package such as Excel. This enables you to enter all data neatly for each participant (this is called raw data) according to categories that are useful to you.

Table 22.6 illustrates raw data from a project which involved asking students on a sports science course to keep a diary for a week, and counting the number of hours they spent on exercise. From this, the researcher summarised the different types of exercise into seven main categories (in a gym, walking etc) and one category for unusual forms of exercise such as trampolining, which she called 'other'. She grouped all the returned diaries into two piles – one for male and one for female – and numbered the males 1–10 and the females 11–20. In this way she was easily able to separate out the data from the two groups to make later comparisons. The use of Excel also allowed her to create a spreadsheet of raw data (this is the name for data that has not been summarised in any form and represents findings from each participant). Using the function button, she then quickly calculated totals and

Theory into practice

1 Use the raw data in Table 22.6 to draw up a table showing the differences between males and females in:

   a total time spent exercising for each group

   b total time spent on each separate activity

   c average time spent on each separate activity

   d average time spent on each activity by gender.

2 Create an appropriate chart or graph to represent the data summaries outlined above. Explain why you have chosen this particular chart or graph.

Participant number	Type of exercise taken								Totals
	In a gym	Walking	Jogging	Swimming	Cycling	Playing team sports	Playing racquet sports	Other	
1	0	3	2	0	0	3	0	0	8
2	3	1	0	2	0	0	0	0	6
3	0	5	2	0	2	0	0	0	9
4	1.5	2	0	3	0	0	2	0	8.5
5	0	4	0	1.5	0	5	0	2	12.5
6	2	0	0	0	5	0	2	0	9
7	3	2	0	0	0	0	2	0	7
8	0	3.5	5	0	0	0	0	0	8.5
9	3	5	0	0	0	0	3	0	11
10	0	2	2	3.5	0	0	2	0	9.5
Totals	12.5	27.5	11	10	7	8	11	2	89
Averages	1.25	2.75	1.1	1	0.7	0.8	1.1	0.2	8.9
11	3	2	0	5	0	2	0	0	12
12	2	0	3	2	0	0	2	0	9
13	0	3	2	4	0	0	3	2	14
14	1.5	2	0	1.5	0	2	0	1	8
15	2	0	3	1	3	0	2	0	11
16	0	3.5	2	0	2.5	2.5	0	0	10.5
17	4	0	3	0	5	3	0	0	15
18	0	2	2.5	3	0	0	0	0	7.5
19	3	1.5	0	5	0	0	2	0	11.5
20	1	3	0	3.5	2	0	3	0	12.5
Totals	16.5	17	15.5	25	12.5	9.5	12	3	111
Average	1.65	1.7	1.55	2.5	1.25	0.95	1.2	0.3	11.1
	In a gym	Walking	Jogging	Swimming	Cycling	Playing team sports	Playing racquet sports	Other	Totals
Males	12.5	27.5	11	10	7	8	11	2	89
Females	16.5	17	15.5	25	12.5	9.5	12	3	111

Table 22.6 A spreadsheet of raw data from 20 participants. The numbers in each cell represent the total hours recorded per activity for each participant

averages for each participant and for the separate groups of males and females. Excel also allowed her, very easily, to create a variety of charts using the data created on the spreadsheet. See the relevant sections for examples of how this can be done.

Remember!

The purpose of graphs, tables and charts is to help the reader to see at a glance a summary of what you have found. Don't give results for every single participant! Choose a method of presentation that clearly links to your aim or hypothesis.

Drawing conclusions

This is where you need to refer back to your original aim and/or hypothesis. You need to summarise your data in such a way that the reader can see at a glance what you have found and whether it supports your hypothesis or not. If you were investigating differences (for example, between males and females on some aspect of health and social care) it would be wise to present your findings in the form of a table of averages and/or percentages and a graph that visually shows what the differences are.

Your conclusion needs to be based on what you have found from your own data. It may be that this is not what you expected to find, in which case you need to make this clear. Be careful not to go beyond what the data tells you. So if, for example, your hypothesis was that females would spend more time taking exercise than males and you find that there is no difference between the two, you have to acknowledge this. From the 'Theory into practice' activity on page 447, you will have analysed the sample and be able to conclude who took more exercise – males or females. You can also draw conclusions about the type of exercise taken by comparing the amount of time spent on different types of exercise by males and females.

Figure 22.6 (on page 443) represents a bar chart created from the raw data shown in Table 22.6. Simply by

looking at the differences between the time spent on different activities by males and females, a number of conclusions can be drawn. For example, it can be clearly seen that most time, overall, was spent on walking, and more males than females spent time on this activity. The second most popular sporting activity was swimming, where women far outnumbered males in terms of total hours spent. A number of other conclusions can be drawn about, for example, the popularity of team sports versus racquet sports, or the total amount of time spent by males and females on sport in the week when the diary activity took place. What you cannot do, is to draw conclusions about *why* females and males chose these particular activities. You could speculate that women prefer gentle sports such as swimming, but you cannot infer this from the data.

Bias

This refers to the possibility that researchers are, intentionally or not, arranging the investigation or collecting information in such a way that their hypothesis will be supported. Two types of bias you need to be aware of are observer bias and subject bias.

■ Observer bias

There may be a tendency for a researcher to notice actions or behaviours that are in line with their predictions and ignore those that aren't. In the example given above of disruptive acts performed by Jo and Sally, it may be that the observer wants to believe that Sally's behaviour is improving and so fails to note disruptive acts by Sally, or exaggerates the importance of disruptive acts performed by Jo. There are a number of ways to avoid this. One is to have someone observing the children's behaviour who does not know the purpose of the observation. They are less likely to interpret events in a biased way. A second method is to have two observers rating actions at exactly the same time. They then compare their observation notes and only select items they reach agreement on. Finally, being really clear about what constitutes a disruptive act is important in avoiding bias. This may involve an initial observation and agreement on what behaviours will be counted as disruptive before the observation starts.

Subject bias

This refers to the situation where an individual taking part in an investigation of any sort behaves differently in order to please the researcher. A famous example of this is known as the Hawthorne Effect. This occurred when a group of researchers were brought into an electrical plant in America to try to improve productivity by varying working conditions (for example, time and length of shifts, lighting and heating conditions etc). It was found that whatever was done to vary conditions, the work rate always improved; it didn't seem to be related in any way to the objective change in conditions. Ultimately it was realised that the workers were responding positively to being singled out for special attention (by being observed) and that, unconsciously, they were improving their work rate in order to 'please' the observers. In an experimental research method, this problem of bias is called 'demand characteristics'. In a questionnaire or interview method there is a similar source of bias known as 'social desirability' where people answer in a way they think is socially acceptable. For example, if asked for an opinion on recycling, a participant may exaggerate either their beliefs about the value of this, or their actual recycling practices, because they know that recycling is generally considered to be a socially desirable thing to do.

Error

Sources of error include factors to do with the sample, confounding variables and problems with the research design.

Ethical considerations

We have discussed earlier the need to conduct research in an ethical way in order to ensure that participants are not harmed in any way. When carrying out research, you must be sure to follow ethical guidelines very thoroughly. However, there are cases where research has been carried out in an ethical way but where the findings are put to uses which may harm participants or groups of participants in some way. This is discussed below in section 22.6, where we look at how research findings can be misused.

Assessment activity 22.4

Carry out the primary research and collect and record appropriate data.

1 Choose an appropriate research method to use (for example, observation, interview, questionnaire). Decide on the type of person you want to obtain your data from (the sample population) and a sampling method and collect the data. Select an appropriate method, of recording the data you have obtained. **P4**

Grading tip for P4

Before you decide upon a method, think about what it is you want to find out. If you are interested in people's opinions, then a questionnaire or interview could be used and you may decide to collect qualitative data. If you want to compare some aspect of people's behaviour (for example, use of a gym, diet etc) a questionnaire might be a good choice. Your ultimate choice will depend on a number of factors including the research hypothesis, the type of sample you will use, the length of time you have available and the type of data (quantitative or qualitative) that will be of most use to you in testing your hypothesis. As you read through the following section, make notes on the advantages and disadvantages of each method so you can include this in your choice of methodology and your evaluation. Ask yourself: 'Are these advantages I can make use of?' or 'Does this disadvantage mean I shouldn't use this particular method?'

Re-read the section on methods of sampling (see pages 433–434) and choose a method that is suitable for your topic.

Select a method of recording your results (for example, a tally chart or an interview schedule with blanks for you to write in the respondents' answers).

Present and report findings in a relevant format, identifying sources of bias or error.

2 Summarise your data using at least one table and one chart. Give them labels and write a brief summary of what they show. List any sources of bias or error you have found. **P5**

Grading tip for P5

In order to select an appropriate method of displaying the data, you need to use descriptive statistics in a way that links to your hypothesis or aim. If you are looking for differences between two groups (for example, males' versus females' use of a gym) a table and graph can help the reader to see at a glance what you have found. Use an average if you want to show differences between participants in each group (for example, the average length of time to complete a maths test with or without taking exercise beforehand). Use percentages if you want to show proportions (for example, the proportion of males and females taking part in different types of sporting activity).

To identify bias you could look at aspects of the method used. For example, were questions worded in such a way that people would be more likely to agree with your hypothesis? If you asked people face-to-face questions, do you think you may have unconsciously used body language or tone of voice that indicated what you wanted them to say? Was your sample biased?

To identify error, look again at the method used and decide whether there could have been something that reduced validity. For example, in a questionnaire if people don't fully understand the question they will not be able to answer it correctly and your findings will not be valid – this is a source of error.

Review the research methods chosen in relation to the results obtained, any sources of bias or error, and ethical considerations.

3 Consider ways in which the research method you chose was useful in testing your hypothesis and collecting data. Identify if there were any aspects of the methodology that were not helpful. For example, you may have asked people about their attitudes and beliefs rather than what they actually do, in order to avoid sensitive issues. This may have meant you did not obtain the results you predicted and expected to find. Your methodology also includes sampling. Could your sample have been biased? If so, why? **M2**

Grading tip for M2

To achieve M2 you could create a table of advantages and disadvantages of the method you have chosen. If you asked your participants for feedback, you can include this here. Issues you might want to consider include the following:

- Was this the best research method to test my hypothesis?
- If yes, why? If not, what could I have done instead?
- Was my sample representative or could it have been biased in any way?
- Was there any aspect of the method (for example, the wording of questions) that could have caused bias?
- Were there any sources of error that I had not anticipated?
- Were the ethical procedures I put into place enough to protect participants? Could I have done anything differently? If so, what?

To help you review your chosen method, you could ask your participants to evaluate the methodology you have used and comment on what they thought was useful and any improvements they think you could make. This will help you to reflect upon and thus evaluate your own research findings.

Discuss how the methodology of the research project could be altered to reduce bias and error.

4   Identify all sources of bias and error in the method used, the sample and the way you collected the data. Discuss the reasons for the bias or error (for example, it may have been unforeseen) and suggest ways you could reduce this. **D1**

Take it further

Research by Cyril Burt into IQ has famously been discredited for being flawed. Find out what the problems were with this research and identify sources of bias within it.

Grading tip for D1

To achieve D1 it may be useful to go back to your original planning. You may, for example, have been trying to avoid being intrusive by carrying out an observational study only to find that this didn't give you the information you needed! If so, explain this and suggest an alternative method that could have been used. If you used a questionnaire but avoided certain questions because of ethical considerations and this affected your findings, explain this here also.

22.5 Evaluating the research project

At the end of your report you need to draw an overall conclusion. You will evaluate the project in terms of the methodology used and make recommendations for further research or for use of your findings.

Evaluation and conclusion

Compare findings with hypothesis

To draw a conclusion about your findings you need to relate your data back to the hypothesis or research question. If, for example, your hypothesis is that 'children who attend pre-school are more likely to show a preference for gender-typed toys than those who do not attend pre-school' you need to show your findings clearly. Suppose you find that the mean number of choices for gender-typed toys (trucks chosen by boys to play with, dolls chosen by girls) is lower among those who attend pre-school, you have to reject your hypothesis and acknowledge that this has not been supported by the data.

Discussion of findings

The first point for a discussion is to compare your findings with those you have outlined in your literature review. It may be that you originally found, and cited, research which found that pre-school children's choice of gender-typed toys was stronger than non pre-school children. In light of *your* data, you need to attempt to explain why you found something different. It may be, for example, that the research was carried out some years ago and that changes have taken place since. It could be that the pre-school facility you investigated has a policy of positive encouragement for children to play with non-gender-appropriate toys and the children have learnt this and acted on it.

Relationships of results to current research

Here you need to explain how your results fit with current research. You may have outlined research, for example, that suggests that parents are most likely to avoid having their child vaccinated because of beliefs about possible side-effects of certain vaccines. If your findings show something different you need to state in what way they are different and suggest possible reasons why.

Identification of limitations of research project

This can sometimes be hard to write since you have probably thought very carefully about how you set up your research in order to avoid limitations! It may be, however, that for practical reasons your sample was very small or not representative of the population as a whole. Many students use other students to take part in their research and there may not be a representative mix of age, gender, ethnic background etc. Or you may have selected a method that you now realise wasn't the best way of investigating your topic. For example, you may have used a questionnaire with closed questions and discovered afterwards that one or two of these questions could have been followed by an open question to enable you to get more information about people's beliefs, feelings and attitudes. It is a good idea to look at all aspects of your methodology in writing this section in order to generate ideas about limitations and possible improvements.

Potential areas for further development of research

For a merit grade you need to discuss the implications that your particular findings may have for current practice. If you were to publish these findings, what organisation might be able to use them to make improvements? What sort of improvements could be made and who would they benefit? Suggest further research that could be carried out to extend knowledge of your topic area.

Consideration of implications

In this section you need to explain what your findings imply in terms of the uses to which they could be put (for example, do they imply that more funding is needed to fund pre-school provision; do they imply that under-16s need better guidance and information on how to practise

safe sex). If there are ethical implications related to these findings, such as human rights issues, state what they are. For example, you may find that people in your sample are openly racist or belong to organisations which infringe human rights. What would you do, and whose advice would you seek if you did come across such a situation? Finally, make suggestions as to how this research could have been improved (for example, by using a different methodology, a different sample etc) and how bias and error could have occurred, or could be excluded.

■ Ethical issues

If you have followed the guidance given in section 22.3 you should have satisfied all the requirements for your project to be ethical. You need at this stage to review all you did to ensure the following requirements.

- **Confidentiality** – did the steps you took to ensure confidentiality achieve this? On reflection, was there anything you could have done differently?
- **Data protection** – how did you ensure you followed the guidelines on data protection? Was this satisfactory? Could or should you have done anything differently?

Use and misuse of research

Research findings can potentially cause harm to others, even if this is unintended. Suppose, for example, you find that the majority of parents at a pre-school you have been working in believe that asylum seekers should be banned from the school; it would cause great harm if this research were to be made known to a member of a pressure group trying to remove these children from the school. Research should only be used for its stated purpose. Similarly, if you were involved in a project interviewing parents who have lost a child, for whatever reason, it would be disastrous for the parents if they could be identified in any way. It is essential that researchers preserve the confidentiality of participants. If you have promised confidentiality you must ensure that any coursework produced is kept safely and is not available to anyone who could possibly identify any of the participants. If you used anyone's name while collecting data (so that you could identify them yourself) make sure you delete this.

Recommendations

It is normal practice for the findings of research in health and social care to be put into practice, and this is no different for your project. You need to show that you can make recommendations based on your findings for how practice could be changed or modified in order to improve services. This applies to both practitioners, who may be guided to carry out their practice in a new way, or to the use of new methods (for example, giving additional control to elderly residents in nursing homes to improve their health outcomes). Recommendations are also made to policy makers who can then conduct further research into a topic. If you read the section on page 460 ('Effects on policy and practice: the impact of key reports') you will see that an important result of the report into the Victoria Climbié case was that six major recommendations were made for social workers and other professionals to follow in future similar cases.

Assessment activity 22.5

Discuss the findings of the research in relation to the original hypothesis.

1 Explain which aspects of your findings support the original hypothesis, using examples from the data. If some of the findings do not support the hypothesis, explain these, again giving examples from the data. **P6**

Grading tip for P6

Start the discussion by stating whether the hypothesis was supported or not, and give some of the data from your findings to illustrate this (for example, 25 per cent more males than females went to a gym once a week). If your hypothesis was not supported, you still need to include data which shows why this was so. You can then move on to a brief discussion of why, despite your literature search which led you to formulate the hypothesis in the first place, you didn't find what you expected.

Analyse the findings of the research in relation to the original hypothesis.

2 Discuss, using examples from the data, where your findings support, partially support or do not support the original hypothesis. Suggest reasons for these findings. **M3**

Grading tip for M3

To achieve M3 you need to go into your findings a bit more deeply than you did for P6. You can look at trends – for example, does the data show a trend in the direction you predicted? If so, would a larger sample have supported your hypothesis? Can your findings be explained in any other way? For example, the research you used may have been old and trends have changed.

Analyse the purpose and role of research in the sectors, drawing on the piece of research undertaken.

3 Explain how your findings could be used in the health and social care sectors. Identify the benefits and difficulties of using these findings. Explain the purpose and role of these findings, giving specific examples of how they could be used. **D2**

Grading tip for D2

To achieve D2 you need to conduct a very thorough and detailed analysis of how your findings could be used in the health or social care sectors. You may find it helpful to consider the following points:

* What was the purpose of this research? Was this purpose partially or completely fulfilled? Explain how and why.
* What role could your findings play in these sectors? Explain how and give examples of how they could be used.

Implications

In this context, implications refer to what appears to be shown by a finding, what conclusions can be drawn from this finding, the consequences that follow and the uses to which such findings can be put. To give a straightforward example, if it is found that the bacteria known as Staphylococcus aureus causes MRSA, it could be concluded that as bacteria can be spread by person-to-person contact, strict hygiene measures could stop the spread of this bacteria from one patient to another. The consequences of this are that hospital administrators could discuss measures that could be taken by all people in contact with hospital patients to improve hygiene. The uses to which such findings could be put are policies and practices to ensure that strict hygiene rules are followed and the monitoring of individuals to ensure they follow such procedures. It is sometimes necessary, however, to look at how trustworthy the findings are before taking action and implementing change.

Who commissions research?

It is important that the organisations which fund specific research projects and sometimes supervise such research are disinterested. This means that they do not have anything to gain from the results whichever way they go. Suppose, for example, that research into the danger of passive smoking were commissioned (requested and paid for) by a tobacco company. It would be expected that the research might be carried out in such a way as to show that the danger is either minimal or non-existent; in addition, the findings might be presented in a biased fashion for the same reasons. A similar problem might exist with research commissioned by a fast food company to investigate if there are any health problems (either short- or long-term) associated with eating their products. It is important, therefore, when evaluating the quality of any research findings, to be certain that the commissioning organisation does not have a vested interest in coming up with a particular finding that supports their cause.

Reflect

There have been many cases of drugs being manufactured and used by members of the public which are later shown to have unwanted side-effects. Thalidomide is an example of one such drug. Discuss amongst yourselves the problems associated with a drug company's researchers being the only people investigating the effects of a new 'wonder drug'. Would you feel comfortable relying on their findings? What alternative set-up could you envisage to ensure that the findings of the research could be trusted by members of the public using this new drug?

Remember!

When you read published research, find out who commissioned the research and ask yourself if you can be certain that they are impartial. If a tobacco company publishes findings that cigarette smoking is not harmful it may be less believable than findings from the Department of Health!

Human rights

In October 2000 the European Convention on Human Rights and Fundamental Freedoms was incorporated into British law as the Human Rights Act. This piece of legislation sets out certain fundamental human rights relating to many diverse aspects of the rights and freedoms owed to any individual in any state. In relation to the conducting of (and participation in) research, the following article is relevant. Individuals have a 'right to respect for private and family life, home and correspondence'. This is taken further in legislation relating to data protection and guaranteed under the Data Protection Act 1998 (see page 458).

Validity

Validity refers to whether a piece of research measures what it set out to measure (valid means true). There are many potential sources of threats to validity, some of which have been discussed above. They include:

- **Demand characteristics** In this instance the participants are behaving in such a way as to please the investigator. What is being measured, therefore, is their ability to act convincingly rather than their actual, normal behaviour. Demand characteristics usually arise when a research set-up is so artificial that participants don't believe in it, so they try to guess the purpose of the research investigation and act accordingly.
- **Social desirability** Here, the results of an investigation may be invalid because participants are responding in such a way as to make themselves seem worthy. They are behaving differently from everyday life (or voicing opinions that don't reflect their own) simply in order to look good in the eyes of the researcher.
- **Investigator effects** This refers to the way in which the characteristics of the researcher influence the behaviour or response of the participants. This is particularly likely to occur if an interviewer or individual administering a face-to-face questionnaire has characteristics which are very different from those of the participants. These characteristics can include accent, way of presenting oneself, social class and gender.

Reliability

Reliability refers to the possibility that the findings of a piece of research can be replicated (repeated) by other researchers using a similar sample and the same methods. If a research investigation is repeated in this way and fails to produce the same findings it is said to lack reliability. This may occur because of flawed methodology. It is very unwise to take action on the basis of findings that are unreliable, particularly when people's health and well-being are at stake. An example of research that was flawed was the theory, proposed by the psychoanalyst Bruno Bettleheim, that autism was caused by mothers who lacked emotional engagement with their children. This research was highly influential at the time and resulted in mothers feeling

What are your thoughts on street crime?

▲ How truthful do you think this young man would be when asked questions by this woman?

blamed and personally responsible for this disorder in their children. Later research has shown that there is strong evidence for a genetic/biological cause of this disorder and Bettleheim's findings have been discredited. He based his theory on case studies of children who already had autism and failed to use a control group to compare the family circumstances of these children with a sample of similar children who did not have autism. Had he done this, before publishing his theories, it would have been shown that there were no significant differences between the mothers of children with autism and those of children who did not suffer from this disorder.

Consequences/benefits of findings

The consequences of findings in terms of public health initiatives must always be considered before research is published. It should be ensured that findings are reliable (can be replicated) before they are incorporated into any public health changes or differences in practice among health or child care professionals. An example of a research finding which had great benefits comes from the observational study carried out by James Robertson in the 1950s of the effects of hospitalisation on children who were separated from their main caregiver. In a famous study called 'A two year old goes to hospital', James Robertson filmed children from the time of entry to hospital to the time of reunion with their parent/ main caregiver. At the time it was current practice to limit contact between children and their parent/main caregiver as it was believed that such visits caused unnecessary upset to the children and hindered the smooth running of the hospital ward. Robertson showed the enormous distress caused to such young children at being separated from the person to whom they had an attachment. Although many doctors were initially reluctant to accept his findings, over time it was acknowledged that more harm than good was done by this separation and as a consequence the practice in hospitals has radically changed. Parents/carers are now actively encouraged to stay with their children to minimise the distress caused by hospital visits; children's wards are often equipped with sleeping facilities to encourage parents/carers to stay for the duration of the child's hospitalisation.

Effects of publication of research

One famous example of the consequences of the effects of publication of research concerns the combined Measles, Mumps and Rubella (MMR) vaccine. In 1998, the findings from a small-scale study were published in the medical journal *The Lancet* suggesting that the MMR vaccine might cause autism in some children. Since the publication of this report, vaccinations for MMR have dropped dramatically. The proportion of children in the UK immunised against MMR by their second birthday fell from 90 per cent in the early and mid-1990s to 81 per cent in 2003/04, while between 1995 and 2001 there were 665 cases of measles in England and Wales. The problem with this research was that it was never replicated. This means that other researchers using a similar sample and a similar methodology did

not come up with the same findings – an example of research that lacks reliability. A report appearing in *The Lancet* in 2004 published the findings of a study carried out by the Medical Research Council comparing a large sample of children diagnosed with autism and similar disorders (1294) with a similar sample of 4469 children of the same sex and similar age. A major researcher in this investigation stated publicly that he had found no evidence that the MMR vaccine caused autism.

Theory into practice

Carry out research into the Atkins Diet and address the following questions.

- How sound was the methodology that was used to formulate this diet plan?
- How many people were estimated, at a given period, to be following this diet?
- Were there any unforeseen side-effects?
- What do opponents of the Atkins diet claim?
- Is there any evidence to support either side?

Access to information

It is essential when research has been carried out that the findings are made public in such a way that *all* members of society can benefit, not just a select few in the medical and nursing (or child health) community who are fortunate enough to be able to read and understand findings that may include statistical data, tables, figures and specialist language. There is an ethical duty, therefore, on all those who come into contact in a professional capacity with a variety of client groups to provide information in a way that is accessible and easy to understand. Action points and advice should also be included to help the client group move forward on implementing findings. Information and advice should also be included in a variety of different languages and formats (for example, Braille) to ensure that everyone can benefit from the new knowledge and feel empowered to act upon it. The Social Care Institute for Excellence publishes many detailed guidelines on how to make information accessible to a range of client groups. To find out more, access the website www.scie.org.uk/publications/misc/accessguidelines-publications.pdf.

Vulnerability of client groups

Certain groups in society may be more vulnerable than others to discriminatory treatment, based on the findings from research. In the area of health prevention, for example, it has consistently been found that people from higher socio-economic backgrounds (managers and other professionals such as teachers, lawyers and architects) are less likely to smoke and more likely to take exercise and eat healthily than those from lower socio-economic backgrounds (for example, manual and unskilled workers). Similarly, asylum seekers are more likely to suffer from preventable diseases such as tuberculosis than the more settled population within the UK. These findings can lead to blame being placed on such vulnerable groups, without taking into account the fuller context such as:

- the strains of living in deprived areas
- the inaccessibility of cheap fresh fruit and vegetables in certain geographical areas
- the lack of privilege which makes it harder for some individuals to take exercise than others who can, for example, afford the time and money to go to a gym.

Ethical issues

Confidentiality

This has been addressed above in the section entitled 'Suitability of topic with reference to ethical issues' on

Remember!

Anyone who carries out research, whether it is a government department or a student, must make ethical considerations a priority. If participants can be harmed in any way by either the research process (for example, being upset by questions or topics) or the way the findings can be used, then this is unethical.

page 429. It is important to note that not only is it good practice to ensure confidentiality because, without it, participants will be reluctant to take part in future research projects, but there is also a legal requirement to protect the confidentiality of participants. This is enshrined in law under the Data Protection Act 1998.

Data protection legislation

There are eight principles of good practice that must be adhered to by anyone collecting data. These are as follows:

1 Data must be fairly and lawfully processed.

2 Data must be processed for limited purposes only (in this case for the purpose of the research project and for no other).

3 Data obtained must be adequate, relevant and not excessive. This means that the researcher must not collect data that goes beyond the scope of the investigation.

4 Data must be accurate and up-to-date.

5 Data must not be kept longer than necessary.

6 Data must be processed in accordance with the individual's rights.

7 Data must be secure (i.e. kept in a place where nobody else can have access to it unless they are part of the research team).

8 Data must not be transferred to countries outside the European economic area unless the country has adequate protection for the individual. This refers to the possibility that information on individuals could be used in countries where there is not such strict regulation on the use of data, in which case confidentiality could be breached.

For more information go to the following website: www.informationcommissioner.gov.uk.

Policy procedures

It is essential that managers, and others who are in charge of drafting policies and procedures for staff to follow, take note of ethical issues and legislation relating to the use and misuse of research findings and statistics, in order to avoid discrimination against certain client groups. In drafting new policies and procedures, attention must be paid to legislation such as the Data Protection Act, issues relating to access to information, anti-discriminatory practices and attention to codes of practice relevant to the particular organisation.

Authenticity

In general, authenticity refers to the credibility and honesty of an object or, in this case, a piece of research. Since the advent of the World Wide Web it is possible for anyone to create a website making all sorts of claims which may be completely untrue! For example, it could be claimed that using dandelion root is an excellent herbal remedy for the early stages of meningitis. This claim would lack authenticity since it could not be backed up by any kind of research. It is important for all researchers to examine the credibility (believability) of any material they read, and credentials (experience and qualifications) of those who conducted the research. You would quite possibly be sceptical about a newspaper headline claiming that Elvis Presley is alive and living in Bournemouth, because this is not credible. On the other hand, if you saw a headline saying 'Dandelion root is wonder cure for meningitis' you may be more inclined to believe this! A way of ensuring authenticity is to find out if claims have been published by a reputable source. Most articles published by reputable medical, social work, nursing or child care journals are likely to have been checked for accuracy before being published. You need to be careful, however, not to believe any claims before ensuring that they have been properly researched before being published.

Inclusion of codes of practice

Researchers must abide by the relevant codes of practice that relate to their area of work. Codes of practice are guidelines issued to members of professional bodies (nurses, social workers, health visitors etc) to give a framework within which to work. It is advisable to seek guidance from the relevant codes of practice of your organisation before conducting any research. The British Psychological Society code of practice for conducting research with human participants is an example, discussed earlier, of guidelines which help researchers to check at every stage that the research project they have planned is

ethical. Other organisations such as nurses, social workers and community care workers all have codes of conduct to guide them in making difficult decisions.

The role of the media

It must be recognised that the main purpose of the media is to find stories that will sell newspapers. This means that snippets of information, or partial findings, might be represented by newspapers and other media sources as the full story, leading members of the public to believe that there is a whole body of research to support the story. This is not always the case. The media may misrepresent findings or give only part of the picture in order to sell their publications.

Use and misuse of data

It is often assumed that statistics represent facts which cannot be disputed in any way because they are based on numbers. However, consider this scenario: a researcher investigates two young children, both of whom have been given the MMR vaccine before their second birthday – one of them has autism. It is quite truthful to say that 50 per cent of the sample investigated have developed autism, and this, together with the information that both infants received the MMR vaccine, gives a very strong impression that the MMR vaccine may well be responsible for the development of autism. This is clearly misleading. When you are reading research findings, therefore, it is important to check the original data on which the statistics are based.

Other examples of potentially misleading statistics come from data on illnesses. Take the case of tuberculosis (TB), for example. This is an infection caused by a germ called the tubercle bacillus or Mycobacterium tuberculosis. In most of the Western world, incidences of TB have been dramatically reduced since the introduction of effective antibiotics which cured the disease. However, since the growth of Auto Immune Deficiency Syndrome (AIDS) and the increase in immigration from countries where tuberculosis is still a prevalent disease, the number of people infected with TB has been increasing. To gain accurate figures on the incidence of this disease, however, it is necessary that everyone who has TB presents to a general practitioner or hospital. Those who, for whatever reason, fail to do so, will not be recorded in official statistics so the statistics recorded for this disease may be inaccurate. Since planned provision is based on an audit of needs which largely comes from official statistics, any misleading statistics will have implications on the level and type of service being provided, to the detriment of those who are 'invisible' in terms of statistical data.

Office of Population Censuses and Surveys

The Office of Population Censuses and Surveys (OPCS) carries out a regular survey on aspects of all individuals and households living within the UK. Data produced by this body ranges from neighbourhood data to national data and includes information for use by government, businesses and communities. Data is broken down to local level so that researchers can access information about specific areas. Information presented includes the categories of people and society, health and care, deprivation, thematic map, economic activity, students, education, skills and training and housing and households. Problems with this data, however, occur because no census ever includes data for all individuals living in each neighbourhood. This could be for a number of reasons including failure to disclose all members of a household surveyed, lack of inclusion of people living in the area who do not have a resident's permit, homeless people and individuals in custody at the time the census information is taken. For this reason, it is important to interpret findings with care. The OPCS is combined with the Central Statistical Office, and is known as the Office for National Statistics (ONS).

Social Trends

Also compiled by the UK government, *Social Trends* is a source of secondary data which collates information on social and economic aspects of life in the UK. It is particularly useful to enable a researcher to gain a broad picture of how society has changed over time. It is broken down into 13 chapters, each focusing on a different area of society. Examples include: the age of the population; the proportion of children living in lone-parent families; convictions for theft; number of people smoking. To find out more, access the following

website: www.statistics.gov.uk/statbase/Product. asp?vlnk=5748&More=N.

As with the OPCS statistics, it must be acknowledged that *Social Trends*, while useful, does not contain a complete picture of society – this is because not every individual living within the UK will be included in the statistics. Furthermore, there are items included in this document which may be inaccurate because of the reliance on subjective reporting. For example, in the 2005 version of *Social Trends*, statistics on smoking for 2003/4 are reported as being highest among adults in manual households and lowest in managerial and professional households. This statistic relies on the self-report of individuals rather than on objective data from, say, consultations with GPs. The possibility of inaccuracy cannot, therefore, be ruled out.

Effects on policy and practice

The impact of key reports

In order for research findings to be of any benefit to the public, it is essential that they are disseminated among all those who need to be aware of such findings. It is also important that those client groups involved have a voice in the collection of data that will form the basis of a report or other recommendation. For example, in 2003 the government published an important report called Every Child Matters. This was inspired by the findings of the enquiry headed by Lord Laming investigating the tragic death of Victoria Climbié, who was killed by her aunt and her aunt's boyfriend. The report makes six major recommendations for improving the care and well-being of children, including:

- being healthy
- staying safe
- enjoying life
- achieving as much as possible
- making a positive contribution
- enjoying economic well-being.

Based on the key objectives of this report, the Commission for Social Care Inspection interviewed young children to gain their opinions on the issues the government considered important. The findings can be accessed at the following website: www.csci.org.uk/publications/childrens_rights_director_reports/default.htm.

It can be seen, therefore, that by publishing policies and recommendations in key reports, attention can be directly focused on the individuals who are at the centre of the issues, and action taken to improve their lives and put right whatever flaws have been identified in a system.

Role of the Social Care Institute for Excellence

The stated aim of the Social Care Institute for Excellence (SCIE) is 'to improve the experience of people who use social care by developing and promoting knowledge about good practice in the sector'. This body researches a wide variety of organisations and service users in order to translate legislation into practice. It publishes information on how to promote effective practice

in a variety of settings and gives examples of how to implement key aspects of legislation. In this way it provides an accessible source of information, based on sound data from practice, which can help organisations to provide good practice in the delivery of a range of services. An example of this is SCIE's research and guidance on implementing an aspect of the Equal Opportunities Act 2004 which applies to carers. Its guide provides a breakdown of the relevant points of the legislation into several topic areas, each of which is divided into sections which make the legislation more accessible to managers and other policy implementers. An extract of the sub-divisions of the topics is given below.

■ Impact of SCIE research on policy

It was mentioned earlier that there is a crisis in recruiting and retaining foster carers (see page 415). One of the key functions of SCIE research projects is to identify the causes of gaps in social care provision

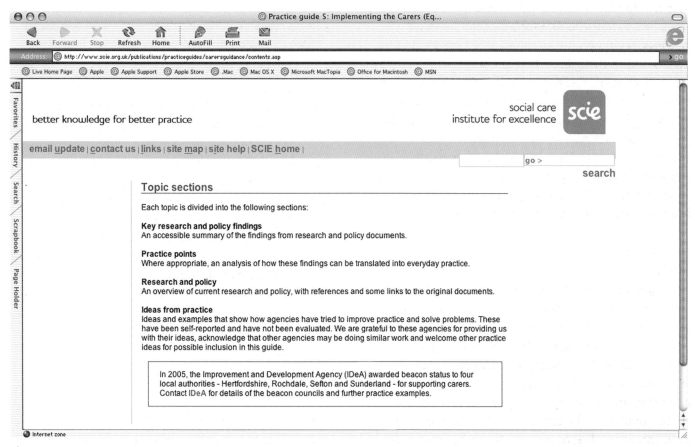

▲ Figure 22.11 A search page from the SCIE website

and suggest ways in which policies and practices can be altered or modified so that these gaps can be filled. Research carried out by SCIE was able to identify the reasons given by foster carers for dissatisfaction with their role and highlighted some important points which could be addressed by those whose responsibility it is to supervise, train and support foster carers. Some of the reasons given for dissatisfaction were:

- late or incorrect payments
- feeling unsupported, resulting in increased feelings of being under strain, and difficulties with a child.

The reasons identified for what keeps foster carers satisfied and happy to continue their work include:

- feeling supported by social workers and their family

- training, support and the chance to meet and get support from other foster carers
- being treated as a member of the team and the opportunity to work with social workers
- adequate information about the child
- good out-of-hours and general support, including access to specialist help and advice.

For more detailed information and to read the full report, visit the website: www.scie.org.uk/publications/practiceguides/fostering/carers/retaining/index.asp.

Based on these research findings, initiatives have been taken by some local authorities to improve the situation of foster carers.

Assessment activity 22.6

Outline any possible improvements to the research, referring to any relevant implications and ethical issues.

1   Suggest ways in which you might have found out more about your topic by using a different sample or a different method. Include reference to the implications of your findings and ethical issues.

Discuss the possible implications that the research results may have on current practice.

2   Explain how your particular findings might be used to alter current practice in the field of health and social care – either in terms of provision or practice.

Grading tip for P7

To achieve P7 you could start by thinking about the implications of your research. What do your findings imply for the professional practice and provision of services? If you had used a different method, or asked additional questions, would you have found out more that would be of benefit? You can also consider whether sensitivity to ethical issues may have led to you avoiding certain issues which you now realise were important to investigate. Alternatively, it may be that aspects of your research were so sensitive that you didn't find out what you needed to find because people felt uncomfortable about disclosing information. Would a different method, or an alteration to your method, have avoided this?

Grading tip for M4

To achieve M4 you could revisit your literature search and go right back to the reasons you chose to investigate this particular topic. It was probably because there was a 'gap' in the research or knowledge base. You will then have formulated a hypothesis and now is your chance to show how your findings could be used to improve or change the way things are done in your area of research.

Knowledge check

1 List four purposes of research in health and social care.

2 What is the difference between primary and secondary data?

3 Name three secondary sources you could use to conduct your literature research.

4 What is the difference between an aim and a hypothesis?

5 List three sampling methods you could use to obtain a sample for your research project.

6 List three potential sources of error in the research process.

7 List four ethical issues that must be considered when carrying out research.

8 Why are descriptive statistics used to present findings?

9 If you wanted to find government statistics about how society has changed over time, what publication would you look in?

10 What legislation governs the use of data?

Grading criteria

To achieve a pass grade the evidence must show that the learner is able to:	To achieve a merit grade the evidence must show that, in addition to the pass criteria, the learner is able to:	To achieve a distinction grade the evidence must show that, in addition to the pass and merit criteria, the learner is able to:
P1 explain the purpose and role of research for the health and social care sectors **Assessment activity 22.1 page 415**		
P2 describe the key elements of research methodologies **Assessment activity 22.2 page 427**		
P3 identify a research topic and carry out a literature search **Assessment activity 22.3 page 438**	**M1** justify the choice of topic and hypothesis **Assessment activity 22.3 page 438**	
P4 carry out the primary research and collect and record appropriate data **Assessment activity 22.4 page 450**		
P5 present and report findings in a relevant format, identifying sources of bias or error **Assessment activity 22.4 page 451**	**M2** review the research methods chosen in relation to the results obtained, any sources of bias or error, and ethical considerations **Assessment activity 22.4 page 451**	**D1** discuss how the methodology of the research project could be altered to reduce bias and error **Assessment activity 22.4 page 452**
P6 discuss the findings of the research in relation to the original hypothesis **Assessment activity 22.5 page 454**	**M3** analyse the findings of the research in relation to the original hypothesis **Assessment activity 22.5 page 454**	**D2** analyse the purpose and role of research in the sectors, drawing on the piece of research undertaken. **Assessment activity 22.5 page 454**
P7 outline any possible improvements to the research, referring to any relevant implications and ethical issues. **Assessment activity 22.6 page 462**	**M4** discuss the possible implications that the research results may have on current practice. **Assessment activity 22.6 page 462**	

Preparation for assessment

Prepare for your assessment by working through the following case study. Imagine you are Jamal's tutor, seeing him through the research process and helping him to think analytically about his procedures and findings. Some of the questions that follow the case study require you to think of ways in which this analysis can be carried out.

Jamal is interested in finding out about the experiences of the elderly when they are admitted to residential care. His 79-year-old grandmother has recently entered a nursing home because of severe arthritis which means she cannot care for herself physically. It is a very well-respected facility and he is confident that she will be well cared for. Some weeks later, however, he notices that she seems to be withdrawing into herself more and is not so lively and interested in what is going on around her. He has recently read about the work of Langer and Rodin in his health and social care course and is interested to find that residents who are given control over aspects of their lives, such as choosing activities and looking after plants, seem to do better than those without such control. He thinks originally about doing an experiment to test this in his grandmother's residential care home, but his tutor warns him that this might be unethical. He then wonders about an observational study, but soon realises that it will be very difficult to find the time to do the observation, so eventually he settles on an interview method.

1 Explain the purpose and role of this research project. **P1**

2 Summarise key features of different research methods and explain the advantages and disadvantages of the method Jamal has chosen. **P2**

3 Write a short statement explaining what topic Jamal is investigating and suggest four sources where he could obtain information for a literature search. **P3**

4 Write a short set of interview questions Jamal could use, and identify whether these are open or closed questions. Give advice on a sampling method and suggest how he could record the data he needs to summarise his findings. **P4**

5 What would be the best way for Jamal to present and report his findings? Explain your reasoning. **P5**

6 Identify any potential sources of bias or error there may be in this research investigation. **P5**

7 Suggest an appropriate research hypothesis Jamal might formulate and discuss how he would know if his findings supported this hypothesis. **P6**

8 Create a list of improvements Jamal could make if he were to conduct this research again. Give examples of how these improvements would affect ethical issues and any relevant implications of the findings. **P7**

9 Explain why this is an appropriate topic to research for health and social care. **M1**

10 Write a relevant hypothesis and justify it based on Jamal's original interest in investigating this. **M1**

11 Write a report giving advice to Jamal on how he could consider the effectiveness of his choice of an interview method. Make suggestions on how he could consider its strengths and weaknesses in relation to potential findings (for example, is he an experienced interviewer?). **M2**

12 Create a set of questions Jamal could answer to help him identify sources of bias or error. **M2**

13 Based on the questions above, create a set of prompts to help Jamal think about how he could have altered his research project in order to reduce bias or error. **D1**

14 Suggest a framework Jamal could use to explain what he did to ensure his project was ethical and

to consider whether this method threw up any unforeseen ethical problems. **M2**

15 Write a set of guidelines Jamal could use to carry out an analysis of findings in relation to his hypothesis. (For example, what kind of answers might he expect if his hypothesis is supported? What elements of his findings do not support his hypothesis?) **M3**

16 Identify any implications of these research findings on current practice and explain how they could be used to improve or change practice. **M4**

17 Give guidance to Jamal on the kinds of information he needs to include to analyse the purpose and role of research in this particular sector, based on the research findings he has come up with. **D2**

Remember that for pass criteria, you need to *describe* and *explain* aspects of the research such as the use of research, different methods that can be used, how to conduct a literature review etc. For merit criteria, you need to *analyse* the choice of research method and problems with different methods. For example, look for reasons why problems may occur and produce evidence to back up your theories. For a distinction, you need to complete an *evaluation*. To evaluate means to weigh up the evidence you have gathered and to draw conclusions from what the evidence shows. You will need to show a good overall understanding of all aspects of the research process to achieve this.

Resources and further reading

Bell, J. (1987) *Doing Your Research Project* Milton Keynes: Oxford University Press

Janis, I.L. (1958) *Psychological Stress* New York: Wiley

Robson, C. (1993) *Real World Research* Oxford: Blackwell Publishers Ltd

Russell, J., Roberts, C. (2001) *Angles on Psychological Research* Cheltenham: Nelson Thorne Ltd

Sarafino, E.P. (1998) *Health Psychology: Biopsychosocial Interactions*, third ed. New York: John Wiley & Sons

Walsh, M. (2001) *Research Made Real: A Guide for Students* Cheltenham: Nelson Thorne

Useful websites

British Medical Association
www.bma.org.uk

Commission for Social Care Inspection
www.csci.org.uk

Every Child Matters
www.everychildmatters.gov.uk

Information Commissioner's Office
www.informationcommissioner.gov.uk

Joseph Rowntree Foundation
www.jrf.org.uk

King's Fund
www.kingsfund.org.uk

Social Care Institute for Excellence
www.scie.org.uk

Social Trends
www.statistics.gov.uk

Vocational experience

Introduction

This unit integrates closely with Unit 6: *Personal and Professional Development* – you will work on both units simultaneously throughout your course. The emphasis of the unit is your professional development. You will use additional time in the same placements to gain a greater understanding of work in health and social care and be expected to engage more fully with a wider range of workplace activities; where appropriate, you will take responsibility for planning and supporting specific activities under supervision. You will investigate in some detail how one of your placements is organised and how it functions. You will extend your learning through more detailed reflection and examine the effectiveness of your contributions to practice in different settings.

You will expand your reflective practice journal (started in Unit 6) and provide full evidence of your additional placement work in your Personal and Professional Development (PPD) portfolio.

How you will be assessed

To achieve this unit you must provide evidence that you have completed 200 hours in placement, in addition to those required for Unit 6. Your journal and portfolio of evidence will demonstrate more involvement with a wider range of activities. Detailed reflection on your learning from this wider experience will be the basis of assessment in this unit.

After completing this unit you should be able to achieve the following outcomes:

- Understand the structure and function of a placement organisation
- Be able to demonstrate knowledge of workplace practice
- Be able to apply knowledge and understanding
- Be able to review personal effectiveness.

Thinking points

In this unit you will continue to apply Kolb's experiential learning cycle to reflect in more detail about how health or social care organisations operate on a day-to-day basis and to think about your contribution to their practice.

With more placement time, you will have greater opportunity to be involved in activities and focus on learning more about health and social care practice.

How does your learning style affect your learning in placements?

What feelings have you experienced in placements? What reasons can you suggest for these feelings?

What strategies have you found most helpful in coping with your emotional responses to placements?

How do you interact with others in placements to support your own learning?

How is your behaviour helping the staff in your placements to support your learning?

How are you obtaining feedback on your performance in placement and how your are using this feedback to improve your performance?

What actions could you take to increase your learning opportunities from placement?

Thinking about these questions should help you to gain the breadth and depth of understanding needed for Unit 44 to build on the concepts introduced in Unit 6.

It is strongly recommended that you read through the whole of this unit early in the programme so you understand how to extend the collection of evidence needed for Unit 6 to meet the requirements of Unit 44. The unit could also support your study for Unit 6.

Introduction

Section 44.1 introduces you to the structure and organisation of health and social care establishments such as a private residential home, a local authority day centre, an infant school, a special school or a hospital. You will focus on one organisation and it should be different from the one you used in Unit 6 to investigate local and national frameworks.

Taking it further

While you are exploring the structure and function of your chosen placement, keep an eye on the media for current news items on health, social care, children's services and related topics.

Reflect on how events and public policy in the news might influence your chosen workplace:

- How might the developments described in the news affect service users in the chosen organisation?
- How might the developments described in the news affect the organisation itself?
- How might the developments highlighted in the news affect the care workers in the organisation?

Discuss the issues with your tutor, peers and staff in your placement to enhance your understanding.

Placement structure and function

For this unit, the structure of the organisation relates to:

- its aims
- its role in providing health or social care services
- the systems, policies and procedures it has in place to enable it to provide these services
- the roles of the workers who work in the organisation.

Organisational aims

The primary purpose of health or care organisations is to provide care for service users. Each organisation will have systems to provide this care for particular service user groups such as people with:

- acute illness
- chronic illness
- injury
- lifelong disorders
- life-shortening illness
- terminal illness
- mental health problems
- mental infirmity in later years
- learning disability
- physical disability
- sensory loss/impairment
- education and development needs

Theory into practice

Find out about your chosen organisation using information that is in the public domain. This could include looking at inspection reports and brochures as well as the organisation's own website. You could compare the information with that available for other similar organisations.

Reflect

Refer to the list of examples of service users given above.

What might the main needs of each service user group be?

What types of care worker are likely to be needed to care for each service user group?

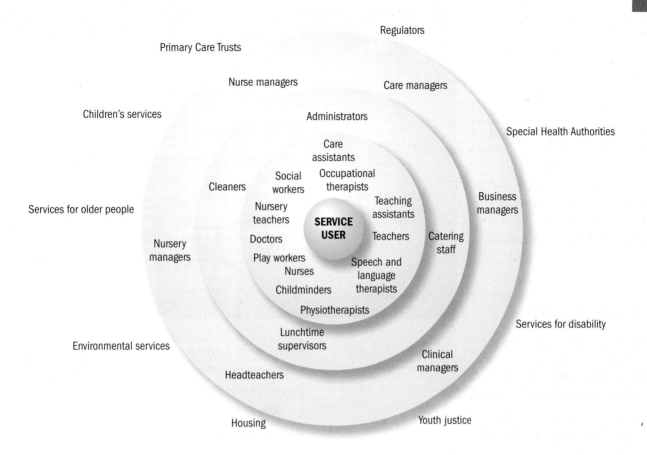

Regulators

Primary Care Trusts

Nurse managers · Care managers

Children's services

Administrators

Special Health Authorities

Care assistants

Social workers · Occupational therapists

Cleaners

Teaching assistants

Business managers

Services for older people

Nursery teachers

SERVICE USER

Nursery managers

Doctors · Teachers · Catering staff

Play workers

Nurses · Speech and language therapists

Childminders

Services for disability

Physiotherapists

Environmental services

Lunchtime supervisors

Clinical managers

Headteachers

Housing · Youth justice

▲ **Figure 44.1 The service user is at the centre of a care organisation's activities**

- special educational needs
- emotional and behavioural disturbance.

All the work activities of the care organsiation will be focused on providing care for its service users.

The type of care provided and the age of the service users will determine the regulatory framework to which the organisation is accountable (see Unit 6).

Some organisations may provide more than one type of care.

Organisational role

An organisation may provide care for service users in a variety of different ways including:

- day care
- residential social care
- long-term residential nursing care
- acute care
- domiciliary care (care in own home)

- care for education and development
- drop-in care (for example, for mental health services)
- emergency care
- respite care
- care for general health and well-being
- specific treatments
- hospice care.

Theory into practice

What are the differences between the different types of care service?

How might the different types of care affect the systems used by health or care organisations to provide the care?

How does the type of care provided affect workers in care organisations?

Levels of responsibility in a care organisation ▶

Organisational structure

The needs of service users influence how a care organisation is structured and the systems it has in place to support its work. Organisations caring for a small group of service users who have similar and straightforward care needs are likely to have a relatively simple structure with a manager, deputy and qualified staff and assistants. Large organisations providing a wider range of specialist care services may be organised into departments, units, teams etc and have more complex structures.

More complex organisations, involving many different specialists, will have many support staff for technical support services, administration of salaries, supplies and to maintain the premises. All but the smallest health or care organisations tend to have a hierarchical structure of workers, supervisors and managers.

Unit managers are responsible for teams of care workers and are accountable to a senior manager who will work closely with the head of the organisation. In your placements, you are most likely to interact with team leaders and possibly middle managers.

Theory into practice

Draw an organisational chart to show the structure of your chosen organisation.

If appropriate, draw a second chart to show how the unit in which you are working is organised.

Describe the main responsibilities in the organisation of each of the departments/sections you have identified on the chart.

How people communicate within an organisation can have a major influence on the experiences of service users and workers who are part of it.

Theory into practice

What is your chosen organisation's mission statement and/or service user charter?

How well do you think it reflects what the organisation does and how it does it?

What are the preferred means of communicating in your chosen organisation with service users, team members, managers and other agencies?

What systems does the organisation have to ensure that the confidentiality of sensitive information is maintained?

How well do you think the communication systems in the organisation contribute to the quality of care received by service users and how workers feel about their work for the organisation?

How effective have the communication systems been in supporting you in your placement?

An organisational chart is a useful way of showing how the people who work within an organisation relate to each other. The NHS has complex management structures but all social care organisations must have a manager who is responsible for all the people in the unit, whether they are service users, workers or visitors. The manager is also accountable to senior managers and regulators for the quality of the care service provided. Under the Care Standards Act 2000, the manager must have a care manager's qualification.

Depending on the structure of the organisation and its purpose, senior managers may or may not be qualified in care and could be based in different premises. Governors and members of NHS Trust boards are likely to be experienced managers or members of the local community.

■ Communication within an organisation

The structure of an organisation can affect how the people in it work together and particularly how people communicate with each other at team level, across teams and with managers within the organisation.

Reflect

How does your unit relate to or interact with other units within your placement organisation?

To what extent is there consultation between the different units?

What is the role of the different units in meeting the needs of the service users in your unit?

How is the work of the different units co-ordinated by the organisation?

What are the advantages and disadvantages of the interactions between different units within the organisation for:

● service users
● workers?

You may reflect on other points to help you gain an understanding of the internal context of the unit to which you are attached in your work placement.

▼ Figure 44.2 Ways of communicating within an organisation

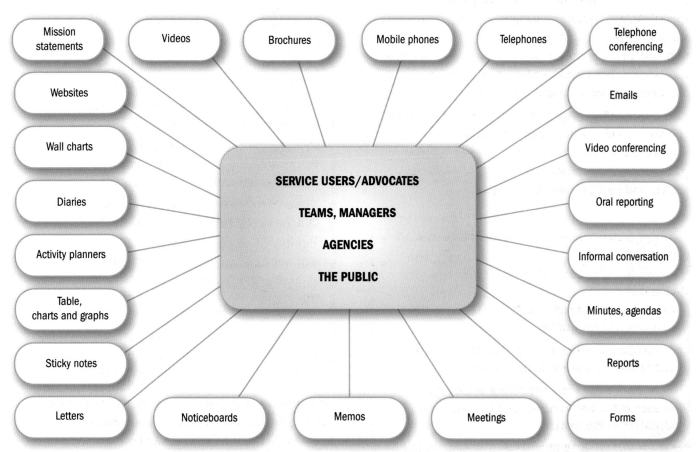

Andy is on placement in a residential care home with 60 social care rooms and an attached unit which provides 15 nursing care beds. The matron is the manager of both parts of the home and she holds a regular meeting of the 10 team leaders on Tuesdays. An agenda is circulated with notes from the previous meeting and the meeting always starts promptly at 2 p.m. and lasts for no more than an hour. Apart from this, the team leaders in the residential unit see the matron only occasionally and when they do, the visit is brief and brisk and involves no interaction with the service users. The team leaders and care workers feel that their work is not valued by the matron. Andy has noticed that negative comments are made and that there is resentment about the amount of attention the smaller nursing unit receives from the matron.

In contrast, Naseem is on placement in a residential home with 25 beds for mentally infirm older adults. Despite the difficulties in communicating with the service users because of their mental confusion, and the challenges that can be presented by their difficult behaviour, the atmosphere is happy and relaxed. The care manager meets the three team leaders for 15–20 minutes each morning and tea or coffee is always available. She also knows the names of all the residents and workers and their family members and always asks how everyone is when she meets them around the home during the day. Formal meetings rarely take place although it appears that all the necessary information is recorded in accordance with regulations. Sometimes requests for more consumable supplies are overlooked so staff have to go to the local supermarket when supplies run out.

Andy and Naseem are sharing their experiences of the first two weeks in their placements. Andy is still not sure what he is meant to be doing and is uncomfortable with the attitudes of the staff whereas Naseem is more relaxed and already feels part of the care team. The manager shows interest in what she is doing and her supervisor is involving her in activities although her explanations of what Naseem should or should not do are not very clear.

1 Why do your think Andy's and Naseem's experiences are so different?

2 What factors have affected their experiences?

3 What strategies could you suggest to help both Andy and Naseem cope with their placement situations and improve their learning experiences?

Policies and procedures

Policies are statements that identify the principles by which an organisation will carry out its activities. All workplaces have a range of policies to comply with legislative requirements. For example, all employers must have a health and safety policy to comply with the Health and Safety at Work Act 1974 and policies to meet other employment law requirements. Health and care organisations have many different policies to address legislative and good practice expectations that are relevant to care (for example, those relating to anti-discriminatory practice, protection from abuse, or for outings and healthy eating). The detail of each policy depends on factors such as the:

- legal requirements
- needs of the service user group
- care service(s) being provided
- number of people in the setting
- features of the location of the setting
- buildings and premises of the setting.

A well-written policy clearly identifies the roles and responsibilities of people in the organisation in relation to the policy.

Procedures are the part of a policy that specifies the actions to be followed to comply with the policy. The procedures need to be specific to each setting and identify, for example, who is responsible for what actions, the order in which the actions should be taken, where critical resources should be stored and how records should be kept.

Theory into practice

Read all the policies for the organisation you are investigating.

How do the policies reflect the care value base?

How do the policies reflect the care needs of the service users?

Share your findings with others in your class group.

To what extent are policies in different care organisations similar or different?

Policies and procedures should be made available to the relevant workers (for example, in a staff handbook) and to service users (or their relatives and partners). Policies and procedures should be reviewed regularly, perhaps annually or every two years as a routine, and when legislative requirements change. It is good practice

In context

Hayley is an early years practitioner with the reception class in a school; she helps the lunchtime supervisors with her class. She is concerned because some children often bring foods in their lunch boxes that are not permitted by the school's healthy eating policy.

1 **What might the healthy eating policy recommend as appropriate for the children's lunch boxes?**

2 **How would you expect the school's healthy eating policy to help Hayley address this problem?**

3 **What policies does your chosen organisation have in relation to healthy eating?**

for the date of the most recent review to be included on the policy and for responsibility for each policy to be assigned to an appropriate manager. The currency and appropriateness of policies is checked by inspection agencies.

Roles and responsibilities

Care workers who provide the day-to-day care directly to service users are usually employees, whereas those who provide care on a more occasional basis may work for a partner organisation. Qualified care workers provide more specialist care direct to service users, for example, devising care plans, administering medicines, changing dressings and giving treatments.

Managers organise the work of the care workers in the organisation. Hospitals will have many specialist clinical and technical workers and most care organisations will have some administrative support.

Theory into practice

Find out about the roles and responsibilities of the workers employed in your chosen care organisation, including care workers, supervisors and those technical and administrative workers or managers associated with the unit in which you are based.

Job descriptions

Workers employed in health or care settings usually have a job description that describes what is expected of them in their work. The job description is usually prepared by the employer before a person is appointed, and might identify the:

- job title
- line manger for the post holder
- essential qualities required of the post holder
- desirable qualities of the post holder
- responsibilities for areas of work
- duties and activities that are expected.

SUNNYSIDE

ANYTOWN

JOB DESCRIPTION

JOB TITLE: Care Assistant

PAY: £5.60 per hour

HOURS: 21

REPORTING TO: The manager

ABOUT SUNNYSIDE

Sunnyside is a purpose-built residential home for up to 48 older people who are infirm and most of whom need some assistance with their personal care. There is a shared dining and recreational area which offers a programme of activities for residents each week.

The post holder will work as part of the care assistant team as directed by the home manager and the care assistant team leader.

PERSON SPECIFICATION:

Essential

- aged 18 years or over
- education qualifications at Level 2 e.g. GCSE, NVQ, BTEC
- ability to communicate appropriately with others
- patience, understanding and ability to be flexible in approach to meeting residents' care needs

Desirable

- NVQ Level 2 in Care/Health and Social Care or willingness to work towards this within an agreed timescale
- experience of work in health or social care
- knowledge of the National Minimum Standards for Social Care

MAIN DUTIES:

The post holder will:

1. assist residents with personal care in accordance with their individual care plan
2. promote the well-being of residents at all times, including assisting residents to participate in recreational activities
3. maintain residents' dignity and privacy at all times
4. work in accordance with Sunnyside's policies and procedures.

RESPONSIBILITIES:

The post holder will be expected to:

- assist residents with washing, toileting, bathing, dressing, feeding and drinking in accordance with each individual's care plan
- respect the confidentiality of residents and their relatives at all times both on and off duty
- assist in maintaining the comfort of residents
- contribute to the planning and delivery of the recreational activities programme and support individual residents to participate as appropriate
- assist residents who have limited mobility to use walking and moving aids as specified in the individual's care plan
- support residents to maintain contact with their family, friends and community
- under the supervision of a senior care assistant, assist with the safe administration of medication in accordance with the administration of medication policy and procedures
- maintain records of all care provided on individual care plans
- when directed by the manager, escort residents on outings to attend, for example, GP or hospital appointments
- inform and discuss matters relating to the care of residents with the care team leader and/or the manager
- undertake certain cleaning, laundering and ironing duties as they relate to the delivery of personal care
- promote the health, safety and security of residents and staff at all times
- contribute to creating a friendly and homely atmosphere for residents through all actions and communications with residents and staff
- receive and report verbal and written communication including answering the telephone and maintaining written records in accordance with policies and procedures
- attend and participate in staff meetings
- attend training in accordance with legal requirements and personal development plan
- after six months in post, and thereafter at an annual performance review, agree and implement a professional development plan.

▲ Figure 44.3 Part of a job description for a care assistant

Theory into practice

What health and/or care workers are employed in your placements?

What qualifications and experience do they have for the posts they currently hold?

What opportunities for professional development have they had in their current post?

Each worker carries out their work according to the role and **responsibilities** described in their job description, with support given during an induction period.

Taking it further

Find out about the recruitment and selection process for workers in your chosen organisation.

Who is responsible for managing the process?

How are posts advertised?

How is the interview process conducted?

What does the induction process involve?

The work activities of an individual tend to change over time. Some workers may take on additional responsibilities, gaining experience for career progression, but this would normally be negotiated with a supervisor or manager to whom workers in health or care must be **accountable**.

Key terms

Responsibility Accepting the duties allocated to you.

Accountability Requiring an individual, group or organisation to justify its actions to another.

Reflect

Review the duties and activities that you have had in your placements.

How have these changed as you have spent more time in each placement?

How has the experience in your first placement helped you cope with the different organisations and their systems in later placements?

■ Gaining qualifications

The Health and Social Care National Occupational Standards include units which relate to supporting learners in the workplace.

In context

For the last 18 months, Jane has been working as a health care assistant in a nursing home and achieved her NVQ Level 3 last month. She is asked by the deputy matron to supervise and mentor a BTEC National student on placement. Jane is interested in gaining more qualifications.

1 **How could Jane best support the student and how might Jane's work towards a qualification affect the student?**

2 **What qualification could Jane work towards?**

3 **How could supervising a student help Jane to develop her career in social care?**

Your responsibilities and accountability in placement

Your responsibilities in placement are identified in Unit 6. A placement manager is responsible for allocating a care worker to act as your supervisor and to ensure that the practices you carry out conform to the minimum standards. Your supervisor is accountable to the manager for your practice and is responsible for ensuring that you comply with organisational practices as described in the workplace's policies and procedures. You should receive an induction to each of your placements.

Theory into practice

How has your college prepared you for your placement experience?

What induction processes have you received in each of your placements?

How do they compare with the experiences of your peers in class?

To what extent have your college and placement inductions helped you settle into each placement?

What strategies have you used to help you cope with starting each of your placements?

Remember!

You are accountable for your behaviour in placements to both your college and to each placement. If your behaviour is not appropriate, or you do not take appropriate responsibility for your attendance, you may be withdrawn from the placement.

Patients or service users

Care organisations usually provide services for one service user group. For example, services for older

Social needs
· Meeting others
· Talking with others
· Creative/social activities

Intellectual needs
· Learning activities
· Recreational activities
· Discussion
· Creative activities

Cultural needs
· Customs e.g. food
· Festivals and celebrations
· Faith needs

Emotional needs
· 'Space' to express emotions
· Affection
· Personal possessions
· Reassurance and routine

Physical needs
· Activities of daily living
· Health and well-being
  – exercise, fitness and diet
  – personal hygiene
· Mobility and co-ordination

Communication needs
· Alternative language
· Language support
· Communication aids
· Sensory aids

▲ **Figure 44.4 Service user needs and how they might be met**

people are likely to be separate from services for babies and toddlers even though some of the services may be similar, for example, help with feeding and toileting. The systems in place in each organisation will be influenced by the needs of the service users.

Theory into practice

Describe the service user group of your chosen organisation.

Identify the group's social, physical, intellectual, communication and emotional needs.

Care planning

Care planning is the process by which the needs of individual service users are assessed and a plan is drawn up to meet the user's individual needs. The service user is at the centre of their plan and is involved in drawing up the plan (together with an advocate and family member/ significant other as appropriate). The plan will identify the care workers involved as well as the care, treatments, equipment etc. The plan is monitored regularly and records are kept in it of all the care that is provided.

Theory into practice

In accordance with the organisation's confidentiality agreements and with appropriate consent, explore how care planning takes place. You are not likely to have access to a completed care plan.

What documentation does the organisation use for care planning and what does it tell you about the process?

When is the care plan drawn up?

Where is it kept?

Who has access to it?

How is it monitored?

Taking it further

From your observations in placements, to what extent is the care planning process successful in meeting service user needs?

What dilemmas and challenges can arise within care planning processes?

In context

Suzie is 4 and has cystic fibrosis. She is due to start school next term but her parents are concerned about how she will cope with it and the demanding treatments she needs three times a day to control her condition.

1 Research the care needs of a young child with cystic fibrosis.

2 What support could help Suzie to be involved in delivering her own care plan once she starts school?

3 What policies and procedures would be needed to support Suzie in school?

In many cases, care plans involve health and care professionals and possibly others, such as teachers.

Inter-agency working

A care organisation may work in partnership with other agencies to ensure that the care needs of individuals are fully met. Workers from the other agencies would be involved as partners in the care team for that individual.

Services and resources

The facilities, staffing, equipment and other resources used by care organisations are all influenced by the needs of their service users.

Theory into practice

Find out how your chosen organisation liaises with other agencies to deliver the care plans for its service users.

How do the care workers from each organisation communicate with each other to ensure that the care plan is delivered effectively?

Facilities

The buildings used for care services may be subject to some specific building regulations, for example, there must be enough fire exits in a residential care setting to be able to evacuate residents quickly from all bedrooms. An organisation providing services for children or for vulnerable adults will have systems to ensure security on the premises, limiting access to authorised personnel only. Physical access is a consideration for those with limited mobility. Appropriate facilities for staff, for example staffrooms, also need to be provided. Specialist areas may need to be designated and kept separate from other areas, for example, food preparation, surgical areas and storage for medication must be secure.

Reflect

How are the facilities organised in your placement organisation?

What specialist areas are there and what is their layout?

How does the organisation of the facilities support the care of the service users?

From your observations, how does the organisation of the facilities affect the care workers in the organisation?

Equipment

Specialist equipment is necessary to meet service user needs in most care organisations. Equipment may be large and fixed in place or mobile if it is to be used in different places. Other resources may be consumable items such as craft materials in a school or may be specially designed, for example, wheelchairs for those with profound or multiple disability, or communication aids.

Theory into practice

What equipment have you seen in use?

In what way does it support the needs of service users?

How does it assist care workers?

Where is it stored and what procedures are followed when it is used?

Who is responsible for its maintenance?

Human resources

Care workers are a valuable resource in health and care organisations and the law requires a minimum number of staff to be on duty at any given time, including overnight stays in residential care.

All workers in social care must meet the induction standards set by the General Social Care Council, and all other workers should receive an induction to their workplace.

Change is a major feature of work in the health and social care sector (see Unit 6). It is therefore important that workers in care organisations keep up-to-date with the legislative requirements, innovations or changes in practice introduced by, for example, the Social Care Institute for Excellence, the National Institute for Health and Clinical Excellence, National Service Frameworks, the NHS Knowledge and Skills Frameworks and other occupational standards. This is in addition to care workers having the opportunity to develop their own careers.

Theory into practice

Research the minimum staffing requirements for:

- child care
- residential social care
- nursing care.

Find the 2006 Induction Standards on: www.gscc.org.uk.

Who is responsible for induction in your chosen care organisation and what does it involve?

What staff development policies does your chosen organisation have? How do these contribute to the quality of care received by its service users?

Reflect

Research professional journals relevant to your chosen workplace (you might be able to find these more easily in the workplace than in your college library) and identify recent (in the last two years) external changes that have affected your care organisation's policies and practices.

What changes has your chosen care organisation made in response to recent external changes?

What staff development activities have workers completed to help them adjust to the changes?

Your role in the placement setting

Establishing a positive working relationship with each of your placement supervisors and the teams in which you work is an important part of your PPD. It will be particularly important because it will help you become more involved in work activities and widen your experience (as required for this unit). You can gather more detailed information by asking open questions and being generally observant of, for example:

- routines
- practical skills involved in direct care, specific equipment and treatments
- record keeping
- dealing with distressed individuals
- implementation of care plans
- working with service users' friends and relatives.

Working with your supervisor for this unit

In Unit 44 you will spend more time in the company of your supervisor or members of their team so you should become more familiar with their practical routines and activities. There will be time for you to build trust with workers enabling you, possibly, to practise the skills demonstrated by your supervisor (subject to placement policies) and observe a wider range of their care activities. You will need to ask for oral feedback on all that you do and use your journal to record this, as well as recording your self-assessment of your performance. You can make improvements over time, supported by your supervisor, and so develop your ability to contribute effectively to work in the placement.

You may also seek support from a mentor, who may be your supervisor, another experienced worker in your placement or a tutor from your college (particularly the person who visits you in placement). A mentor may only see you occasionally but they can provide valuable guidance and advice to support the extra learning and understanding you need to obtain from placements in this unit.

It is important for you to recognise that **coaching** and **mentoring** are an essential part of your reflective observation: this will help your abstract conceptualisation (see page 275 of Unit 6 and Kolb) and the personal development needed to analyse your effectiveness in this unit.

Key terms

Coaching Training to develop specific skills.

Mentoring When a more experienced person provides support and advice.

Remember!

In most placements, the priority of workers is to meet the needs of service users rather than the needs of students. You will have to be adaptable, considerate and creative in how you use your time with your supervisor to gather the knowledge and understanding needed for this unit. Planning ahead, in particular identifying the placement-specific knowledge you need to gain (e.g. from the 'Theory into practice' questions), and communicating clearly and concisely, will be helpful both to you and your supervisor/mentor. You will need to take the initiative in quiet times to carry out research through general observation of others or from reading policies, for example.

Confidentiality

Because you will be spending more time with work teams in Unit 44, you are more likely to hear conversations in which confidential information is discussed. It is therefore important that you continue to be vigilant about how you talk and write about your work in placements.

Reflect

How do workers in the organisation work with confidential information?

What procedures does the organisation have to address breaches of confidentiality?

What dilemmas relating to confidentiality have you encountered in your work in placements? How have you coped with these dilemmas?

It is relevant to this unit to consider these issues in relation to each of your placements, but particularly the one chosen for this section of the unit.

Consent

Obtaining consent (see Unit 6) from the appropriate manager or supervisor remains an essential responsibility

in this unit, particularly if you are using the additional time in placement to engage in more practical activities and widen your experience in the setting.

Assessment activity 44.1

Describe the structure and function of one health or social care organisation.

Complete this activity for ONE of your placement organisations (it must be different from that used for P6 in Unit 6). **P1**

1 Write a detailed description of the care organisation to include its:

- aims and values and its role within local health and social care frameworks
- structure and organisation of staff including management structures, work teams and job roles
- policies and procedures
- service users, their needs and how these needs are met by the organisation
- facilities and equipment
- interactions with other agencies involved in providing services to meet service users' health and/or care needs.

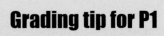

Grading tip for P1

Throughout, illustrate points made in your description using examples taken from your observations and experiences working in the organisation and recorded in your journal and practice evidence.

2 Describe your own job role within the placement in the context of your placement's expectations of your contributions and the aims and objectives you have set for yourself during your time in the placement.

Grading tip for P1

Your aims and objectives for the placement could relate to your PPD action plan for Unit 6 and work for other units.

Introduction

You will draw on your learning from *all* of the placements you have during your course for this section. As in Unit 6, you should provide *evidence* in your portfolio of how you have *used* your knowledge and understanding of practice in these placements.

All the boxed activities included in this unit and Unit 6 address points that should help you to develop your knowledge and understanding from each placement. It would be useful to go through each activity for each placement, keeping the dated notes in your journal.

Theory into practice

Throughout *each* placement, obtain witness testimonies and observation records (for example, competence checklists) of your practice as evidence of your knowledge and understanding of workplace practices.

Make sure each is signed and dated by your supervisor. File each record systematically in your portfolio.

On a regular basis, make more detailed notes in your journal of your feelings, any oral feedback received, descriptions of placement activities and other details you might find useful when reviewing your practice.

Knowledge and understanding

Your additional 200 hours in placement enable you to reflect with greater *breadth* and *depth* as well as acquire *more evidence* of your personal and professional development. Unit 44 places more emphasis on the professional aspects of working in health and care settings than is required for Unit 6.

Using reflection

The Kolb Experiential Learning Cycle (see Unit 6) will help you to develop your knowledge and understanding of workplace practice. Your reflection for this section could be structured by means of comparisons between practices according to different:

- placement organisations
- units within the organisation
- service user groups and their needs
- work teams
- work activities.

Your knowledge and understanding can be consolidated to assist your active conceptualisation (Kolb) through:

- discussion with supervisors and mentors
- independent research in college (for example, about a disease or the Foundation Stage curriculum)

In context

Anna is in placement in a residential home and has helped a service user to make an Easter bonnet in an activity led by the activities supervisor. The service user had difficulty attaching the flowers on the bonnet so Anna did this for her. During feedback, the supervisor said that she should not have carried out the task for the service user but admitted that the activity she had planned was quite hard. Anna was asked to plan a further creative activity with the theme of 'spring'.

1. **What aspects of the care value base did Anna overlook when she completed the bonnet for the service user? What could she have done instead?**

2. **How should Anna prepare for her 'spring' activity and show she has learned from the experiences of this activity?**

3. **What practice skills could Anna develop when she carries out the 'spring' activity?**

- observing and listening as a non-participant
- practising your use of equipment (for example, hoists)
- participation in routines (for example, mealtimes)
- visiting other units in the organisation.

With more time, you have more opportunity for active experimentation when carrying out tasks on repeated occasions.

Additional breadth and depth of knowledge may be gathered as indicated in the table below.

Breadth	• The range of different individual needs within service user groups • Observing a wider range of approaches to meeting service user needs • Working with different teams • Understanding the wider context of each unit/setting • Participating in a wider range of activities and routines • Understanding how routines vary over longer periods of time
Depth	• Detail relating to service user needs • Participating in one-off events, for example, a service user outing, an inspection • Researching specific health conditions and treatment processes • Exploring complexity or interrelatedness of different factors affecting practices
PPD	• More involvement with individual service users • More practice of routine skills, observation/practice of a wider range of skills • An enhanced confidence to take initiative in contributing to routines and activities • Developing your own team-working skills • A greater awareness and development of how your own values are evolving towards those expected of care workers • A better understanding of rationales behind policies and procedures and how they operate in practice • An enhanced understanding of your own strengths and weaknesses in relation to care work • A better understanding of the roles of other workers and agencies in contributing to care for service users

Table 44.1 Extending the breadth and depth of your knowledge and practice

Reflect

One way of gaining knowledge and understanding is to use open questions beginning with:

What?
Why?
Who?
Where?
When?
How?

You can use this in oral questions but also as a prompt list for yourself when you are making notes in your journal or preparing written work for assessment. This will ensure that you address a topic fully.

Information

Work organisations usually have formal methods of communicating through meetings, emails, reports, newsletters etc. Information is often communicated through informal channels over cups of coffee.

Reflect

How do your placements use formal methods of communicating with work teams and individuals?

What sort of information have you observed being shared when staff meet together informally in the staff room?

How do the methods of communicating affect:

- confidentiality
- the culture of the organisation?

An important aspect of your developing practice is to recognise how confidential information in health and care settings is recorded, used and stored.

Reflect

Review your life experiences, health and private concerns and identify information about yourself that you would not be prepared to share with others, for example, with your parents, siblings or other family members, partner, friends, doctor, a professional who does not know you, a stranger.

- What are the factors that influence your willingness to share personal information about yourself with other people?
- How would you feel if confidential information about you was given to someone whom you didn't want to share it with?
- In what circumstances would you be prepared to share the most sensitive information about yourself and with whom?

Keep only outline notes for the first part of this activity in your journal; you should only share information with others that you are comfortable sharing.

Remember!

All information relating to service users should be treated as confidential. However, you may also overhear or become aware of confidential information that relates to another worker. This information should not be shared with others.

Communication skills

Communication skills (see Units 1 and 6) are fundamental to work in health and care and underpin much of the care value base. In this unit you will have time to observe the skills used by workers in more complex situations and note less obvious skills used across a wider range of situations.

Reporting and recording

Practices relating to recording information about service users are important but as a student in placement you will not have the authority to carry these out.

For written information you should observe:

- what type of information is recorded
- how it is recorded
- who makes the record
- when the records are made
- why the record is made
- where the record document is stored and for how long
- how secure the information is.

You should note what, when, why and where information is communicated orally and who is communicating it.

Skills for teamwork

Work teams

The concept of team working was introduced in Unit 6 but, for this unit, you will have more time to develop your team-working abilities in placement settings.

Depending on the purpose of the team, members may meet daily or periodically. Members of a care team may work in a partner organisation and only visit the service user organisation occasionally.

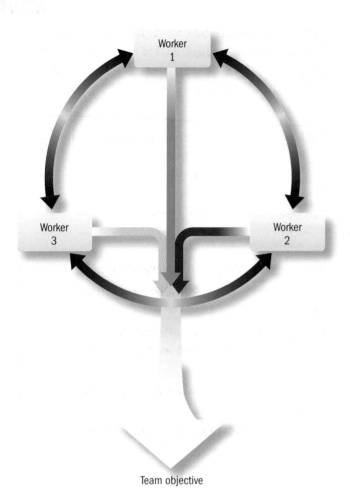

Theory into practice

Identify a care team which includes a range of care professionals. Describe:

- how each member of the care team contributes individually to the care of service users
- how the work of the team members is co-ordinated
- how the team members support each other.

Team objective

▲ **Figure 44.5 A model of team work**

Taking it further

Investigate the training, qualifications and experience required for three of the specialist roles identified in Figure 44.6.

To what extent would any one of these specialisms provide a possible career option for yourself?

What would you need to include in your PPD plan to meet the requirements for entering such a career?

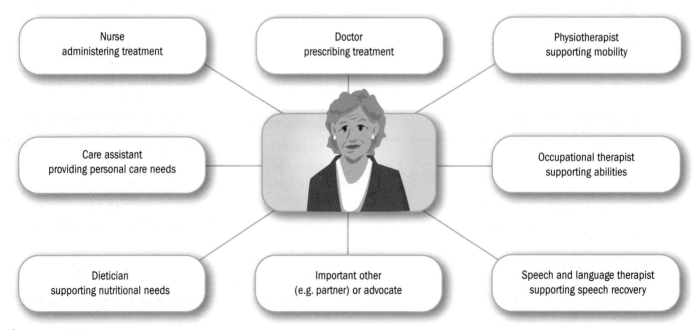

Nurse administering treatment	Doctor prescribing treatment	Physiotherapist supporting mobility
Care assistant providing personal care needs		Occupational therapist supporting abilities
Dietician supporting nutritional needs	Important other (e.g. partner) or advocate	Speech and language therapist supporting speech recovery

▲ **Figure 44.6 How service user needs are met through a team approach to care**

Skills for team effectiveness

An effective team is one in which all the members contribute their best efforts to give the support needed by individuals, the team and its goal. It is essential when working in a team that there is open communication between all members. This means that everyone must:

- feel they can express their views without fear of criticism
- communicate frequently through meetings, email etc
- keep records of their discussions, actions and progress
- check on the progress of each other's contributions to the team effort
- support each other to achieve the team's goals.

Team work requires everyone to carry out the share of the work that has been agreed between members. If you arrive late or are slow to return from breaks, your lack of punctuality means that other members of the team have to do your work until you arrive. Similarly, if you are unreliable because you do not carry out a task as agreed, or you take on the task of another team member, you are no longer working together effectively and the team goals may not be met, or the work becomes an individual rather than a team effort.

Reflect

Using your experiences of group work in class sessions and in placements, what is the difference between a group and a team?

What factors contribute positively to team work?

What factors have a negative influence on team work?

From your placements, what factors have you observed influencing the effectiveness of work teams?

What have you learned about your team-working skills in placements?

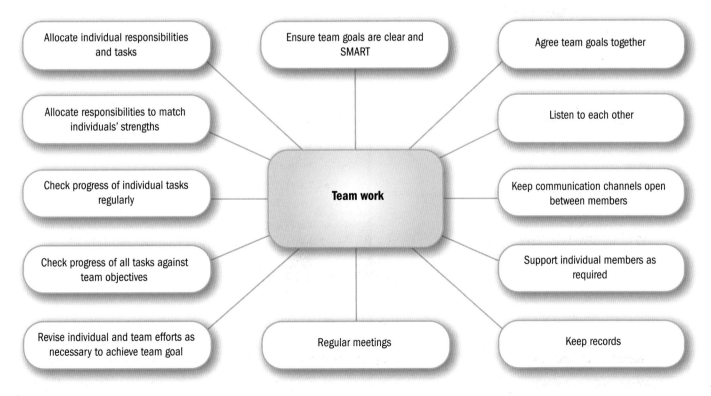

- Allocate individual responsibilities and tasks
- Ensure team goals are clear and SMART
- Agree team goals together
- Allocate responsibilities to match individuals' strengths
- Listen to each other
- Check progress of individual tasks regularly
- **Team work**
- Keep communication channels open between members
- Check progress of all tasks against team objectives
- Support individual members as required
- Revise individual and team efforts as necessary to achieve team goal
- Regular meetings
- Keep records

▲ **Figure 44.7 Skills for teamwork**

A care worker may be a member of several work teams and you will work with different combinations of workers in your placements – you may observe that teams work with variable effectiveness.

Remember!

As you learned in Unit 6, SMART goals are those which are specific, measurable, actionable, relevant and timely.

Reflect

Identify the different teams in which you have worked in each of your placements.

What responsibilities did you have in each team?

How did your responsibilities contribute to the effectiveness of the team in addressing the group task(s)?

In what ways did you support the other members of the team in carrying out the group task(s)?

To what extent were you effective in using team-working skills to maximise the effectiveness of the team?

Effective teamwork needs commitment from all members of the team and your team-working skills will develop if you:

- reflect on the team experiences you have in each of your placements
- include a focus on these skills in your PPD action plan.

■ Taking the initiative

With more time in placement, you should be able to gain the confidence you need to take more initiative in planning and taking responsibility for activities with team members and service users.

Remember!

You should never work with service users if you are unsupervised.

Initiative might take the form of:

- anticipating what has to be done or what equipment and resources are required and preparing them to support your supervisor, rather than waiting to be asked to do this
- planning and delivering an activity for a small group with greater independence and less direction (but with sufficient consultation)
- carrying out different types of observation (possibly in early years settings) using recognised methods
- carrying out activities that are more complex or better integrated within a programme (a series of related activities)
- developing and presenting a full programme of activities
- working more directly with service users.

Taking it further

This activity would be appropriate towards the end of a placement in a setting.

Access the following websites as appropriate for your chosen setting:

- www.skillsforhealth.org.uk
- www.skillsforcare.org.uk
- www.ssda.org.uk.

Identify the knowledge and skill sets within the Health and Social Care Knowledge and Skills Framework (KSF) that most closely describe your placement role in the setting.

1 Use the skill sets to make up a job description of your role.

2 Analyse the extent to which your work activities in the placement setting are enabling you to develop the skills, knowledge and understanding required within the KSF identified.

3 How would you need to modify or develop your PPD action plan to address the gaps in your skills, knowledge and understanding for the identified units within the health and social care KSF?

Assessment activity 44.2

Present and review a portfolio of evidence demonstrating knowledge and understanding of workplace practice.

Note: Your portfolio will be the same as that which you present for Unit 6 but will include more evidence of wider ranging activity in placements and more reflection on this.

1 Present a portfolio of evidence demonstrating knowledge and understanding of workplace practice. Review the portfolio at regular intervals to show how your practice and your knowledge and understanding of the practice of others is developing over time.

Grading tip for P2

Start collecting detailed evidence of your practice from your first placement onwards and continue for each placement.

Make sure that your practice evidence reflects the extra depth and breadth of your skills, knowledge and understanding developed in this unit.

Draw up appropriate evidence documents to capture the depth and breadth of your practice abilities, for example, checklist observation records.

Choose additional practice themes to those targeted for Unit 6 for your development, for example, working in multidisciplinary teams, partnership working, the use of specialist communication skills such as signing, and reflect on these.

Check your evidence at least once before the end of each placement and seek additional evidence if it does not fully reflect your abilities, learning and development from the placement.

Cross-reference your reviews to specific evidence in your portfolio, including your journal.

Links between theory and practice

Reflect

A reflective account is a piece of writing that shows your understanding of situations, events and practice. It should use theory and observation to describe the situation, present discussion and suggest possible reasons and explanations. It may include analysis and evaluation.

The theories of Kolb and Honey and Mumford (Unit 6) are useful for structuring reflection on learning from practice situations. Objective evidence noted in your journal and PPD portfolio should be used to support points you make in your reflective writing.

For this section of the unit you will expand your journal entries to write specific *reflective accounts* at intervals throughout your National programme to show how your *own* knowledge, understanding and skills are developing.

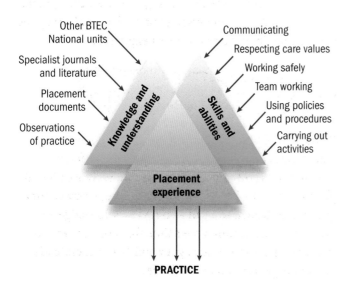

▲ Figure 44.8 Using the PPD model to integrate theory, skills and experience relating to work in health and care

Theory into practice

Complete the activities in this unit and in Unit 6 for each of your placements, keeping notes in your journal and dating each entry.

Make notes specifically to record how your knowledge and understanding have developed from one placement to another.

As you spend more time in placement experience, your study skills (Unit 6) will develop and you will find it easier to make links between theory and practice. For example, you have investigated national and local frameworks for Unit 6 and the function and structure of one care organisation in the previous section of this unit.

Reflect

What is the local and national framework for each of your placements and how are these influenced by social policies?

What models of care are used in your placement organisations/units and how do they relate to their structure and practices?

Using knowledge and understanding acquired for one aspect of assessment and applying it more broadly (in this case, to all your placement organisations) shows that you are reflecting on your experiences.

You can use your journal to make notes of your reflections, linking the theory and practices you observe in your placements. Your PPD portfolio of evidence should reflect the increased depth and breadth of your experience.

	Unit of study (abridged title)	Links to work experience
1	Communicating	Skills, interactions with service users as a carer
2	Equality and diversity	Care practices for diversity, how legislative requirements are met
3	Health safety, security	Observations of settings, survey of community environment for a service user group
4	Development through life stages	Development needs and influences on different age groups
5	Anatomy & physiology	Routine measurements of body functions, how physiology affects care needs
6	PPD	Study skills, codes of practice and conduct, HSC workforce, career pathways
7	Sociological perspectives	Social and medical models of health in practice
8	Psychological perspectives	Strategies for managing service user behaviour
9	Values and planning	Care planning processes, the service user at the centre of service provision
10	Caring for children and young people	Early years setting only; promoting children's learning and development, partnerships with parents, child protection
11	Supporting adults	Minimising abuse, POVA
12	Public health	Protection of health of individuals, factors affecting health
13	Physiology of fluid balance	Disposal of hazardous waste, what body fluids can indicate about health
14	Physiological disorders	Care and treatment in practice for specific conditions
22	Research methodology	Access to workers and other specialist sources of information, practice of research techniques

Table 44.2 Possible links between your studies and your placement experiences

Reflect

What resources does the placement have to assist your learning and development?

There are many links between your placement experiences and the knowledge and theory you acquire in the units of the course.

All units (core and specialist) within the National programme can be related to practices you observe in placement, either as underpinning knowledge and understanding of, for example, service users, or of practices.

If your formal learning for a unit comes after you have reviewed an activity, experience or placement, you can always refer back to the situation later in your journal writing and formal reflective writing. This is especially useful if the knowledge and understanding you have gathered gives you a greater insight into the earlier experience.

Different care practices, organisations and service user groups

By the end of your programme you should have had placement experience in at least three different organisations and settings. Each should serve a different purpose and involve working with different service user groups and teams. You can also review knowledge and understanding acquired over time from specific events and activities, for example, your ability to generate ideas for, and organise, creative activities.

You will need to keep on top of your work for Unit 44 (and Unit 6), especially as it is drawn out over the whole of your course and will require careful planning and regular monitoring. You will find it much easier if you write up accounts of individual events and activities as soon as possible after they have taken place. This practice will also help you to build your portfolio, and if the work is seen by your tutor, you will receive feedback on your learning and development right from the start of the course.

■ Reviewing your accumulated knowledge and understanding

You will be encouraged by all your tutors to make links between your placement experiences and the knowledge and theory associated with different units. For these other units, you can include relevant examples of understanding of service users and work practices within the body of your writing or other work for the unit to which it is relevant. By doing this, you can show that you are applying your knowledge and understanding (it may be appropriate to include the work prepared for the other unit in your portfolio). Often, however, the written feedback you receive from your tutor can serve as witness testimony of your ability to apply knowledge; this could be sufficient, provided it is clear when and in what context the feedback was generated and by whom.

You should also prepare reviews that are specific for your placement units. A single review which includes the depth and breadth required for Unit 44 may also be sufficient for an aspect of evidence needed for Unit 6, but it is unlikely that a review prepared for Unit 6 criteria will have the depth and breadth required for Unit 44. Appropriate times for reviews are:

- immediately after the start of a placement
- at the end of a placement
- in the middle of a placement (or the middle of the period between placements if taken as blocks)
- immediately after **critical incidents**.

Remember!

Critical incidents often provide valuable learning experiences for organisations and teams as well as for those on a programme of study. Such incidents test the robustness of policies and procedures.

Evidence

Unit 44 requires you to gather more detailed evidence of your performance; it may be in different forms but must include sufficient and relevant detail to fulfil the assessment requirements of the unit.

Reflect

Assuming that you are the person who is most familiar with your PPD plan and the assessment requirements for this unit, how can you help workers in your placements to provide you with sufficient and relevant evidence for your assessment needs?

Consult with your peers in college and with your tutors and supervisors to generate ideas and practical solutions for specific purposes.

The following can all be sources of objective evidence of your practice, performance, knowledge and understanding:

- checklists
- observation records
- witness testimonies
- placement reports
- feedback records on assessments.

However, each must be specific for its purpose.

Key term

Critical incident This is an unplanned event, such as a violent outburst, a breach of security or a breakdown in plans due to exceptional circumstances beyond the organisation's control.

Assessment activity 44.3

Maintain a reflective practice journal to monitor development of your knowledge, understanding and skills.

1   Keep a reflective practice journal to monitor the development of your own knowledge, understanding and skills.

2   At the end of each term, write a formal (typed) reflective account of the development of your knowledge, understanding and skills from your study on the whole course. Describe the progress in your development from your initial self-assessment (Unit 6) up to the last review.   **P3**

Grading tip for P3

Date all entries in your journal, making entries before, during and at the end of each placement at the very least.

Make reflective entries in your journal regularly throughout your programme, as indicated in Unit 6. Your entries will include handwritten notes describing routines, activities and events in placements and work in class.

Your reflection should identify your feelings, overall judgements about specific aspects of your practice, reasons for these, suggestions of how to improve and a justification of revised targets.

Submit your journal and each formal review to obtain interim feedback from your tutor.

At the end of the course, submit a summative review of your development over the whole course.

44.4 Reviewing personal effectiveness

In this section you will explore the links between knowledge and understanding and how effective your contributions are to work practice in health and social care workplaces.

As you progress through each of your placements, you can start to make comparisons, identifying similarities and differences between the placement organisations and settings. Contrasts will be more apparent if your placements provide different types of service.

Review your own practice

Reflection

Throughout your work for Units 6 and 44, you will have support from tutors and placement supervisors

Remember!

You will need to show how practice skills are linked to the theory and knowledge that you have explored in all units of the course and explain how this can lead to improved practice.

You should describe your own effectiveness when working in health and social care: explain how you have developed so that your contributions in placements have benefited service users, either directly or indirectly, through your contributions to team work.

You should evaluate your development as a result of your experience in placements.

as teachers, coaches and mentors. The feedback and conversations you have with them will help your reflective observation and abstract conceptualisation. If time allows, you can repeat activities, using each opportunity to make amendments and improvements in response to feedback. Thus you will be using active experimentation and concrete experiences to consolidate your learning.

You also carried out a self-assessment of your skills and abilities for Unit 6 at the start of the programme; you identified your strengths and weaknesses. This helped you to identify areas for development and to plan to address these using a SAP approach:

S = Strengths

A = Areas for improvement

P = Plans for development.

The self-assessment provided you with a benchmark against which you could measure your progress. You should return to the benchmarks you identified and measure the progress you have actually made over the whole course. You will have been monitoring your personal development plan as part of the assessment for Unit 6 and you may have made alterations to the plan as a result. In particular, you may have made choices about

your career progression (you will have had to include or emphasise different aspects of your personal and professional development for this).

Your learning from college-based study and from placements will have increased your knowledge base and enabled you to develop some practical work-based skills and abilities and you can review your development as a learner and as a care worker.

Remember!

Skills as a carer *and* as a learner are important for workers in health and social care.

Your own effectiveness

Evidence from your portfolio, periodic reviews and feedback on assessed work will be valuable in providing objective assessment of your abilities which you can compare against:

- your initial self-assessment
- recommended best practice
- your previous performance
- trends in your performance over time.

You can also judge your performance in different contexts working with different service users, settings, organisations and teams.

Remember!

You should always include reflection on how well you have communicated, respected the values of care and considered health, safety and security in your practice.

You can use a variety of contrasting perspectives to help you to reflect and judge what difference you have made to your own development or to others around you in the workplace or learning environment.

Opposing perspectives	
strengths	weaknesses
advantages	disadvantages
coping strategies	challenges
similarities	differences
successful	less successful
opportunities	barriers
omissions	excesses
within capabilities	beyond capabilities
achievement	non-achievement

Table 44.3 Contrasting perspectives

Effectiveness as a learner

Aspects of your learning that you could explore as part of the reflection on your skills as a learner/student might include:

- identifying what you need to know
- the appropriateness of your responses to feedback
- using journal and portfolio evidence as a resource
- accessing and using other sources of information
- the development of IT skills to obtain information and for use in the workplace
- the ability to relate theoretical knowledge to the health or care workplace
- the ability to relate experience in one context to learning in a new context
- judging your own performance objectively.

Effectiveness as a care worker

Core abilities that are expected at this stage of your development as a care worker include:

- communication
- health, safety and security of individuals
- respecting the value base of care.

You should continually use the knowledge and understanding you have gained from study, practice and feedback to develop your skills and abilities in these aspects of practice.

Depending on the function of each placement organisation, you will have developed specific knowledge and understanding and participated in a range of routines and specific activities. It would be useful to identify themes that you can relate to *all* of your placements when you are reviewing your effectiveness during the whole of your placement experience. Examples could be:

- working one-to-one with service users
- working with service users in small groups
- team-working skills
- relating to managers
- working with workers in partner agencies
- planning and leading therapeutic and/or creative activities
- fitness, mobility, exercise/sport for service users
- diet and nutrition of service users
- supporting sensory, learning and communication needs
- supporting physical disability.

Recommendations for your future development

After reviewing your effectiveness at the end of the course, you can use the SAP approach to identify areas for your further personal and professional development and make recommendations towards planning for these. Any recommendations you make will be set in the context of your aspirations for your future, perhaps for professional training in a health or care profession, employment or a gap year.

There may be some uncertainty about the detail of your plans in the short-term (six months), and the long-term (greater than six months), but your recommendations should take account of your strengths and areas for improvement. You should also review and identify your aims and priorities and include an outline of how these might be met.

Assessment activity 44.4

This activity should be completed at the end of the unit. For the criteria below, you will use different examples from your placements, journal and portfolio.

Identify links between knowledge and understanding and effective practice.

1   Produce a piece of writing (it could be linked to P2 and P3) that identifies links between knowledge and understanding and effective practice in health and social care. **P4**

Grading tip for P4

Use examples from your experience in placement to illustrate the points you make.

Explain how development of knowledge and understanding can be linked to improved practice.

2   Include in your writing for P4 explanations of how increasing knowledge and understanding can lead to improved practice in the health or care workplace. **M1**

Grading tip for M1

Use your knowledge of theories from any of the units of the course to support your explanations.

Describe your effectiveness in work in health and social care.

3   Describe the effectiveness of your contributions to work in health and social care. **P5**

Grading tip for P5

Use additional specific examples to those used for P4. Refer to theory and to evidence in your portfolio and journal of the quality of your practice to support the points you make about your effectiveness.

Explain how improving your personal effectiveness can enhance the experience of the patient/service user.

4   Explain how the improvements you have made in your personal effectiveness have benefited the service users you have cared for. **M2**

Grading tip for M2

Reflect on your practice from the perspective of service users.

Evaluate your development as a result of workplace experiences.

5   Using your journal, evidence from placements and your reflective accounts, evaluate how your development has been influenced by your experiences in placements. **D1**

Grading tip for D1

To evaluate, you should make judgements, justified by a range of arguments, about your development through placements.

Knowledge check

1   How does organisational structure affect the care received by service users?

2   What is the difference between a policy and a procedure?

3   Compare the job roles of the same type of care worker in different care organisations, for example, a nurse in a hospital and a nurse working in the community.

4   How does partnership working enhance the care that service users receive?

5   Compare procedures for a) reporting, and b) recording information about service users in different care organisations.

6   To what extent do routines for ensuring the health, safety and security of people differ in different care organisations?

7   What are the similarities and differences in the values that underpin work in health and social care compared to those that apply to children's care, learning and development?

8   What positive and negative influences have you observed on the effectiveness of team work in different organisations?

9   In what ways have your contributions in placements made a positive difference to the experiences of service users and the work of care workers?

10 To what extent have you been able to make effective links between your experiences in placement and your learning in class?

Grading criteria

To achieve a pass grade the evidence must show that the learner is able to:	To achieve a merit grade the evidence must show that, in addition to the pass criteria, the learner is able to:	To achieve a distinction grade the evidence must show that, in addition to the pass and merit criteria, the learner is able to:
P1 describe the structure and function of one health or social care organisation **Assessment activity 44.1 page 480**		
P2 present and review a portfolio of evidence demonstrating knowledge and understanding of workplace practice **Assessment activity 44.2 page 487**		
P3 maintain a reflective practice journal to monitor development of own knowledge, understanding and skills **Assessment activity 44.3 page 491**		
P4 identify links between knowledge and understanding and effective practice **Assessment activity 44.4 page 494**	**M1** explain how development of knowledge and understanding can be linked to improved practice **Assessment activity 44.4 page 494**	
P5 describe own effectiveness in work in health and social care. **Assessment activity 44.4 page 494**	**M2** explain how improving own personal effectiveness can enhance the experience of the patient/service user. **Assessment activity 44.4 page 494**	**D1** evaluate own development as a result of workplace experiences. **Assessment activity 44.4 page 495**

Preparation for assessment

1 Use one of your placements and find out about its structure and function. Describe how the organisation meets the needs of its service users and how it works with other organisations to do this. Draw an organisational chart to show the relationship between the different workers and summarise the job roles and responsibilities of the people you have identified within it. Research the policies of the organisation and describe how they affect the procedures, routines and practices you observe in the placement. You should include an outline of your job role in the chosen placement and where you fit within the organisational structure. **P1**

2 Collect evidence from each of your placements that has the depth and breadth expected in Unit 44 (the evidence could also support Unit 6) and file it systematically in your portfolio. Clearly identify and annotate the location of your evidence for *each* grading criterion for this unit, for example, 44P1, 44M1, 44D1, to distinguish it from the evidence that supports Unit 6 criteria. Use separate tracking sheets for Unit 6 and Unit 44.

Evidence could include: plans for activities and routines with evaluations of their implementation; descriptive accounts of unforeseen events, for example, service user trips or unplanned events from which you have learnt about workplace practice (for example, a service user fall or behaviour management incident). It is your responsibility to ensure that the evidence you collect records your knowledge and understanding of workplace practices to the depth and breadth required in this unit. This may mean providing, for example, detailed descriptive accounts or specifically designed checklist observation records, always verified by a professional's signature.

Keep a log of your attendance in placement (the total for this unit must be at least 200 hours). **P2**

3 Make regular and detailed notes in your journal throughout the course, with several entries for each placement. Your notes should relate to specific events and to your overall progress and development in placement and the course as a whole. You should quote from your journal notes to illustrate points you make in your reflective writing about the development of your practice.

Set specific and challenging targets for yourself for each placement to help you improve and/or extend your practice in each placement. To help your reflection, participate professionally in as wide a range of work activities and routines as possible, for example, by producing written plans when leading activities and evaluate these activities against their objectives in relation to a) the service user, and b) your learning. Show initiative in your work:

- with service users, both one-to-one and with groups
- with a range of care workers, one-to-one and as part of a team
- when working independently.

Ask for feedback on your performance whenever possible through targeted questioning or specifically produced observation records. Note informal/oral feedback in your journal and file formal written feedback in your PPD portfolio.

Compare the most recent evidence of your practice with earlier evidence and describe your progress (or otherwise). Write periodic summative *reflective* statements about your experiences, for example, after induction, at the end of each term, at the start and end of each placement and at the end of the course. The statements should refer to your journal and portfolio evidence and to theory from the course to describe the progress of your PPD. **P3**

4 When writing reflectively, explicitly reference your writing about practice to theory from the course

and use examples from placements to illustrate
theoretical concepts. **P4**

5   Explain how greater knowledge and understanding
can help improve practices in the workplace. Use
examples of your own practice or that observed by
others to illustrate the points you make. **M1**

6   In each reflective statement, make judgements about
how effective you have been in your placements.
Describe in what ways your actions in working
with service users and carers have been helpful or
unhelpful. **P5**

7   Explain how the improvements you have made to
your practice have benefited service users. **M2**

8   At the end of each placement, evaluate your own
learning from that setting. At the end of the course,
review what you have learnt from all your placement
experiences and evaluate how you have developed
as a result of your workplace experiences as a whole.
Compare your contributions to the work of different
settings, service user groups, care workers and work
teams. Evaluate how well you have been able to develop
specific skills, knowledge and understanding. **D1**

Keep up-to-date throughout the course with
a) collection of evidence, and b) reflective statements.

Further reading

BTEC National in Children's Care Learning and
Development, Oxford: Heinemann

Hull, C., Redfern, L., Shuttleworth, A. (2005) *Profiles and
Portfolios: A Guide for Health and Social Care*, second
ed. Basingstoke: Palgrave

Jasper, M. (2003) *Beginning Reflective Practice*
Cheltenham: Nelson Thornes

Nolan, Y., Moonie, N., Lavers, S. (2005) *Health and
Social Care (Adults)* Oxford: Heinemann

Tassoni, P., Bulman, K., Beith, K., Robinson, M. *S/NVQ
Level 3 Children's Care Learning and Development*
Oxford: Heinemann

Useful websites

Care Council for Wales
www.ccwales.org.uk

Chartered Institute of Personnel and Development
www.cipd.org.uk

Children's Workforce Development Council
www.cwdcouncil.org.uk

Commission for Social Care Inspection
www.csci.org.uk

General Social Care Council
www.gscc.org.uk

Health and Safety Executive
www.hse.gov.uk

Healthcare Commission
www.healthcarecommission.org.uk

Learning and Skills Council
www.lsc.org.uk

NHS
www.nhs.uk

NHS Careers
www.nhscareers.nhs.uk

Northern Ireland Social Care Council
www.niscc.org.uk

Nursing and Midwifery Council
www.nmc-uk.org.uk

Sector Skills Council for Health: Skills for Health
www.skillsforhealth.org.uk

Sector Skills Council: Skills for Care and Development
www.skillsforcare.org.uk

Glossary

Abdomen also known as the stomach or 'tummy'

Accountability when an individual or organisation is required to justify its actions

Absorption taking up of substances to be used by the body cells and tissues

Anaphylactic shock a sudden, severe allergic reaction causing a sharp drop in blood pressure, a rash, and breathing difficulties, following exposure to an allergen, such as nuts, shellfish or bee venom. Can be fatal if emergency treatment such as injection by an 'Epipen' is not given immediately

Aseptic technique method used to keep patient free from contamination, so that micro-organisms are prevented from entering wounds to cause infection. Includes use of sterile equipment and fluids during procedures that pierce the skin

Assertion being able to negotiate a solution to a problem, distinct from submission and aggression

Attachment theory the idea that children need to form a secure and long-lasting attachment to an individual (usually the primary care-giver) in order to have positive psychological development in later life (John Bowlby (1907-1990))

Benchmark standard against which an action, activity or performance can be measured

Bibliography list of texts that have been used to provide general information and background knowledge

Biomedical model approach to health and illness which identifies health as the absence of disease

Bullying when an individual or group of people intimidate or harass others

Caring presence being open to the experience of another person through a 'two-way' encounter

Chest (or thorax) separated from the larger abdomen (also known (inaccurately) as the stomach or 'tummy') by a fibro-muscular sheet known as the diaphragm

Coaching training to develop specific skills

Cognitive abilities ways of thinking that make use of knowledge and experience

Collagen fibrous structural protein, generally in the form of fibres for added strength

Conditioned response learnt response to the new, conditioned stimulus

Conditioned stimulus new, neutral stimulus that has been paired with the unconditioned stimulus and can be substituted for this

Confidentiality usually achieved in a research project by specifying that no participant will be identified to anyone other than the researcher, and that no details of their results will be published or otherwise made available to anyone outside it. Can be achieved by giving each participant a number instead of a name

Conflict model sociological approach first associated with Karl Marx which sees the institutions of society organised to meet the interests of the ruling classes

Confounding variables variables that are not intended to be measured but which, if left uncontrolled, may spoil the experiment. They are a potential source of error.

Continuing Professional Development (CPD) further learning *after* qualifying

Critical incident an unplanned event, such as a violent outburst, a breach of security or a breakdown in plans due to exceptional circumstances beyond the organisation's control

Critique process of detailed analysis

Culture the values, beliefs, customs and behaviours that distinguish a group of people

Cultural difference influence of cultural systems of meaning. Different cultures interpret words, phrases and body language differently. Also known as **Cultural variation**

Dangerous occurrences include fire, electrical short circuit, needle stick injury and collapse of lifting equipment

Debriefing occurs at the end of an investigation, and aims to restore participants to the physical or psychological state they were in at the start. This usually involves telling them the true aim and hypothesis of the research, reassuring them that their response is 'normal' and answering any questions they may have.

Deception when some details of an investigation are withheld from the participant to ensure that their behaviour remains true-to-life. Participants are therefore unable to give informed consent.

Demographic data describing populations and their properties or characteristics. For example, demographic data will describe the age groups and perhaps income categories of people living in certain places. Other characteristics of demographic data include race, religion, political preferences, spending preferences, family size etc.

Dependent variable performance of participants as a result of manipulation of the independent variable

Descriptive statistics data which is summarised in numerical form, such as mean, median or mode. This forms the first stage of data analysis for calculating inferential statistics, and is normally shown in a table and graph.

Development describes complex changes involving quality as well as straightforward increases in some measured quantity

Developmental norms average set of expectations with respect to an infant or child's development

Deviance People who do not conform to the norms of the society or group are said to be deviant.

Dialect words and pronunciation specific to a geographical community. For example, people living in the north of England might use a different dialect from Londoners.

Diaphragm fibro-muscular sheet which separates the upper chest (thorax) from the abdomen

Digestion conversion of food into simple, soluble chemicals capable of being absorbed through the intestinal lining into the blood and being utilised by body cells

Disability impairment restricted further by inappropriate attitudes and inadequate facilities

Disabling environment social context where adaptations and other facilities are not in place to ensure that people with impairments can take full part in a social life

Discrimination treating some people less well than others because of social differences

Disease incidence number of new cases of a specific disease occurring in a population during a specified period of time

Disease prevalence total number of cases of a specific disease in a population during a specified period of time

Diversity recognising that everyone is different in some way. Importantly this also means 'valuing' the difference.

Egalitarian society society without hierarchies, where all members are regarded as equal

Egestion process involved in eliminating waste material from the body

Ego part of the mind that develops at around the age of 3, whose function is to moderate the demands of the id, and prevent the superego being too harsh

Ego defence mechanisms unconscious protective devices which prevent us from being overwhelmed by anxiety. If a traumatic event occurs before we are ready psychologically to deal with it we may use the ego defence mechanism of repression to push the event into our unconscious. The type of ego defence mechanism which is used tends to reflect the source of anxiety we are trying to avoid.

Empowerment enables a service user to make choices and take control of their own life, opposite of dependency.

Equality treating all individuals equally – legally enforced in this country

Experiment research method involving a high level of control

Extensors carry out extension which increases the angle between two bones, for example, triceps is used to straighten the forearm after flexion.

False consciousness In Marxist theory, this is the process and common occurrence of the proletariat taking on the views and beliefs of their class enemy – the bourgeoisie. They do not realise that, by working hard, they are serving the interests of the capitalists much more than their own.

First language The first language that a person learns to speak is often the language that they will think in. Working with later languages can be difficult as mental translation between languages may be required.

Flexors carry out flexion which is decreasing the angle between two bones, for example, raising the forearm uses biceps, a flexor.

Formal care provided by workers who are part of a health or care service organisation

Functionalism sociological approach which sees the social institutions of the society working in harmony with each other, making specific and clear contributions towards the smooth running of the society

Gender roles social and cultural expectations about the different ways men and women should behave

Group values Group members need to share a common system of beliefs or values in order for the group to communicate and perform effectively. You may be able to identify these values when you watch a group at work.

Growth an increase in some measured quantity, such as height or weight

Guidelines statement of a policy or procedure to assist in following regulations or laws

Hazard anything that can cause harm

Health hazard can include incidents leading to illness

Holistic assessment approach to care which addresses the physical, social, emotional and spiritual health of the client, and attempts to meet the needs of the 'whole' person

Holistic development People usually experience physical, intellectual, emotional and social development as a whole. Analysing development under these categories can help us identify issues, but life is unlikely to be experienced using these categories.

Hypothesis precise, testable statement which makes a prediction about the findings the researcher expects to make. For example, 'the more control elderly residents are given in a nursing home, the better their health outcomes.'

Id part of the psyche which we are born with. It consists of all the raw emotions we are capable of feeling. The id operates on what is called the 'pleasure principle': it wants what it wants, when it wants it!

Identity the way a person understands themself, including self-esteem and self-image as well as other social and personal issues

Impairment restrictions on day-to-day activity caused by a physical or mental dysfunction or abnormality, for example, the loss of a limb, a sensory impairment or a learning difficulty such as Down syndrome

Independent variable aspect of an experimental set-up that is controlled by the researcher

Infant mortality rate number of deaths occurring to infants under one year old per thousand live births

Inferential statistics mathematical calculation looking into the probability that an outcome happens by chance. For example, if a group of participants who have taken vigorous exercise do better in an arithmetic test than a similar group who took no exercise, it may just be chance, in which case we cannot draw strong conclusions from these findings. However, if an inferential statistical test shows us that there is a 95 per cent probability that this didn't happen by chance, we would be safe to say that exercise improved performance.

Informal care is provided for others on a good neighbourly basis

Informed consent when participants in research projects are given full details of the aim of the research, the methodology to be used and the likely outcomes in terms of how it will affect them. They must be told this before the research is carried out. With this information they are able to make an informed choice about whether or not they wish to take part.

Ingestion taking food, drink and drugs by the mouth

Interactionism sociological approach which focuses on the influence of small groups on our behaviour rather than the power of large institutions. These theorists believe that our behaviour is driven by how, in smaller groups, we interpret situations – how we see ourselves in relation to other people in the group, how we see other members and how they see us.

Internalise taking in information from the outside world and building it into our sense of self. If we are consistently valued, loved, praised, given positive attention etc we will believe ourselves to be valuable, lovable, worthwhile, etc.

Jargon words used by a particular profession or group that are hard for others to understand

Latent learning taking on board a new way of doing something (such as performing a breast examination) but not using it until it's needed

Legislation law or group of laws

Life course a map of what is expected to happen at the various stages of the human life cycle

Life expectancy the average number of years that a person can expect to live

Lifestyle the way a person spends their time and money

Major injury fractures, dislocations, loss of sight, unconsciousness, poisoning and anyone requiring resuscitation

Maturation development that is assumed to be due to a genetically programmed sequence of change

Measures of central tendency a method used to summarise the mid-point of a set of data, including the mean, median and mode

Mentoring providing support and advice based on experience

Minimum Standards the smallest acceptable standard of practice

Model an individual with characteristics which inspire us to follow their example

Modelling basing behaviour, attitude, style of speech or dress on someone we want to be like

Morbidity rate the number of people who have a particular illness during a given period, normally a year

Mortality rates number of people who have died in the population in a given year, expressed as the number of deaths in a year per thousand of the population

MRSA short for Methicillin-Resistant Staphylococcus Aureus. Sometimes known as a 'superbug', it has developed resistance to many antibiotics, and even those that are effective against it have to be given in higher doses over longer periods to work

Nature genetic and biological influences; those human characteristics that are genetically determined

Norms guidelines or rules that govern how we behave in society or in groups within that society

Nurture social, economic and environmental influences; those human characteristics that are learnt through the process of socialisation

Objective assessment is free from bias because judgements are based on evidence from independent sources, so are free from personal feelings and opinions

Objective data is collected without any need for interpretation by the researcher (for example, the number of students on a health and social care course; or the total immunisations given to children aged between 18 and 36 months in a local health centre)

Observational learning comes through watching someone else doing something. This new behaviour (such as smoking, drinking, wearing a cycle helmet) can be learnt, but may not be carried out unless the individual chooses to do it.

One-tailed hypothesis predicts the nature of the finding. For example, you may predict that *more girls than boys take up smoking in order to fit in with their peer group* (*see* Two-tailed hypothesis)

Osteo- prefix associated with bone

Overt open and transparent

Peer-reviewed This means that before an article is printed in a specialist journal (such as *The Lancet* which is for doctors and other medical professionals) it must first be scrutinised by other doctors and specialists in the field. They will examine the method and sample used and scrutinise the findings to make sure that any claims made about the findings are accurate and truthful. This method ensures that only high-quality research is published and made available to the general public.

Pelvis lower, narrower part of the body below the abdomen

Personal and Professional Development (PPD) learning acquired from experience *before* you qualify as a professional

Policies general statements of intent

Power in the context of interpersonal behaviour, 'power' means the ability to influence and control what other people do

Pressure ulcers areas of damage to the skin and deeper tissue which can affect all patients (formerly known as pressure or bed sores) which can give discomfort and become infected. In extreme cases, they can damage muscle and bone, leading to a longer stay in hospital.

Presumptive consent when a group of people similar to the sample that will be used in a research investigation are told the full details of that investigation and asked if they think it is acceptable. If they agree that it is, the researcher can be said to have gained presumptive consent.

Primary socialisation the first socialisation of children that normally takes place within the family

Prior general consent when a researcher asks participants beforehand if they would object in principle to being deceived about aspects of the investigation. If they say no, then prior general consent has been obtained.

Prioritisation understanding the order of importance of certain actions, and doing them in that order

Procedures step-by-step instructions telling you what to do in certain situations

Protection from harm the obligation on the part of a researcher to ensure that no physical or psychological harm will occur to the participant. It is the responsibility of the researcher to do all they can to foresee any potential harm and either change the design of the study or, if this is not possible, make the participant aware of this before they take part.

Psyche structure of the mind consisting of three dynamic parts

Qualitative information is based on description, using words and images

Quantitative information is described by using numerical data, for example, tables, charts or graphs.

Raw data refers to data as it is collected, for example, completed questionnaires, participants' test papers, an observation schedule with tally marks, etc. It is the data which you then summarise to present as findings.

Reference acknowledging the original author of a source text used that gave rise to a specific idea, opinion, quotation, statistic, fact, diagram, chart, etc

Regulation principle, rule, or law designed to control or govern behaviour

Reliability is a measure of the methods used to generate information

Replication when a research investigation is based on a previous one, and uses a similar sample and the same methodology, and thus comes out with the same findings

Reportable diseases relevant to health and social care workers include hepatitis, tuberculosis and meningitis

Researcher bias when a researcher interprets data in a way that suits their hypothesis. If an answer is given that is ambiguous (i.e. it could be interpreted in different ways), they may interpret it in a way that supports what they wanted to find out in the first place. Alternatively, they may give some sort of prompt, or cue, to the participant in a face-to-face study which influences the participant to behave in a particular way (sometimes called 'investigator effects' or 'demand characteristics').

Research question investigation into a broad area of research which does not have a specific prediction. For example, you may just want to find out what the factors are that distinguish those girls (or boys, or both) who do take up smoking from those who do not.

Responsibility duties you are expected to carry out within your role

Rights roles and responsibilities attached to being an individual living and working within wider society

Right to withdraw To ensure that participants in a research project are true volunteers, they must be given every opportunity to withdraw from the process if, at any point, they wish to do so. At the end of the project, usually after the debriefing, it is advisable to remind participants that they have the right to withdraw their data for any reason. They should not be forced to justify their reasons for wishing to withdraw.

Risk the chance, high or low, that someone will be harmed by a hazard

Role a person's function, such as a manager or youth worker

Role conflict exists where the demands of the social roles that you are expected to perform are not consistent with each other and it is difficult, or even impossible, to meet all demands

Role-play acting out a role, behaving in such a way that other people can – at least temporarily – believe in the character you are acting out

Safety hazard includes incidents leading to injury or to damage to equipment or buildings

Sample group of participants chosen from the target population. To avoid bias, samples must be representative of the target population.

Secondary socialisation the socialisation that takes place as we move into social settings beyond the family or place of our primary socialisation, for example, nursery, school and friendship groups.

Security hazard includes intruders, theft of property or information, and service users either being abducted or leaving without consent

Self-awareness perception of the way a fact or situation relates to ourselves

Self-concept the way in which we see ourselves. In early life this comes from what we are told about ourselves ('you're so pretty', 'you're a good footballer', 'what a kind girl you are' etc). As we grow older, our ability to think about ourselves develops and we begin to incorporate our own judgments ('I did well at that test – I'm good at maths', 'I wasn't invited to that party – I must be unpopular').

Self-esteem The way in which we value ourselves, believe ourselves to be worthy, lovable, etc. This is learnt from the way we are valued and loved by others. Self-esteem is not stable. It can go up and down according to our personality and the way we typically view the world and our past experiences. People can, however, be taught how to increase their self-esteem.

Self-image how we see or imagine ourselves

Simulation does not require you to act or portray a character. If you simulate a conversation, you simply say (or sign) the appropriate responses. You do not expect people observing your behaviour to perceive you as anyone but yourself. Both simulation and role-play involve thinking through appropriate responses, but role-play involves a greater level of acting skill.

Slang informal words and phrases that are not found in standard dictionaries but which are used within specific social groups and communities

Social control strategies used to ensure that people conform to the norms of their society or group

Social institution a major building block of society which functions according to widely accepted customs, rules or regulations, for example, the family, the education system or the legal system

Social mobility process of moving from one social stratum to another, either upwards or downwards

Social role expectations associated with holding a particular position in society or group

Social stratification term borrowed from geology which describes the hierarchies in society – how some groups have more status and prestige than others

Socialisation process of learning the usual ways of behaving in a society

Socio-economic status an individual or family's social and economic status and ranking compared with other groups in society (for example, a doctor is seen as having a higher social status and economic means than a hospital porter)

Socio-medical model focuses on the social and environmental factors that influence health and illness, including the impact of poverty, poor housing, diet and pollution

Stereotyping making generalisations and holding expectations about an issue or a group of people

Subjective data data that expresses a personal point of view (for example, the reasons for choosing to study health and social care; beliefs about the causes of mental disorder)

Superego aspect of the mind roughly equivalent to a conscience: it internalises learned morals and aspects of right and wrong, and contains an image of our ideal self

The bourgeoisie In Marxist theory, the bourgeoisie (or capitalists) are the powerful class in society who own the factories, land and other capital and organise the economy and other important institutions to their own advantage.

The proletariat In Marxist theory the proletariat are the 'working class' who have only their labour to sell. They work for and are exploited by the bourgeoisie.

Two-tailed hypothesis is a theory with two strands, for instance you might predict there are different reasons for girls and boys taking up smoking, but you don't yet know what they are. Your hypothesis will be tested against the data collected to find out if, in fact, there are different reasons.

Unconditional positive regard a totally non-judgmental way of viewing a client: not liking or approving at certain times and disapproving at others, but valuing the client in a positive way with no conditions attached

Unconditioned response instinctive response provoked by a stimulus (for example, the startle reflex in response to a slammed door)

Unconditioned stimulus a naturally occurring event which provokes a response (for example, a door banging)

Validity a measure of the quality of information and how it is used

Value consensus general agreement as to the values and beliefs of a society

Index

Key terms are shown by bold page numbers. Tables and pictures are shown by italic page numbers.

primary socialisation **336–7**
prior general consent 431
prioritisation **305**
private homes 110
private sector organisations 315
probes 28
procedures 87–91, **124,** *125,* 125–6, 132, 323, 472–3
professional training and registration 326
proletariat **344**
promotion
    of anti-discriminatory practice 91–3
    equality and rights 66–9, 87, 92
prompts 28
protection from danger and harm 72–3, **429**
protoplasm **203**
psyche **382**
psychodynamic approach 382–7, *384–5*
psychological changes during ageing 193–4
psychological needs of users 27–9
psychologists 37
Psychology of Personal Constructs 393
puberty 158–9, *159*
public sector organisations 315
publication of research 457
pulmonary circulation 231
pulse rate measurement 255–7

Q

qualitative information **288–9**
qualitative research *416,* 416–17
quality issues 88–9
quantitative information **288–9**
quantitative research *416,* 416–17
questionnaires 417–18, *418,* 420–2
questions 28, 420–2

R

racism 63
radio as source of research material 426
rates of pay 111
raw data **440**
reciprocal influence 180
record-keeping
    accidents and incidents 130
    and confidentiality 68–9
    health and safety 135
recruitment of staff 132
reference **291**
reflection on experience 309, 311, *312,* 488–94, *492, 493*
reflective listening 12–13, 16
regional patterns in health and illness 364
regulation, definition of **118**
Regulation of Care (Scotland) (2001) 125

regulation of health and social care services 320–1
regulations 118–24
reliability **289,** 456
reminiscence work *193,* 193–4
renal system 217, *217*
replication **417**
reportable diseases **120**
Reporting of Injuries, Diseases and Dangerous Occurrences
    Regulations (RIDDOR) 120
reproductive system *219,* 219–20
research
    access to information 457–8
    action plan for 434, *435*
    bias 449–50
    books 427
    charts and diagrams 443–6
    choosing a topic 428–30
    commissioning of 455
    consequences/benefits of 456–7
    drawing conclusions 449
    ethical issues 429–31, 450, 453, 458–60
    evaluation and conclusion 452–3
    formal and informal observation 423–5
    Human Rights Act 455
    hypothesis 428, 432
    impact of key reports 460–1
    internet 425–6
    interviews 418–22
    journals 426
    leading to discrimination 458
    literature search 428, *429*
    manageable aims 432
    methodology 433
    percentages 441
    presentation methods 443–7
    primary 417–25
    publication of 457
    purpose of 408–11
    questionnaires 417–18, *418*
    rationale for 434
    recommendations 454
    reliability 456
    report structure and contents 439–50
    role of 411–15
    sampling 433–4
    scientific experiment 422–3
    secondary 425–7
    Social Care Institute for Excellence (SCIE) *461,* 461–2
    spreadsheets 447–8, *448*
    statistical presentation of findings 441–3
    target group 433–4
    television and radio as source 426–7
    triangulation 440

work experience placements 284, 292–3, 302–8, 475–6, 479–90
    see also organisations
work in health and social care settings 324, *324*
work teams 327, 483–6, *484, 485*
working practices 88
    effect of legislation on 125–6
    monitoring of 134
    MRSA *113,* **113–14,** *114*

working with others, skills in 287
workplace practice, demonstrating knowledge of 481–7
written communication 18

Zimbardo, P.G. 185–6